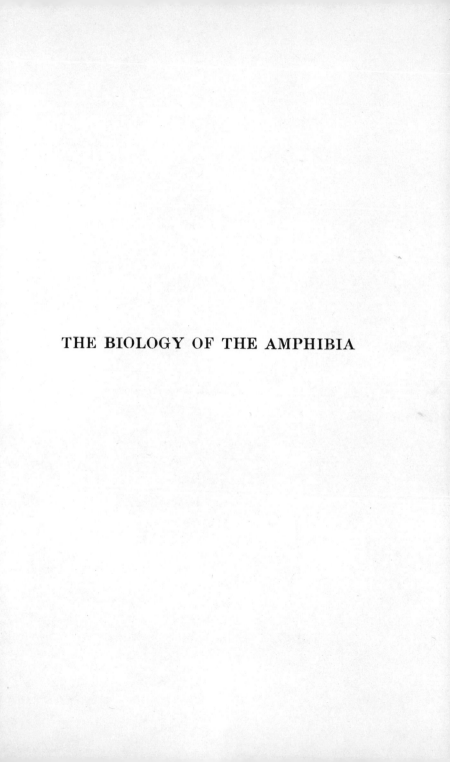

THE BIOLOGY OF THE AMPHIBIA

the biology

of

the amphibia

by G. Kingsley Noble

Dover Publications, Inc. New York 10, N. Y.

BIOGRAPHICAL NOTE

Gladwyn Kingsley Noble was born September 20, 1894 in Yonkers, New York, the son of Gilbert Clifford Noble and Elizabeth Adams. From earliest boyhood he displayed a marked interest in the world of nature and long before graduating from the Yonkers High School he had made up his mind to become a naturalist.

Majoring in zoology at Harvard, he received his A.B. in 1916 and his A.M. in 1918. Much of his time in Cambridge was spent at the Museum of Comparative Zoology working as assistant to the late Thomas Barbour. His early enthusiasm was for birds, and his first scientific paper, published when he was nineteen, dealt with the depredations of cats among the nesting gull colonies of Muskeget Island. It was chiefly as a bird student and collector that he was sent to Guadeloupe at the end of his freshman year and to Newfoundland the following summer. In 1916 a third Harvard expedition took him as general zoologist to the Marinan Valley in northwestern Peru. Dr. Barbour encouraged his field activity, gave him a thorough grounding in taxonomy, published several herpetological papers with him, and undoubtedly was responsible for stimulating his interest in reptiles and amphibians. His first paper on frogs was largely taxonomic but gave promise of depth and versatility in its histological drawings and data.

The young scientist's career was interrupted early in 1918 when he obtained a commission as ensign and was sent to Washington to serve in the Office of the Chief of Naval Operations. At the close of the war he came to the American Museum of Natural History as assistant curator in the department of herpetology. At the same time he began working for his doctor's degree at Columbia University with Dr. William K. Gregory as his faculty adviser and later his deeply esteemed friend. His thesis, entitled "The Phylogeny of the Salientia," was published in 1922 and was soon recognized as a major herpetological contribution. In it he reclassified frogs and toads on the basis of such fundamental characteristics as vertebral articulation and thigh musculature. Subsequent papers also reflected his intense training at Columbia in morphology, phylogeny, and palaeontology.

In 1921 he married Miss Ruth Crosby, a member of the museum educational staff, and many of his later field trips were taken with her and with their two sons. Much as he delighted in field work, he never had a keen desire to explore the far corners of the world, feeling that for him the mysteries of laboratory and countryside offered adventure enough. Short excursions were frequently made to study or collect forms in which he was particularly interested, such as the aquatic lizards of Cuba, the giant tree frogs and iguanas of Santo Domingo. He loved the pine barrens and cedar swamps of south Jersey with their Anderson's tree toads, carpenter frogs, and fence lizards; the heron and gull colonies of Long Island, Nantucket, and the Jersey coast; the cave creatures of the Ozark mountains; the fish life of the Florida reefs and the Marineland Aquarium. Intimate contact with these creatures brought him to the realization that life history, like structure and physiology, could indicate evolutionary relationships. A number of ontogenic papers were published and later summarized in "The Relation of Life History to Phylogeny within the Amphibia," read before the British Association for the Advancement of Science in 1925.

That summer and fall were spent in England and Europe visiting universities, museums, zoological gardens, and aquaria—studying not only the collections of animals but also techniques of storing, cataloguing, and exhibition.

During his comparatively short career he published about 180 papers. From 1916 to 1932 four-fifths of these were on amphibians. His interest in life history lead inevitably to a closer study of courtship and social behavior, and of the effects upon them of the endocrine glands, especially in salamanders. He learned that much of this behavior, so difficult to spot in the field, could be induced artificially in the laboratory. Reptiles and amphibians proved to be excellent subjects for experimental work because of their basic position in the evolutionary scale and because they were easy and economical to rear in the laboratory. A long series of studies were made on the physiology and behavior of various frogs, salamanders, snakes, and lizards. Many of the results were woven into this book originally published in 1931.

Henry Fairfield Osborn, long president of the museum, had followed these researches with consistent enthusiasm, and in 1928 the trustees voted funds to establish a separate department of experimental biology—a department which is still producing regularly and which is undoubtedly Dr. Noble's greatest memorial.

The last twelve years of his life were devoted chiefly to problems of physiology and behavior; characteristically, he prepared himself to meet them by taking courses in endocrinology, neurology, and psychology. To some extent reptiles and amphibians gave way to fish and once more to birds. Fish had the advantage of more frequent breeding cycles, and bird reactions were perhaps more spectacular.

At various times, Dr. Noble was a lecturer in biology at Columbia University, a visiting professor at the University of Chicago and at New York University. On several occasions he was offered university posts of distinction and responsibility; although he enjoyed a university environment, he decided not to change. He had a sincere devotion to the museum and a tremendous desire to see it develop—not as a storehouse—but as a dynamic educational force which would interpret the fundamental principles of life. He felt, too, that his own particular type of research could best be carried on in the museum. Always he remained a naturalist at heart, fully recognizing the importance of the more technical "ologies" but accepting them only as tools to the deeper understanding of birds, frogs, and men.

1954   R. C. N.

PREFACE

With the increasing use of both frogs and salamanders in experimental biology, the need has arisen for a general textbook which summarizes the relations of Amphibia to one another and to their environments. The salamanders, for example, are commonly believed to be more primitive than frogs, although this is true for only certain features of their anatomy. Again, Necturus, which is now frequently employed in university courses of zoölogy, is often described as a very primitive type, without further reference to its systematic position among the Caudata. There is no book written in English since Gadow's volume in the "Cambridge Natural History" (1901) which attempts to combine both the natural history and the biology of Amphibia in a single volume. Holmes's splendid book on "The Biology of the Frog" has accomplished this task for Rana, and in extending the field to all the Amphibia, I have been influenced by this work in the selection of material.

Although the present volume was written primarily to introduce the student to the biology of both frogs and salamanders, technicalities have been avoided wherever possible and much has been included which should be of interest to the field naturalist or traveler. The systematic names employed are those in current use by naturalists and not the more familiar ones of the experimental laboratory. The difference between these two nomenclatures is not sufficiently great, however, to cause confusion.

The sections dealing with the physiology of Amphibia are necessarily greatly abridged, but reference has been made wherever possible to the more comprehensive papers and summaries where a historical treatment of the subject may be found. Unfortunately, the extensive account of the Amphibia by Professor Franz Werner in Kükenthal's "Handbuch der Zoologie" appeared after my manuscript had gone to press and no reference is made to this authoritative work in the following pages.

In the preparation of the text I have received help from many sources. My thanks are due first to Professor Henry Fairfield

Osborn for his enthusiastic interest and for the many facilities I have enjoyed at the American Museum where the work was carried forward. I have received considerable bibliographical assistance from Dr. Cora S. Winkin and Mr. Ludwig Hirning, who have also collated various parts of the text. Dr. Winkin has contributed original notes to the chapters dealing with the nervous system and with metabolism. Professor Frank H. Pike has kindly read the chapters on the nervous system and on respiration. Dr. Thomas Barbour has loaned for study valuable material preserved in the Museum of Comparative Zoölogy. The drawings are the work of Mrs. E. L. Beutenmuller and many are based on original material in the American Museum. I am especially appreciative of the aid given throughout the course of the work by my research assistant, Miss Gertrude Evans.

G. K. N.

THE AMERICAN MUSEUM OF NATURAL HISTORY
NEW YORK, N. Y.,
April, 1931.

ACKNOWLEDGMENTS

Many of the figures used in the text have previously appeared in my papers published in the *Bulletin* and in *Novitates* of the American Museum as well as in the *Annals* of the New York Academy of Science. I am indebted to the authorities of the Museum and to the Academy for the privilege of republishing them. Many others have been taken from various scientific journals and books and I wish to express my obligation to the publishers and the authors for the opportunity of redrawing these figures for the present work. Acknowledgment of this courtesy is made to the following sources:

Académie Royale des Sciences, des Lettres et des Beaux-Arts de Belgique for Fig. 68 from *Bull. Acad. Roy. Belg. Cl. Sci.*

Akademische Verlagsgesellschaft, for Fig. 100 from *Zool. Anz.*, Figs. 65, 92, 92*D* from *Morph. Jahrb.*, Figs. 118, 119 from *Zeitschr. Wiss. Zool.*

American Microscopical Society for Figs. 103*A*, 103*B*, 114*B*, 138 from *Trans. Amer. Micr. Soc.*, Figs. 78*A*, 78*B*, 115 from *Proc. Amer. Micr. Soc.*

Bergmann-Verlagsbuchhandlung, J. F., for Figs. 117, 122 from *Anat. Hefte.*

Bonnier, Albert, for Fig. 114*A* from *Acta Zoologica.*

Cambridge University Press and The Macmillan Company for Fig. 130 from Coghill, "Anatomy and the Problem of Behaviour."

Crowell Company, Thomas Y., for Fig. 126 from Papez, "Comparative Neurology."

Deutsche geologische Gesellschaft for Fig. 3*B* from *Zeitschr. Deutsch. Geol. Gesellschaft.*

Essex Institute, The, for Fig. 82 from *Bull. Essex Inst.*

Fisher, Gustav, for Figs. 60, 64, 72 from *Anat. Anz.*, Figs. 6*B*, 6*C* from *Biol. Unters.*, Fig. 97 from Hertwig's "Handbuch der vergleichenden und experimentellen Entwickelungslehre der Wirbeltiere," Fig. 125 from *Jena. Zeitschr. Naturw.* Fig. 9 from Keibel's "Normentafeln zur Entwicklungsgeschichte der Wirbeltiere," Fig. 128*C* from Kuhlenbeck "Vorlesungen über das Zentralnervensystem der Wirbeltiere," Fig. 123 from *Zool. Jahrb., Abt. Allg. ·Zool. Physiol. Tiere*, Figs. 111, 128*A*, 129 from *Zool. Jahrb., Abt. Anat.*

Folia Anatomica Japonica, Editors of the, for Figs. 84*A*, 84*B*, 84*C*, 84*E*, 128*B* from *Folia Anat. Japonica.*

Hokkaido Imperial University for Fig. 133 from *Jour. College Agr.*

Hollandsche Maatschappij der Wetenschappen and F. J. J. Buytendyk for Fig. 134 from *Arch. Neerland. de Physiol. de l'Homme et des Animaux.*

Marine Biological Laboratory for Figs. 7*A*, 52, 103*C* from *Biol. Bull.*

ACKNOWLEDGMENTS

New York Zoological Society for Fig. 133F from *Zool. Soc. Bull.*

Royal Society, The, for Figs. 1, 2, 83 from *Phil. Trans. Roy. Soc. London*, Figs. 56A, 56B from *Proc. Roy. Soc. London.*

Smithsonian Institution for Figs. 77, 139 from *U. S. Nat. Mus. Bull.*

Springer, Julius, for Figs. 3A, 10 from "Ergebnisse naturwissenschaftlicher Forschungen auf Ceylon" (Sarasins), Figs. 13, 55 from *Arch. Mikr. Anat.*, Fig. 8 from *Zeitschr. Zell. Gewebel.*

Taylor and Francis for Figs. 4, 85 from *Ann. Mag. Nat. Hist.*

Thieme, Georg, for Figs. 79, 106, 132 from *Biol. Zentralbl.*

University of California Press for Fig. 137 from *Univ. Calif. Pub. Zool.*

University of Chicago Press for Fig. 16 from *Physiol. Zool.*

University of Wisconsin for Fig. 71 from *Bull. Univ. Wis.*

University Press Cambridge for Figs. 12, 112 from *Brit. Jour. Exp. Biol.*

Wegner, Julius E. G., for Fig. 133D from *Blätt. Aquar.-Terrar.-Kde.*

Wistar Institute of Anatomy and Biology for Fig. 109 from *Anat. Rec.*, Fig. 108 from *Amer. Anat. Mem.*, Figs. 69, 70, 75 from *Amer. Jour. Anat.* Figs. 113, 116, 120, 124, 127 from *Jour. Comp. Neurol.*, Figs. 15, 101, 107 from *Jour. Exp. Zool.*, Figs. 6D, 10A, 14, 93, 98, 102, 105, 121 from *Jour. Morph.*

Zoological Society of London and Dr. O. M. B. Bulman for Fig. 5 from *Proc. Zool. Soc.*

CONTENTS

CONTENTS

PART II

RELATIONSHIPS AND CLASSIFICATION

THE BIOLOGY OF THE AMPHIBIA

THE BIOLOGY OF THE AMPHIBIA

PART I
THEIR STRUCTURE AND FUNCTIONS

CHAPTER I
THE ORIGIN OF THE AMPHIBIA

There are many backboned animals which lead an amphibious life. The crocodile and the seals live at times in water and again on land. The name "Amphibia," first used by Linnaeus for a rather odd assemblage of more or less aquatic vertebrates, referred to this amphibious habit of the members of the group. Today the name is restricted to that class of vertebrates which is intermediate between fishes and reptiles. The group includes the frogs, salamanders, caecilians, and many fossil creatures, frequently of large size and bizarre form.

The living Amphibia are cold-blooded vertebrates possessing limbs instead of paired fins like the fish and having a soft, moist skin lacking the protective hair or feathers of higher vertebrates. Salamanders are often confused with lizards, which they resemble superficially. The latter have a dry, scaly skin similar to that of other reptiles. Minute scales are present between the transverse body rings of caecilians but these are rarely seen without making a dissection. Amphibia may, therefore, be defined as cold-blooded vertebrates having a smooth or rough skin rich in glands which keep it moist; if scales are present, they are hidden in the skin.

The development of Amphibia, also, serves to distinguish them from reptiles, birds, or mammals. The eggs are usually laid in the water and the larvae pass through an aquatic stage before metamorphosing into the adult. Many frogs and salamanders lay large-yolked eggs on land and the young never enter the water. These terrestrial eggs lack the calcareous shell of reptiles

1

and birds. Further, the embryo as it develops is never surrounded by the protective amnion or equipped with a respiratory
allantois as in the case of higher vertebrates. Modern Amphibia
differ from reptiles in many details of their skeletal anatomy,
but some Carboniferous and Permian Amphibia, especially the
Rachitomi, were so similar to contemporary reptiles that it is
impossible to draw a sharp line of distinction between them.
Palaeontological discoveries have also done much to fill in the
gap between Amphibia and fishes but even here all the intermediate stages have not yet been found. Modern Amphibia
have arisen from a group of more or less aquatic tetrapods which
flourished from at least early Carboniferous to Triassic times.

The term "Batrachia" is frequently used for the class
Amphibia, as, for example, by Cope in his monumental "The
Batrachia of North America." Linnaeus included crocodiles,
lizards, snakes, and turtles in his group Amphibia, and he was
followed by some later students. Brongniart was the first to
distinguish the frogs and salamanders from the reptiles but his
choice of the term batraciens for the group was unfortunate, as
this name was already a synonym of Salientia. Various other
names were later proposed for the class. It was not until 1825
that Latreille restricted the name Amphibia to the frogs, toads,
and salamanders, leaving the caecilians with the reptiles. The
term Amphibia, therefore, originates from the Linnaean name
as restricted by Latreille, the caecilians being later added to
the group. Rules of priority are not strictly applied to groups
higher than genera, and as Linnaeus included reptiles in his
category, there are some students who would use another name
for the class. Since none of the later names proposed has met
with wide acceptance, the majority of recent students utilize the
Linnaean name Amphibia in its restricted sense. (Noble, 1929.)

The First Tetrapods.—If we compare a frog sitting on the
edge of a pond with the perches, catfish, or eels in the water, the
difference between a tetrapod and a fish seems tremendous. A
scrutiny of their detailed structure brings forth such a series of
differences in skull, appendages, and breathing apparatus that
the change from fish to frog would seem to be one of the most
radical steps in the evolution of the vertebrates.

This step does not seem less tremendous when we compare the
aquatic newt with the fish, for the former is a typical tetrapod
which has secondarily taken up a life in the water. It is no

wonder that anatomists were puzzled for many years as to how the first tetrapod arose, and even today there is no agreement between those who study only the recent forms.

When the evidence from palaeontology is available, this must necessarily be placed ahead of all our other evidences. The gaps in the palaeontological record of the Amphibia are great, but the combined researches of recent years (especially Gregory, 1915; Watson, 1917, 1919, 1926; Williston, 1925) have thrown much light on the beginnings of land life among the vertebrates. Further, most amphibians pass their early life in the water. The morphological changes of metamorphosis would seem to reflect to a greater or lesser extent the changes which took place when the first vertebrate became established on land. As with all other problems of phylogeny, the evidence of palaeontology, of anatomy, and of development must be weighed one against the other for the final solution of the problem.

If the modern fish were to be changed into a tetrapod, a number of important transformations of structure would have to be accomplished. The gills would have to be lost, and the lungs developed and the nasal passage extended to form internal nares for the ingress of air when the mouth is closed. The fins and body would have to be modified for land locomotion and the integument changed to resist drying. The latter would mean the development of a cornified epidermal covering and a series of integumentary glands discharging by ducts on to the surface, at least over those parts not provided with an armored skin. Specialized glands would be required to keep the nasal passage and mouth from drying. The eyes, formerly bathed by the water, would be especially sensitive to the new conditions and must either develop a horny, protective cover as in modern snakes or produce softer eyelids out of dermal folds. In either case a lacrimal gland and drain would be needed for cleansing the eyeball. To keep the nasal passage clean a muscular closing device would be required at the outer end of each nasal inlet. If the first tetrapod were to succeed on land, the sense organs of the fish would have to undergo considerable modification, for, while the lateral-line organs would be no longer required, the auditory, optic, and olfactory centers would gain a higher importance, demanding in some cases fundamental changes in the structure of the organs. If the head were flat as that of many frogs, special muscles to raise the eyes above the surface of the skull would be needed if the eyes were to be at all efficient. Lastly, the loosely hung jaw of the majority of teleosts would have to be firmly fixed to the brain case.

How the first tetrapod accomplished all these changes will never be known. The evidence available shows conclusively that it was not by such sudden revolution as maintains in the metamorphosis of most modern forms. The outstanding contribution of the palaeontological data is the proof of how slight a structural alteration changed the primitive fish ancestor into the first land vertebrates. Similarly, the first reptiles evolved from the embolomerous amphibians and the first mammals from cynodont reptiles by very gradual steps.

Piscine Ancestors.—Today there are a few fish which live both in and out of water. Some of these have been recently carefully studied by Harms (1929) and it is interesting to note how closely they parallel the Amphibia in their adaptations to life on land. Protection against drying is secured by the development of a horny skin growth in the gobies and a cuticle in the blennies. Skin respiration is improved by the penetration of capillaries into the epidermis. An extensive saccular enlargement of the buccopharyngeal cavity increases the efficiency of buccal respiration. Gulped air is prevented from escaping through the gill slits by a modification of the gill covers. The eyes are modified to project above the surface of the head, and the limbs, especially the posterior, are strengthened by bony rays so arranged as to permit terrestrial locomotion. There are also changes in the cutaneous sense organs which protect them against drying. These fish undergo a certain metamorphosis into partly terrestrial animals, and Harms found that this metamorphosis was influenced by the thyroid hormone, as in the case of Amphibia.

The first tetrapods did not come from modern fish. Already in Carboniferous times three distinct orders of tetrapods—labyrinthodonts, lepospondyls, and phyllospondyls—had developed. The first two were both present in the Lower Carboniferous. Footprints are known from the Devonian of Pennsylvania. Hence the tetrapods must have arisen in at least Devonian and possibly Silurian times. The tetrapods arose from ancestors in the fresh waters, for their earliest remains are associated with fresh-water deposits. All fresh-water fishes of Devonian times were ganoids (in the broad sense), dipnoans, or aberrant sharks, and hence our search for the tetrapod ancestor narrows down to these lines of primitive fishes.

If we compare the modern dipnoans and ganoids with modern Amphibia, especially urodeles, certain obvious resemblances will at once appear. Both breathe to a large extent by lungs and the distributions of blood vessels to and from these organs have a close resemblance. Other similarities may be found in certain features of the skull (Wintrebert, 1922), the brain (Herrick, 1924), the urogenital system, and early development. But these similarities will not bear a close inspection, for they differ in many details.

It is, however, hardly reasonable to compare a modern amphibian with a modern dipnoan when the ancestral stocks of both groups are available for study as fossils. The most primitive dipnoans, those from the Middle Devonian, may have possessed some of the urodele resemblances listed above, but they also possessed a number of distinctive characters which would preclude them from the direct ancestorship of modern Amphibia. This is especially true of the skull which had already begun the formation of the large tooth-plates so characteristic of modern lung fishes. In many other features of their skull the primitive dipnoans differ widely from their tetrapod contemporaries.

This leaves only the ganoids among which to find the ancestor of all tetrapods, since the sharks are obviously off the main line of ascent. One family of Devonian crossopterygian ganoids, the Osteolepidae, agree so closely with the primitive Amphibia in most important skeletal features that there can be no doubt that the first tetrapods branched off from a fish very closely allied to this family. The work of Dollo, Watson, Gill, etc., has made it clear that the dipnoans and the osteolepids sprang from the same stock. Whether the Amphibia sprang from this ancestral stock or from the very base of the crossopterygian stem is not known. They agree in structure more closely with the Osteolepidae than with the earliest fossil dipnoans. In seeking the beginnings of tetrapod organization in the fishes, our attention must, therefore, be turned not to modern dipnoans nor to crossopterygians, nor to the fossil dipnoans, but to the osteolepid crossopterygians of Devonian times which differed but slightly from the actual ancestors of the Amphibia.

The most primitive Amphibia are the Embolomeri, an extinct suborder which lived from Lower Carboniferous to the Permian

(Fig. 1). Our knowledge of the skeletal details of the Embolomeri are chiefly due to the brilliant researches of Watson (1926).
The Embolomeri, like many later groups of Amphibia, very
early underwent an enormous adaptive radiation. Already in
Carboniferous times the group contained, as shown by Watson
(1926, page 192), "primitively aquatic animals which show no
signs of ever having possessed terrestrial ancestors," others
obviously terrestrial, and still others secondarily returned to
life in the water. "Despite these diverse habits. the funda-

FIG. 1.—*Eogyrinus attheyi*, a primitive embolomerous amphibian. Reconstruction of the skeleton. (*After Watson, Phil. Trans. Roy. Soc. London*, 1926.)

mental morphology of the skeleton is strikingly uniform throughout the group." The ancestral fish, as shown by Watson,
changed into a tetrapod before the latter became permanently
adapted to land life.

Labyrinthodontia.—The earliest Amphibia as represented by
Eogyrinus, recently made known by Watson (1926), swam in
the waters with their piscine ancestors. Amphibia were prepared for life on land before they were forced into the terrestrial
world. Still it is probable that a need for terrestrial adaptations
existed at the time the Amphibia were evolving. Eogyrinus
apparently lived in pools of a rather arid and quickly drying
country. With the drying of the pools Eogyrinus would have
been forced to make overland journeys to new pools. Locomotion over land was probably made very much in the manner
of an eel.

The first Amphibia were essentially fishlike in most of their
skeletal anatomy. In the osteolepid fishes a long tract of the
basis cranii remained unossified permitting a certain movement
of the skull, while in the embolomerous Amphibia this had
ossified (Fig. 2). The fish hyomandibular was converted into a
stapes in the earliest Amphibia even though no opening for its
insertion into the otic capsule was present. A true stapes in
these Embolomeri suggests that a tympanic membrane was
present covering the spiracular notch. As in fish, the pectoral

girdle of some Embolomeri was attached to the skull by the post-temporal bones and closely resembled that of fish except that a new dermal element, the interclavicle, had been added to its ventral surface in the midline. The pelvis of these early Embolomeri gave evidence that the first Amphibia were not primarily

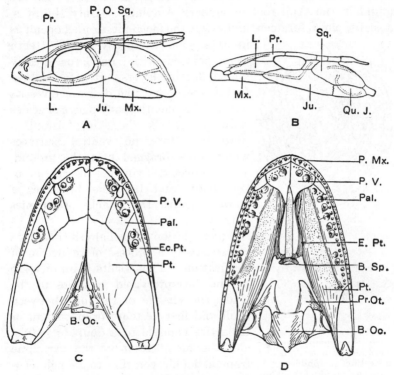

Fig. 2.—Skull of an osteolepid fish and an embolomerous amphibian compared. Side view: *A. Osteolepis macrolepidotus. B. Palaeogyrinus decorus.* Palate view: *C.* Baphetes. *D.* Eusthenopteron. *B.Oc.*, basioccipital; *B.Sp.*, basisphenoid; *Ec.Pt.*, ectopterygoid; *E.Pt.*, epipterygoid; *Ju.*, jugal; *L.*, lacrimal; *Mx.*, maxilla; *Pal.*, palatine; *P.Mx.*, premaxilla; *P.O.*, postorbital; *Pr.*, prefrontal; *Pr.Ot.*, pro-otic; *Pt.*, pterygoid; *P.V.*, prevomer; *Qu.J.*, quadratojugal; *Sq.*, squamosal. (*After Watson, Phil. Trans. Roy. Soc. London, 1926.*)

terrestrial. The long sacral ribs lay below an elongated ilium, indicating that the latter element was attached to them by muscles, exactly as the scapula is attached to the pectoral ribs. The limbs were small but as far as known more like those of later Amphibia than like the fins of the osteolepoid fishes. Fingers and toes were present and the limbs assumed a normal position at right angles to the axis of the body. The limbs of the Embolomeri perhaps more than any other part of the skeleton show an advance over the homologous structures of fish.

The Embolomeri are grouped with other crocodile- or salamander-like Amphibia in the order Labyrinthodontia. These have a skull with a solid covering of many more bones than are found in the skull roof of modern Amphibia. Only the eyes, nostrils, pineal foramen, and rarely the facial pit, formed openings in this solid skull cover. The teeth were pointed with simple or greatly folded dentine layers. It is from these folded teeth that the order receives its name. Frequently bony plates or scales were present in the skin, forming a protection for the ventral surfaces which were dragged over the ground, also a cover delaying the desiccation of the body and in some instances a cuirass against the attacks of enemies (Fig. 3).

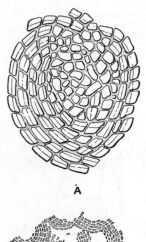

FIG. 3.—Comparison of the scales of a modern and an extinct amphibian. *A.* A single scale of Ichthyophis, a caecilian *(after the Sarasins).* *B.* Several scales of Discosaurus, a labyrinthodont *(after Credner).*

The evolution of the Labyrinthodontia is essentially a process of reduction of ossification. This results in an increase in the interpterygoid vacuities of the skull, the change of the joint between skull and first vertebra from a single or tripartite condyle to a double condyle, and the modification of the vertebrae from a double centrum to a single centrum type. These changes in the skeleton are considered in further detail in Chap. X, while a classification of the order is given in the concluding chapter.

The suborders Embolomeri, Rachitomi, and Stereospondyli represent successive grades in the evolution of skull and vertebrae. The vertebrae evolved away from the reptile type for the intercentrum (basiventral) was emphasized in the Stereospondyli at the expense of the pleurocentrum which tends to disappear (or remain cartilaginous). In modern Amphibia this reduction is carried even further; an ossification in the connective tissue sheath surrounding the chorda forms the greater part of the centrum, although the basidorsal and usually the basiventral are represented by cartilages. The pleurocentrum (interdorsal and interventral) may remain unossified, forming the cartilaginous joint between the successive vertebrae, or the greater part may ossify as the "ball" of the centrum. If this ball attaches itself to the vertebra anterior to it, the vertebra is procoelous; if to the one behind, it is opisthocoelous.

Phyllospondyli.—Contemporaneous with the Embolomeri there occurred in both Europe and America a group of small Amphibia which were apparently destined to give rise to the frogs and salamanders at a later period. These were the Phyllospondyli (Fig. 4) as represented by Eugyrinus in Lancashire, England, and Pelion in the Pennsylvanian of Linton, Ohio (Romer, 1930). Pelion retained such primitive features as an ectopterygoid, as well as an articulation of the pterygoid with the anterior margin of the basisphenoid region much as in the Embolomeri. Large labyrinthodont teeth were present medial to the row of marginal teeth. Romer considers this form ancestral to the typical branchiosaurs in which the labyrinthodont teeth were greatly reduced or lost and the pterygoid had a more posterior position and was presumably firmly fixed to the cranium. Typical branchiosaurs as represented in the late Pennsylvanian horizon of Bohemia had short, broad skulls, still retaining the tabulars and the dermosupraoccipitals, lost by all modern Amphibia (Fig. 5). The ribs were short and straight as in frogs and salamanders and were carried by transverse processes from the side of the vertebrae. Primitive frogs agree so closely with salamanders in vertebrae and skull that it would seem certain they had a common origin. The branchiosaurs resembled salamanders closely in body form. No fossils have been found with skull or pectoral girdle intermediate between that of branchiosaurs and urodeles. Nevertheless the ribs, limbs, pelvis, and vertebrae of branchiosaurs resemble those of urodeles so much that it seems highly probable that salamanders and also frogs arose from the

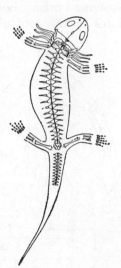

Fig. 4.—Restoration of *Branchiosaurus flagrifer.* (*After Whittard.*)

branchiosaurs. At least there is no group of fossil Amphibia which they resemble more fully.

In the coal measure deposits there are found a variety of other small Amphibia which cannot be grouped with the Labyrinthodontia. Some of these in the Linton formation, such as Colosteus and Stegops, may be considered aberrant branchiosaurs (Romer, 1930). It is interesting that the latter should have "horns" projecting from the posterior angles of its skull. In frogs a similar horn development occurs in certain genera but here involving other bones. Stegops also exhibits dentigerous plates in the roof of the mouth underlying the eye sockets.

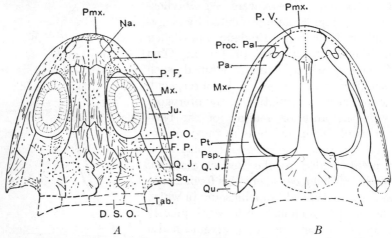

FIG. 5.—Reconstruction of the skull of *Leptorophus tener*, a branchiosaur amphibian. *A.* Dorsal surface. *B.* Palate view. *D.S.O.*, dermosupraoccipital; *F.P.*, postfrontal; *Ju.*, jugal; *L.*, lacrimal; *Mx.*, maxilla; *Na.*, nasal; *Pa.*, palatine; *P.F.*, prefrontal; *Pmx.*, premaxilla; *P.O.*, postorbital; *P.V.*, prevomer; *Proc.Pal.*, *Processus palatinus* of maxilla; *Psp.*, parasphenoid; *Pt.*, pterygoid; *Q.J.*, quadratojugal; *Qu.*, quadrate; *Sq.*, squamosal; *Tab.*, tabular. (*After Bulman and Whittard.*)

A similar development of crushing plates occurs in certain species of the salamander, Desmognathus. Other parallels may be drawn between vertebrae, limbs, and various other features of these Phyllospondyli with similar structures in either frogs or salamanders.

Lepospondyli.—In the same deposits as the Phyllospondyli and Labyrinthodontia there occurs a variety of other amphibian types which may be grouped together in another order, Lepospondyli, although they seem to have little in common. The vertebrae are usually formed of a single piece without sutures, the centrum being hourglass shaped, and the ribs are generally intercentral in position. There are, however, exceptions to both these rules. The Adelospondyli, considered by Watson (1926a) a distinct order, has the neural arch joined by suture with the centrum which is cylindrical in shape and indented by a deep pit on either side. The transverse process is anterior in position and the rib is thus nearly intervertebral in position. The centrum is solid except for a small notochordal foramen and is not the thin shell found typically in branchiosaurs. The group is represented in America by Cocytinus of the Pennsylvanian and Lysorophus of the Permo-Carboniferous. If this group arose from the Embolomeri it must have split off in Devonian times. The best-known genus is Lysorophus (Sollas, 1920). In many characters of the skull it resembles the caecilians closely. Limbs and a well-ossified branchial apparatus were present, however. Lysorophus has been described as a Permian "urodele," but its principal urodele characters, other than those just mentioned, are found also in caecilians. The structure of its vertebrae and skull excludes it from the order Caudata.

Legless Amphibia were present in the Carboniferous but these resemble caecilians in neither skull nor vertebrae. These were the Aistopoda which may be considered a suborder of Lepospondyli. They differ from typical lepospondyls in their large transverse processes and distinctive ribs.

One of the most bizarre groups of lepospondyls is the Nectridia which specialized in the development of a "horn" on either angle of the head. In the last of the line in America, Diplocaulus of the Permo-Carboniferous, the head had the form of a Colonial cocked hat. Diplocaulus, as shown by Douthitt (1917), retained various reptilian features such as a separate coracoid and possibly a fifth finger. The primitive Nectridia had a skull structure resembling the embolomerous plan and hence it seems probable that the group arose at the time the Embolomeri were evolving on one hand into reptiles and on the other into higher labyrinthodonts. Well-developed transverse processes are present on the vertebrae of the Nectridia, a parallel to the Phyllospondyli. These Nectridia were too specialized in skull structure to be considered ancestral to any modern Amphibia. While various lepospondyls approach the urodeles in the structure of their vertebrae they possess other characters which exclude them from the direct line of ancestry. On the other hand, the caecilians, which are more primitive than any other modern Amphibia in many details of their anatomy, may have directly evolved from lepospondyls. If this is true, caecilians had an independent line of evolution from Lower Carboniferous or Devonian times. The many differences between the structure of caecilians and that of other modern Amphibia would support such a view.

Modern Amphibia.—The three orders of Amphibia living today may be distinguished at a glance from one another. The Salientia, or frogs and toads, have short, tailless bodies in adult life and long hind legs, the latter being effective organs for leaping. The Caudata, or salamanders and newts, retain the larval tail throughout life and have short legs of use in walking but not in rapid flight. The Gymnophiona, or caecilians, are wormlike, burrowing creatures of the tropics with a very short tail usually resembling the head in form and without any indication of limbs. All three orders differ radically from the extinct orders of Amphibia in having lost many skeletal elements. The suppression of bones in the orbital series makes possible a proportionately larger eye in modern forms. The loss of the dermal bones along the posterior margin of the skull gives them a more compact skull. Both temporal and back muscles tend to cover the otic region even in the most primitive of the modern Amphibia and the temporal bones of the extinct groups are either lost or greatly modified in modern forms. There are also marked differences in other parts of the skeleton; these will be considered in further detail below. Modern Amphibia are frequently considered more primitive than reptiles which are supposed to form the next "higher" class of vertebrates. The primitive reptiles grade imperceptibly into the Embolomeri and many living reptiles retain primitive structures which have been lost in all modern Amphibia. The reptile skull, with its more complete skull roof and its twelve cranial nerves, is more primitive than that of modern Amphibia. The shoulder girdle of many reptiles, especially that of lizards with a well-developed interclavicle, is more primitive than the girdle of modern Amphibia. The highly glandular skin, the development of cutaneous respiration, the loss of the external ear in many species represent deviations from the primitive conditions which were not shared by most reptiles.

Nevertheless, all reptiles have advanced beyond the first tetrapods in the direction of birds and mammals in their manner of protecting the eggs against desiccation and of embryonic modifications for respiration and storing of waste products. The labyrinthodonts passed through an aquatic larval stage in the water as shown by the retention of the larval respiratory apparatus in certain forms such as Dwinasaurus. This indirect method of development was handed on to the branchiosaurs and to modern Amphibia. Reptiles, at a very early stage in their evolution, succeeded in producing a leathery or calcareous cover to their egg. Further, the growing embryo forced into the large yolk produced a cover for itself, the amnion, by folding over the extra-embryonic tissue immediately surrounding it. The embryo removed from the surface of the egg next succeeded in producing a saclike diverticulum of the cloacal region, the allantois, which served both for respiration and for storing solid wastes of metabolism. Although many modern Amphibia lay eggs on land and some embryos are partially forced into the yolk as they develop, no amphibian has succeeded in making these important changes in egg and growing embryo which were so important for the future evolution of land vertebrates. An aquatic larval life is not characteristic of all Amphibia, but none develops from eggs with calcareous shells, and none produces an amnion or allantois.

Modern Amphibia are mostly small creatures. The giant salamander, Megalobatrachus, reaches a length of over 5 feet, the Goliath Frog may reach a length of nearly a foot in head and body length, but most salamanders and frogs are not over a foot in total length.

References

DOUTHITT, H., 1917: The structure and relationships of Diplocaulus, *Contrib. Walker Museum*, II, No. I, 3–41.

GREGORY, W. K., 1915: Present status of the problem of the origin of the Tetrapoda, with special reference to the skull and paired limbs, *Ann. N. Y. Acad. Sci.*, XXVI, 317–383.

HARMS, J. W., 1929: Die Realisation von Genen und die consecutive Adaption; I, Phasen in der Differenzierung der Anlagenkomplexe und die Frage der Landtierwerdung, *Zeitschr. Wiss. Zool.*, CXXXIII, 211–397, 5 pls.

HERRICK, C. JUDSON, 1924: "Neurological Foundations of Animal Behavior," New York.

NOBLE, G. K., 1929: Amphibia "Encyclopaedia Brittannica," 14th ed., I, 832–840.

ROMER, A. S., 1930: The Pennsylvanian Tetrapods of Linton, Ohio, *Bull. Amer. Mus. Nat. Hist.*, LIX, 77–147.

SOLLAS, W. J., 1920: On the structure of Lysorophus as exposed by serial sections, *Phil. Trans. Roy. Soc. London*, Ser. B, CCIX, 481–527.

WATSON, D. M. S., 1917: A sketch classification of the Pre-Jurassic tetrapod vertebrates, *Proc. Zool. Soc. London*, 1917, 167–186.

———, 1919: The structure, evolution and origin of the Amphibia—the "orders" Rachitomi and Stereospondyli, *Phil. Trans. Roy. Soc. London*, Ser. B, 1920, CCIX, 1–73.

———, 1926: The evolution and origin of the Amphibia, *Phil. Trans. Roy. Soc. London*, Ser. B, CCXIV, 189–257.

———, 1926a: The Carboniferous Amphibia of Scotland, *Palaeontologica Hungarica*, I, 221–252, 3 pls.

WILLISTON, S. W., 1925: "Osteology of the Reptiles," Harvard Univ. Press, Cambridge.

WINTREBERT, P., 1922: L'Evolution de l'appareil pterygo-palatin chez les Salamandridae, *Bull. Soc. Zool. France*, XLVII, 208–215.

CHAPTER II

DEVELOPMENT AND HEREDITY

The egg of frog or salamander, when freshly laid, is a single cell. If fertilized, it develops by a series of orderly changes into a complex organism, an adult amphibian. The processes of development and heredity are so closely interwoven that they are conveniently considered together.

Development begins with the fertilization of the eggs or ova. These are produced by the ovary and they have a long growth period before they are released from that organ. The spermatozoa are formed in the testes and represent single cells greatly elongated and modified for locomotion. The spermatozoa of Salientia exhibit a great variety of form according to the species, while those of the urodeles are singularly uniform (Fig. 6). The acrosome or point of the urodele spermatozoon is frequently bent like the barb on a fishhook. The head is lance-shaped and formed by the transformation of the nuclear matter of the male germ cell. Before this transformation takes place the number of chromosomes in each germ cell is reduced by half by a division which gives half the number of whole chromosomes to the daughter cells, instead of the whole number of chromosomes, divided longitudinally in half, as in ordinary cell division. The middle piece and tail of the spermatozoa are formed from the cytoplasm or from structures in the cytoplasm of the germ cells.

Fertilization.—The eggs of most frogs are fertilized externally and usually by the male who is embracing the female when the eggs are laid. The egg capsules absorb water rapidly after laying and soon can be no longer penetrated by the sperm. The ovoviviparous frogs of Africa, Nectophrynoides, practice internal fertilization, although no external organs for transfering the sperm are known in these frogs. In the "tailed" frog of America, Ascaphus, the "tail," an extension of the cloaca, serves as an intromittent organ. External fertilization characterizes the two most primitive families of urodeles,

15

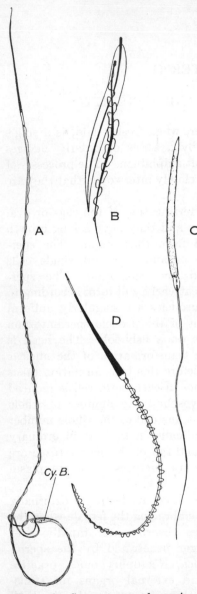

FIG. 6.—Spermatozoa of various amphibians. *A. Desmognathus phoca.* *B. Bombina bombina (after Retzius).* *C. Hyla arborea (after Retzius).* *D. Cryptobranchus alleganiensis (after Smith).* *Cy.B.*, cytoplasmic body.

Hynobiidae and Cryptobranchidae, but all higher groups except the specialized Meantes possess a series of tubules in the roof of the female cloaca which retain, for varying periods, the spermatozoa usually picked up *en masse* in the form of a spermatophore (Fig. 7) by the female with her cloacal lips. These tubules known collectively as the "spermatheca" are homologous with a smaller or greater part of the pelvic gland of the male (Noble and Pope, 1929). It has been assumed that the eggs are fertilized as they pass by the spermatheca, but there is evidence that in Salamandra at least, the spermatozoa migrate up the oviduct before the time of egg laying (Weber, 1922).

The spermatozoa make their way through the gelatinous capsules of the egg, aided by the swimming movements of their tails and apparently also by the digestive action they exert on the capsules (Wintrebert, 1929). In the case of the primitive frog, Discoglossus, the spermatozoa, although more than 2 mm. in length, are almost completely immobile (Hibbard, 1928). Nevertheless, they are carried through a thickened portion of the egg capsules overlying a depression in the surface of the egg by their digestive powers. Why the spermatozoa accumulate only in the region of this depression has not been determined. Miss Hibbard suggests that the nuclear fluids which collect at the bottom of the depression may exert a chemotactic effect on the sperm. In the common frog, Rana, although a much higher type than Discoglossus, there is less localization of the area of penetration. The first spermatozoon to reach the darker hemisphere of the egg sets up a fertilization reaction. After it

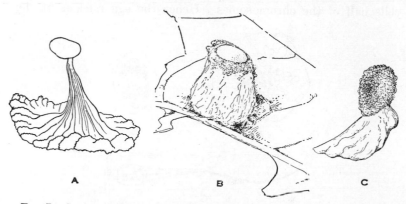

Fig. 7.—Spermatophores of common salamanders. *A. Triturus viridescens* (*after Smith*). *B. Desmognathus fuscus* (*after Noble and Weber*). *C. Eurycea bislineata.*

has entered the egg, the latter forms a fertilization membrane which prevents the entrance of other spermatozoa. In Caudata several spermatozoa normally enter the egg but only one sperm nucleus combines with the egg nucleus, the others degenerating before segmentation is far advanced. The number of spermatozoa which may safely enter the urodele egg, without causing irregularities of development leading to death, stands roughly in proportion to the size of the egg. Polyspermy obtains among eggs, such as those of Cryptobranchus, in which the mass of yolk is considerable. It seems to be a device for large eggs, insuring that one sperm at least shall enter at a point near the egg nucleus. Fertilization includes two processes: activation or the removal of the block to development, and syngamy or the union of the nucleus of the egg with that of the spermatozoon. The first process may be induced artificially in frogs by pricking the egg with a needle (Bataillon, 1910). The second process makes possible the transmission of hereditary factors received from the male and may be considered in more detail.

Eggs extracted from the ovaries of the frog before they have escaped into the body cavity cannot be fertilized. This seems due to the failure of such eggs to maturate. In this process two successive divisions of the egg result in the throwing off near the animal pole of two minute bodies which are actual daughter cells although very small and difficult to see. One of these divisions results in relegating to the small functionless daughter cells half of the chromosomes. Hence the egg nucleus at the

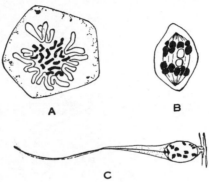

Fig. 8.—Stages in the spermatogenesis of *Rana temporaria*. *A*. Metaphase of a spermatogonial division showing the 26 chromosomes characteristic of this species. *B*. Second maturation division showing the x and y chromosomes (in outline) between the autosomes. *C*. Immature spermatozoon. (*After Witschi.*)

moment of fertilization has only half the chromosome number found in the body cells (Fig. 8). The union with the male nucleus (which by a similar pair of divisions has reduced its chromosome number by half) results in the restoration of the original somatic number of chromosomes. This number is constant for the species, ranging from 32 for Alytes to 12 for Pelodytes. Several frogs and salamanders have a somatic number of 24. In *Rana pipiens*, *R. palustris*, and *R. sylvatica* there are 26 chromosomes; in several species of Bufo only 22 (Stohler, 1928).

The spermatozoon brings to the egg little besides this nuclear matter. The acrosome or point (Fig. 6) is formed by the transformation of certain cytoplasmic materials, the product of the Golgi bodies, and may possibly represent a secretory granule which sets off the fertilization reaction (Bowen, 1924) or at least digests the egg capsules. The middle piece, or neck, is derived from other cytoplasmic material and carries one or two bodies, the centrioles, one of which forms a center of cell division after the sperm enters the egg. In urodeles the neck is better marked than in Salientia and formed of only a single centriole. The tail, which is long and vibratory, is left outside when the spermatozoon enters the egg. There is at present no definite evidence that any of these cytoplasmic materials play any part in heredity. The hereditary factors of the male parent are brought in by the sperm nucleus while those of the female are located in the nucleus of the egg. It is known from the combined researches of genetics and cytology that the chromosomes, the most conspicuous part of the nuclei, are the bearers of genes, the determiners of heritable characters. The genes lie in a linear order along the chromosomes. Their ultimate nature is still unknown but they have been compared with protein bodies and have been assumed to release enzymes which take part in the catalytic reactions in the cytoplasm of the cell.

The chromosome complex is handed on by cell division to all the cells of the body. Since the cells of the skin have the same number of chromosomes (except in certain unusual cases) as the fertilized egg, the question arises: What has determined that they will become skin instead of remaining germ cells? What, in brief, produces differentiation?

The frog's egg, even before fertilization, has a certain organization which affects the pattern of differentiation. It has an apicobasal polarity, as shown externally by the distribution of the pigment. The pigmented pole has less specific gravity than the yolk-laden vegetative pole and hence floats uppermost. This is made possible by the extrusion from the egg of a fluid which collects under the vitelline membrane, facilitating the rotation of the egg within the capsules. During development the egg rotates further and this apicobasal axis becomes the longitudinal axis of the tadpole. The other two axes are established at the moment of fertilization. A gray crescent, caused by the retreat of the pigment from the surface opposite the point of penetration of the spermatozoon, gives the egg bilaterality, and as this crescent is on the future dorsal side, the dorsoventral axis is indicated. Pricked frogs' eggs have gray crescents without relation to the point of pricking (Herlant, 1911). Hence eggs

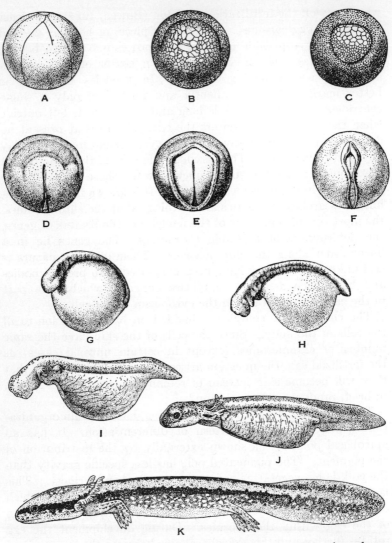

Fig. 9.—The development of *Necturus maculosus*. *A*. Side view of egg 1 day and 8 hours after deposition, showing second and third cleavage grooves. *B*. Bottom view of egg 6 days and 16 hours old. The crescentic blastopore lip sharply separates the large-yolk cells from the small cells of the blastodisc. *C*. Bottom view of egg 10 days and 10 hours old, showing large circular blastopore. *D*. Top view of egg 14 days and 4 hours old. Blastopore smaller. The beginning of neural fold formation, especially anteriorly. *E*. Top view of egg 15 days and 15 hours old. Yolk plug still visible. Neural fold prominent. Its free ends reach nearly to the blastopore. *F*. Top view of egg 18 days and 15 hours old with three or four pairs of myotomes visible. *G*. Dorsolateral view of embryo 22 days and 17 hours old; length 8 mm.; 16 to 18 myotomes. *H*. Side

probably have an initial bilaterality of their own which is over-
ridden by the stimulus introduced by the spermatozoon.

Cleavage.—The fertilized egg divides into many cells (Fig. 9).
As the egg increases only slightly in size during the period of
cleavage, the nuclear material is brought into close relationship
with smaller units of cytoplasm. At every division nuclear
material is liberated into the cytoplasm; enzymes or other
substances released by the genes are thus brought in close association with the cytoplasm. The cleavage pattern has little phylogenetic significance. All amphibian eggs are comparatively
soft and cleavage is total. If the yolk of the frog's egg is packed
down by centrifuging, cleavage may be partial as in higher
vertebrates without detriment to the embryo (Hertwig, 1899).
The eggs of Amphibia vary enormously in the amount of yolk
they contain and there is considerable evidence that the simplified
cleavage pattern found in the common frog has been secondarily
imposed by a reduction in the amount of yolk in the egg. The
cleavage of Hemidactylium is more diagrammatic than that of
Eurycea, for although a more specialized type, its eggs contain
less yolk (Humphrey, 1928). A cleavage which is diagrammatic
is not necessarily primitive in any vertebrate. Cleavage is a
period of rearrangement of nuclear material in relation to the
cytoplasm. Qualitative changes do not occur, hence alteration
of cleavage pattern by pressure has no permanent effect on the
embryo. Cleavage results in the formation of a hollow sphere
with walls usually several cells thick. The hollow or blastocoel
is frequently very shallow and in the large-yolked species may be
merely a slit between apical cells and underlying yolk.

Gastrulation.—A certain amount of differentiation occurs
before cleavage. This is revealed externally by the formation
of the gray crescent alluded to above. If this region is cut
away from the egg the latter is unable to develop (Moszkowski,
1902). In the urodeles, a gray crescent has been described in
the axolotl (Vogt, 1926) but it is scarcely visible in the European
newts which have been extensively studied by Spemann and his
associates. During cleavage the cells of the pigmented hemisphere of the egg divide more rapidly than the heavily yolk-

---

view of embryo 26 days old; length 11 mm.; 26 to 27 myotomes; eye, ear, nasal
pits, and mouth well defined. *I*. Side view of embryo 36 days and 16 hours old;
length 16 mm.; 36 to 38 myotomes. *J*. Side view of larva 49 days old; length 21
mm. *K*. Side view of larva 97 days old; length 34 mm. (*After Eycleshymer and
Wilson.*)

laden cells of the opposite pole. A continuation of this process causes the cells of the first region to tend to grow over those of the second. The gray crescent region takes the lead in cell proliferation and becomes the dorsal lip of the blastopore, growing as a crescentic fold over a section approximately 100 degrees of the egg. The slitlike cavity between lip and infolded yolk cells represents the archenteron, or rudiment of the gut. This eventually either opens at its anterior end into the blastocoel or obliterates it by crowding. Since the overgrowth of the cells of the dorsal hemisphere extends completely around the egg, the blastopore becomes a gradually diminishing circular fold engulfing

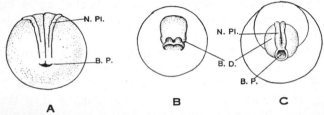

A   B   C

Fig. 10.—Blastopore of a salamander and caecilian compared. In salamanders and most frogs the overgrowth of cells of the dorsal hemisphere during gastrulation extends completely around the egg; in caecilians the blastodisc or overgrowth forms a circular blastopore while the yolk hemisphere is still uncovered. *A.* Late blastopore of Cryptobranchus (*after Smith*). *B* and *C.* Two stages in the formation of the blastopore of Ichthyophis (*after the Sarasins*). *B.D.*, blastodisc; *B.P.*, blastopore; *N.Pl.*, neural plate.

the more slowly dividing yolk cells. In some plethodontid salamanders, the circle remains incomplete ventrally and the blastopore takes the form of an inverted crescent (Humphrey, 1928). The embryo-forming materials of the gray crescent are at first broadly distributed as a ring or crescent about the circumference of the egg. They are brought together not only by overgrowth during gastrulation but also by concrescence of the two halves of the gray crescent in the midline. Hence the point of concrescence, namely the dorsal lip of the blastopore, comes to have a more important role in organ formation than the ventral lip.

In frogs and salamanders the whole of the yolk hemisphere is covered over as the blastopore closes, but it is a very interesting fact that in the caecilians, which seem to have descended independently from primitive tetrapods, the blastopore becomes circular while the yolk hemisphere is still largely uncovered (Fig. 10). In this way the blastopore becomes surrounded by blastodisc while the latter still remains on the upper surface of a partly divided egg. This is a very important step in the direction of reptilian development. If the developing embryo should sink into this blastodisc until the surrounding tissue folded over it as an amnion, if cleavage were further delayed in the yolk hemisphere, and if, as development proceeded, the urinary bladder were converted into a large respiratory membrane, the allantois, the gap between amphibian and reptilian types of development would be bridged. The earliest Amphibia, as revealed by their fossil skeletons, were hardly separable from the earliest reptiles. It seems likely that their mode of development resembled that of the caecilians, many of which today lay their eggs on land. In any case, the result of gastrulation is the development of a double-layered sac out of a single-layered hollow sphere, and this event is of great significance in the origin of structures.

Larvae.—The frog embryo, as it develops within the egg capsule, shows various conformations which can be identified as the anlage of organs. The head end exhibits two swellings which may be recognized as eyes. Between them, and sometimes extending posteriorly in the midline, is a more densely pigmented stripe. This is the site of the unicellular hatching glands (Chap. VI) which are destined to free the larvae of both frogs and salamanders from their egg capsules. A conspicuous pit in the developing head of the frog embryo may be recognized as the mouth. At this early stage the deepest part of the pit in some species of Rana is formed by the hypophysial ingrowth of the pituitary (Chap. XIII). The position of the future external nares is indicated by a pair of depressions, above and usually lateral to the mouth. Below the mouth a pair of pigmented eminences, or frequently a V-shaped furrow, is the first indication of the growing adhesive organs (Fig. 11). At the time of hatching these structures form a pair of adhesive organs of value in permitting the larva to hold to its egg capsule, or other objects. In most salamander larvae these adhesive organs find their homology in a pair of glandular stalks, the balancers, which project from near the angle of the mouth and have the same function as the adhesive organs of tadpoles. These structures are further discussed in the following chapter.

Immediately caudal to the optic eminences a series of three or four ridges indicates the developing branchial arches of both

frog and salamander larvae. The external branchiae early
begin to sprout on these arches as a number of small buds. With
development a fold appears anterior to the first of these gills.
In the frog tadpole this is destined to grow back over the external
gills and form an opercular sac which remains in communication
with the exterior by one or two small openings, the spiracles.
An opercular fold is represented in salamander larvae but it

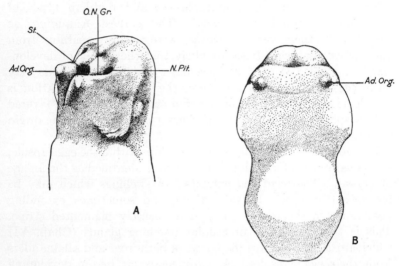

FIG. 11.—The head structures of the early larva of a toad, *Gastrophryne carolinensis*. The adhesive organs function at the time of hatching to hold the tadpole to objects in the water. The oro-nasal groove forms the beginning of the nasal chamber. *Ad.Org.*, adhesive organ; *N.Pit.*, nasal pit; *O.N.Gr.*, oro-nasal groove; *St.*, stomodaeum.

never completely covers the branchial arches until the time of
metamorphosis.

The chief difference between the larvae of frogs and salamanders lies in the mouth region. In most frog tadpoles, lips
are formed and these acquire a series of horny teeth arranged
in rows above and below a pair of strong mandibles. These
nippers are supported internally by a pair of cartilages, called
"superior" and "inferior labial cartilages." The former, which
articulate with cartilaginous processes of the brain case, are
destined to form the premaxillaries of the adult; the latter,
the mento-Meckelian bones. The inferior labial cartilages are
supported by a pair of short cartilages, the very rudimentary
Meckelian, or lower jaw cartilages. Most remarkable is the

forward extension of the palatoquadrate cartilage of each side to give support to these Meckelian cartilages. In salamanders, horny teeth or typical mandibles never appear, and the jaws which are well provided with true teeth are long from the first stages of development. This apparently enormous difference in the structure of the mouths of tadpole and salamander is bridged over by various intermediate types. As stated below (page 52), some salamanders have horny plates on their jaws, and many frog tadpoles, as, for example, most Brevicipitidae, lack horny teeth.

Some of the developing internal organs are indicated on the outer surface of the embryos or larvae of frogs and salamanders. Of these, the most conspicuous is the pronephros. The developmental history of these structures is given in the following chapters, and only the external changes of development need be indicated here. The adhesive organs and balancers are lost at about the time the larvae begin to feed. The gills elongate and in salamanders assume a form more or less characteristic of the species. In frogs the extent of the operculum and the position of its spiracle differ with the species. The vent, which becomes perforated at this time, may lie on the side of the tail fin or ventral to it, and this position is again a character of systematic importance. The intestine in most frog tadpoles becomes very long and coiled like a watch spring. As discussed in a following chapter, this is an adaptation to the vegetarian diet of most tadpoles and is not characteristic of all species. In frog tadpoles the forelimbs develop within the opercular sac and do not appear until the time of metamorphosis. The hind limbs of both frog and salamander continue their growth during larval life. The lungs are present in the larvae of most frogs and salamanders and function both as hydrostatic and respiratory structures. At the end of larval life the frog tadpoles lose their larval teeth, tail, and gills. The eyes develop lids, and many pronounced changes of skull and viscera occur. Metamorphosis in salamander larvae is less revolutionary, for a broad mouth and true teeth are already present. Nevertheless, many changes occur in the skull, skin, and respiratory system. These changes are discussed in detail below (Chaps. VI, VII, and X).

Mechanics of Development.—The tissues which take part in the formation of the various structures of Amphibia are being analyzed experimentally by an increasingly large number of investigators. Some of their more general conclusions may be considered here, for they have an important bearing on the causes of the diversity of structure distinguishing species. At the close of gastrulation the potencies for organ formation are segregated in various parts of the embryo, although there may be no external evidence of this mosaic formation of qualitatively unlike regions. Little or no regulation can occur if one of these regions is removed. Thus, if an area destined to produce a forelimb is dissected away from an Ambystoma embryo at the time of the appearance of the tail bud, the region will remain permanently limbless (Harrison, 1915). In considering the origin of structure one must examine first the origin of potencies.

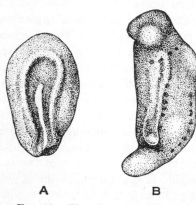

FIG. 12.—The effect of an organizer. A. Neurula of the newt, *Triturus taeniatus*, with a secondary medullary plate (the narrow white band) induced by a transplanted organizer from another species of newt, *T.cristatus*. B. Embryo of *T.taeniatus* seen from the left side. The secondary embryonic growth consists of neural tube and some associated structures. (*Both after Spemann.*)

At the very beginning of gastrulation the embryo of the newt is not a mosaic of potential parts. If a piece of ectoderm which would become neural plate is transplanted into the place which would become gills, it develops into gills. A little later in gastrulation the same operation will produce no change, for the presumptive neural plate tissue remains neural plate. If the exchange is made at the beginning of gastrulation between the embryos of two species of newts readily distinguished by their color, the tissue which would have become neural plate is molded into gill tissue as before, but the tissue resembles that of the donor species in color and character. During gastrulation, transplanted tissue may be molded by the host embryo (Figs. 12, 13) but this tissue does not lose its specific identity (Spemann, 1928).

What is the nature of this molding influence? Spemann and his associates have shown that it emanates from the turned-in dorsal lip of the blastopore, the gray crescent region of the frog's egg. Geinitz (1925) transplanted a piece of this potential chorda-mesoderm into the archenteron of a European newt and found that it induced the overlying ectoderm to form a neural plate. Since the secondarily induced embryo need not have the same orientation as the primary one, the organizer has a longitudinal axis of its own. Further, it has some laterality, for if dorsal lip tissue from one side is replaced by tissue from the opposite side of another egg, two similar half embryos tend to develop from the egg. Nevertheless, the molding influence, or

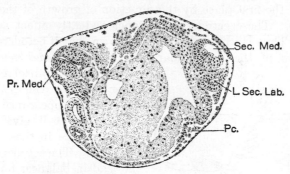

FIG. 13.—Section of an egg of the newt, *T. taeniatus*, in which a piece of dorsal lip from the egg of *T.cristatus* has been transplanted and has induced there a secondary embryo. *L.Sec.Lab.*, left secondary ear vesicle; *Pc.*, pericardium; *Pr.Med.*, primary medullary tube; *Sec.Med.*, secondary medullary tube. (*After Spemann and Mangold.*)

"organizer," as it is called, is nothing specific. Geinitz (1925) showed that gray crescent material from a frog, Bombina, could induce a secondary embryo in a newt. The organizer seems to be something retained in the tissues for a considerable time. A neural tube induced by a piece of dorsal lip tissue when transplanted into the archenteron of a young gastrula induces another neural tube to form in the overlying ectoderm. Mangold and Spemann (1927) have shown that brain tissue from a free-swimming tadpole can induce the formation of a medullary plate. This makes it appear likely that the organizer is chemical in nature. Nevertheless, the organizer seems to require contact for its spread. Brachet (1923) found that it could not exert its influence beyond a cut.

As development continues, the organized tissue becomes in turn an organizer, influencing the development of adjacent tissue. The anterior part of the neural plate folds over to form a brain, and evaginations from the sides of the inturned plate extend toward the now overlying ectoderm. In several species of

Amphibia, each evagination which becomes the optic cup of that side induces a lens to form in the overlying ectoderm; foreign ectoderm transplanted over the cup is similarly modified. During gastrulation in the urodele, but apparently earlier in some species of frog (Brachet, 1927), but not in others (Schotté, 1930), the potencies for many structures are localized in the ectoderm. Areas which are to give rise to gills, balancer, nose, ear, hypophysis, etc., are segregated according to a pattern which seems controlled in the first place by the direction of growth of the dorsal lip tissue. These ectodermal potencies greatly affect adjacent tissues. Thus Harrison (1925) has shown that if ectoderm from the region of the mandibular arch of *Ambystoma maculatum*

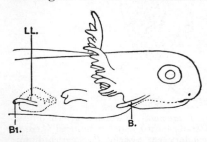

FIG. 14.—The influence of the ectoderm in balancer formation in Ambystoma. A supernumerary b a l a n c e r developed from ectoderm transplanted from another individual shortly before the normal appearance of its balancer. *B*, balancer of host; *B₁*, balancer developed from grafted ectoderm; *LL.*, lateral line sense organs appearing in the grafted ectoderm. (*After Harrison.*)

embryos is transplanted to other parts of the body just before the appearance of the balancer, it will give rise to this structure in these regions (Fig. 14). The ectoderm takes the lead in balancer formation and seems to condense the underlying intercellular ground substance into a fibrillar membrane which gives support to the ectoderm. Harrison suggests that this modifying influence may be a type of enzyme action. As development continues the balancer attracts a twig from the mandibular branch of the fifth nerve. If the balancer rudiment is transplanted to a posterior position it may attract a twig from a more posterior nerve or even from similar nerves in a frog tadpole.

Epigenesis.—Many other striking cases of the effect of one tissue on the growth of another tissue have been demonstrated by experimental embryologists. The parts of a structure may effect one another during growth, while together they may mold adjacent tissues or be influenced by nutritional or hormonal conditions of the body. For example, the two common salamanders *Ambystoma maculatum* and *A. tigrinum* grow at different rates and the latter reaches a much larger size than the former. If the eye of *A. tigrinum* is transplanted during an embryonic stage to' the embryo of *A. maculatum,* it will continue to grow in this new environment at its own specific rate and will reach the same large size as the eye which was not transplanted (Harrison, 1929). Three or four months after the operation, the transplanted *A. tigrinum* eye is approximately double the size of the *A. maculatum* eye of the host and demonstrates in a convincing manner that even such matters as size may be determined by factors within the tissues of an organ. If the grafted eye should be taken from an older animal, its growth is at first retarded (Twitty, 1930). This is apparently due to the fact that the body of the host had not yet developed to the point where it could release the growth mechanism of the grafted eye. Even though the potential size of the eye is determined by intrinsic factors of the eye tissue, the realization of this potentiality depends upon certain changing conditions of development in the body of the host (Twitty, 1930).

If the lens ectoderm alone is transplanted from *Ambystoma tigrinum* to *A. maculatum* embryos, a lens is produced which is at first too large for the eye (Harrison, 1929). The growth of this lens is retarded but it in turn stimulates the bulb to more rapid growth so that it becomes 30 per cent larger in diameter than the bulb of the control. The bulb may also have an effect upon the lens, for if the lens ectoderm of *A. maculatum* is transplanted to *A. tigrinum,* the lens which was at first too small for the bulb retards the growth of the latter while its own growth is accelerated. The size of the trabecula which forms the lateral wall of the brain case in the orbital region is influenced by the size of the adjacent eye. If the eye of *A. tigrinum* is transplanted into the site of an *A. maculatum* eye, the trabecula on this side shows a marked enlargement throughout most of its length (Twitty, 1929).

The skeleton is of importance in phylogenetic studies, chiefly because it is usually the only part of extinct species which is preserved in the fossil and therefore serves as the only basis of comparison with living forms. The close correlation between the skeleton and adjacent tissues is not a chance relation. The eye, as shown in the above experiments, controls the size of the trabecula. The auditory vesicle migrating from the overlying ectoderm induces the development of a cartilaginous capsule about itself even when transplanted to the region of the eye (Luther, 1925). The cartilaginous nasal capsules of Ambystoma were shown by Burr (1916) to be dependent on the nasal sacs for their conformation. In brief, the skull is not merely molded by the paired sense organs; parts of it are unable to develop a normal form unless the sense organs are present.

Cartilage usually arises in the mesenchyme by a condensation and transformation of this mesodermic tissue. But the tissue which produces the branchial arches of both urodeles and frogs migrates for the most part from a portion of the neural crest. The removal of this portion of the ectoderm or mesectoderm in the branchial region results in marked deficiencies in the hyobranchial apparatus in urodeles (Stone, 1926). A similar operation in frog embryos has demonstrated that the mesectoderm gives rise to Meckel's cartilage, the palatoquadrate, the supra- and infrarostral cartilages, the anterior portions of the trabeculae, and the hyobranchial skeleton exclusive of the basihyal and second basibranchial (Stone, 1929).

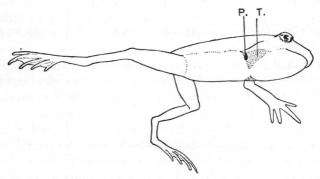

Fig. 15.—Part of the mechanism of metamorphosis in *Rana pipiens*. Histolysis of the operculum by the degenerating gills. The forelimb was removed at an earlier stage. *P.*, perforation; *T.*, histolysized area. (*After Helff.*)

Secondary organizers are not confined to the ectoderm but are located in various parts of the body. The potencies for limb formation with the resulting cartilage and bone development are first localized in the mesoderm and these influence the overlying epidermis. The potencies for gill formation occur in the entoderm but they can act only on a limited portion of the ecto- and mesoderm (Severinghaus, 1930). This influence of one tissue upon another is not restricted to the earlier stages of development. The frog tadpole during metamorphosis does not thrust its forefeet through the overlying membranes by sheer force.

Helff (1926) has shown that the atrophying gills produce a substance which digests two neat holes in the confining cover (Fig. 15). Further, the metamorphosing tadpole owes the formation of its eardrums to the influence of the annular cartilages which come to underlie the integument of the ear region. Foreign integument

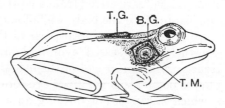

Fig. 16.—The effect of the annular tympanic cartilage on the formation of the tympanic membrane. Skin transplanted from the back to the tympanic region develops a tympanic membrane by the influence of the underlying tympanic cartilage. Skin from the tympanic region transplanted to the back fails to develop a tympanum. *B.G.*, back-skin graft; *T.G.*, skin graft from tympanic membrane region transplanted to the back; *T.M.*, tympanic membrane. (*After Helff, O. M., Studies on Amphibian Metamorphosis, Physiol. Zool., Vol. I, No. 4, adapted from Plate IV, Fig. 13.*)

transplanted over an annulus is molded (Fig. 16) into a tympanum (Helff, 1928).

Basis of Homology.—The induction of structures by organizers of various grades is probably due to chemical substances, and these may have different positions in such related types as the frog and the newt. In Rana the roof of the archenteron persists as the dorsal lining of the alimentary tract, a median strip of topmost cells becomes the notochord, and the dorsal mesoderm splits off from the roof on either side of this. In the newt, the whole roof of the archenteron in the midline becomes converted into notochord, and the gut is completed dorsally by the ingrowth of yolk cells from the side. Undoubtedly homologous structures such as the gut of the frog and the newt may thus differ considerably in their manner of origin. The organ-inducing materials are most probably homologous but their center of activity has been shifted. Similar changes of position of organ-forming substances in the developing embryo may have been responsible for the different final positions of various parts such as the limbs in frogs and urodeles. The somites which form these structures in the two types may be those nearer or farther from the head, but the hind limbs of the first are nevertheless homologous with those of the second in spite of these different muscle-segment origins.

At an early stage of development the potencies for organ formation may extend beyond the region which eventually gives rise to a structure. This manifests itself in the tendency for transplanted tissue to form more than it would in the course of normal ontogeny. Thus, Adelmann (1929) found that a small median piece of neural plate, removed from a newt or Ambystoma embryo and transplanted into the body wall of another one, gave rise to a single eye in addition to dorsal parts of the brain, while the donor, nevertheless, possessed eyes and brain of normal proportion. Hence, the anterior end of the neural plate of these salamander embryos possesses generalized eye-forming potencies, any portion of which is capable of forming an eye. A median piece of the neural plate removed from its normal environment and thereby released from the influences of surrounding parts differentiates into an eye, although in the normal course of ontogeny this tissue would have had a different fate.

The organ-forming substances may produce their effects at different times in different Amphibia. In the eggs of some frogs the potencies are apparently localized earlier than in the newts (Brachet, 1927), and this may be one of the reasons why the mesoblastic pouches, obviously primitive structures, still appear in the development of some urodeles but not in pouch form in the frogs. On the other hand, two such closely related frogs as *Rana fusca* and *R. esculenta* may differ considerably in the localization of potencies. The first requires the presence of the optic cup to induce lens formation, while in the second species the lens is self-differentiating. There is some evidence that even in the newt a certain amount of self-differentiation occurs in the neural plate independent of the inturned dorsal lip (Lehmann, 1926), and a sharp line cannot always be drawn between dependent and self-differentiating development. In fact, some tissues may be under some circumstances dependent and under others independent. This principle of double assurance (Spemann, 1928) is probably widespread in early stages of development.

Development of Limbs.—Further, there must be considered the phenomenon that one axis of a structure may become fixed before another. Thus, in the early limb buds of Ambystoma, the dorsoventral axis can be inverted and yet the palm, as it develops, will appear face downward, for the dorsoventral axis is not established at this stage. The anteroposterior axis, however, is fixed at the same stage and an inversion of the bud brings the first digit, when it appears, in the position of the last (Harrison, 1921). This polarization of the anteroposterior axis resides in the limb mesoderm and not in the surrounding tissue. Detwiler (1929) showed that when the mesoderm of a forelimb of Ambystoma was inverted and grafted into slightly older embryos, a limb with reversed asymmetry differentiated.

The determination of the anteroposterior axis of the limbs is made long before they appear as rudiments (Detwiler, 1929). The anterior extremities develop much later in *Ambystoma tigrinum* than in *A. maculatum;* nevertheless the dorsoventral axis of these limbs is determined at about the same time in the two species (Ruud, 1926). Brandt (1927) finds that the fixation of the limb axes of Pleurodeles, a primitive salamandrid, occurs at approximately the same time as in Ambystoma. This is of interest, for in Triturus, a more specialized salamandrid, this fixation of limb axes occurs at an earlier stage of development. The same is true of the shoulder girdle, its axes being determined earlier in Triturus than in Ambystoma (Brandt, 1927). The shoulder girdle and limb, in spite of their close functional correlation, are determined independently, the latter at an earlier stage of development than the former (Swett, 1928). It would seem from these few cases that determination occurred earlier in the more specialized species and that it was not correlated with the time of appearance of the limbs, or with the period of girdle determination.

The limb as it develops is subject to influences which may modify it considerably. Schmalhausen (1925) showed that malnutrition or abnormally high temperatures retarded the development of the postaxial portions of the limbs of the axolotl. In some cases a fusion of the tarsal or carpal bones may occur as a result, either the tibiale with the mediale I, or the intermedium with centrale, or certain tarsalia with one another or with the fibulare. This was apparently due to the fact that growth and morphogenesis were retarded more than histogenesis in these regions. These observations invite a comparison with limb development in salamanders which normally differentiate rapidly and at a small size. In many of these, such as Manculus and Hemidactylium, it is the postaxial part of the feet which has suffered the greatest reduction.

Influence of Function.—Many structures, after they have appeared as rudiments, are dependent on function for their complete elaboration. If the legs of a tadpole are early removed, the hind brain will remain stunted (Dürken, 1912); if the eyes are removed, the optic lobes of the brain become reduced (Steinitz, 1906). Constitutional growth factors of heart, gills, and apparently of pronephros are readily modified if such organs are transplanted to parts of the body where they may grow but are unable, because of conditions there, to realize their normal functions.

The influence of function is especially well marked in the development of the nervous system. Excitations received from the sense organs have an important influence on the growth of the nerve centers in the central nervous system during each ontogeny. In the cord, moreover, there is a proliferation and arrangement of cells in response to the growth of descending fiber tracts. Such a growth makes possible the individuation of reflexes out of the primary behavior pattern. When function is lost in the forelimb of Ambystoma, the cellular areas within the branchial segments may be reduced to 60 per cent of the normal (Nicholas, 1929), and this reduction is apparently due to the failure of cell proliferation in the absence of descending fiber connections.

The need of the functional stimulus of light for the retention of a well-developed retina is discussed below in the case of the Cave Salamander, Typhlotriton. There is no sharp separation of the period when function will exert its effect from that when chemodifferentiation prevails. Thus, the extent of muscular development in the tail of tadpoles is apparently correlated with the amount of exercise they receive, but the color change of the tail skin which occurs at metamorphosis is inherent in the skin and not produced by the degenerating tissue below. Tail skin transplanted to the back undergoes the usual color change at metamorphosis (Lindeman, 1929). The nervous system is not indispensable for the development of limbs nor for the histological differentiation of its tissues (Mangold, 1929). A nerveless limb does not reach the size of a normal one and here lack of function would seem to be exerting an influence.

During development there arises a series of organs which release secretions having an effect not merely on adjacent tissues as in the case of organizers but frequently on many parts of the body.

These are the glands of internal secretion such as the pituitary and the thyroid. We shall consider them in greater detail in another chapter, although some have an important influence on development.

From this outline of the mechanics of development it is clear that any one of many alterations of development might account for the differences between two species. The integument of the head of a frog might be able to produce a tympanum but if—due to some modification of development—the tympanic annulus were held at a distance from the integument, no tympanum would develop. Brachet (1927) concluded from his experiments with *Rana fusca* that the amount of gray crescent material present in the egg at the time of fertilization determined the size attained by the adult frog. It may be inferred from the work of Uhlenhuth (1920) on salamanders that the amount of hormone released by the anterior lobe of the pituitary of the growing individual has an important effect on size. Burns and Burns (1929), however, united embryos of *Ambystoma tigrinum* with *A. maculatum* in pairs and noted that the larvae as they developed retained their specific growth rates and grew to the size characteristic of their own species. Thus, capacity for growth would seem to be inherent in the tissues of a species, although the addition or removal of some endocrine substances from the body may influence the result (see Chap. XVIII). No doubt the reduction or loss of some chemodifferentiators in the early embryo is the immediate cause for the failure of certain structures to appear. Thus, Harrison showed that ectoderm from the balancer region of the early embryo *Ambystoma tigrinum*, which usually lacks a balancer, if transplanted on the head of *A. maculatum*, fails to induce a balancer in this species which normally possesses one. There is something missing in the ectoderm of the mandibular arch ectoderm of *A. tigrinum* which is present in that of *A. maculatum*.

Although lack of function or of certain chemodifferentiators at critical stages of development may be the immediate cause of differences existing between two species, these embryonic conditions are in turn determined by the specificity of the germ plasm itself, which is provided by the chromosomes with their equipment of genes. Every cell of the embryo's body has the same complement of chromosomes as the fertilized egg. Developmental changes are due to a progressive change in the cytoplasm, and this change is produced presumably by the chromosomes in the first place, since these alone are known to be the bearers of hereditary characters. The establishment of the center of rapid cell division in the gray crescent and the development of gradients of cell activity from this center give the necessary conditions for localizing potencies in different parts of the embryo along these gradients. Once "the embryo in the rough" is established, however, development is not merely an unfolding of these potencies, for the tissues containing the potencies react on one another and are modified by function and by environmental influences. Every animal possesses more potentialities than are ever realized; the conditions of development, and especially the environment, determine what characters will appear.

Regeneration.—Larval salamanders frequently snap off each others' legs or gills if they are crowded together in dishes. Some terrestrial salamanders, especially plethodontids, will leave part of their tail in the hand which attempts to seize them. The autotomy of the tail resembles that of many lizards, although it is not so spontaneous as in the geckonids, and the split occurs between the vertebrae instead of along an intravertebral split. Nevertheless, the tail of some plethodontids seems modified in anticipation of its being lost, for a constriction occurs around its base at the point where the tail readily breaks off. The lost parts of both young and old are regenerated. The phenomenon of regeneration seems to be a highly adaptive mechanism in these aquatic larvae and terrestrial plethodontids, permitting these forms to succeed under difficult conditions of livelihood. Ability to regenerate is, however, not closely correlated with liability to injury in Amphibia. Newts may regenerate their hyoids (Bogoljubsky, 1924) and frogs their lungs (Westphal, 1925). The protected gills of tadpoles may regenerate, while the exposed gills of axolotls may not attain on regeneration the form of the original structures (Wurmbach, 1926). Natural selection has played only a minor part in the distribution of the capacity to regenerate. The latter is a common faculty of the tissues of animals but one which has been reduced during phylogeny (Korschelt, 1927).

The power of regeneration diminishes with increasing organization usually during both ontogeny and phylogeny. Adult newts can regenerate new limbs but do this more slowly than larvae of the same species. In reptiles and especially in higher vertebrates the capacity to regenerate is greatly restricted. The Salientia on the other hand, which are more primitive than salamanders in many features of their skeleton, show only slight regenerative ability during adult life. Alytes can restore extremities if they are cut off just before metamorphosis, but even this capacity is lost in the more advanced Salientia. Metamorphosed frogs, however, have been reported to regenerate single digits and partial limbs.

Relation of Regeneration to Development.—The tissues which take part in regeneration may be derived from already differentiated cells, but more usually undifferentiated cells are marshaled together to form the new structures. The regeneration of the lens illustrates well the first kind of regeneration. Although the lens is formed originally from ectoderm under the influence of the optic cup, it may regenerate from the iris in both frogs and salamanders. The iris cells undergo a loss of pigmentation, dedifferentiate, and develop a new type of structure to form a lens. In the more usual type of regeneration, connective tissues form a mass below the surface of the wound and begin to grow and differentiate in the manner of embryonic tissues. Regeneration may be described as the induced development of undifferentiated tissues.

The close relation of regeneration to development is well shown in the recent work which has been done on the growth of limbs in Amphibia (see reviews by Mangold, 1929; Korschelt, 1927; and Przibram, 1927). When the limb of a salamander larva is cut off, the new limb bones develop not from the bone rudiments in the stump but from the blastema growing over the stump (Weiss, 1922). A boneless forelimb transplanted to the back of a salamander will regenerate its proper bones (Bischler, 1926). A complete foot can develop from a cross-section of only half an extremity. There is no part-for-part influence even when regenerating bones and bone stumps lie adjacent to one another (Weiss, 1925). The blastema lying above the wound contains the determinants of the complete part within itself. Weiss (1926) removed the skin from a limb stump and covered it with lung tissue to prevent necrosis. The stump regenerated skin as well as skeleton and musculature. Sections revealed that the skin of the regenerated limb had no corium in the part covered by the lung. Hence the corium of the regenerated limb skin had apparently been derived, like the skeleton, from the blastema of the stump.

Extremities have been induced to develop on the side of the body at a distance from the original limbs by introducing into the side portions of the otic capsules or pieces of celloidin (Balinsky, 1926, 1927; Filatow, 1927). In these cases it would seem that material from the normal extremity, either anterior or posterior to the wound, had been attracted to the new wound surface. These undifferentiated cells of the extremities in the new locality become organizers of the surrounding material to form a limb. G. Hertwig (1927) transplanted the limb buds of haploid newt larvae on diploid individuals of the same species. The haploid material partially degenerated through lack of vitality and was replaced by diploid host cells. The diploid tissue was thus organized by haploid limb rudiments. The organizing center would seem to lie in the mesoderm and not in the ectoderm as would appear to be the case of the balancer, since covering of a limb rudiment by foreign ectoderm does not prevent the development of mesoderm into extremities (Detwiler, 1922; Ekman, 1922).

With the development of the limb rudiment, functional adjustments between the parts take place. Although an extremity can develop without a girdle (Brandt, 1926), or two girdles may be present with one limb, secondary adjustments take place which may be correlated with function during development. Brandt (1927) showed that one girdle possessing two extremities will develop two glenoid cavities or one wide one for the two heads of the humeri. Swett (1926) found that the glenoid fossa did not develop at all when the extremity was absent. Although the nerves are not necessary for the early growth of the limbs, they appear necessary for the full elaboration of these structures. If the nerves are prevented from growing into the limb bud, the latter differentiates normally, but the resulting limb is 10 per cent shorter and 50 per cent narrower than normal limbs. The atrophy is most marked during the functional stage. Hence, function has an important influence on the quantity of tissue and on the maintenance of its form.

When a limb regenerates from the base of another one and forms a duplication, the secondary limb is usually a mirror image of the primary limb. This has been explained by assuming that every extremity anlage has the potentiality of forming two mirror image extremities, but normally one of these is inhibited by the growth of the other. Triplicate formation of limbs may be experimentally produced, however, making further assumptions necessary. A simpler explanation assumes that the anterior-posterior axis of the secondary limb rudiment is influenced by the primary limb and develops as a mirror image of it. The dorsoventral axis is determined by the factors at the base of the growing limb. Since the anteroposterior axis of the limbs, whether primary or secondary, is generally determined in Amphibia much earlier than the dorsoventral, a reversal of the lateral quality is induced by the inversion of the antero-posterior axes of the secondary buds (Swett, 1927). The determination of the axes in regenerating limbs would, according to this explanation, follow the same course as in normal development, with an interval between the determination of each of the axes. The effect of injuries which produce duplications consists in the weakening of the dominance in the limb center so that one or, rarely, more peripheral regions of the rudiment become independent and sprout as additional limbs.

Regenerative Capacity.—The regenerative capacity is greater in the tail than in the extremities and greater in the posterior than in the anterior limbs (Ubisch, 1923). This may be due to the fact that the posterior regions are growing more actively than the anterior. The foot of the toad loses its power of regeneration at a stage before it is completely differentiated, while the newt, as stated above, conserves the power of regeneration its entire life. It has been suggested that the salamander limb may contain more undifferentiated cells than the developing limb of the toad, but there is little histological evidence in favor of such an assumption. The factors which have brought about the restriction of the regenerative capacity in some groups of Amphibia but not in others are still unknown. Many factors influence the rate of regeneration. If the wound surface is sewed together or its healing hastened, regeneration may be prevented or delayed in salamanders (Schaxel, 1921). Swimming movements not only hasten the regeneration of the tail but may actually prevent its growth in an oblique direction (Harms, 1910). If function has such a marked effect on the regeneration of the tail, it probably has an equal effect on its normal growth. Hormones which influence growth affect regeneration. Thyroidectomy retards the regeneration of the hind limbs of salamanders (Walter, 1911), while hypophysectomy prevents the regeneration of limbs and tail in the adults (Schotté, 1926). Since large losses up to a certain limit are repaired more rapidly than small ones, there is apparently an increase in the energy of regeneration with increase in the size of the wound.

The regenerative repair of injuries may lead to many kinds of growths in Amphibia. Salamanders may develop forked tails, extra digits, or complete supernumerary limbs. The healing of wounds represents a type of regeneration. After blood clotting, the epithelial cells of the edges of the wound grow out over the exposed surface. If a young Necturus is beheaded, the wound heals and the body may continue to grow and differentiate for two months (Eycleshymer, 1914). Structures which regenerate show no decrease in the rate of regeneration after successive removals (Zeleny, 1916).

Regeneration is a type of developmental regulation which results in the replacement of parts normally lying peripherally to the cut surface. In adult Amphibia the body is a mosaic of regenerative territories, having different morphological potentialities. The complete extirpation of one of these regions prevents its regeneration. Transplanting it to some other part of the body does not destroy its specificity (Guyénot and Ponse, 1930).

There are other types of regulation which may be confused with regeneration. If a limb bud is split in the growing larva it will develop into two limbs. The latter phenomenon is comparable to the twinning produced by restricting the fertilized egg of the newt in the midline during the two cell stage.

Hybridization. —Hybrids between different species, genera, and even families of Amphibia, have been reported, but such individuals rarely grow to maturity and in many cases may be false hybrids resulting from the activation of the egg by the sperm without the transmission of the paternal characters. The European newts have been the most extensively hybridized. A large percentage of the species have been successfully crossed by Wolterstorff, Schreitmüller, Poll, and others (Schreitmüller, 1912). In some cases species which have never been known to cross in nature produced true hybrids in the laboratory tanks (Schreitmüller, 1913). Newts carry the spermatozoa for long periods in the spermatheca of the female and possibly also in the oviduct where fertilization occurs. Hence, the identification of the young as the offspring of any particular male becomes often difficult. In some cases hybrids may be recognized by the appearance of specific characters of the male in the offspring. True hybrids with characters of the male species have been produced various times among European newts, perhaps most recently by Bataillon (1927). There seems to be no doubt that very distinct species of Triturus are able to hybridize.

European Salientia have frequently been crossed. As long ago as 1883, Héron Royer described hybrids of the interfamily cross *Rana fusca* × *Pelobates fuscus* as exhibiting characters of both parents. Crosses between different species of Discoglossus and between species of Bufo gave hybrids with some male characters (Héron-Royer, 1891). The hybridization of various European Salientia and newts had recently been carefully studied by Hertwig (1918), who finds that true hybrids result from crossing a number of different species. Among the frogs studied, only *Rana arvalis* ♀ × *R. fusca* ♂ and *Bufo communis* ♀ × *B. viridis* ♂ developed into healthy adult hybrids. Crosses between Bufo and Rana gave, in some cases, true hybrids which, however, developed poorly. Usually the intergeneric and most interfamily crosses, if successful, developed into false hybrids, the male nucleus not entering into the cross. This was shown in hybrids of *Bufo communis* ♀ × *Pelobates fusca* ♂ where the nuclei of the body cells were only half the size of those of normal toads and hence were presumably haploid. In other cases, however, they were of the normal size and presumably diploid. Similar full-sized nuclei may appear in the progeny produced by irradiated sperm. As previous experiments had shown such sperm not to be functional, the diploid number of chromosomes had apparently been restored by a doubling of the maternal set of chromosomes. A similar restoration of the diploid number may occur in eggs developing parthenogenetically after pricking with a needle (Parmenter, 1920). From the work of Hertwig (1918) it would seem that most cases of intergeneric crosses were cases of activation by the spermatozoa without union of the hereditary material. Apparently, the nuclear material of widely separated species is incompatible and unable to enter into the formation of a zygote. This makes it especially important that the few reported cases of true intergeneric crosses should be confirmed. In no such case was an anatomical study made to determine how the generic characters combined.

Hybrid Salientia frequently develop slowly and often die at gastrulation when growth takes place at the expense of the yolk. Apparently the sperm nucleus in the foreign egg is unable to utilize the foreign yolk. Cell size varies with the species and the difference may be considerable in such closely related species as *Bufo vulgaris* and *B. viridis*. Hertwig (1930) suggests that the quantity of nuclear material available is a factor regulating the rate of yolk elaboration. If the nuclei transmit specific developmental potencies quantitatively proportional to their volume, one of the chief reasons for the failure of hybrids to develop may lie in this quantitative difference between available nuclear material and amount of yolk to be elaborated.

The study of hybridization has an important bearing on the origin of species. The hybrid between the European newts *Triturus cristatus* and *T. marmoratus* was described as a distinct species, *T. blasii*. Rollinat showed that hybrids were fertile *inter se* and with the parent stock (Boulenger, 1898). *T. blasii* occurs in France where the ranges of the two parent forms overlap. It is not considered a distinct species by some systematists. As discussed in another chapter, the criteria of a species are frequently difficult to define.

Frogs and toads combining the characters of two very distinct species are sometimes found in regions where the ranges of these forms overlap. These have sometimes been considered hybrids. Examples may be found among the African tree frogs which have been called *Leptopelis tessmanni* (Noble, 1924) and among the African toads described by Power (1926). In none of these cases have breeding experiments confirmed the hybrid character of these individuals.

Although experimental evidence is lacking, it seems certain that hybridization often occurs in nature where the ranges of two closely related subspecies overlap. Museums contain many specimens which cannot be more definitely assigned to one species than to the other. Crossing makes possible the recombination of characters and if the environment permits such hybrids to isolate themselves until a stock is well started, a new form may arise. This subject will be discussed more fully below. Aside from theory, the material available in museums suggests that hybridization of subspecies is a far more frequent phenomenon in nature than the crossing of species.

References

ADELMANN, H. B., 1929: Experimental studies on the development of the eye; II, The eye forming potencies of the median portions of the urodelan neural plate (*Triton teniatus* and *Amblystoma punctatum*), *Jour. Exp. Zool.*, LIV, 291–318.

BALINSKY, B. I., 1926: Weiteres zur Frage der experimentellen Induktion einer Extremitätenanlage, *Arch. Entw. Mech.*, CV, 718–731.

———, 1927: Über experimentelle Induktion der Extremitätenanlage bei Triton mit besonderer Berücksichtigung der Innervation und Symmetrieverhältnisse derselben, *Arch. Entw. Mech.*, CX, 71–88.

BATAILLON, E., 1910: L'embryogenèse complète provoquée chez les Amphibiens par piqûre de l'oeuf vierge, larves parthénogénésiques de *Rana fusca, Compt. rend. Acad. Sci.*, CL, 996–998.

———, 1927: Les croisements chez les Urodèles et l'androgénèse hybride, *Compt. rend. Soc. Biol.*, XCVII, 1715–1717.

BISCHLER, V., 1926: L'influence du squelette dans la régénération, et les potentialités des divers territoires du membre chez Triton cristatus, *Rev. Suisse Zool.*, XXXIII, 431–560, 3 pls.

BOGOLJUBSKY, S. N., 1924: Die Regeneration des Hyoidapparatus und des Unterkiefers beim Triton, *Rev. Zool. Russe*, IV, 168–169.

BOULENGER, G. A., 1898: [Exhibition of a hybrid male newt], *Proc. Zool. Soc. London*, 127.

BOWEN, ROBERT H., 1924: On the acrosome of the animal sperm, *Anat. Rec.*, XXVIII, 1–14.

BRACHET, A., 1923: Recherches sur les localisations germinales et leurs propriétés ontogénétiques dans l'oeuf de Rana fusca, *Arch. Biol.*, XXXIII, 343–430.

———, 1927: The localization of development factors, *Quart. Rev. Biol.*, II, 204–229.

BRANDT, W., 1926: Extremitätentransplantationen an Triton taeniatus, *Anat. Anz. Ergheft.*, LXI, 36–43.

———, 1927: Extremitätentransplantationen an Pleurodeles waltlii, *Anat. Anz. Ergheft.*, LXIII, 18–25.

BURNS, ROBERT K., and LUCILE M. BURNS, 1929: The growth of the whole organism and of the limbs in two species of Amblystoma united in parabiosis, *Jour. Exp. Zool.*, LIII, 455–477.

BURR, H. S., 1916: The effects of the removal of the nasal pits in Amblystoma embryos, *Jour. Exp. Zool.*, XX, 27–57.

DETWILER, S. R., 1922: Experiments on the transplantation of limbs in Amblystoma; Further observations on peripheral nerve connections, *Jour. Exp. Zool.*, XXXV, 115–161.

———, 1929: Transplantation of anterior limb mesoderm from Amblystoma embryos in the slit-blastopore stage, *Jour. Exp. Zool.*, LII, 315–324.

DÜRKEN, BERNHARD, 1912: Über frühzeitige Exstirpation von Extremitätenanlagen beim Frosch; Ein experimenteller Beitrag zur Entwicklungsphysiologie und Morphologie der Wirbeltiere unter besonderer Berücksichtigung des Nervensystems, *Zeitschr. Wiss. Zool.*, XCIX. 189–355, 1 pl.

EKMAN, G., 1922: Neue experimentelle Beiträge zur frühesten Entwicklung der Kiemenregion und Vorderextremität der Anuren, *Comm. Biol. Soc. Sci. Fenn.*, I, 3–96.

EYCLESHYMER, A. C., 1914: Some observations on the decapitated young Necturus, *Anat. Anz.*, XLVI, 1–13.

FILATOW, D., 1927: Aktievirung des Mesenchyms durch eine Ohrblase und einen Fremdkörper bei Amphibien, *Arch. Entw. Mech.*, CX, 1–32.

———, 1928: Über die Verpflanzung des Epithels und des Mesenchyms einer vorderen Extremitätenknospe bei Embryonen von Axolotl, *Arch. Entw. Mech.*, CXIII, 240–244.

GEINITZ, BRUNO, 1925: Embryonale Transplantation zwischen Urodelen und Anuren, *Arch. Entw. Mech.*, CVI, 357–408.

GUYÉNOT, E., and K. PONSE, 1930: Territoires de régénération et transplantations; Il, La réaction du territoire queue chez le triton et le lézard, *Bull. Biol. France et Belgique*, LXIV, 263–271.

HARMS, W., 1910: Über funktionelle Anpassung bei Regenerationsvorgängen, *Arch. ges. Physiol.*, CXXXII, 353–432.

HARRISON, Ross G., 1915: Experiments on the development of the limbs in Amphibia, *Proc. Nat. Acad. Sci. Wash.*, I, 539–544.

———, 1921: On relations of symmetry in transplanted limbs, *Jour. Exp. Zool.*, XXXII, 1–136.

———, 1925: The development of the balancer in Ambystoma, studied by the method of transplantation and in relation to the connective tissue problem, *Jour. Exp. Zool.*, XLI, 349–428.

———, 1929: Correlation in the development and growth of the eye studied by means of heteroplastic transplantation, *Arch. Entw. Mech.*, CXX, 1–55.

HELFF, O. M., 1926: Studies on amphibian metamorphosis; I, Formation of the opercular leg perforation in anuran larvae during metamorphosis. *Jour. Exp. Zool.*, XLV, 1–67, 6 pls.

———, 1928: Studies on amphibian metamorphosis; III, The influence of the annular tympanic cartilage on the formation of the tympanic membrane, *Physiol. Zool.*, I, 463–495, 4 pls.

HERLANT, M., 1911: Recherches sur les oeufs di- et trispermiques de grenouille, *Arch. Biol.*, XXVI, 103–336, 5 pls.

HÉRON-ROYER, L. F., 1883: Note sur l'hybridation des Batraciens anoures et ses produits congénères et bigénères, *Bull. Soc. Zool. France*, VIII, 397–416.

———, 1891: Nouveaux faits d'hybridation observés chez les Batraciens anoures, *Mem. Soc. Zool. France*, IV, 75–85.

HERTWIG, G., 1918: Kreuzungsversuche an Amphibien; I, Wahre und falsche Bastarde, *Arch. mikr. Anat.*, XCI, 203–266, 3 pls.

———, 1927: Beiträge zum Determinations und Regenerationsproblem mittels der Transplantation haploidkerniger Zellen, *Arch. Entw. Mech.*, CXI, 292–316.

———, 1930: Ungleichartige Ergebnisse reciproker Kreuzungen und ihre Ursachen, *Sitz. Abh. Naturf. Ges. Rostock.* (3), II, 113–117.

HERTWIG, O., 1899: Beiträge zur experimentellen Morphologie und Entwicklungsgeschichte; IV, Über einige durch Centrifugalkraft in der

Entwicklung des Froscheies hervorgerufenen Veränderungen, *Arch. mikr. Anat.*, LIII, 415–440, 2 pls.

HIBBARD, HOPE, 1928: La fécondation chez "Discoglossus pictus" Otth. *Compt. rend. Ass. Anat.*, XXIII, 191–195.

HUMPHREY, R. R., 1928: Ovulation in the four-toed salamander Hemidactylium scutatum, and the external features of cleavage and gastrulation, *Biol. Bull.*, LIV, 302–323.

KORSCHELT, E., 1927: Regeneration and Transplantation, I, Regeneration, Berlin.

LEHMANN, F. E., 1926: Entwicklungsstörungen in der Medullaranlage von Triton, erzeugt durch Unterlagerungsdefekte, *Arch. Entw. Mech.*, CVIII, 243–282.

LINDEMAN, V. F., 1929: Integumentary pigmentation in the frog Rana pipiens during metamorphosis, with especial reference to tail-skin histolysis, *Physiol. Zool.*, II, 255–268, 2 pls.

LUTHER, A., 1925: Entwicklungsmechanische Untersuchungen am Labyrinth einiger Anuren, *Comm. Biol. Soc. Sci. Fenn.*, II, 1–48.

MANGOLD, O., 1929: Das Determinationsproblem; II, Die paarigen Extremitäten der Wirbeltiere in der Entwicklung, *Ergebn. Biol.*, V, 290–404.

MANGOLD, O., and H. SPEMANN, 1927: Über Induktion von Medullarplatte durch Medullarplatte im jüngeren Keim, ein Beispiel homöogenetischer oder assimilatorischer Induktion, *Arch. Entw. Mech.*, CXI, 341–422.

MOSZKOWSKI, M., 1902: Zur Frage des Urmundschlusses bei R. fusca, *Arch. mikr. Anat.*, LX, 407–413.

NICHOLAS, J. T., 1929: An analysis of the responses of isolated portions of the amphibian nervous system, *Arch. Entw. Mech.*, CXVIII, 78–120.

NOBLE, G. K., 1924: Contributions to the Herpetology of the Belgian Congo based on the collection of the American Museum Congo Expedition; Part III, Amphibia, *Bull. Amer. Mus. Nat. Hist.*, XLIX, 147–347.

———, 1925: The evolution and dispersal of the frogs, *Amer. Naturalist*, LIX, 265–271.

NOBLE, G. K., and S. H. POPE, 1929: The modification of the cloaca and teeth of the adult salamander, Desmognathus, by testicular transplants and by castration, *Brit. Jour. Exp. Biol.*, VI, 399–411, 2 pls.

PARMENTER, C. L., 1920: The chromosomes of parthenogenetic frogs, *Jour. Gen. Physiol.*, II, 205–6.

POWER, J. H., 1926: Note on the occurrence of hybrid anura at Lobatsi, Bechuanaland Protectorate, *Proc. Zool. Soc. London*, 1926, Part III, 777–778, 1 pl.

PRZIBRAM, H., 1927: Deutungen spiegelbildlicher Lurcharme, (Zur Verständigung mit R. G. Harrison u. a.), *Arch. Entw. Mech.*, CIX, 411–448.

RUUD, G., 1926: The symmetry relations of transplanted limbs in Amblystoma tigrinum, *Jour. Exp. Zool.*, XLVI, 121–142.

SCHAXEL, J., 1921: Auffassungen und Erscheinungen der Regeneration; Untersuchungen über die Formbildung der Tiere, Berlin.

SCHMALHAUSEN, J., 1925: Über die Beeinflussung der Morphogenese der Extremitäten von Axolotl durch verschiedene Faktoren, *Arch. Entw. Mech.*, CV, 483–500.

SCHOTTÉ, O., 1926: Hypophysectomie et régénération (et métamorphose) chez les batraciens, Compt. rend. Soc. Physiol. Hist. Nat. Genève, XLIII, 67–71.

———, 1930: Der Determinationszustand der Anurengastrula im Transplantationsexperiment, Arch. Entw. Mech., CXXII, 663–664.

SCHREITMÜLLER, WILHELM, 1912: Weitere Bastardierungen (auf natürlichem Wege erzeugt) verschiedener Molcharten, Blätt Aquar.-Terrar-Kde., XXIII, 225–6, 258–9.

———, 1913: Über eine gelungene Kreuzung zwischen Triton vulgaris L. (♂) und T. palmatus Schneid. (♀) (auf natürlichem Wege erzeugt), Blätt. Aquar-Terrar-Kde., XXIV, 387–8.

SEVERINGHAUS, AURA E., 1930: Gill development in Amblystoma punctatum, Jour. Exp. Zool., LVI, 1–31.

SPEMANN, H., 1928: Organizers in animal development, Proc. Roy. Soc. (B), CII, 177–187.

STEINER, K., 1928: Entwicklungsmechanische Untersuchungen über die Bedeutung des ektodermalen Epithels der Extremitätenknospe von Amphibienlarven, Arch. Entw. Mech., CXIII, 1–11.

STEINITZ, E., 1906: Über den Einfluss der Elimination der embryonalen Augenblasen auf die Entwicklung des Gesamtorganismus beim Frosche, Arch. Entw. Mech., XX, 537–578.

STOHLER, R., 1928: Cytologische Untersuchungen an den Keimdrüsen mitteleuropäischer Kröten (Bufo viridis Laur., B. calamita Laur., B. vulgaris Laur.),·Zeitschr. Zellforsch. mikr. Anat., VII, 400–475, pls. IX–XIV.

STONE, L. S., 1926: Further experiments on the extirpation and transplantation of mesectoderm in Amblystoma punctatum, Jour. Exp. Zool., XLIV, 95–131.

———, 1929: Experiments showing the role of migrating neural crest (mesectoderm) in the formation of head skeleton and loose connective tissue in Rana palustris, Arch. Entw. Mech., CXVIII, 40–77.

SWETT, F. H., 1926: On the production of double limbs in amphibians, Jour. Exp. Zool., XLIV, 419–473.

———, 1927: Differentiation of the amphibian limb, Jour. Exp. Zool., XLVII, 385–432.

———, 1928: Studies on the shoulder-girdle of Ambystoma punctatum (Linn); I, Determination of its dorsoventral axis, Jour. Exp. Zool., LI, 389–402.

TWITTY, VICTOR C., 1929: Correlation in development of structures associated with transplanted eyes, Proc. Soc. Exp. Biol. Med., XXVI, 726–727.

———, 1930: Regulation in the growth of transplanted eyes, Jour. Exp. Zool., LV, 43–52.

UBISCH, L., 1923: Das Differenzierungsgefälle des Amphibienkörpers und seine Auswirkungen, Arch. Entw. Mech., LII, 641–670.

UHLENHUTH, E., 1920: Experimental gigantism produced by feeding pituitary gland, Proc. Soc. Exp. Biol. Med., XVIII, 11–14.

VOGT, W., 1926: Die Beziehungen zwischen Furchung, Hauptachsen des Embryo und Ausgangstruktur im Amphibienei, nach Versuchen mit örtlicher Vitalfärbung, Sitz. Ges. Morph. Physiol. München, XXXVII, 60–70.

WALTER, F. K., 1911: Schilddrüse und Regeneration, *Arch. Entw. Mech.*, XXXI, 91–130.

WEBER, A., 1922: La fécondation chez la salamandre alpestre (Sal. atra Laur), *Compt. rend. Ass. Anat.*, XVII, 327–329.

WEISS, P., 1922: Unabhängigkeit der Extremitätenregeneration vom Skelett (bei Triton cristatus), *Anz. Akad. Wiss. Wien*, LIX, 231–3.

———, 1925: Unabhängigkeit der Extremitätenregeneration vom Skelett (bei Triton cristatus), *Arch. mikr. Anat. Entw. Mech.*, CIV, 359–394.

———, 1926: Morphodynamik; Ein Einblick in die Gesetze der organischen Gestaltung an Hand von experimentellen Ergebnissen, *Abh. Theor. Biol. Schax.*, XXIII.

WESTPHAL, KURT, 1925: Über Lungenregeneration bei Anurenlarven, *Zeitschr. Anat. Entw.*, LXXVII, 144–163.

WINTREBERT, P., 1929: La digestion de l'enveloppe tubaire interne de l'oeuf par des ferments issus des spermatozoïdes et de l'ovule chez Discoglossus pictus Otth, *Compt. rend. Acad. Sci.*, CLXXXVIII, 97–100.

WURMBACH, H., 1926: Über Kiemenregeneration beim Axolotl, *Zool. Anz.*, LXVII, 309–322.

ZELENY, CHARLES, 1916: The effect of successive removal upon the rate of regeneration, *Proc. Nat. Acad. Sci. Wash.*, II, 487–490.

CHAPTER III

THE MODE OF LIFE HISTORY

Many Amphibia do not lay their eggs in water as in the case of Rana and Ambystoma but deposit them on land and sometimes even in nests constructed by one or both parents. The eggs and larvae which develop in these situations are often modified in adaptation to their surroundings. It has recently been recognized that these modifications have usually evolved slowly and the various steps by which extreme stages have been reached may often be still found in related species. The mode of life history and the modifications of eggs and larvae thus often give clear evidence as to the affinities of a species.

Cryptobranchidae.—The American giant salamander, *Cryptobranchus alleganiensis*, lays its eggs in two long chains (Smith, 1912). Fertilization is external and the larvae which escape from the egg capsules are short limbed with no dorsal fin on the body and no balancers such as occur in Ambystoma. Have these characters any phylogenetic significance? Cryptobranchus, as far as known, has exactly the same life history as Megalobatrachus, the giant salamander of Japan and China. These two genera belong to the same family and hence only one type of life history is found throughout this family. The Cryptobranchidae, moreover, have been derived from the Hynobiidae and may be considered merely permanent or partly metamorphosed hynobiid larvae of large size. The hynobiids are the only other salamanders (except the Sirenidae) which practice external fertilization. All of the genera lay their eggs in two sacs and, although these are not so elongate as the egg chains of Cryptobranchus, and consequently have thicker walls, they have much in common. Hynobius, the least specialized genus of the family, lays some 35 to 70 eggs, 2.5 to 3.2 mm. in diameter, within each egg sac. The younger larvae, as far as known, are all Ambystoma-like, with dorsal fins, balancers, and long external gills. The eggs are laid in ponds, temporary pools, springs, or even slow-moving streams. Within the family there are two

48

genera which live in or near mountain brooks. The egg sacs of one of these, Ranodon, are fastened to the under sides of flat stones, beneath which water flows. The eggs are larger than those of Hynobius and fewer in number. The larvae hatch in a more mature condition, and their digits are shorter than in that genus. Apparently the dorsal fin is also reduced (Schmalhausen, 1917). In Onychodactylus there is no dorsal fin and the digits are not only short but are equipped with horny claws. Further, their external gills are comparatively short. It is apparent that the Cryptobranchidae have received their method of fertilization and general character of their egg capsules from the family Hynobiidae as a whole, while their short gills, reduced

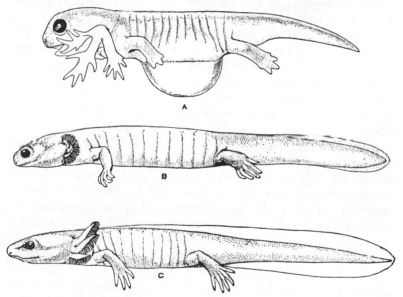

FIG. 17.—The principal types of urodele larvae. *A.* Terrestrial type: *Plethodon vandykei.* *B.* Mountain-brook type: *Dicamptodon ensatus.* *C.* Pond type: *Ambystoma paroticum.*

fins, and short toes may have been inherited from mountain-brook ancestors, presumably of the same family. Apparently also the large eggs (although not particularly large when compared with the body length of the parent) may also be considered a mountain-brook inheritance. These large eggs and "swift-water features" of the larvae frequently appear in species of other families of salamanders (Fig. 17) which live in mountain brooks.

It is difficult to tell *a priori* which character will prove the most conservative in evolution, but in general the more specialized a structural modification may be the greater is the probability that it will be modified only gradually during evolution.

In all the higher salamanders except the Sirenidae, fertilization is internal. Very little is known about the breeding habits of Siren and Pseudobranchus, except that the eggs of both are large, pigmented, and laid singly or in small groups. The larvae of both, soon after hatching, have elongate bodies approaching the form of the adult. This in itself would suggest that the Sirenidae is an isolated group. The larvae of both genera, as they mature, have the ability of reducing their gills to mere stumps if respiratory conditions in the aquatic medium are not suitable to them. This is not a metamorphosis but merely a temporary loss of the gills. The larvae never undergo a complete metamorphosis although, as discussed under the heading of this subject (page 103), they normally transform certain structures, especially the integument in Siren.

Proteidae.—The Proteidae, which includes the well-known genus Necturus, are also somewhat isolated structurally from other salamanders and, like the Sirenidae, never complete their metamorphosis. The two genera Necturus and Proteus of this family agree in laying their eggs singly in the water, attached to the under surface of rocks, boards, or other objects in still water; but they have also been recorded in streams. Since the habit of selecting the under surface of rocks is common to mountain-brook salamanders of two other families, it is possible that the Proteidae may have arisen in mountain brooks. In fact, Proteus in its subterranean habitat must be subject to a current for a considerable part of its life. Further, the eggs of both genera are large and the larvae are devoid of dorsal fins and have short limbs. These mountain-brook characters, if such they be, are common to other larvae living in a similar habitat and hence give no clue as to the ancestors of these genera. In this case we do not have extreme larval modifications pointing the way to relationships, but as both genera of the family have the same mode of life history in spite of the fact that the adults occupy totally different regions, we have further evidence of the stability of breeding habits in phylogeny.

Proteus, under certain conditions, does not lay eggs but retains them in its oviducts where one or two may undergo their development, finally to be born as salamanders resembling their parents in most particulars. No especial modifications of either the larvae or of the oviducts are known to occur to permit this change in the mode of life history. The phenomenon is very similar to the case of some species of lizards, such as certain horned toads which may either lay eggs or give birth to their young alive. The phenomenon is, however, very rare in the salamanders and very much in need of further study.

Ambystomidae.—The best-known genus of American salamander is Ambystoma. Most of the common eastern species, *maculatum*, *tigrinum*, and *jeffersonianum*, lay their eggs in the water in early spring, but *opacum* lays them in the fall on land, and the female curls about them. The young, which hatch on the advent of the rains, make their way into the water and have all the larval characters of the other species of the genus. These are the broad body and tail fins, the balancers (rarely absent), and the elongate gills, each provided with a central rachis and many pairs of filaments. The middle-western *A. annulatum* lays its eggs in the water (occasionally on land), and the larvae, as far as is known, resemble the other species of the genus. The Ambystoma larvae are similar to those of Hynobius, and the eggs of some species are laid enclosed in a common gelatinous capsule, apparently resembling the egg sacs of Hynobius but not so elongated. The Ambystomidae are closely related to the Hynobiidae but they have advanced beyond that group in developing a complex mechanism for internal fertilization. Nevertheless, the mode of life history seems to have been evolved out of a type common to the most primitive genus of that family. The Ambystomidae include two mountain-brook genera, Rhyacotriton and Dicamptodon. The latter of these lays small clumps of eggs in the cool lakes of the west coast of the United States (Storer, 1925). The egg capsules, which are two and three in Ambystoma, are apparently reduced to one in this species. The larvae, at least in some part of the species range, make their way into mountain streams where they assume all the characters of the mountain-brook larvae discussed above. Rhyacotriton lays large pigmentless eggs attached singly to stones. It is a much smaller salamander than Dicamptodon and like many other dwarf forms lays fewer eggs than its larger relative. The larvae which hatch from the eggs possess the mountain-brook characters of Dicamptodon larvae. Rhyacotriton and Dicamptodon are more closely allied to one another than they are to Ambystoma, and their larval characters tend to confirm this relationship.

Ambystoma has one larval character which is found elsewhere among salamanders only in the hynobiid Onychodactylus. Anterior to the teeth on the lower jaw, there is found a horny beak very similar to the larval mandible of frog tadpoles. This beak has been described only in the axolotl and in one species of Onychodactylus, but it is so distinctive a structure that probably it will be found in other species of these families. The Sirenidae, which may possibly have had hynobiid ancestors (Noble, 1929), have developed horny sheets on both jaws. Since no other salamanders have horny jaws, we may consider this character as evidence that the forms are related.

Salamandridae.—The Salamandridae seem to have evolved from some prehynobiid stock, for the most primitive genera differ markedly from Hynobius in structure. These primitive genera, Tylototriton, Pleurodeles and some species of Triturus, lay their eggs in loose chains or short bunches very similar to the eggs of *Ambystoma tigrinum*. The larvae which emerge from them have the dorsal fins, broad tail, and long gill characteristics of Ambystoma. The other newts were apparently derived from this primitive stock which seems to have been widespread in both Asia and Europe. The pond species lay their eggs singly, attached to water weed. This habit of laying single eggs appears as a variation in *Triturus torosus* and *Ambystoma tigrinum*. Differences occur in the various species. The American newt, *T. viridescens*, lays small eggs, approximately 1.5 mm. in greatest diameter and spherical in shape. Each is enclosed in a more or less oval mass of jelly which during the later period of development is well separated from the egg by a fluid, oddly enough of a greenish color. The American newt is also distinctive in that the female usually wraps a leaf about the single eggs which further protects them. Although all the more specialized pond newts lay single eggs, there are various specific differences in the form of the egg capsule, shape of the egg, and method of oviposition.

The mountain newts of Europe are sometimes referred to a distinct genus, Euproctus. The eggs are slightly larger than those of most pond newts, averaging approximately 2.5 mm. in diameter without the egg capsule in the case of *E. asper*. The eggs are laid singly on the under side of stones in running water. Despax (1923) has suggested that the large egg size of the latter may be due to the cold water in which the eggs are laid and he has drawn a comparison in the egg size of certain cold- and warm-water fish. The American newt, *Triturus viridescens*, will lay its eggs on stones if no vegetation is available (Moesel, 1918), but they are not laid under the stones and, of course, are not of larger size. Mountain-brook salamanders of all families tend to reduce their lungs and develop habits of crawling under stones in the water. Hence, the method of egg laying found in Euproctus was probably evolved out of the method found in the pond newts, the change of egg-laying site being conditioned by the changed habits of the adult. The larvae as they develop have short external gills and lack the dorsal fins, thus representing another instance of convergent evolution in the mountain-brook habitat. In the frogs and toads there are many instances where the method of oviposition is more important than the larval characters. The reason for this is that yolk size has changed frequently in evolution and has necessitated marked change in the details of development in closely related forms.

An instance of this fact may be seen in the European land salamanders. Wunderer (1910) describes various differences between the embryos of two species of Salamandra and is inclined to believe that they are not closely related. *Salamandra salamandra* and *S. atra*, however, both retain the eggs for a part of their development within the female body. The larvae of both species as they develop are equipped with long filamentous gills which absorb oxygen from the highly vasculated oviducts (Fig. 18). *S. atra* gives birth to fully metamorphosed young, while *S. salamandra* usually gives birth to larvae, although some individuals from Spain have been found to produce metamorphosed young as well. *S. atra*, being equipped with less yolk, secures some nutriment from its parent's body during development but it develops no especial mechanism for accomplishing this act other than the elongation of the gills. Both species, as they develop, exhibit one larval character which shows that both forms have been derived from pond-breeding ancestors. A rudimentary balancer appears in both forms while within their parent's oviduct. Balancers have been recorded only from pond-living salamander larvae, never from mountain-brook forms. Further, Escher (1925) reports lateral-line organs, a

character of pond larvae, in *S. atra*. Hence, certain larval
characters in Salamandra indicate that these species are closely
related, the method of carrying their eggs until the young are
well advanced further supporting this conclusion. The differences between the early embryos are brought about by differences in amount of yolk. When the Amphibia are considered
as a whole, many other instances may be found where yolk size
has changed apparently suddenly in phylogeny. For example,
in the Marsupial Frogs, Gastrotheca, the species carry their eggs

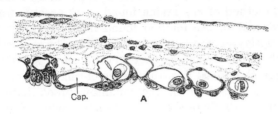

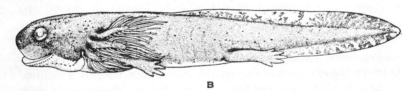

Fig. 18.—*A*. Section through the wall of the oviduct of a gravid *Salamandra
salamandra* showing proximity of capillaries to lumen of the duct. *B*. Larva
removed from oviduct of a gravid female. *Cap.*, capillary.

in sacs on the back of the female, and the larvae as they develop
have extraordinary bell-shaped gills. If the eggs are small-yolked,
the embryos soon assume the characters of tadpoles; while if
considerable yolk is present, they develop directly into froglets.
In either case both the character of the gills and the method of
carrying the eggs are evidence that the species are related.
Further, when the phylogeny of the group is considered, it is
found that the ancestral forms, which are grouped in the genus
Cryptobatrachus, all have large-yolked eggs. Hence, in this
case it would seem certain that the small-yolked eggs were derived
from the large-yolked ones. Similarly, there is considerable
evidence that the high mountain *Salamandra atra*, with its small
eggs, has evolved from the large-egged *S. Salamandra* of the low
altitudes.

Amphiumidae.—In making comparisons of life histories there is always the danger that the likenesses are due to superficial resemblances. For example, the large American salamander, Amphiuma, lays its eggs on land and the female curls about them. This method is essentially like that of the Dusky Salamander, *Desmognathus fuscus*, although the detailed character of the eggs is different. The eggs of Amphiuma are laid in long rosaries, while in a branched clump in Desmognathus. Amphiuma has been derived from Salamandridae, while the Plethodontidae, which include Desmognathus, arose from the same stock. The mode of life history in many cases does not establish but merely suggests where the relationships actually are to be found. The anatomy of the adults must be considered in reaching a final conclusion. The allantoic placenta is characteristic of the placental mammals, but it occurs again in certain skinks but not in all lizards. In any case the more specialized the modification the better is the chance of its being the same in related groups.

Plethodontidae.—The Plethodontidae, which embrace the majority of North American salamanders, afford an excellent illustration of the close correlation of change in life history with change in phylogeny. The family evolved from the Salamandridae, and some of the primitive genera of both lay their eggs under stones in running streams. Each plethodontid egg is comparatively large, unpigmented, and attached separately by a gelatinous stalk. The eggs are usually crowded together on the under side of a single stone, and in some cases, at least, the female parent remains near them. Apparently some of the primitive plethodontids have departed somewhat from this method. Gyrinophilus and Eurycea, as well as *Pseudotriton ruber*, retain this primitive mode of egg laying inherited from mountain-brook salamandrids. *P. montanus*, according to Brimley (1923), lays its eggs singly or in small groups on dead leaves in the outlets of springs. This species, unlike its relative *P. ruber*, is partial to muddy springs, and hence a breeding site like that selected by the stream forms might not be available to it in this habitat. Further data are needed concerning the breeding of *P. montanus* before the degree of divergence in the mode of life history may be determined. Manculus, a dwarf derivative of Eurycea, lays relatively large, pigmentless eggs, attached by short stalks to the under sides of leaves in flowing spring water.

The commonest plethodontid salamander in eastern United States is Desmognathus, the Dusky Salamander. This genus is particularly interesting because within it there is found a gradual evolution of the mode of egg laying from the ancestral condition, where eggs are laid under stones in the water, to a terrestrial condition. Although all adults live both in and out of water, the progressive change in the mode of egg laying closely follows the phylogeny of the group. The most primitive species is *D. quadra-maculatus*, a large and powerful species of the southern Appalachians. *D. phoca*, which is rather more advanced in structure, lays its eggs in a similar manner but apparently always deposits out of water. The common Dusky Salamander, *D. fuscus*, which is still more specialized, lays its eggs in one or two grapelike clusters in small excavations in the soft earth, beneath stones or logs. The excavation is generally one or two feet from the water. This is an advance over the primitive methods of the larger species of the genus, not only in the form of the egg capsules but also in the life history of the young. The recently hatched individuals remain for 15 or 16 days on land, or at least with their heads out of the water. These terrestrial young show various adaptations to their habitat. The posterior limbs are longer in proportion to the trunk region than during any other period in later development. The tail lacks a fin. In brief, the young Dusky Salamander, during the first two weeks of its life, is not merely a little larva which chances to be hatched at a distance from its aquatic habitat, but it is a terrestrial salamander fully able to move about in the damp cracks and crannies leading from the nest to the nearest pool. In the most terrestrial form of the genus, namely *D. fuscus carolinensis*, the breeding site and apparently the mode of life history remain the same. This illustrates the general rule that salamanders do not lay their eggs wherever they happen to be but that during the breeding season they move into environments which are most suitable to the egg-laying requirements. Further, the mode of life history gradually changes in phylogeny and this change, while moving toward terrestrialism, does not progress so fast as the change in habitat preference exhibited by the adults.

In spite of this rapid change in breeding-site preference and of adaptive changes in the young, certain larval characters appear which stamp the group as related. The young of *Desmognathus fuscus*, after its sojourn between land and water, finally takes up a purely aquatic life and develops the tail fin and gills of a mountain-brook larva. It lives in the same streams as *Eurycea bislineata* but may be distinguished from that species by its differently formed gills. It has three pairs, as most of the salamanders have, but these are devoid of a distinct central ramus so characteristic of Eurycea and Gyrinophilus. There are only from three to seven branches to each gill in the brush projecting from a central axis. This shows that while swift currents may oppose a limit to the growth of gills, probably for the good reason that cold swift water is better supplied with oxygen than most pond water, nevertheless, the character of the gills is determined by the heredity of the species and, in the case of Desmognathus, affords one of the best identification marks of the larvae. It does not follow that gill structure in other groups will always afford important clues as to relationships.

Terrestrial Plethodontids.—Another common salamander in the eastern United States is *Plethodon cinereus*. It is a terrestrial form and during the breeding season apparently shows a preference for coniferous woods. The female lays from 3 to 12 large, white eggs in a single mass, usually in crannies in the logs. The egg cluster is usually attached to the roof of the cavity, each egg being laid separately adhering to those previously laid, the fused outer capsule seemingly forming a single envelope. The embryos develop rapidly and soon show large external gills. These are lost on hatching, when the young have the same form as the adults. This same mode of life history is apparently found throughout the entire genus. One of the most primitive species is the large, slimy salamander, *P. glutinosus*, which has been found to lay its eggs deep underground in the walls of caves. In such situations there is an abundant water supply; nevertheless *P. glutinosus* has exactly the same mode of life history as its smaller relative *P. cinereus*, even to the details of egg-capsule structure and gill form. *P. glutinosus*, being a larger form, lays more eggs; larger species of all genera usually lay more eggs than smaller species of the same group. The immediate ancestors of Plethodon seem to have been lost, but the mode of life history practiced by the genus may be evolved from the pattern found in the more terrestrial species of Desmognathus.

Plethodon has given rise to a number of derived groups. Some of these genera, such as Aneides and Batrachoseps in the West, are considerably specialized but nevertheless retain the mode

of life history found in Plethodon.   Differences appear in the
form of the gills and, as discussed in Chap. VIII, may be correlated
with the increased efficiency of the blood of Batrachoseps
as a carrier of oxygen.   It is perhaps not surprising that Batrachoseps has very small external gills while Aneides has them not
only elongated but fused at the base to large leaflike structures.
Incidentally, *Aneides aeneus*, which in the character of its skull
is the most primitive member of the genus, has its gill form intermediate between that of Plethodon and *Aneides lugubris*.
Other differences appear in the form of the egg capsules: while
the eggs of both Plethodon and Batrachoseps are attached to
one another and each egg surrounded by three capsules, those of
Aneides are separate and attached by a single twisted peduncle
to the roof of the nest chamber.   In Ensatina, another derived
genus, the eggs are stuck together and only one egg capsule has
been recorded.   Hence, while differences exist in both the character of the egg capsule and the gills of the young, all the species
agree in laying their eggs on land, there to develop directly into
salamanders without going through an aquatic period.   This
mode of life history is not merely a consequence of the terrestrial
habit of the adults; other terrestrial salamanders, such as
Ambystoma opacum, have a very different life history.

Not all the derivatives of Plethodon have retained this
mode of life history.   The four-toed salamander, Hemidactylium, seems structurally very closely allied to Plethodon but
is obviously a derived and not an ancestral form, because it
has only four toes on its rear feet and a double constriction
around the base of the tail.   Both of these characters represent an
advance over the conditions in Plethodon.   Hemidactylium
lays its eggs on land near sphagnaceous or at least wooded ponds.
The female twists her body around and attaches the eggs to
strands of moss lying over her head.   This habit is found in
Plethodon but also in Eurycea which lays its eggs on the under
side of stones.   The eggs are more numerous than with Plethodon
and the larvae which hatch out make their way into the adjacent
water.   The eggs without their capsules are from 2.5 to 3 mm.
(Bishop, 1919), while those of *Plethodon cinereus* vary from 3.5
to 4.5 mm. in diameter.   The yolk is very early absorbed by the
larva of Hemidactylium which develops a low dorsal fin approaching that of many other pond salamanders in form (Fig. 19)
but not found elsewhere in the Plethodontidae.   The larva does

not, however, develop the balancer or elongate digits of primitive pond salamanders and hence is merely a "plethodontid larva" with a low dorsal fin. It has been suggested that the life history of Hemidactylium may be explained by assuming that Plethodon was originally aquatic or at least laid its eggs in the manner of Eurycea and that the life history of Hemidactylium is a retention of this primitive condition. It seems more likely, however, after a consideration of the yolk reduction of *Salamandra atra* and some

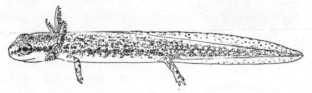

FIG. 19.—The larva of *Hemidactylium scutatum*.

Marsupial Frogs, that the aquatic period in the life of Hemidactylium is a derived condition induced by the reduction and early absorption of the yolk in the embryos.

The European cave salamander Hydromantes shows in its osteology an affinity both to Eurycea and to Plethodon. It retains the eggs in the oviduct and gives birth to fully transformed young. The same habit is found in the neotropical salamander Oedipus structurally allied to Hydromantes. This would seem to afford evidence that these genera are closely related. Many tropical frogs pass their whole lives on land. There are opportunities for laying their eggs in water but the dominant groups are those which have given up this primitive habit. Similarly, Oedipus, which has freed itself from the necessity of returning to water during the breeding season, represents a highly successful stock. From the data available, it cannot be determined whether Oedipus evolved from Plethodon or from Eurycea. At least we may conclude that the ovoviviparity of Hydromantes and Oedipus is further evidence of the close affinity of these two genera.

Salientia.—Turning to the frogs and toads, there are far more genera to consider and their life histories are less known than those of urodeles. Still, there is abundant evidence that their mode of life history has usually changed gradually in phylogeny and that a specialized method of caring for the young may be common to many related species and even to several allied genera. The recognition of this fact has helped greatly in elucidating the relationships of various genera. For example, Protopipa and Pipa are the only frogs which carry their eggs in individual dermal chambers on the back of the female parent and are undoubtedly closely allied. Similarly, Phyllobates and Dendrobates, which until recently were placed in separate families, are the only genera which transport their tadpoles on the back of the male parent to streams where they complete their metamorphosis. The South American tree frogs, Cryptobatrachus, Hemiphractus, Gastrotheca, and Amphignathodon, have been variously relegated by herpetologists. Since they are the only frogs which carry their eggs in a single mass on their backs (Fig. 20), whether or not this mass is exposed or covered by a fold of skin forming a veritable sac, it appears probable that they are closely allied. This conclusion is supported by the fact that all the larvae have distinctive bell-shaped gills (Fig. 21 *B-C*). Many other frogs lay their eggs out of water and yet the larvae of none of them have bell-shaped gills.

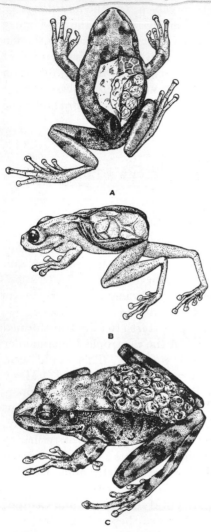

Fig. 20.—The evolution of the dorsal brood pouch of the Hylidae. *A. Gastrotheca marsupiata*, the purse-like brood pouch cut open on the side to show the eggs within. *B. Gastrotheca pygmaea*, female with the eggs removed from the widely open brood pouch. *C. Cryptobatrachus evansi*, female with eggs.

Many frogs and toads lay their eggs in the water and the polliwogs which emerge may have distinctive characters of value to the systematist in defining relationships. Some tadpoles may have narrow

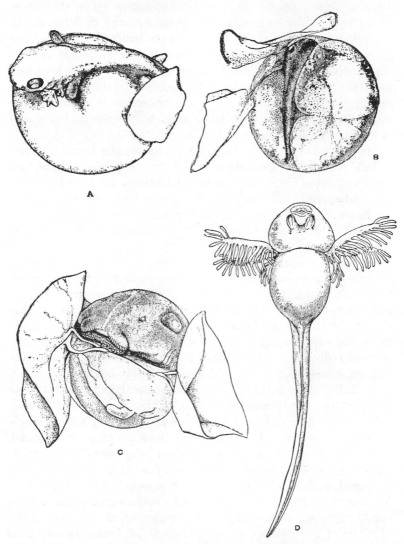

Fig. 21.—Larval respiratory organs of some neotropical frogs. *A. Eleutherodactylus inoptatus. B. Cryptobatrachus evansi. C. Gastrotheca marsupiata. D. Hyla rosenbergi.*

tail fins which permit them merely to wriggle along over the bottom of the pond. Others may have broad fins and well developed lungs, the latter functioning primarily as hydrostatic organs. Such tadpoles, as for example those of *Hyla versicolor*, are usually graceful swimmers. The characters which these tadpoles exhibit are of importance in defining the species. A synopsis of the tadpoles of the United States has been given by Wright (1929), those of California by Storer (1925). The tadpoles of many exotic species have also been described (see bibliography in Noble, 1927). In the present summary, reference may be made to only the more extreme modifications, especially to those which have been employed as indicators of the course of phylogeny.

Brevicipitidae.—The narrow-mouth toads, the Brevicipitidae, include the most specialized of all the Salientia. Some are narrow-snouted, burrowing types and others are broad-headed, arboreal species. Nevertheless, all of their larvae, whether they are hatched in the open ponds of our western prairies or between the leaves of banana plants in the mountains of East Africa, have the same distinctive characters (Fig. 22*C*). The only exceptions are found among those forms which lay large-yolked eggs hatching directly into frogs and among certain South African brevicipitids which may possibly have evolved separately from some ranid stock. This characteristic brevicipitid tadpole is devoid of the usual horny teeth of the Rana polliwogs. It lacks the suprarostral cartilage which supports the upper jaw of most tadpoles, and the lower lip carries a series of folds which in some species may be protruded considerably beyond the mouth (Fig. 22*B*). The external nares do not break through until late in larval life; the spiracle is median, unlike that of all other tadpoles of the more advanced families of Salientia, with a single possible exception. Apparently the toes as they develop are always webbed, although this webbing may be entirely lost at metamorphosis. The eggs, when laid free in ponds, are usually equipped with a ridge on the outer capsule and the egg itself lies eccentrically in the upper half of the egg capsule. Such eggs have been described for Gastrophryne of America, Kalophrynus of the Philippines, and Kaloula of Asia. Hence, it is possible that they will be found throughout other genera of the family which lay floating eggs, although they have not been recorded elsewhere.

Various brevicipitids produce large eggs which develop directly into frogs without passing through the tadpole stage. These

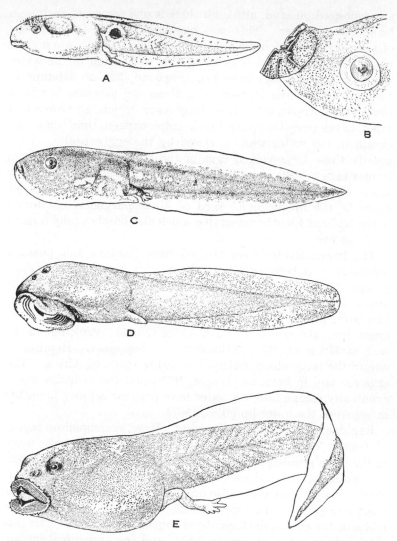

FIG. 22.—Tadpole mouths. The shape is frequently correlated either with the type of habitat or with the method of feeding. The umbrella mouth (*B*) characterizes surface film feeders, while mountain-brook forms (*D*) frequently possess large suctorial lips. Cannibalistic tadpoles (*E*) have strong mandibles and sometimes broad lips. Some species, notably the Brevicipitidae (*C*), undergo very little modification in spite of radically different feeding habits. *A. Rana alticola. B. Microhyla heymonsi. C. Gastrophryne carolinensis. D. Ascaphus truei. E. Ceratophrys dorsata.*

are deposited on land, although there is one record of such eggs being laid in water. This case was probably due to a flooding of a stream near which the eggs had been laid. There are several records of large-yolked eggs being able to develop in the water after the egg capsules have been removed, but no attempt to raise such eggs without removing these egg capsules has been successful. Apparently these large eggs which go through a rapid development require much more oxygen than they can obtain in the water while enclosed by the egg capsules. How greatly these large-yolked eggs of the brevicipitids differ from similar eggs of other families is not entirely clear, for only a few forms have been described in detail. Differences exist; for example, the mucilaginous cord of Mantophryne is not found in the bufonid Eleutherodactylus which also hatches fully formed from the egg.

The Brevicipitidae have evolved from Ranidae and possibly represent a polyphyletic assemblage, for the South African genera, Hemisus, Cacosternum, and Anhydrophryne lack the distinctive tadpoles of other Brevicipitidae. In the case of the two latter genera it was possible to trace in their anatomy their origin from the ranids in South Africa (Noble, 1926), but in the case of Hemisus, the relationships are less clear. Hemisus is one of the most characteristic burrowing toads of Africa. The eggs are laid in burrows (Wager, 1929) and the tadpoles which eventually escape into the water have peculiar sensory filaments attached to the lower lip (Bles, 1907).

Ranidae.—The Ranidae represent a large, cosmopolitan family of frogs. Their tadpoles exhibit various modifications, some of the more peculiar being common to natural groups of species. For example, the tadpoles of all species of Staurois are characterized by an adhesive disc on the ventral surface behind the mouth (Fig. 23). This permits the tadpoles to hold tightly to rocks in the mountain torrents of southeastern Asia. The disc was evolved out of the musculature and the abdominal integument of Rana tadpoles but few intermediate stages in the genesis of the structure exist today (Noble, 1929 a). A second ranid modification is found in the Philippine Cornufer. C. guentheri lays large eggs which hatch directly into froglets. These are provided with a series of pronounced folds along each side of the body. A similar modification is found in the young Discodeles opisthodon which also hatches fully formed. In the latter species the folds were described as respiratory structures but histological examination has shown that they are merely folds of the body wall produced by the rapid absorption of the yolk. This, apparently, is a very trivial feature in the organization of these young frogs; nevertheless, it occurs only in these closely related species.

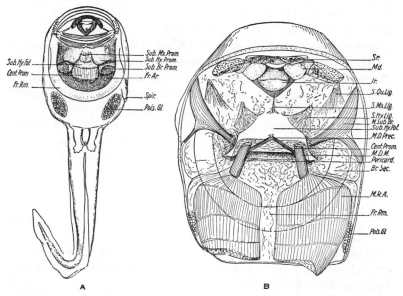

Fig. 23.—Suctorial disc of a mountain-brook tadpole. *A*. Tadpole of *Staurois ricketti* as seen from the ventral surface. *B*. The disc dissected free and viewed from its dorsal aspect. *Br.Sac.*, branchial sac; *Cent.Prom.*, central prominence; *Fr.Ar.*, friction area; *Fr.Rm.*, free rim; *Ir.*, infrarostrale; *Md.*, mandibulare; *M.D.M.*, M. diaphragmatobranchialis medialis; *M.D.Prec.*, M. diaphragmatopræcordialis; *M.R.A.*, M. rectus abdominis; *M.Sub.Br.*, M. subbranchialis; *Pericard.*, ligamentous posterior wall of pericardium, cut edge; *Pois.Gl.*, poison gland; *S.Hy.Lig.*, subhyoid ligament; *S.Mx.Lig.*, submaxillary ligament; *Spir.*, spiracle; *S.Qu.Lig.*, subquadrate ligament; *Sr.*, suprarostrale; *Sub.Br.Prom.*, subbranchial prominence; *Sub.Hy.Fol.*, fold over M. subhyoideus; *Sub.Hy.Prom.*, subhyoid prominence; *Sub.Mx.Prom.*, submaxillary prominence.

The tadpoles of the numerous species of Rana exhibit few modifications. Those which live in swift waters resemble the mountain-brook larvae of salamanders in lacking body fins and in having the tail fins greatly reduced (Fig. 22*A*). Unlike salamanders their lips are frequently enlarged and assist them in adhering to rocks (Fig. 23). In many of these species the number of tooth rows is correspondingly increased. Some of the Indian species of Rana, while enlarging their lips, tend to lose their tooth rows. Where the latter are increased in number, as in *Rana boylii boylii* of the western United States and in various Indian species of Rana, this cannot be taken as evidence of relationship between the forms but merely of parallel evolution. In many other groups of frogs, as, for example, in the hylas of Haiti or of Central America, closely related species may show marked differences in the size of the mouth and in the number of tooth rows. Such differences are usually correlated with the rapidity of the current in which the tadpoles live, the species with larger mouths and most teeth occurring in the swiftest water. There is, however, an individual and an age variation in the number of rows which may make the identification of forms difficult (Scott-Biraben and Fernandez-Marcinowski, 1921).

One or two oriental species of Rana and another from South Africa (Rose, 1929) have been reported to lay their eggs out of water on leaves or stones or in the mud, but these egg masses are unmodified and the larvae which escape soon make their way into the water. The habit of laying eggs out of water is found, however, in other ranids, as, for example, in one South African species of Phrynobatrachus. Since other species of the genus lay floating eggs, Wager (1930) considered this habit evidence for retaining the species in a separate genus Natalobatrachus. The habit finds a close parallel in certain neotropical tree frogs of a very different family, to be discussed below.

Polypedatidae.—The Polypedatidae are Old World tree frogs which have evolved from ranids and they have taken up the habit of laying the eggs out of water and further elaborated it. The most primitive genus is the well known Asiatic East Indian genus, Rhacophorus or Polypedates. The vast majority of the species in the genus lay their eggs over or near water and beat the egg mass with their hind legs into a foam. This procedure beats air into the developing spawn, an important feature, since the outer surface of the foamy "nest" soon dries forming a resistant crust to the nest. The central part of the nest liquefies as the tadpoles develop and the latter are soon freed to take up a life in the water. The older tadpole usually has a broad tail fin which extends forward along the back. Two species of the genus have succeeded in increasing the yolk content of the eggs and these are no longer beaten into a foam. These large eggs are probably hatched directly into frogs but observations on this point are incomplete. In the Bufonidae the habit of making a foam nest has been evolved independently but here the eggs are laid in contact with or very near the water, while the tadpoles never develop the larval characters of Polypedates. It is, nevertheless, interesting that the habit of making foam nests should have independently evolved in these two unrelated groups.

All the genera which show anatomical evidence of having evolved directly from Polypedates have retained the same mode of life history. Several species living in the same region as Polypedates have been found to have the same habit, while the African Chiromantis which is another derivative of Polypedates has exactly the same way of caring for its eggs. The life histories of African frogs related to Chiromantis are incompletely known, but some such as Hyperolius, lay their eggs in small clusters in the water (Rose, 1929) and here it is apparent that the spawn-beating habit has been given up. *Kassina senegalensis* is closely related to Hyperolius and has also given up the egg-beating habit. Its eggs are small, only 1.5 mm. without the capsules, pigmented, and laid singly or in pairs in the water (Power, 1926). The mature tadpoles are of the back-finned Polypedates type; the tooth rows, however, are more reduced than in most species of the ancestral group. Although Kassina and Hyperolius have succeeded in giving up their spawn-beating habit, they still show in the tadpole form some evidence of their origin. Further, the tadpole of Kassina develops a rigid convex upper lip and a pair of horny plates obliquely arranged in the angle of the mouth. Such structures are known only in the tadpoles of Hylambates, a genus more closely related to Kassina than to Hyperolius. Until recently Hylambates was confused with another genus of polypedatids, Leptopelis. Since the tadpoles of one South African species lack these plates (Wager, 1930), it remains to be discovered if the genera Leptopelis and Hylambates may be distinguished on the basis of different larval modifications.

Hylidae.—The typical tree frogs, Hylidae, show no close relationship to the Polypedatidae; they have evolved from bufonids, not ranids. As already indicated, one group of hylids, which may be defined as Gastrothecinae, carries its eggs on the back of the female, some exposed and others enclosed in a sac. None of the other hylids shows any indication of this mode of life history, nor are the larvae equipped with bell-shaped gills which are found throughout the first subfamily. All of the latter hylids lay their eggs in pools. Some, such as *Hyla rosenbergi* and the closely related *H. faber*, build basins of mud either near the edge of pools or in the bed of the pool itself. In the case of the former species, at least, the male does all of the building and he attracts the female to the basin with his voice, after the walls are constructed. The tadpoles (*H. rosenbergi* at least) which are developed within these muddy cups have enormous pinnate gills which adhere to the surface film of the basins. Similar gills have been described in *Leptodactylus ocellatus* which is not closely related to *H. rosenbergi*. The former lays its eggs in a foamy mass similar to other species of the genus Leptodactylus and no mud basin is constructed. The gills, while long (Fig. 21*D*), have the simple structure of the gills of other species of Hyla and hence their hypertrophy, which seems to be correlated with the poor oxygen supply of the basins, has brought no radical change in their structure. Other tree frogs of the genus Hyla lay their eggs in small basins of water existing in nature. For example, the tree frogs of Jamaica lay their eggs in water between the leaves of bromeliads. In such a habit we apparently have the beginning of the basin-building habit of *Hyla rosenbergi* and *H. faber*. The two latter species are more closely related to one another than to any other tree frog whose life history is known and they have similar modes of nest building different from that of any other frog.

Within the genus Hyla, other closely related groups of species have similar habits. All the hylas of Jamaica lay their eggs in bromeliads and the larvae are modified for living in close confinement. The larval tooth rows have been reduced and also the larval gills. Hence, these tadpoles apparently secure most of their oxygen directly from the atmosphere. The food supply in these situations is limited and the tadpoles have developed the habit of eating the eggs of their own or related species laid in the same situation. It is interesting that brevicipitid toads of the genus Hoplophryne should have adopted a somewhat similar habit of laying their eggs in or near basins of water. They also exhibit a reduction of the gills and both possess a powerful development of the jaws (Noble, 1929*a*). Apparently the latter modification assists them in cutting through the capsules of the eggs they eat. In spite of the parallelism of habit and diet, the tadpoles of each group show definite evidence of their group relationship. Those of Hoplophryne have the characteristic brevicipitid features described above, while hylas resemble one another in the reduction of the larval tooth rows (Fig. 24).

Other species of Hyla have adopted still other modes of life history. *Hyla uranochroa*, for example, apparently lays its eggs out of water on leaves and the tadpoles which finally make their way into the water are forced to live in the rapid streams where they find themselves. This tree frog has a red iris similar to many species of the genus Phyllomedusa. The latter is merely a Hyla which has undergone various reductions in the length of certain digits. All species of Phyllomedusa, as far as is known, lay their eggs over water. They do not beat this egg mass into foam as in the case of Polypedates, but in some species the parents may fold the leaves together over the mass of eggs. The tadpoles which hatch have a broad back fin similar to *Hyla versicolor*. One species of the genus has been recorded to have its mouth produced into a funnel which apparently assists it in surface feeding. A similar umbrella mouth has

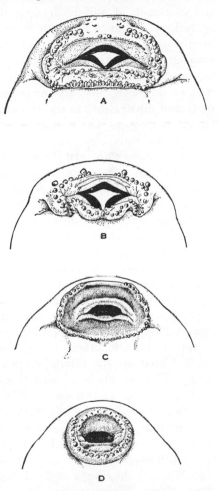

FIG. 24.—The modification of the mouth parts of the tadpoles of Jamaican tree frogs: *A. Hyla lichenata.* *B. Hyla brunnea.* *C. Hyla marianae.* *D. Hyla wilderi.*

been recorded in the brevicipitids, *Microhyla achatina* and *M. heymonsii* tadpoles, as well as in many species of the pelobatid Megalophrys and in one species of the brachycephalid Phyllobates (Fig. 22B). Some of these species live in mountain brooks and others in ponds.   The funnels differ in detailed form but in all cases they are umbrella-like extensions of one or both of the larval lips. No doubt the funnels assist some species, if not all, in increasing the efficiency of surface feeding, but when one considers the sporadic occurrence of these enlarged lips in totally unrelated groups of frogs, it becomes clear that they do not afford a good evidence of relationship.   Since tadpoles with and without enlarged mouths are sometimes found together in the same ponds, it does not seem that the presence of these enlargements is a matter of life or death in the economy of these species.   It would be interesting to know whether the tadpoles with the large mouths invariably feed on a different kind of food from that on which the others do.   In the adult frogs there is no specialization of food habits permitting two closely related species to live in the same region.   Possibly competition is avoided in these tadpoles by the very different mouths of the larvae.

Brachycephalidae.—A second family of predominantly neotropical Salientia is the Brachycephalidae.   Like the Hylidae they also evolved from toothed bufonids but they specialized in terrestrial life.   As mentioned above, Phyllobates and Dendrobates are closely related and the males of both genera carry their tadpoles on their backs, at least while transporting them to the pools from the site where the eggs were laid.   The habit is known from a series of species, some living at high altitudes in the Andes and others at sea level in tropical jungles.   The habit forced on the group by phylogeny was found useful in many different kinds of situations.   How the habit actually developed is not known since the life history of the genera immediately ancestral to Phyllobates has not yet been worked out.

A second group of Brachycephalidae seems to have had an independent origin from bufonid ancestors.   This group includes the diminutive frogs of the genus Sminthillus.   Their anatomy suggests that they have evolved directly from Syrrhophus or its close relative Eleutherodactylus.   Like the latter genus, *Sminthillus limbatus* of Cuba lays large eggs on land.   Apparently these undergo the usual devclopment of Eleutherodactylus. Sminthillus is very small, and each female, as far as known, lays only a single egg, while the many species of Eleutherodactylus, whose life histories are known, lay considerably more.   Such a reduction in egg number is apparently correlated with the small size of the species.

There is one genus of Brachycephalidae, Rhinoderma (Fig. 25), which has attracted attention for many years because the male carries the eggs in his vocal pouch until they hatch as fully formed frogs. The tadpoles during this period have typical larval mouth parts, although these remain uncornified. The papillae about the mouth resemble more closely those of the bufonid Paludicola, as described by Fernandez (1927), than those of the brachycephalid *Dendrophryniscus stelzneri*, described by the same author. No intermediate stages between this remarkable habit of carrying eggs in the vocal pouch and the more usual habit of laying eggs in the water are known. Many fish are "mouth breeders," that is, they carry their eggs for various periods during development in the buccal cavity, but no species of frog has this habit, although an African form was incorrectly described as doing so.

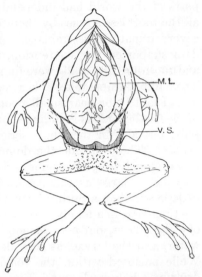

FIG. 25.—A dissection of the vocal pouch of *Rhinoderma darwinii* showing several partly metamorphosed larvae. The young undergo their larval development within the vocal sac of the male. *V.S.*, vocal sac; *M.L.*, metamorphosing larva.

The retention of larval structures in situations where they cannot function finds a parallel to Rhinoderma in other groups. The South African *Arthroleptella lightfooti* develops a branchial sac devoid of a spiracle, although the species undergoes its entire development on land and is unable to swim when placed in the water. Again, the African *Breviceps parvus* undergoes even a more direct development from egg to frog but nevertheless possesses a branchial sac within which the forelimbs develop (de Villiers, 1929). Possibly these or other larval retentions may afford a clue to the ancestry of these groups, but so little is known concerning the larvae of the Brachycephalidae that the phylogenetic significance of the larval teeth of Rhinoderma cannot be stated.

Bufonidae.—Mention has been made of the direct development of Eleutherodactylus. This genus belongs to the large group of tooth-bearing toads formerly called "Leptodactylidae." A study of the anatomy of the toothed and the toothless toads in various parts of the world disclosed that many genera in different parts of the world had independently lost their teeth. Placing all the toothless species by themselves in a separate family made a very unnatural assemblage. As indicated above, life history data supported this contention, for various groups of toothless and tooth-bearing toads were found to have the same life-history. The habit of Eupemphix of beating its egg mass into a foam which it had laid in or near small pools of water was found not only in the toothed genus Paludicola, immediately ancestral to Eupemphix, but also in the whole series of species referred to several genera. These include the dominant group of South American frogs, namely Leptodactylus. Some species of the latter genus may be as large as the American Bullfrog and others only a little larger than a Spring Peeper, *Hyla crucifer*, and yet they all lay their eggs in a foamy mass. A parallel occurs in some species of Polypedates, but here the egg mass is not laid in contact with water, and the larvae, as they develop, are differently modified. While enclosed within the foamy mass, the larvae of Leptodactylus, Paludicola, and Eupemphix have very slim bodies which may be of assistance in their efforts to break through their slimy nests to the adjacent water. Differences appear in the various species; for example, in the length of the gills. Nevertheless, there is a general agreement of nest form and larval habitus which runs through the whole group.

The only exception known at the present time to foam nest building as characteristic of all species of Leptodactylus and its allies is found in a species at present referred to the genus Pleurodema. Fernandez (1927) reported this species to lay its eggs in regular masses, but since the eggs were not collected by Fernandez, there is some possibility of error. The evidence as given would indicate that a life-history mode may remain constant throughout a great many related species and genera and suddenly, within a single genus, change to a totally new type. Within many genera egg size may increase and species with the largest eggs will develop into frogs instead of going through the tadpole stage. But there is very little evidence of radical changes in the mode of life history among closely related species which pass through the tadpole stage.

Although egg size may shift within closely related species, it is interesting that it frequently remains constant throughout a large series of forms. For example, all species of Eleutherodactylus apparently lay their eggs on land; the eggs are devoid of peduncles and are not beaten into a foam. The embryos as they develop may or may not be provided with external gills. They are all equipped with a broad, thin tail which functions as a respiratory organ. No other species of frogs laying eggs on land is equipped with this respiratory tail at the time they are enclosed within the egg capsule, except certain East Indian brevicipitids. In these brevicipitids, the eggs are laid in the form of a rosary and the tadpoles which develop are not known to have the powerful egg teeth of Eleutherodactylus (Fig. 26).

Fig. 26.—The egg teeth of two frogs. A. *Eleutherodactylus abbotti*. B. E. *inoplatus*.

The egg teeth in Eleutherodactylus usually have the shape of a pair of bull's horns which help the little frog when mature to escape from the capsule. There are, thus, apparently important details of development to distinguish the mode of life history found in Eleutherodactylus from that in other frogs laying eggs on land. Again, these differences are not sufficiently known in any number of species for us to be sure which are the most diagnostic.

That the form of the egg capsule really may be an important character uninfluenced by environmental factors is well shown in the case of the common toad. Species of Bufo are found throughout the greater part of the world. Species laying their eggs in deserts, in jungles, or on mountain tops all produce the same characteristic string of eggs found in our common Bufo. There is, to be sure, one exception from the East Indies which has not been accounted for (Noble, 1927) and also the instance of the Oak Toad of Florida which sometimes lays its eggs in small rods instead of strings (Wright and Wright, 1924). The latter case may be accounted for by assuming the modification to be due to the extremely small size of the adult. Since the Bufo stock of South America must have been separated from that in South Africa for many thousands of years, and both must have migrated across jungle and plain to reach their present-day ranges, it is remarkable that both are able to succeed so well with this simple mode of egg laying. It is probable that factors other than the mode of life history have been chiefly responsible for the toad's success; nevertheless, the method of laying the eggs in strings has not been detrimental to the species under these various environmental conditions, or the stock would have died out.

Ovoviviparous Bufonids.—Within a single family there may be several modes of life history. In the Plethodontidae discussed above, some species lay their eggs in water, others on land, and still others retain them in the oviducts until fully formed young emerge. Similarly in the Bufonidae different ways of propagation may occur. There is one group of African frogs, referred to the genus Nectophrynoides, the two species of which are structurally very different. Until recently they have been kept in separate genera, but both give birth to their young alive. No copulatory organs have been described, and how the spermatozoa are transmitted to the oviduct is not known. The embryos as they develop have very slim tails which no doubt are of little use as locomotory organs. The tails are well vascularized, however, and greatly elongated. This seems an adaptation to securing oxygen from the vascular uterine wall. The number of larvae within a single uterus of *N. vivipara* is often over a hundred, and the long tails apparently function as so many pipe lines bringing oxygen to the larvae kept away from the uterine wall by the bodies of their brothers and sisters. As in the case of Rhinoderma, the stages by which this ovoviviparity in Necto-phrynoides was secured are unknown. In fact the many peculiar life histories of tropical frogs are known so fragmentarily that we are able to compare only the general mode of life history rather than the details of development. Where these details are known, however, they sometimes exhibit marked adaptations which have no especial phylogenetic significance. Examples may be found among the tadpoles of Ceratophrys, two species of which have large mouths and many tooth rows as an adaptation toward a cannibalistic diet. Mountain-brook tadpoles may have large mouths which assist them in holding on to rocks in midstream. In these cases tadpoles with few, and others with many tooth rows may be closely related.

The mode of life history thus forms a guide rather than an infallible proof of the relationship of frog or toad. Where the affinities of genera or species are in doubt the mode of life history frequently gives an important clue. For example, the torrent frogs of Rio de Janeiro, called *Hylodes petropolitanus* and *Borborocoetes miliarus*, have peculiarly flattened tadpoles adapted for gliding over wet stones or trickles on the edge of the torrents. These tadpoles are so different from any other species that there can be little doubt as to the close affinity of the two forms. More recently, Lutz (1928, 1929) has shown that the tadpoles of two species of Cycloramphus resemble these flat tadpoles closely but are more elongate and may have different mouth parts and spiracles. The eggs of all these species are apparently laid out of water among the rocks and the tadpoles are more truly amphibian, that is, both aquatic and terrestrial, than those of any other frog of South America. This habit and habitus of the tadpoles is not an ontogenetic modification produced by a peculiar environment. In the same mountain torrents there are various species of Elosia which frequent the rocks but produce large tadpoles of the usual torrent type. The edges of mountain torrents are attractive to many species of frogs but each holds to its own mode of life history which is primarily dependent on the heredity of the species. In the present instance the mode of life history would seem to be a better clue to relationships of the species than many of the so-called generic characters. In other words, marked changes in the dilation of the digits, the webbing between the toes, and various other external characters of the adults have occurred, while the mode of life history remained the same.

Primitive Salientia.—Finally, mention should be made of the most primitive families of frogs and toads—Liopelmidae, Discoglossidae, Pipidae, and Pelobatidae. With the exception of the last, there are few genera to consider and these are widely separated geographically. No doubt the first three represent ancient stocks and hence the mode of life history is often strikingly different within each family. Nevertheless, all are characterized by the pelvic embrace of the male during breeding, while most higher frogs and toads practice the pectoral amplexus, although occasionally the amplexus may be pelvic in very stout species. The observations of Fletcher (1889), that the Australian Limnodynastes, Hyperolia, Pseudophryne, and Crinia employ a pelvic embrace is of interest, for it strongly suggests that these toads are more primitive than other bufonids. Nearly all tadpoles of liopelmids, discoglossids, and pelobatids exhibit smooth edges to their larval teeth, which frequently appear in duplex rows. A doubling of the sets of teeth within each tooth row appears extremely rarely among higher forms, and the tadpole teeth of the latter are usually serrated. Where specializations occur in the life history, these are unique. Mention has been made of Protopipa and Pipa as the only two frogs which carry their eggs in separate pockets on their back. Mention has been made also of Ascaphus (Fig. 22D), whose tadpoles live in the mountain torrents of the West. The arrangement of the tooth rows of Ascaphus is unique among the Salientia. While the species of these primitive genera are too few to trace out their progressive evolution in their mode of life history, nevertheless, in general they support the view that the mode of life history is usually of considerable phylogenetic significance.

Gymnophiona.—The caecilians, which have been found to be primitive in many features of their anatomy, possess large-yolked eggs. Some of these are laid on land as in Ichthyophis, and the female guards them until the larvae hatch and take up a life in the water. Others skip over the aquatic larval stage and a few have specialized external gills. One genus, Typhlonectes, is ovoviviparous. No caecilian has a less specialized life history than that of the more primitive genera Ichthyophis and Rhinatrema. The life histories of Ichthyophis, Hypogeophis, and Typhlonectes show a gradual specialization of life history accompanying a specialization in adult structure.

The Primitive Type.—Lastly, it should be emphasized that there is no reason for assuming that the small eggs of Rana are primitive. The branchiosaur ancestors of frogs and urodeles arose from labyrinthodonts and these ancient Amphibia were almost indistinguishable from some cotylosaur reptiles. Possibly these labyrinthodonts had not developed the amnion, allantois, or calcareous egg membranes of modern reptiles, but it is not improbable that the eggs were well provided with yolk. Another inheritance from fish ancestors was the gelatinous egg capsules which serve not only as a protective cover but also as a regulator of osmotic conditions in the egg. In species exposing their eggs to the sun the capsules have the additional function of conserving heat by checking radiation.

References

BISHOP, S. C., 1919: Notes on the habits and development of the four-toed salamander, *Hemidactylium scutatum* (Schlegel), *N. Y. State Mus. Bull.*, 219–220, 251–282.

BLES, E. J., 1907: "Notes on anuran development; Paludicola, Hemisus, and Phyllomedusa," The Work of John Samuel Budgett, Cambridge, 443–458, pls. XXII–XXVII.

BRIMLEY, C. S., 1923: The dwarf salamander at Raleigh, N. C., *Copeia*, N. Y., No. 120, 81–83.

DESPAX, RAYMOND, 1923: Contribution à l'étude anatomique et biologique des Batraciens urodèles du groupe des Euproctes et specialement de l'Euprocte des Pyrénées, *Thèses pour Docteur Sci. Nat. Toulouse*, Sér. A, No. 929.

DE VILLIERS, C. G. S., 1929: Some features of the early development of Breviceps, *Ann. Transvaal Mus.*, XIII, 142–151.

ESCHER, KONRAD, 1925: Das Verhalten der Seitenorgane der Wirbeltiere und ihrer Nerven beim Übergang zum Landleben, *Acta Zool.*, VI, 307–419.

FERNANDEZ, K., 1927: Sobre la biologia y reproduccion de batracios argentinos (Segunda parte), *Bol. Acad. Nac. Cien. Cordoba*, XXIX, 271 338, 4 pls.

FLETCHER, J. J., 1889: Observation on the oviposition and habits of certain Australian Batrachia, *Proc. Linn. Soc. N. S. Wales* (2), IV, 357–390.

LUTZ, A., 1928: Biologie et metamorphose des Batraciens du genre Cyclorhamphus, *Compt. rend. Soc. Biol.*, XCVIII, 640.

———, 1929: Taxonomy and biology of the genus Cyclorhamphus, *Mem. Inst. Oswaldo Cruz*, XXII, 16–25, 5 pls.

MOESEL, J., 1918: Thesis: a study of the Caudata of the Cayuga Lake Basin, *Cornell Univ. MS.*

NOBLE, G. K., 1926: The importance of larval characters in the classification of South African Salientia, *Amer. Mus. Novit.*, No. 237.

———, 1927: The value of life-history data in the study of the evolution of the Amphibia, *Ann. N. Y. Acad. Sci.*, XXX, 31–128, 1 pl.

———, 1929: Further observations on the life history of the newt, Triturus viridescens, *Amer. Mus. Novit.*, No. 348.

———, 1929a: The adaptive modifications of the arboreal tadpoles of Hoplophryne and the torrent tadpoles of Staurois, *Bull. Amer. Mus. Nat. Hist.*, LVIII, Art. VII, 291–334.

POWER, J. H., 1926: Notes on the habits and life histories of certain little-known Anura, with descriptions of the tadpoles, *Trans. Roy. Soc. S. Africa*, XIII, 107–117, pls. VI–IX.

POWER, J. H., and WALTER ROSE, 1929: Notes on the habits and life histories of some Cape Peninsula Anura, *Trans. Roy. Soc. S. Africa*, XVII, 109–115, pl. V.

Rose, Walter, 1929: "Veld and Vlei: An account of South African frogs, toads, lizards, snakes and tortoises," Cape Town.

Schmalhausen, I., 1917: On the extremities of Ranidens sibiricus Kessl, *Rev. Zool. Russe*, II, 129–135.

Scott-Birabén, M. T., and K. Fernandez-Marcinowski, 1921: Variaciones locales de caracteres específicos en larvas de anfibios, *An. Soc. Cient. Argentina*, XCII, 129–142.

Smith, Bertram G., 1912: The embryology of Cryptobranchus alleghen-iensis, including comparisons with some other vertebrates; Part I, Introduction: the history of the egg before cleavage, *Jour. Morph.*, XXIII, 61–154; Part II, General embryonic and larval development, with special reference to external features, *Jour. Morph.*, XXIII, 455–579, 10 pls.

Storer, T. I., 1925: A synopsis of the Amphibia of California, *Univ. Cal. Pub. Zool.*, XXVII, 1–342, 18 pls.

Wager, Vincent A., 1929: The breeding habits and life histories of some of the Transvaal Amphibia, II, *Trans. Roy. Soc. S. Africa*, XVII, 125–135, 5 pls.

————, 1930: The breeding habits and life histories of two rare South African Amphibia, I, *Hylambates natalensis*, A. Smith; II, *Nataloba-trachus bonebergi*, Hewitt & Methuen, *Trans. Roy. Soc. S. Africa*, XIX, 79–92, 5 pls.

Wright, A. H., 1929: Synopsis and description of North American tadpoles, *Proc. U. S. Nat. Mus.*, LXXIV, Art. 11, 1–70, 9 pls.

Wright, A. H., and A. A. Wright, 1924: A key to the eggs of the Salientia east of the Mississippi River, *Amer. Naturalist*, LVIII, 375–381.

Wunderer, Hans, 1910: Die Entwicklung der äusseren Körperform des Alpensalamanders (Salamandra atra Laur), *Zool. Jahrb. Anat. Abt.*, XXIX, 367–414, pls. XXV–XXXIII.

CHAPTER IV

SPECIATION AND ADAPTATION

It is self-evident that Amphibia are more or less adapted to their environment. Burrowing toads are equipped with tarsal "spades" (Fig. 27), pond salamanders with lateral line organs, arboreal frogs with large adhesive discs. If Amphibia were not in more or less harmonious relation with the habitats in which

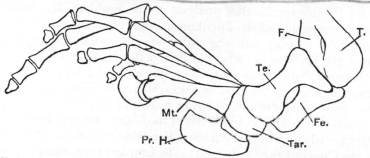

Fig. 27.—A fossorial adaptation. Skeleton of the right foot of *Rhinophrynus dorsalis*, mesial aspect. The prehallux and first digit are modified for digging. *F.*, fibula; *Fe.*, fibulare; *Mt.*, metatarsal of first digit; *Pr.H.*, prehallux; *T.*, tibia; *Tar.*, fused tarsalia; *Te.*, tibiale.

the different species spend the greater part of their lives, be that aquatic, terrestrial, or arboreal, they would eventually succumb. Each of the chapters devoted to the structure of Amphibia discusses some illustration of the adjustment or modification of organs and tissues as correlated with the particular needs of the organism. Amphibia, like most other organisms, when under the stress of unusual environmental conditions, can modify during development the full expression of various structures. But the alterations of development will explain very few of the extraordinary adaptations found in the group. In considering the latter, some account must be given of the mechanism by which both species and their distinctive characters come into existence. Emphasis will be laid on the origins of adaptations rather than on a detailed description of them.

Species Defined.—Species are groups of individuals having one or more characters in common which distinguish them from related groups of individuals. Groups exhibiting characters in common but intergrading with those of a closely related group are usually defined as subspecies and a third name is added to the species name. For example, *Desmognathus fuscus carolinensis* is the subspecies of the common Dusky Salamander *D. fuscus*. Species may embrace several subspecies but they may also include many variants, incipient species, and sometimes "sports." The relation of these various infraspecific categories to species is still a controversial matter in spite of the efforts of many investigators (*cf.* Cuenot, 1921; Morgan, 1923; Robson, 1928; Rensch, 1929). The Amphibia have contributed little to an experimental analysis of the problem, but various facts concerning their distribution and phylogeny have been used to bolster up now one view, now the other. Since it has been the systematist who has first defined and has been most concerned with species as steps in evolution, some reference may be made to the kind of data which have been employed by the systematist when considering species origin.

Variation.—The individuals of any one species frequently vary greatly among themselves. Variation of color is well known in the Cricket Frog, Acris, and in the Leopard Frog, *Rana pipiens*. Variation has been described in toe number in Hynobius, vertebrae number in Dendrobates, and egg size in some species of Rana. Similar differences when fixed have been used in defining other groups of Amphibia. The toad, *Bufo americanus*, is not so variable as many species of Salientia, but Kellicott (1907) found many differences in the 13 characters he considered in a single colony of the species. In various species of Salientia individuals may appear with a conspicuous dorsal stripe, and as similar stripes may be characteristic of other species but not those under consideration, they have been considered sports or pronounced mutations (Mertens, 1926). Darwin was familiar with such differences, but he rejected them as a possible source of species formation. He appealed to the small heritable variations found in all species of animals as furnishing the material for species production. Since Darwin's time, naturalists have greatly increased the number of instances of species differing from others merely by slight differences of color or form. On the other hand, geneticists have demonstrated that these small differences are also due to germinal mutations and that they arise and are inherited in the same way as the large heritable changes or sports. In brief, the systematist considers the same kind of data which Darwin utilized, only more examples are available today and much more is known of the way the characters are inherited.

Hereditary Units.—All heritable differences distinguishing species which have been adequately studied have been found to be produced either by recombination of the genes (the hereditary factors) upon crossing; by aberrations of the chromosomes, the bearers of these hereditary factors; or by mutation, that is, change in the individual genes. Most variation displayed by a population of a single species in nature is usually due to recombination of preexisting mutations. Because recombination occurs so much more frequently than mutation, each individual is not the final member of a single series but of converging lines of descent which ramify throughout the entire specific group (Fisher, 1930). Most wild species are heterozygous, that is, unlike in a number of pairs of homologous genes derived from father and mother, respectively. As a result, the effect of any one member of the pair may be modified, and different grades of any one variation may appear within a species. Such variation may appear to be continuous, in striking contrast to the pronounced mutations first studied in domesticated animals and plants. This has led many naturalists to assume that speciation was continuous; mutation, discontinuous. In every case where the material has been subjected to adequate breeding tests, however, this distinction was found to be non-existent. Large and small heritable differences were found to have the same kind of chromosomal basis. Geneticists have shown that the greater the effect of a single mutation, the more likely it is of being not viable. Mutations which produce relatively slight changes are least likely to be harmful and therefore most likely to be preserved by natural selection. It is for this reason that the differences which distinguish species of Amphibia are usually very slight. There is, however, some evidence that mutations of some magnitude have played a rôle in the evolution of the Amphibia.

Unfortunately for the present review, the genetic analysis has not proceeded far enough to determine how many mutations distinguish any one species of Amphibia from another. The albino axolotl is known to differ from the normal colored phase merely by a single Mendelian factor (Haecker, 1908), although there appear to be various degrees of albinism in this species which may be due to other genetic factors. Amphibia are slow-breeding creatures and we may never know how many gene mutations distinguish the axolotl from the other species of Ambystoma. In the meantime, geneticists have brought to light additional facts which give an explanation for the essential requirements postulated by many naturalists for the origin of species in nature.

Isolation in Species Formation.—It has long been recognized that "without isolation no species" will be formed. Recent investigations have emphasized that isolation alone is not so effective as isolation plus change of environment (Grinnell, 1924; Chapman, 1926). Random mating in a natural population of any one species tends to distribute all the different genes throughout the population. Since most mutations occur in only one member of a pair of genes and are recessive (Morgan, 1926), they cannot come to expression until they meet with other like genes on crossing. Isolation encouraging inbreeding hastens the appearance of the characters, and continued inbreeding tends to change the isolated group into one which is homozygous for these characters. Hence stocks isolated on islands, on mountain tops, or in well-defined ecological niches soon exhibit and fix characters which their wide ranging, freely interbreeding ancestral stocks fail to show. If in addition to this uncovering process the isolated community is subjected to new environmental conditions, the stock will be reduced to only relatively few individuals of those best fitted to survive. The uncovering will proceed more quickly, and natural selection will presumably favor individuals unlike those of the original stock. It is thus no wonder that while some species of tree frog have a wide range in Central America, each of the Greater Antilles has its own species. Nor is it surprising that mountain ranges with their diverse topography, whether in the Old or in the New World, usually have a greater number of distinctive types of frogs and toads than the adjacent low country of much greater area.

It may be noted, however, that continued isolation does not improve the strain beyond a certain point. No change will occur in this pure line until a mutation happens to occur in some gene. Isolation favors the rapid purification of hidden strains but has no influence on inducing new mutations.

It is frequently supposed that inbreeding within an isolated community leads to a decrease of vigor. This does not always follow. In a wide-ranging species individuals with dominant genes having unfavorable effects are soon eliminated in the struggle to live. Unfavorable recessive genes, on the other hand—those which do not have any visible effects—may become widely spread throughout the population. Inbreeding of a sample of this population leads to the appearance of these effects, for the inbred individuals tend to become homozygous for these genes. Hence isolated communities of small size are usually less vigorous than communities of a larger size which are frequently "mixing" their germ plasm. If this small group is suddenly thrown into competition with a wide-ranging group, it will usually succumb because it is less vigorous due to its genetic constitution. It is of course possible, however, that the pure line produced by isolation and inbreeding would be more vigorous than a wide-ranging stock due to the selection of certain favorable genes. The chances, however, are very much against such a possibility in nature.

Kinds of Isolation.—Multiplication is so rapid within any species of animal that a balance of numbers is soon struck, dependent on available food and other conditions limiting life in a particular habitat. Competition is most keen between organisms whose food and other requirements are most alike. Hence a decided premium is placed on mutations which tend to throw their owners out of competition with their near relatives. Geneticists have shown that a single gene mutation may affect many organs of the body at one time and also influence physiological processes of great importance in the life of the animal. As Morgan (1923) has said, it is these physiological effects which have played the most important rôle in evolution. In the first place, they might tend to isolate the individuals possessing them as effectively as a river barrier. It is chiefly physiological differences which induce species to select different breeding sites or appear at different seasons or take up an abode in different habitats. In the second place, they might affect the reactions of one individual to another or even induce infertility. Systematists have not been concerned with the characters which have created the species. For example, the Japanese tree frog, *Polypedates schlegelii*, has a form *arborea* differing from the typical form in its slightly more pointed snout and smaller size (Okada, 1928) but it differs radically from the typical form in laying its eggs in frothy masses on leaves over the water instead of in holes in the banks of rice fields. The difference between the two forms is so slight that they are not considered good species. Since the forms, however, are apparently completely isolated during the breeding season, the two "varieties" will continue to accumulate small mutational differences until they become good species. Outside the breeding season many species of frogs and salamanders may occupy the same habitat. Robson (1928) in his review of species formation failed to find isolation an important factor, apparently because his data on the kinds of isolation were incomplete. Geographic isolation is the most obvious but by no means the only important kind of isolation which may occur. For example, *Plethodon cinereus* and *P. glutinosus* are two common salamanders of eastern United States. As shown by Shelford (1913), the latter is more sensitive to dry air than the former and this would explain why the latter is usually found in more moist situations than the former. Further, *P. cinereus* lays its eggs in logs or under stones in the woods, while *P. glutinosus* seeks a subterranean retreat for egg laying. Lastly, the two species are of very different sizes and hence would not compete for the same food. If a derived stock is thrown out of competition with the ancestral group and cross-breeding is prevented due to morphological or physiological change, the first step in the origin of a new species has been made.

Not all closely related species are isolated, and some may be thrown into direct competition. In such cases the factors permitting survival may be complex. Recently Piersol (1929) has found that *Ambystoma jeffersonianum*, although breeding in the same ponds as *A. maculatum*, maintains the same relative abundance from year to year in the Toronto region. The first species breeds a little earlier than the second and a higher percentage of its eggs fail to develop. Piersol has shown that this loss is due to the cold, which in some cases may prevent the sperm from entering and in others may favor an abnormal polyspermy leading to irregular changes and death. Further, low temperatures below 5°C. result in such a slowing of development that the egg materials tend to stratify and the egg dies. These losses, however, are compensated for by the cannibalistic tendencies of the larvae and the earlier start they obtain in life. Piersol showed that when the larvae of the two species were crowded and starved, the *jeffersonianum* larvae devoured the *maculatum*. If *jeffersonianum* larvae were not so aggressive and voracious, *maculatum* would soon replace *jeffersonianum* as a species, for it has inherited a breeding season rhythm better fitted to the Toronto climate.

Not only the time of breeding but the duration of the breeding season may be due to genetic factors. Witschi (1930) found that two strains of *Rana temporaria* differed in the length of the breeding season. When the rapid breeders were brought into the laboratory, they deposited their eggs in 24 hours while the slow breeders under the same conditions required a longer period. Correlated with this difference in breeding rate was an inherited difference in rate of sex differentiation. Further, the rapid breeders came from regions with long winters and short though relatively hot summers. Their breeding rhythm was adapted to the habitat of the strain. No doubt natural selection had been instrumental in localizing each strain in that region most suited to its particular rhythm.

Space and Time in Evolution.—Species change with space and time: with space because they meet new environments and this permits new isolations and new selections, with time because any one locality is undergoing a cyclic climatic change (Matthew, 1915) which will eventually alter both the physiography and flora of the region. Since species usually avoid competition by migrating into new territory, Jordan (1926) has postulated that the nearest relative of any species is not likely to be found in the same region, but in a neighboring one separated by a geographical barrier. Since an active or passive migration is occurring at all times, various naturalists, such as Taylor (1913), have assumed that the older the group the greater will be its range. Exceptions occur to both these rules but they frequently afford valuable clues in tracing the history of a group.

Species arise chiefly by an accumulation of gene mutations (chromosome aberrations have not been investigated in Amphibia). The genes are the hereditary factors and they lie in linear order in the chromosomes. They have been compared with catalysts and their size and number estimated in the case of the fruit fly (Muller, 1929). Although naturalists have frequently assumed that the hereditary material may be altered by the environment, the proof of such an alteration is a matter of recent demonstration. Muller and others have shown that X-rays and radium may induce mutation in the fruit fly and other organisms including plants. Goldschmidt (1929) has induced a series of mutations in Drosophila by exposing the eggs for short periods to a temperature of 37°C. Whether or not air temperatures or radioactive substances in the earth have any influence on mutation in Amphibia, it should be noted that the mutations so far induced in animals or plants are no more adaptive to particular environmental conditions than the usual mutations of the laboratory. Adaptation results from the fact that nature permits those individuals to survive which are equipped with useful or at least non-harmful mutations. Indifferent mutations make up the bulk of specific differences. Darwin considered specific differences to have been gradually improved by natural selection, but more recent field observations have failed to show the survival value of many characters, such as the color differences of the various species of Ambystoma or Plethodon. The red and gray phases of *P. cinereus,* for example, are nearly equally abundant in regions where enemies, such as the screech owl, are known to be abundant. It would thus appear that physiological differences, such as habitat or breeding-season preferences, which actually throw a derived stock out of competition with its ancestral form, are the real characters favored by natural selection. Linked with the genes which determine these physiological characters are still other genes which determine the visible differences.

Natural Selection.—The great variety of apparently useless characters found in Amphibia is due to the nature of the hereditary mechanism. In other groups of animals it has been shown that each gene may produce several visible effects. Some of these may be favorable, others neutral, but they are either accepted or rejected as a unit by nature. The survival of any particular individual or species is not determined by the perfection of any one character but by the total fitness of an organism for some particular environment. Since it is obvious that natural selection weeds out those variants which are least fitted to survive, we might expect that any species which has existed in one environment for a long time would be as well-adapted as its genetic constitution would permit. The possibilities of viable mutations are, however, fewer than usually believed. In spite of the fact that many groups of Amphibia were in existence since the early Tertiary, we find many species still bungling along with mechanisms not perfectly adjusted to any one environment. The reason for this lack of complete adaptation in all characters lies in the nature of the hereditary mechanism and the possibility for neutral characters being carried along in the evolutionary stream.

It was noted by Darwin (1859) that wide-ranging species usually exhibit more variation than forms having a smaller range. These variations may show no intergradation with the ancestral stock and in some cases have been given specific names. Thus, *Rana burnsi* is a spotless *Rana pipiens* found in the same locality as the latter and yet not intergrading (Weed, 1922). In the same region *Rana kandiyohi* may be described as a mottled *Rana pipiens* which does intergrade. In other groups of animals mutations may show a perfect or incomplete dominance. In the latter case the hybrids appear intermediate in character.

It is probable that both *Rana burnsi* and *R. kandiyohi* owe their origin to one or more mutations but the determination of the exact number will have to await a genetic analysis. The adaptive value of the color differences, which is the distinguishing character of these three species of Rana, is apparently very slight; the same may be said of the color patterns of many other species of Salientia. On the other hand, the coloration of arboreal frogs and salamanders, which expose themselves to the attacks of enemies, may be highly protective. *Aneides aeneus*, for example, closely resembles the blue-green algae on the trees it frequents, while *Hyla andersoni* has acquired the apple green of the swamp magnolia on which it often rests. Such close correlations owe their existence to natural selection and are found in species most open to attack.

In the same way any rigorous habitat will foster more adaptations than a less selective one. The tadpoles and salamanders of mountain streams are equipped to hold tight and to expose little surface to the current. They reduce their lungs which might function as hydrostatic organs. The degree of adaptive modification bears no relation to the degree of specialization attained in their phylogeny. Ascaphus, America's most primitive frog, lives in the mountain streams of northwestern United States. In apparent adaptation to this habitat it has given up its voice and reduced its auditory apparatus and lungs. The males during the breeding season crawl along the bottom of the streams in search of the females. External fertilization is uncertain in swift currents, and the males of Ascaphus are equipped with a vascular extension of the cloaca, which can be carried forward and inserted into the cloaca of the female. Although there are many mountain-brook urodeles, few Salientia live habitually in these currents. One of the reasons may well be that urodeles have adopted a method of internal fertilization. Ascaphus has accomplished the same result by a different method. Although Ascaphus is highly adapted to a mountain-brook habitat, it retains all the primitive features of anatomy which disclose its true relationships. The habitus characters of Amphibia are not to be confused with the heritage of less plastic features which indicate the phylogenetic position of the species.

Divergent Evolution.—A species is usually distinguished from a subspecies by the arbitrary criterion that the former does not intergrade while the latter always merges gradually into its nearest relatives occupying contiguous ranges. Most species are also distinguished from subspecies by the fact that they are unable to cross with their nearest relatives. This sterility which emerges with the birth of a species seems to be a consequence of the difference in many genes; the greater the number of different genes the more the likelihood of incompatibility on fertilization or during development of the hybrid. Whenever two groups of individuals are effectively isolated they tend to accumulate different mutations, merely by chance, and hence continue to diverge. Obviously, once this infertility is complete the opportunities for divergence are greatly increased.

Parallel Evolution.—One of the most interesting features of speciation is that the same characters frequently appear independently in the descendants of a single stock. This phenomenon has frequently been noted in plants (Vavilov, 1922) and in many groups of animals. It is even a feature of the evolution of the opalinid parasites in the recta of frogs (Metcalf, 1928). It is also an important characteristic of amphibian speciation, as examination of the data in Chap. V will show. For example, Boulenger (1918) in considering the subspecies of the common European frog, *Rana esculenta*, showed that *R. e. chinensis* repeated the principal characters of *R. e. lessonae* although both are independently derived from *R. e. ridibunda*. An even better case is found in the West Indian tree frogs. Several species of Hyla in Hispaniola have been evolved independently of the Jamaican series from a common *Hyla brunnea-H. dominicensis* stock and in both islands certain distinctive

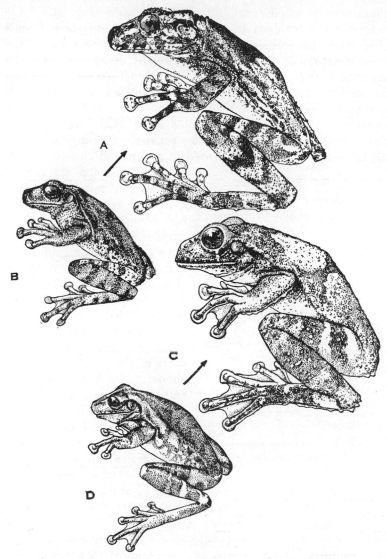

F‌ɪɢ. 28.—Parallel evolution.   The life history data indicates that the large
tree frogs, *Hyla lichenata* (*A*) and *H.vasta* (*C*), have been independently evolved
from smaller ancestors, *H.brunnea* (*B*) and *H.dominicensis* (*D*), respectively.
Nevertheless, the larger species agree among themselves not only in size but in
their rhomboid pupil and rough skin.   Many other instances of the independent
origin of identical characters may be found among the frogs and toads.

characters of pupil form, skin rugosity, and body size have independently evolved in the derived species on these islands (Fig. 28). In many groups of animals the reappearance of the same character in species not closely related has given rise to the suggestion that one species may be mimicking another which has certain other characters of survival value. This mummery has been brought about by the action of natural selection on small mutations. In the Amphibia many characters of dentition, pupil form, pectoral girdle, tongue form, digital scutes, digital loss, etc., have reappeared in groups not closely related.

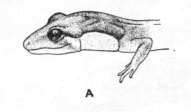

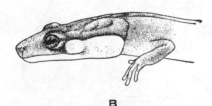

FIG. 29.—Mimicry in salamanders. A reddish cheek patch is characteristic of *Plethodon jordani* (*B*) and appears as a variation in specimens of *Desmognathus fuscus carolinensis* (*A*) living in the Great Smoky Mountains, the habitat of the former species.

It would seem that the various families of Amphibia had only a limited repertoire of germinal changes. Many of these parallel changes have no known functional significance.

In some cases the retention of a character once it has reappeared in a different stock may be aided by natural selection. Some polypedatid and hylid tree frogs from different parts of the world may appear almost identical externally, and it is possible that the slow weeding out of natural selection has brought this about. Natural selection, however, would seem to have had little effect on shaping the color pattern of some Amphibia. For example, *Plethodon jordani* of the Great Smoky Mountains is dark bluish with a conspicuous reddish cheek. *Desmognathus fuscus carolinensis* of the same region occasionally shows an almost identical color pattern (Fig. 29). It would seem remarkable that this distinctive color pattern should have occurred in two species in the same region, but at Durbin, West Virginia, bright orange specimens have been found, others with a stripe on each side and a plain back, or a stripe on each side and a row of spots in the middle of the back, or a series of small vermiculations on the side, or several other distinctive patterns which are well-marked even in young metamorphosed individuals. Some of these color patterns appear again in species of *Plethodon* and *Eurycea*. It is thus clear that *D. f. carolinensis* is able to produce in a single locality many of the patterns of the Plethodontidae, and while some of these patterns may appear with intergrades such as the reddish-cheeked variant of the Great Smokies, others may show little intergradation. If any of these well-marked color variants of Durbin could isolate themselves in a distinctive range or ecological niche, few systematists would hesitate in calling them species.

The case of reddish-cheeked Plethodon and Desmognathus occurring together in the Great Smokies and nowhere else in the United States has been considered an instance of mimicry. The phenomenon may be compared with the parallel modification of bent terminal phalanges in certain African ranids (Fig. 30). Why the only species of Rana having claw-shaped terminal phalanges actually perforating the integument of the digit tips should be found in the only part of the world where this modification occurs in other genera not closely related to it is difficult to account for on the basis of natural selection, since neither this modification nor the reddish cheeks seem to have a survival value. It is possible that parallel modifications in unrelated genera are linked with physiological mutations having such a value, but at present there is no evidence for such an assumption.

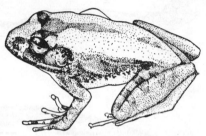

FIG. 30.—The African *Gampsosteo-nyx batesi* with recurved terminal phalanges which normally protrude through the skin of the toes to form claws.

Function in Phylogeny.—Structural characters may also exhibit in some cases an apparent gradual change, in others an apparent sudden modification. Various genera of frogs differ from their closest relatives merely by a loss of teeth, but tooth loss in some bufonids such as Batrachophrynus was brought on gradually. Similarly, while the salamanders Manculus, Hemidactylium, Salamandrella, and Salamandrina differ from their ancestral stocks chiefly or at least in part by lacking the outer toe of each hind foot (Fig. 31), toe reduction in *Batrachoseps* *pacificus* and some species of *Hynobius* is a variable phenomenon. Related frogs with and without the teeth apparently take the same food. Similarly, no functional change has been noticed in the locomotion of salamanders which have lost the outer digit.

FIG. 31.—Four-toed salamanders. The loss of the fifth or outer toe has occurred frequently in the phylogeny of the salamanders. Four-toed species of three different families are shown here: *A. Hynobius keyserlingi. B. Hemidactylium scutatum. C. Salamandrina terdigitata.*

Tree frogs of Santo Domingo which have a rhomboidal pupil and other species with an oval pupil are both nocturnal; and since both live in the same valley, they would seem to have had little reason for difference in the shape of the pupil. Whether a character has taken its final form gradually or suddenly, natural selection would frequently seem to have played little part in its genesis. The effect of natural selection may, however, be indirect, in the present instance favoring frogs of different sizes, and the rhomboidal pupil may be another manifestation of the gene or genes producing large size. Although the subject is highly speculative, it is important to emphasize that many characters of Amphibia have no functional significance but nevertheless have appeared independently several times in phylogeny.

Adaptation.—Most Amphibia are well adapted to the particular environments in which they live. These adjustments have been brought about by the elimination over a long period of time of those variants which decreased the efficiency of the species in any particular locality. Species are therefore preadapted by gene mutations, very few of the great many mutations produced (to judge from the kinds of variations in any one species) being retained in future generations. As indicated in Chap. III, function may play an important part during the later stages of ontogeny in shaping certain organs or tissues of the body. There is, however, no evidence that this effect is ever inherited. For example, the blind salamander, *Typhlotriton spelaeus* as a larva, lives chiefly near the mouths of caves and it retains functional eyes throughout larval life. During metamorphosis, however, it penetrates deeply into the caves and soon the lids draw together, fuse in part, and the rods and cones of the retina degenerate (Fig. 32). If the larvae are kept in the light during this critical period they retain and further develop both the functional eyes and pigmentation (Noble and Pope, 1928). Typhlotriton has been losing its eyesight every generation for presumably a very long period, since it represents one of the most primitive plethodontids, and yet the effect of cave life has not been inherited. Give the young, metamorphosed Typhlotriton the stimulus of light, and it will develop functional eyes (Fig. 32). The same is true to a lesser extent of the European blind salamander. Proteus will redevelop cutaneous pigment in the light (Werner, 1892) and further develop its larval eyes under certain conditions of red and white light not to be expected in nature (Kammerer, 1912). Although many modifications produced during ontogeny resemble heritable features of other species, this is no evidence that the modification frequently repeated can impress itself on the germ. | Thus, while cold has been shown to induce the European land salamander to retain the young for longer periods in the oviducts even until metamorphosis (Kammerer, 1907) and this condition is typical of the related *Salamandra atra* (a high mountain species), Lantz (1927) found that the former species, *S. salamandra,* may sometimes also produce metamorphosed young in nature at a moderate elevation.

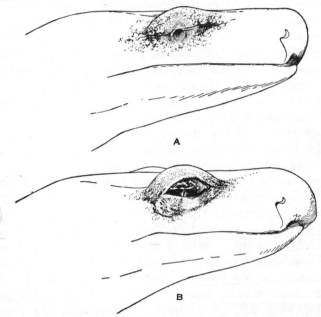

FIG. 32.—The influence of light on the eye of the cave salamander, *Typhlotriton spelaeus*. *A*. A blind adult reared in the dark for 203 days after the beginning of metamorphosis. *B*. Another, reared in the light for approximately the same period, retains and further develops the functional eyes both possessed while larvae.

Mutations in other groups of animals have frequently been found to resemble modifications, but there is no experimental evidence that modifications produced during life in the body can be transferred to the germ plasm and become hereditary. Those who believe this possible would postulate long periods of time to accomplish this result. The evidence available is, however, against such an assumption (Cuenot, 1925).

Preadaptation.—Instances of preadaptation are given in the discussion of behavior (Chap. XVI) and in the origin of the brooding habit (Chap. XVII). The "sucking discs" of tree frogs are frequently considered highly adaptive organs. They are really adhesive and friction discs equipped with a series of glands and a network of fine grooves (Chap. VI). Each cell is free distally from its neighbor and being stiffened by a fibrous modification of its cytoplasm catches in irregularities of the surface in much the same way as the fine bristles covering the toe pads of gecko lizards. Further, there is a series of fibers within the pad which automatically squeeze the fluid from the glands when the body weight of the frog pulls on the gripping toes (Noble and Jaeckle, 1928). This modification of glands, epidermis, and pad fibers was found to be present in frogs such as Phyllobates, which do not climb, and others such as Acris, which have given up the arboreal habits of their tree-frog ancestors. In general, tree frogs must have pads of a certain size in order to be able to climb, but there is little correlation between the actual width of the pad and the amount of tree climbing the species practices. In general, large frogs ascend to greater heights than small frogs. *Hyla vasta* adheres with difficulty to the side of a glass aquarium, while the much smaller *H. crucifer* may adhere for days, nevertheless the former species lives in tall trees, while the latter rarely if ever climbs at all. Possibly small frogs become desiccated more quickly and hence are forced to keep near the ground. According to Gadow (1901), the European tree frog lives the first two years of its postlarval life in the grass. It would be interesting to know if other tree frogs were terrestrial before they reached a certain size in their ontogeny.

Salamanders which habitually climb trees have the digits either more or less webbed or joined by a thick pad as in Oedipus, or the terminal phalanges may be Y-shaped and bent downward as in Aneides. Nevertheless, many other salamanders can readily climb smooth vertical surfaces. The climbing salamanders are few, and although one species of Aneides is apparently entirely terrestrial (Storer, 1925) it is not clear that their climbing equipment arose first in terrestrial species, as seems certain in the case of the frogs. Many tree frogs have broad webs which may assist in climbing, while others, chiefly the South American genus Phyllomedusa, may reduce the webs and transform both hands and feet into gripping organs. The latter would seem to be a modification closely correlated with arboreal life. Webbed feet are also found useful in the aquatic medium, and digital reduction, if on a different plan, occurs in many different families of

Salientia whose habits are apparently very distinct one from another.

Fig. 33.—Burrowing toads. Fossorial toads of several different families resemble one another in their narrow, pointed heads and conspicuous 'spades,' the digging tubercles of the hind feet. *A. Hemisus marmoratum*, a brevicipitid. *B. Rhinophrynus dorsalis*, a bufonid.

The integument, which is the tissue first to come into contact with the environment, might be expected to show the greatest number of adaptations. But Protopipa and Pipa from the ponds of Guiana have a very different degree of skin rugosity. *Hyla vasta* and *Eleutherodactylus inoptatus* live in the tall trees of Hispaniola and yet the first has a rough and the second a smooth skin. Smooth-skinned toads such as *Bufo alvarius* of Arizona live only near water, while rough-skinned species may be found far from water in the desert. Thus, the structure of the integument apparently restricts the range of the species, but the correlation between skin structure and environment is not always close. Many Salientia (Figs. 33 and 34) burrow to avoid desiccation. The Spade-foot Toads are equipped with large metatarsal tubercles which are doubtless of great assistance in this

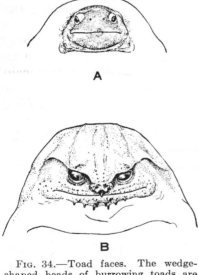

Fig. 34.—Toad faces. The wedge-shaped heads of burrowing toads are variously modified. In *Rhinophrynus dorsalis* (*A*) the snout is truncate; in *Rhombophryne testudo* (*B*) it is covered with sensory papillae.

operation. Salientia of other families may be similarly equipped, and some forms such as Helioporus and Chiroleptes make more or less permanent underground passageways. The latter genus is remarkable for its ability to absorb water rapidly until it assumes the rotundity of a tennis ball (Buxton, 1923). The Australian aborigines were found by the Horn Expedition to use these toads as a source of drinking water.

Some burrowing species such as the Spade-foot Toads, Scaphiopus and Pelobates, have blunt, bony heads, the subcutaneous tissues of the head being infiltrated with bone tissue. A similar casque develops in species such as *Hyla dominicensis*, which only rarely burrow. Other burrowing species have sharp, narrow snouts with or without dermal ossifications. The aquatic salamander, Amphiuma, is a notorious burrower and its sharp snout and long body would seem to be produced expressly for this purpose. Batrachoseps, which may be considered a long-bodied Plethodon with a lost or reduced outer toe, is not, however, more of a burrower than *Plethodon glutinosus*. Further, the long-bodied Siren does not burrow at all. Still, Pseudobranchus, a close relative of Siren, having a much more pointed head, readily burrows into the sand covering the bottom of aquaria. The long-bodied fish are looked upon as having evolved from short-bodied forms under a variety of ecological conditions. Occasionally the long body in both fish and salamander is put to some special use, but neither seems to have evolved in correlation with the burrowing habit alone.

Physiological Characters.—Many adaptations are not morphological but apparently physiological. Why should *Salamandra salamandra* avoid limestone while Proteus and Typhlotriton live well in limestone regions? Within the genus Eleutherodactylus some species, as *lentus*, are found only in limestone regions, and others never in such situations. The rough-skinned *Hyla arenicolor* is found on rocks close to streams, while the smaller and apparently more delicate *Hyla regilla* has a wide range in many kinds of habitats (Storer, 1925). The factors which hold *Rana virgatipes* and *Hyla andersoni* to the Atlantic Coastal Plain are not known, but they would seem in some way associated with the acidity of the water (Noble and Noble, 1923). Many cases of habitat preference, however, would seem to evolve several factors. The Gopher Frog, *Rana aesopus*, for example, breeds in the same ponds as several species of Rana, but it alone leaves these ponds for a solitary life at the entrance of Gopher Turtle burrows.

Although no determination has been made of any of these factors, it was found that temperature may be of importance in restricting the range of Typhlotriton to the vicinity of caves (Noble and Pope, 1928). This species will not stand temperatures so high as *Eurycea multiplicata*, which is found in the same caves, and which, on the other hand, ranges far beyond the caves in regions where water temperatures are considerably higher. Presumably temperature limits the northern distribution of many species of Amphibia and no forms are found in northern regions where the subsoil remains permanently frozen throughout the year.

As indicated in the discussion of the endocrine organs (Chap. XIII), cold may prevent the functioning of the thyroid, and various urodele larvae at high altitudes may become neotenous. The adaptation of perennibranchs to the aquatic habitat is due to the failure of the tissues to react to the thyroid hormone. This condition has apparently been brought about by genetic factors. It is, nevertheless, interesting to note that thoroughly aquatic frogs such as the Bullfrog, *Rana catesbeiana*, and such tropical species as *Pseudis paradoxa* usually have a longer larval life than species which become terrestrial on metamorphosis. Similarly, the aquatic *Eurycea bislineata* has a more extended larval period than the more terrestrial Ambystomas. It would seem that slowly maturing thyroid glands in the larvae are in some way correlated with more or less aquatic preferences in the adult.

Hormones in Evolution.—It is not known whether genetic factors have produced species of Amphibia by controlling the endocrine organs alone. Nevertheless, in many different genera, pairs of species live side by side, one form half or less the size of the other and approximating the young of the larger species in appearance.

In Cuba the diminutive *Bufo dunni* agrees well in form and color with the young of *B. peltacephalus* of the same island. It has not the cranial ossifications of the adult of the latter, but these ossifications develop slowly during adult life in *B. peltacephalus*, and one would not expect to find them in a derived form which had ceased to grow much beyond metamorphosis. Similarly, the diminutive *Necturus maculosus lewisi* (Fig. 35) is a dwarf derivative of *N. m. maculosus* living in an adjacent area. In some cases the dwarfism is correlated with mountain life.

The dwarf species of Oedipus have large nostrils, not in adaptation to any particular needs of mountain life but merely because large nostrils characterize the young of Oedipus. These species are essentially forms which have failed to grow up as do the primitive species of the genus. This phenomenon of arrested development has been recognized for a long time in various groups of vertebrates (Franz, 1927). Cope (1889) made extensive comparisons between the young and adult stages of various

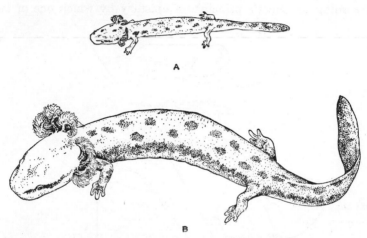

FIG. 35.—Speciation by dwarfing. An adult *Necturus maculosus lewisii* (*A*) compared with an adult *N.m.maculosus* (*B*) drawn to the same scale. The former race has apparently developed from the latter by dwarfing.

genera of frogs. When species living in contiguous areas are compared and the adults of one species found to agree closely with the young of the other, it would seem probable that the phenomenon of arrested development had played an important part in the genesis of the smaller species.

Many characters of adult frogs resemble ontogenetic stages in other species. *Hyla vasta* develops an extensive web between its fingers (Fig. 36) and dilates its sacral diapophyses during postmetamorphic life. Can the short webs and narrow sacral diapophyses of some species of Hyla be considered arrested stages of more primitive larger species? All specific changes appear first during ontogeny. New species are not produced by the addition of stages to more primitive species but by a modification of the processes of development of the former. This modification may mean a loss of growth, an extension of the growth period, or a disharmonic growth of parts. Hence, if two species are found together in the same or adjacent areas and one never develops beyond a juvenile stage in the ontogeny of the other, it does not always follow that the former species has been derived from the latter.   It is equally possible that the reverse is the case and the "adult" characters represent a further modification of the ontogeny characteristic of the other species. It is also possible that the pair of species may have evolved according to Eimer's principle of epistasy by which one of two

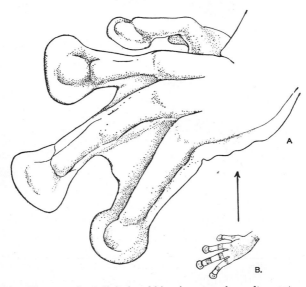

Fig. 36.—The growth of digital webbing in a tree frog after metamorphosis. Left manus of *Hyla vasta* viewed dorsally: *A*. Adult.   *B*. Recently metamorphosed individual of the same species.

related forms becomes more modified in phylogeny than the other. The bright salmon tints of the spring salamander, Pseudotriton, may have been derived from the more primitive *Gyrinophilus danielsi*. The purple salamander, *G. porphyriticus*, has similar bright colors in some recently metamorphosed individuals, however.   Hence, the bright colors of both *danielsi* and Pseudotriton may be the retention of a juvenile character of *G. porphyriticus*.   In such cases a knowledge of the evolution of the group as a whole and its routes of dispersal will sometimes afford important evidence as to which possibility is more probable.

Phylogeny is the result of ontogeny; specific differences occur in the genes of the eggs or sperms of the species, and they produce effects which become more manifest as development proceeds. Genes may occur which induce modifications only during larval life. For example, although the species of Megalophrys appear to be closely related, the larvae of some species differ remarkably from the larvae of others. On the whole, however, evolution has proceeded more rapidly in the adult than in the larval forms and hence we have been able to conclude that the structure of the larva may afford better evidence of relationship than many adult characters (Chap. III).

Ontogeny does not repeat phylogeny. Amphibian larvae in their external gills, adhesive organs, and body form resemble the larvae of crossopterygian and dipnoan fish but not the adults. This repetition of characters in corresponding stages is evidence of relationship in the same way that the distinctive brevicipitid larva common to Gastrophryne and Microhyla shows that these genera are related. The brevicipitid larva has not the slightest resemblance to an adult ranid from which the Brevicipitidae evolved, and, as Garstang (1922), Sewertzoff (1927), and Franz (1927) have recently emphasized, the adult stage of the ancestor is not pressed back into earlier stages of development in the descendants of any groups of animals. Over a century ago, von Baer concluded that the young stages in the development of an animal were not like the adult stages of other animals lower down on the scale but were like their young stages, and this conclusion seems equally well founded today.

Nevertheless, certain characters distinctive of an adult stage may appear earlier in a descendant. This may be due to the earlier functioning of the genes producing these characters, but there are various conditions of development of Amphibia which may also be considered. While the primitive frogs have arciferal pectoral girdles, the more specialized frogs show firmisternal girdles which are formed by two halves coming together to fuse in the midline during ontogeny. This is apparantly the only way possible for the firmisternal girdles to develop while maintaining a lateral position in connection with the forelimbs. The branchial arches of amphibian larvae bear a resemblance to those of fish. Some frogs may skip the tadpole stage and in these cases the arches may develop directly into the hyobranchials without serving as respiratory structures. There is a recapitulation of successive grades of differentiation but the repetition of ancestral adult stages is usually lacking during ontogeny. Nevertheless, bone may replace cartilage during development, or the anlage of originally separate organs may form separately and fuse later. As Garstang (1922) has pointed out, it is this formative dependence of one organ or tissue on another which confers upon ontogeny its recapitulative character.

Permanent Larvae.—Growth and differentiation, as discussed in Chap. XIII, are controlled by the hormones of the glands of internal secretion. The relation of hormones to the genes is well shown in the phenomenon of metamorphosis. At this period the salamander larva and the frog tadpole undergo an extensive reorganization and differentiation and emerge as tetrapods capable of land life. The gills are lost, the branchial clefts fused, the larval branchial skeleton is changed into the adult hyobranchial. The eyes bulge, lids are formed, palate, jaws, and skull bones undergo marked changes. In the tadpole the larval epidermal teeth are lost, the tail is absorbed, while in urodeles the spike teeth of the larva are usually replaced by bicuspid ones, and the fin on body and tail is reduced. Wilder (1925) has described some of the many changes which take place at the time of metamorphosis in the larval *Eurycea bislineata.* Not all of these occur in other species. For example, the maxillary bones are formed long before metamorphosis in the axolotl but not in Eurycea. Endocrinologists seize upon the shedding of the skin in one or more large pieces as the criterion of metamorphosis in the urodeles. Correlated with this skin change the large Leydig cells are lost and the stratum corneum develops as an adaptation to resist the drying effect of the air.

Some urodeles never metamorphose and others seem to begin the process and not complete it. When incomplete metamorphosis occurs, it is not due to the absence of the thyroid hormone, which induces metamorphosis in other species, but to the fact that certain tissues are no longer sensitized to this hormone. These tissues do not react to thyroid extracts injected into the animals' bodies (Chap. XIII). For the present discussion it is interesting that the hyoid apparatus of Necturus and Amphiuma on its first appearance has the reduced form of the adult of these species just as if not enough branchial arch-forming material had been present (Noble, 1929). Further, the palatoquadrate bar in Siren splits into the usual two parts at a time when the skin retains its typical larval structure. Although the physiological block to complete metamorphosis in these permanent larvae is not known, it is obvious that structural changes are taking place at such early and disconnected stages that they cannot be considered metamorphosis. Nevertheless, if we focus our attention only upon the most obvious changes of metamorphosis, namely the development of limbs, of maxillary bones, the loss of gills, and reduction of branchial arches, Siren and Pseudobranchus would be considered forms which have ceased to differentiate beyond a very early stage of larval life; Proteus and Necturus, forms which have reached a later stage of urodele ontogeny; Cryptobranchus, one which has begun its metamorphosis; and Megalobatrachus and Amphiuma, forms which have nearly completed their metamorphosis. If we examine the skin of the last three genera it will be found to have metamorphosed completely and thus run ahead of this scheme. Further, the skin of the adult Siren has the typical metamorphosed structure while that of the closely related Pseudobranchus is larval. The skin of Necturus does not react to the thyroid hormone, while that of Cryptobranchus does (Noble and Farris, 1929). There is, of course, little advantage to be gained by the latter change since both of these genera are entirely aquatic. The thyroid hormone reacts on tissues which are sensitized to its action, and this sensitization is produced presumably by genetic factors without any relation to the future use of this modification.

The thyroid hormone may produce its influence on metamorphosis very indirectly. For example, Maurer (1921) found that removing the forelegs of a tadpole did not prevent perforations from developing in the operculum during metamorphosis. He assumed that this could be explained only on the basis of the inheritance of acquired characters, the forelegs having been pushed presumably through the operculum for so many generations that now the holes would form even when no legs were present. But Helff (1924) showed that the perforation of the operculum was due to a secretion of the degenerating gills which would induce a similar histolysis of the integument on other parts of the body. Thus, the thyroid hormone by inducing a degeneration of the gills caused the production of a cytolysin which released the forelimbs. An even more complex situation is to be found in the tail of a tadpole during metamorphosis. If skin from the body region is transplanted to the tail before metamorphosis,

this piece of skin does not degenerate with the remainder of the
caudal appendage at the time of transformation (Reis, 1924).
In addition to the hormones producing metamorphosis, there
are cytolysins released which are specific for certain skin, namely
that of the tail, but have no effect on other skin which differs
structurally in no essential way.   Since moreover, skin from the
anterior part of the tail grafted to the back of frog tadpoles undergoes histolysis at a greater speed than skin from near the tail
tip similarly grafted, there exists a gradient of response to these
cytolysins in the skin of the tail (Clausen, 1930).   The tail is
not absorbed from the tip forward as commonly supposed; the
degeneration of tissue is more rapid at the base.   Metamorphosis
even within the tail of Amphibia is a very complex process.

The Course of Phylogeny.—It may be noted by referring to
other sections (Chap. I, Part II) that neoteny in the usual sense
of the word, namely the retention of larval characters during
sexual maturity, has played no part in the phylogeny of the
Amphibia.   Typhlomolge is a plethodontid salamander because
it possesses characters in common with plethodontid larvae.
Necturus and Proteus are isolated in a separate family of Caudata
by taxonomists because they possess several striking features
not shared by other salamanders, larval or adult.   These perennibranchs owe their position in the system to the degree they have
diverged from apparent ancestors and not because of their
larval features *per se*.   The more advanced types of any group
of animals are frequently highly modified and consequently
restricted to particular environments but it does not follow that
primitive types are always more "plastic," more able to cope with
varying conditions of habitat.   Ascaphus, the most primitive
frog in America, can live only in or near cold mountain streams.
Primitiveness rests on resemblance to ancestral types and not at
all on any physiological peculiarities.

In tracing the evolution of the Amphibia (Chap. I) we noted
various trends of evolution, especially the reduction in the number
of skeletal elements and the increase in cartilage.   The latter may
be described as a progressive foetalization.   Similarly, the loss
of teeth in various groups of Salientia may be considered a retention of a larval condition, since teeth in other Salientia do not
appear till metamorphosis.   The same process of progressive loss
may be traced in the evolution of higher classes of vertebrates.
Another parallel is to be found in the secondary production of

snakelike forms. In salamanders and lizards, the elongation of the body in phylogeny is accompanied by the reduction in the length of the limbs. Among the Amphibia these elongate types have not proved highly efficient, at least they have not split up into many species, while in the Reptilia the success of the snakes is familiar to everyone. Similarly, the birds which are specialized reptiles have succeeded extraordinarily well and show the danger of concluding that a specialized group is in any way senescent.

References

BOULENGER, G. A., 1918: On the races and variation of the edible frog, *Rana esculenta* L., *Ann. Mag. Nat. Hist.* (9), II, 241–257.

BUXTON, P. A., 1923: "Animal Life in Deserts; A Study of the Fauna in Relation to the Environment," London.

CHAPMAN, FRANK M., 1926: The distribution of bird-life in Ecuador, *Bull. Amer. Mus. Nat. Hist.*, LV, 784.

CLAUSEN, H. J., 1930: Rate of histolysis of anuran skin and muscle during metamorphosis, *Biol. Bull.*, LIX, 199–210.

COPE, E. D., 1889: The Batrachia of North America, *Bull. U. S. Nat. Mus.*, No. 34.

CUENOT, L., 1921: "La genese des espèces animales," 2d ed., Paris.

———, 1925: "L'adaptation," Paris.

DARWIN, CHARLES, 1859: "Origin of Species," New York.

FISHER, R. A., 1930: "The Genetical Theory of Natural Selection," Oxford.

FRANZ, V., 1927: Ontogenie und Phylogenie, *Abh. theor. Organ. Entw.*, III, 51.

GARSTANG, W., 1922: The theory of recapitulation: A critical restatement of the biogenetic law, *Jour. Linn. Soc. London*, XXXV, 81–103.

GOLDSCHMIDT, R., 1929: Experimentelle Mutation und das Problem der sogennannten Parallelinduktion. Versuche an Drosophila, *Biol. Zentralbl.*, XLIX, 437–448.

GRINNEL, JOSEPH, 1924: Geography and Evolution, "Ecology," V, 225–229.

HAECKER, V., 1908: Über Axolotlkreuzungen; II, Mitteilung (Zur Kenntnis des partiellen Albinismus), *Verh. deutsch. zool. Ges.* 18. *Vers.*, 194–205.

HELFF, O. M., 1924: Factors involved in the formation of the opercular leg perforation in anuran larvae during metamorphosis, *Anat. Rec.*, XXIX, 102.

JORDAN, D. S., 1926: Isolation with segregation as a factor in organic evolution, *Ann. Rep. Smithson. Inst.*, 1925, 321–326.

KAMMERER, PAUL, 1912: Experimente über Fortpflanzung, Farbe, Augen und Körperreduktion bei Proteus anguinus Laur, *Arch. Entw. Mech.*, XXXIII, 349–461, 4 pls.

KELLICOTT, W. E., 1907: Correlation and variation in internal and external characters in the common toad (*Bufo lentiginosus americanus*), *Jour. Exp. Zool.*, IV, 575–614.

LANTZ, L. A., 1927: Quelques observations nouvelles sur l'herpétologie des Pyrénées centrales, *Rev. Hist. Nat. Appl.*, VIII, 16–22, 54–61.

MATTHEW, W. D., 1915: Climate and evolution, *Ann. N. Y. Acad. Sci.*, XXIV, 171–318.

MAURER, F., 1921: Zur Frage von der Vererbung erworbener Eigenschaften, *Anat. Anz.*, LIV, 201–205.

MERTENS, ROBERT, 1926: Über Färbungsmutationen bei Amphibien und Reptilien, *Zool. Anz.*, LXVIII, 323–335.

METCALF, M. M., 1928: Trends in evolution: a discussion of data bearing upon "orthogenesis," *Jour. Morph. Physiol.*, XLV, 1–46.

MORGAN, T. H., 1923: The bearing of Mendelism on the origin of species, *Sci. Monthly*, XVI, 237–247.

———, 1926. "The Theory of the Gene," Yale Univ. Press., New Haven.

MULLER, H. J., 1929. The gene as the basis of life, *Proc. Int. Congr. Plant Sci.*, I, 897–921.

NOBLE, G. K., 1929: Further observations on the life-history of the newt, *Triturus viridescens*, *Amer. Mus. Novit.*, No. 348.

NOBLE, G. K., and E. J. Farris, 1929: A metamorphic change produced in Cryptobranchus by thyroid solutions, *Anat. Rec.*, XLII, 59.

NOBLE, G. K., and M. E. JAECKLE, 1928: The digital pads of the tree frogs; A study of the phylogenesis of an adaptive structure, *Jour. Morph. and Physiol.*, XLV, No. 1, 259–292.

NOBLE, G. K., and R. C. NOBLE, 1923: The Anderson tree frog (*Hyla andersonii* Baird); Observations on its habits and life-history, *Zoologica* II, 417–455.

NOBLE, G. K., and S. H. POPE, 1928: The effect of light on the eyes, pigmentation and behavior of the cave salamander, Typhlotriton, *Anat. Rec.*, XLI, No. 1, 21.

OKADA, Y., 1928: Notes on the breeding habits of Rhacophorus in Japan, *Annot. Zool. Japon.*, II, 279–285, 1 pl.

PIERSOL, W. H., 1929: Pathological polyspermy in eggs of *Ambystoma jeffersonianum* (Green), *Trans. Roy. Canadian Inst.*, XVII, 57–74, 1 pl.

REIS, K., 1924: Sur le comportement des greffes de la peau dans la queue du tetard pendant metamorphose, *Compt. rend. Soc. Biol.*, XCI, 701–702.

RENSCH. B., 1929: "Das Prinzip geographischer Rassenkreise und das Problem der Artbildung," Berlin.

ROBSON, G. C., 1928: The species problem: An introduction to the study of evolutionary divergence in natural populations, *Biol. Monog. and Manuals*, No. VIII, Edinburgh.

SEWERTZOFF, A. N., 1927: Über die Beziehungen zwischen der Ontogenese und der Phylogenese der Tiere, *Jena. Zeitschr.* LXIII, 51–180.

SHELFORD, V. E., 1913: The reactions of certain animals to gradients of evaporating power of air: A study in experimental ecology, *Biol. Bull.*, XXV, 79–120.

STORER, T. I., 1925: A synopsis of the Amphibia of California, *Univ. Cal. Pub. Zool.*, XXVII, 1–343, 18 pls.

TAYLOR, J. W., 1913: Geographical distribution and dominance in relation to evolution and phylogeny, *Trans. Congr. Ent. Oxford*, II, 271–294, pls. 6–9.

VAVILOV, N. L., 1922: The law of homologous series in variation, *Jour. Gen.*, XII, 47–89.

Weed, Alfred C., 1922: New frogs from Minnesota, *Proc. Biol. Soc. Wash.* XXXV, 107–110.

Werner, Franz, 1892: Untersuchungen über die Zeichnung der Wirbelthiere, *Zool. Jahrb. Syst.*, VI, 155–229, 5 pls.

Wilder, I. W., 1925: "The Morphology of Amphibian Metamorphosis," Smith College, Northampton, Mass.

Witschi, E., 1930: Studies on sex differentiation and sex determination in Amphibians; IV, The geographical distribution of the sex races of the European grass frog (Rana temporaria L.); A contribution to the problem of the evolution of sex, *Jour. Exp. Zool.*, LVI, 149–166.

CHAPTER V

SEX AND SECONDARY SEX CHARACTERS

Sex is the physical, chemical, and psychical difference between male and female animals. The difference is primarily correlated with the production of male and female sex products and the facilitation of their union. Sexual reproduction hastens evolution, for it combines the characters existing in a population in a variety of different ways and brings new mutations into relation with old combinations, thus giving natural selection more kinds of individuals on which to work. It is thus biologically important that the egg should not develop until it receives the male chromosomes in the process of fertilization. As discussed in Chap. II, frogs' eggs may be made to develop in other ways, but under natural conditions the egg does not divide until activated by a spermatozoon.

The sexual characters form a well-defined group, usually sharply distinguished from somatic characters both in structure and function. The genetic analysis of these characters in animals other than Amphibia has shown conclusively that they owe their origin to changes in the same chromosomal mechanism which through its mutations has produced the somatic characters (Crew, 1927; Morgan, 1926). Various other explanations have been given for the origin of secondary sexual characters in Amphibia, but none of these fits the facts of sexual divergence as exhibited by related species. These divergences may be considered in some detail, for they have an important bearing on the origin of characters in relation to the use which is finally made of them.

Under the term "secondary sexual characters" are included all the differences between the two sexes other than those connected with the gonads and their ducts. The latter are considered in the chapter dealing with the urogenital system. The best-known secondary sexual characters are the nuptial pads which appear on the prepollex region of many frogs and toads during the breeding season, or the bright colors and crests of certain male European newts during the same period. These, like the majority of secondary sexual characters of vertebrates, are brought to expression by the hormone of the testes (Chap. XIII). Many, such as the elongate, premaxillary teeth of Desmognathus, are potentially present in both sexes and can be made to develop in an adult female if a testis is transplanted into the body. The hormone acts upon characters determined by heredity but able to develop only in the presence of the testicular hormone. Other secondary sexual characters resemble those of invertebrates in that they do not require the testicular hormone to maintain their appearance. It is interesting that this should be true of certain characters, such as the vocal pouch of *Rana esculenta* (Champy, 1924) which has a great functional value in the male, and also equally true of others, such as the cloacal papillae of certain newts (Nakamura, 1927) which have a doubtful functional significance. Both those characters dependent on a testicular hormone and those independent of it find their hereditary determiners in genes and hence may be considered together in the present discussion.

Functional Significance of Secondary Sex Characters.—It is well known that the nuptial pads of frogs are used for maintaining a firm grip on the back of the female during egg laying. Pads are also present on the upper arm of the male Pleurodeles which swims below his partner during the courtship (Chap. XVI). This would seem to be an inappropriate position to take but it is actually well adapted to the method of fertilization by spermatophores. The male, after a time, frees one foreleg and by bending his body forward deposits a spermatophore opposite the female's snout. The male *P. waltl* then crawls forward until the female's cloaca is directly over the spermatophore. In *P. poireti* there is a circling movement with the clutched arm as the pivot leading to the same result (Klingelhöffer, 1930). It is interesting that the male Salamandra grips the female the same way, although courtship proceeds on land (Van Leeuwen, 1907). The hedonic glands, found on the tails and other parts of the body of male plethodontids (page 136) and on the cheeks of the male *Triturus viridescens*, are other mechanisms nicely adjusted to play a certain part in the complex courtship of these animals. The method of courtship varies with each group of salamanders, and hence different secondary sexual characters might be expected in the various groups.

Instinctive habits, often quite different in the two sexes, appear during the breeding season under the influence of gonads and may be classified as secondary sexual characters. In the Salientia, associated with the greater activity, louder voice, and retentive grip of the male sex, many structural differences of fluctuating or more permanent character may appear. The forelimb bones may be greatly molded by the muscles of the male as in *Leptodactylus ocellatus* (Fig. 37) and *Rana spinosa*, and less pronounced skeletal differences have been found between

Fig. 37.—Sexual dimorphism of the forelimbs in the South American frog, *Leptodactylus ocellatus. A. Female. B. Male.*

the sexes of almost all Salientia which have been intensively studied (Dauvart, 1924; Kandler, 1924; Klier, 1926; Harms, 1926; Saller, 1927). There are correlated differences of muscle weight (Gaule, 1900). The abdominal muscles of the male have such an important function in forcing air from the lungs in producing the call and are correspondingly more powerful than those of the female, but differences are also to be found even in the tendons of the two sexes (Kahn, 1919). The lungs of many male frogs are larger than those of the female, markedly so in Bombina (Boulenger, 1897). This may be correlated not only with the louder voice but also with the higher metabolism and greater activity of the male. The red blood count of the male frog is higher (Zepp, 1923), its brain weight greater (Komine, 1924), its liver heavier (Yunge, 1907). In the case of the African *Astylosternus robustus*, a species with greatly reduced lungs, a compensatory vascularization of the integument occurs in both sexes, while in the male patches of vascular villosities appear on the thighs and sides, and in reference to these the species has been given the name of "Hairy Frog" (Fig. 63). These villosities apparently supply the frog with the greater amount of oxygen his sex demands (Noble, 1925). The difference between the sexes of frogs may thus extend to many details of their anatomy and physiology and may include many little-understood differences, such as the shorter intestines of the male of some European frogs (Yunge, 1907). Sex differences may be demonstrated in the functioning of the heart (Appelrot, 1930) and these may possibly find their explanation in the higher calcium content of the tissues of the male frog. A similar variety of secondary sexual differences may be found without doubt in urodeles. Ueki (1930) noted that the sexual differences occurred in many parts of the viscera, brain, and eyes of the Japanese newt, *Triturus pyrrhogaster*. Although these modifications probably have some functional correlation, it is difficult to account for the much softer skin of the male, since neither secretions nor rubbing movements are known to play a part in the courtship of this species.

As indicated in the discussion of habits (page 410), the methods of courtship and embrace are singularly uniform throughout the Salientia, differences appearing only in the position of the forelimbs about the body or the relation of the fists to the female's body or to each other. Nevertheless, the differences in the nuptial pads of closely related species may be extraordinary. The nuptial pads usually consist of a cluster of black epidermal spines covering a swelling on the prepollex region of each hand. The swelling is formed by numerous acinous glands having a distinctive granular cytoplasm at the height of the breeding season. Some species, such as *Bufo vulgaris*, lack the glands (Kandler, 1924), and others, as *Hyla arborea* and *Hemisus marmoratum*, may lack the asperities. Pigmented breeding pads have extended to the mesial surfaces of the three inner digits in some species of ranids and bufonids. Spines similar in appearance to those on the pad may rarely occur on various parts of the appendages, as along the edges of the toe webbing in Discoglossus, or along the toes in Pelodytes, or as patches on three of the toes in *Bombina variegata*. They also occur under the toes in a position where they could not function in certain higher forms such as in *Hyla leprieuri* (Boulenger, 1912). Pigmented spines occur on the ventral surfaces of the forelimbs in the breeding males of some discoglossids, pipids, and ranids. They extend to the chest and chin of a few discoglossids, pelobatids, bufonids, and ranids. In the case of certain species of Rana this spread of the spiny area to the chest is correlated with a life in mountain torrents. In such situations the ability to maintain the grip on the female is placed at a premium, and Pope (1931) has shown that the frogs breeding along certain Chinese torrents either had spiny chests or the males were much smaller than the females and hence offered little resistance to the current when carried on their backs. The tendency to form pigmented spines in the male is by no means always correlated with obvious advantages. In fact, the tendency seems to run riot in the males of some frogs, for the spines may appear on almost any part of the body. The males of one or more species of Bufo, Hylambates, Chiromantis, Megalixalus, Phrynobatrachus, and Eleutherodactylus have their dorsal surfaces covered with spines, while the females are smooth above. In many of these species no asperities at all appear on the prepollex and hence the dorsal rugosity cannot be considered an extension of the nuptial pad area. If sex recognition in these species is accomplished by trial embrace, as in *Rana sylvatica* (Noble and Farris, 1929), the dorsal spines might serve the courting male to distinguish quickly between the sexes. Such an explanation does not work out well in detail, for while the male, *Bufo marinus* and *B. regularis* are more spinous above, the females of *Bufo funereus*, *B. vulgaris*, and *B. americanus* are the more spinous or rugose. In *Bufo canorus* the male has both fewer and smaller warts than the female (Storer, 1925). In other genera also the differences between the skin of the two sexes may be great or slight according to the species, making it doubtful if skin "feel" could play a part in sex recognition throughout the group.

In various salamanders there may be a difference of texture in the skin of the two sexes. The western "water dog," *Triturus torosus*, as well as the above-mentioned *T. pyrrhogaster*, is much smoother skinned in the male. Fisher (1905) showed that "during the fall the dermis of the female frog is thinner and less resistant to acids and alkalis and digestive fluids than that of the male." Zepp (1923) found that the skin of certain European frogs (excluding that of the head) was much heavier in the male sex. Such differences might be assumed to be correlated with the chain of anatomical differences alluded to above and to have no specific functions in the breeding act.

Unexplained Sexual Differences.—Such an assumption would not explain the spinosity of other species of frogs. For example, the males of some African tree frogs, as *Megalixalus fornasinii* and *M. leptosomus*, are spinose above, while spines of similar character are found over the dorsal surfaces of both sexes of the closely related *Megalixalus spinosus*. Although these spines are slightly better developed in the breeding male, they are an important feature in both sexes and represent an instance of a phenomenon frequently found in birds and mammals where a character found only in the males of one species appears fully developed in both sexes of another (Pycraft, 1914).

A similar phenomenon is to be observed in the European newts. In various species (*italicus*, *montandonii*, etc.), the males have the tip of their tails extended into a whip lash which may serve to direct the secretion of the abdominal glands toward the female during courtship, although other species seem to get along without the lash. This secondary sexual character appears in both sexes of the related *T. palmatus* where its function in the female is a mystery. Other cutaneous hypertrophies in Amphibia present equal difficulties when their possible functions are considered. For example, the male European toads, *B. vulgaris* and *B. viridis*, exhibit a slight extension of the webbing between the toes during the breeding season. This involves a growth of the toe and tarsal ridges to form fringes in the male *Pelodytes punctatus*, while in the male Elosia and Crossodactylus a similar hypertrophy produces broad folds. In the wood and grass frogs of America and Europe, (*Rana sylvatica*, *temporaria*, etc.), the toe webbing of the male is extended to form a convex edge during the breeding season, but a detailed study of the breeding of the first species did not give proof of the use of these structures (Noble and Farris, 1929). If we assume that all of these toe webs must be used in some way in swimming, we have still to account for their sporadic occurrence in only one or two species of very distinct families. Any explanation in terms of function is complicated by the fact that a slight seam appears along the fingers of both the male Crossodactylus and Elosia in the breeding season. Further, in *Crossodactylus gaudichaudii* the second finger of the male is spatulated, while in *Phyllobates nubicola* (Dunn, 1924) it is the third finger which is thus modified. If field observations should demonstrate that these broadened fingers are pressed against the female in amplexus, we have still to explain why female frogs from the other side of the world have a similar modification. For in *Lechriodus melanopyga*

(Fig. 38) the two inner fingers are spatulated, while in *Limno-dynastes dorsalis* the second finger is broadly spatulated and the third hypertrophied along its preaxial edge.

Although certain modifications of the appendages would seem to have considerable use, they are frequently found in

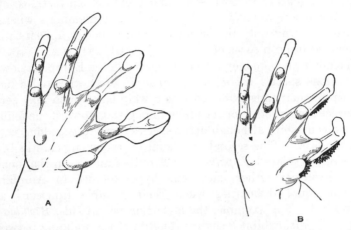

Fig. 38.—Secondary sexual modification of the manus in *Lechriodus melano-pyga*. *A.* Right hand of female as seen from below. *B.* Right hand of male, same aspect.

only a few species of a related group. The European mountain brook newts of the genus Euproctus are notorious in the way they court. The males lie in wait among the rocks and snare passing females with their prehensile tails. So forceful and pro-

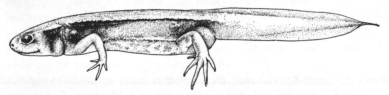

Fig. 39.—The male *Triturus pyrrhogaster* with the glandular hypertrophies, the elongated digits, and the pointed tail, characteristic of this sex.

longed is the grip that it frequently kills the captured animal. *E. montanus* apparently assists the grip with the spikelike processes which protrude from its fibulas (Klingelhöffer, 1930). Nevertheless the related *E. asper* succeeds well without these spurs. Again, the toes of some newts, especially those of *Triturus vittatus* and *T. pyrrhogaster* (Fig. 39), are elongated in the breeding males. These apparently balance themselves on their digit tips while waiting expectantly for a female. The attitude is, however, not very different from the usual posture of aquatic salamanders when on the alert. It is difficult to believe that male salamanders "well up on their toes" have a decided advantage in courtship or that the elongated digits *per se* have a great selective value.

Perhaps the most discussed secondary sexual characters of vertebrates are the color differences. Darwin tried to explain these differences in birds by his well-known theory of sexual selection, the female being supposed to select the most attractive male and hand on his characters to her male progeny. Such a selection has been denied in fishes (Kyle, 1926) although in some groups sexual differences in color seem to aid sex recognition. In the European newts, which have bright colors in the male, there is a certain amount of display which apparently tends to raise the female to such a state of sexual excitement that she will pick up the spermatophore when it is later emitted by the male. But in the blind salamander of Europe, *Proteus anguinus,* two rows of light spots appear on the side of the tail during the breeding season (Chauvin, 1883) and these certainly would not be appreciated by his sightless mate. In all Salientia where the courtship and mating has been adequately analyzed, sight has been found to play almost no part in sex recognition (Noble and Farris, 1929) other than to inform the male of the approach of another object of suitable size or movement. Nevertheless, some species as distantly related as *Bufo canorus* of the Yosemite (Storer, 1925) and *Arthroleptella lightfooti* of South Africa (Rose, 1929) may show a marked difference in color and color pattern in the two sexes. Some differences of color may be directly correlated with physiological changes which take place in the male during the breeding season. Thus Leydig (1892) showed that in both *Rana fusca* and *Triturus cristatus* the dermis of the integument undergoes a marked swelling in the breeding male. This is not due merely to an absorption of water, for while the lymph spaces increase in size the lymph becomes gelatinous in some of the spaces. The yellow color of the throat of the male Cricket Frog, Acris, and the dark tone of breeding toads' throats are correlated with the enormous expansibility of this region during the breeding season. Still, such seasonal changes would not account for the marked sexual difference in color pattern seen in some frogs and salamanders.

Most Amphibia, unlike lizards and birds, show little or no sexual difference in color. Male lizards make great use of their conspicuous colors in bluffing possible rivals, while many birds engage in elaborate courtship displays. In most vertebrates

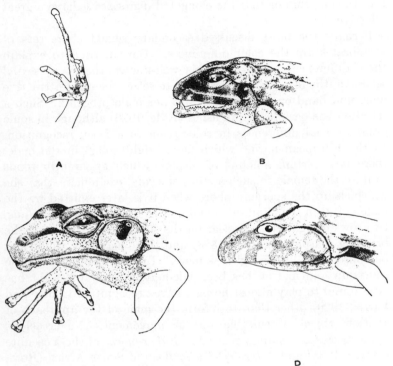

Fig. 40.—Secondary sexual characters in Old World frogs. *A.* Left manus of *Dimorphognathus africanus* as seen from below, showing the elongated third finger of the male. *B.* Head of the male of the same species with the pseudo-teeth of the lower jaw characterizing this sex. *C.* Head of the male *Petropedetes newtonii* showing the columella process, the spike-like metacarpal I and distinctive chin spines. *D.* Head of *Rana pileata* with the frontal swelling peculiar to the male.

where marked sexual differences in color appear these have an important rôle in sex recognition or courtship. The types of courtship found in Amphibia are usually not such as would foster a sexual divergence in color.

Phylogeny of Secondary Sex Characters.—The phylogeny of other secondary sexual characters is instructive when considered in relation to the apparent phylogenies of the various species. Although the more familiar frogs and toads have the prepollex region of the male covered with a nuptial pad, the prepollex itself or the adjacent digits may be modified into a spine or "dagger" in other species.   In *Petropedetes newtoni* the metacarpus of the first digit is enlarged, spikelike, and protrudes through the skin

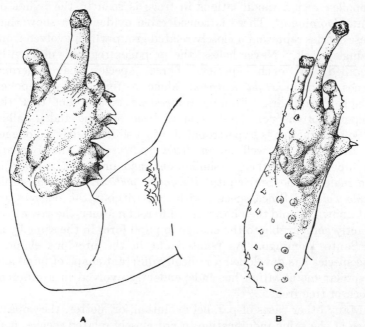

A   B

FIG. 41.—Closely related frogs frequently have markedly different secondary sexual characters.   The forelimb of the male *Hoplophryne uluguruensis* (*A*) compared with the forelimb of *H. rogersi* (*B*), seen from the same ventral aspect.

as an effective instrument for holding the female (Fig. 40C). In *Telmatobius jelskii* the same element is enlarged, in Discoglossus it is broadened, while in *Leptodactylus ocellatus* it is bifid with two spines.   In other frogs it is the prepollex which is hypertrophied to form a recurved spine.   There is no evidence of a progressive enlargement of this spine in any Salientia.   For example, in the recently described "Banana Frogs" of East Africa, a pad of sharp dermal spines occurs on each side of the chest in the male *Hoplophryne uluguruensis* and another cluster of large dermal spines over the prepollex region of each hand (Fig. 41A).   Such a formidable array of spines rarely occurs in any frog, and one would imagine that this diminutive frog was amply equipped to hold his own with any struggling female. But in the closely related *Hoplophryne rogersi* of an adjacent mountain range, the rudimentary prepollex of *uluguruensis* has enlarged to form a formidable spine (Fig. 41B).

An equally convincing case of the discontinuous nature of prepollex region modifications in frogs is seen in the hylids of Santo Domingo. There is considerable evidence to show that these species represent a closely related group which evolved from a single stock. Nevertheless, the prepollex region is differently modified in each species. Three species have dermal spines, and in *Hyla heilprini* alone a formidable prepollex "dagger" appears. Equally interesting is the fact that the prepollex of the not closely related *Hyla maxima* and its allies of South America is hypertrophied into a similar recurved dagger in the male, as well as in *Hyla pollicaris* of the Bismark Archipelago. Further, a similar enlarged prepollex appears in the male of the brevicipitid *Phrynella pollicaris* and the ranid *Rana holstii*. Since species with and without the daggers are not known to hold their hands in a different manner, the case seems exactly comparable to the change in pupil form in the same hylas of Santo Domingo. As pointed out in the previous chapter, one species has developed a radically different shape of pupil and a similar modification has independently evolved in a different stock of tree frogs.

Many other cases of parallel evolution, or, better, the appearance of the same modification in not closely related species, may be found among the secondary sexual characters. For example, a sharp, recurved spine appears on the proximal end of the humerus in *Hyla humeralis* but in none of the closely related species of the same region, while an identical spine reappears in the male Centrolene on the other side of the world but is not found in any of its relatives living in that region. All plethodontid salamanders possess hedonic glands which serve to attract the females (Chap. XVI). These glands usually manifest themselves as a swelling on the chin, or as a scattering of enlarged glands on the lower eyelid, or along the cheeks of the male. In *Eurycea multiplicata* they form a prominence on the dorsal surface of the tail base which appears even in the male larva (Fig. 42C). An apparently homologous glandular appendage develops above the base of the tail in *Salamandra caucasica* and *S. luschani*,

members of a different although ancestral family. Turning to
the Salientia, many cases of glandular hypertrophies are found
in the male sex but none is known to play any part in attracting
the female. All species of Cycloramphus (Fig. 42B) have glandular pads in the inguinal region, and similar but more extensive
glands appear on the sides of the body of *Hyla rosenbergi*. Pelobates has a pad of glandular tissue on the outer side of the upper
arm where it could not function in the embrace, and a similar
pad crops up in many species of Rana (the Hylorana group).
In the African tree frogs, *Leptopelis rufus* and *L. aubryi*, a pair of

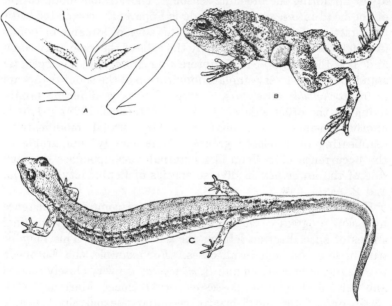

Fig. 42.—Hypertrophied glands as secondary sex characters. The glandular
mass at the tail base of the male *Eurycea multiplicata* (*C*) is employed to attract
the female. The functional significance of the hypertrophied glands on the
thighs of the male *Mantidactylus luteolus* (*A*), viewed ventrally, and in the inguinal
region of the male *Cycloramphus asper* (*B*) is at present unknown.

glandular patches appears on the chest of the male and would
be assumed to function in holding the female. But in various
pelobatids (Scaphiopus, Cophophryne, and some Megalophrys), a
similar pair of pads appears in both sexes. Perhaps this is another
instance of the inheritance of male characters by the female, but
the Pelobatidae are far more primitive than the polypedatid
tree frogs and hence presumably represent the primitive condi-

tion. In this connection we might compare the inguinal glands of Cycloramphus with those of *Pseudophryne guentheri*. In the latter they appear in both sexes, but most developed in the large females. In *Bufo punctatus* the paratoid glands, which would seem to have no direct rôle in the breeding process, are most pronounced in the male. Whatever may be the function of these various glandular hypertrophies it is interesting that they crop up in unrelated families, sometimes in both sexes and again only in one.

The males of many species of the neotropical frog, Leptodactylus, develop a pointed snout with a horizontal ridge along the upper lip during the breeding season. This strange modification of the head into a veritable spade is apparently correlated with the practice of digging holes near the edge of streams or ponds in which the females, attracted by the calls of the male, may come and lay their eggs. It is interesting from the phylogenetic standpoint that a very similar modification of the snout reappears in *Batrachylodes vertebralis*, a frog of a very different family living on the other side of the world (Mertens, 1929). This is another instance of similar secondary sexual modifications reappearing in unrelated groups. It is exactly comparable to the occurrence of balloon-like external vocal pouches on each side of the lower jaw in diverse species of Leptodactylus, Hyla, and Rana.

Have these secondary sexual characters come into existence by a slow progressive change and do they represent only the final stages of specialization left on the earth today? This may be true in some but not in all cases. For example, the European toads, *Bombina bombina* and *B. variegata*, are very closely related and yet only the former possesses vocal pouches (Mertens, 1928). Again one of the most bizarre secondary sexual characters is found in the African *Petropedetes newtoni*. Here the columella is thrust through the drum of the male and, covered by the derm, it forms a prominent projection (Fig. 40*C*). There are five species in the genus but only *newtoni* exhibits this peculiar structure. *P. newtoni* agrees with many other Salientia in that it has apparently suddenly developed a very distinctive type of secondary sexual character. The modification is further surprising in that the eardrum shows very little sexual dimorphism throughout the Salientia. In the Bullfrog, *Rana catesbeiana*, the Pond Frog, *Rana clamitans*, and allied species, the eardrum of the male is distinctly larger than that of the female (Fig. 43). This is a case where a secondary sexual character is found throughout an allied group of species and stands in striking contrast to the conditions in Petropedetes. Why the male frog would have need of a more elaborate hearing organ than the female is not at all clear.

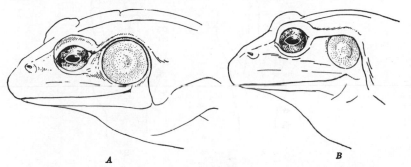

Fig. 43.—Sexual dimorphism in the Bullfrog, *Rana catesbeiana*. The tympanum is markedly larger in the male (*A*) than in the female (*B*) of the Bullfrog and allied species.

Relation of Secondary Sexual to Somatic Characters.—The secondary sexual characters of Amphibia are highly discontinuous in their occurrence. Further, almost identical modifications may appear in unrelated groups. The only adequate theory which will explain the origin of secondary sexual characters is that they are due to gene mutations which occur either in the sex chromosome or in the autosomes but in the latter case can come to expression only in the male or the female body, as the case may be. Natural selection has tended to preserve those mutations which facilitate sexual union, but just as in the case of the somatic changes some mutations have given rise to "neutral" characters, those which are neither harmful nor useful, but which are carried along by the hereditary stream. There are several possible ways by which a sex-linked or sex-limited character may lose this bondage to one sex and appear in both. Genetic evidence as to the nature of this change is lacking for the Amphibia. Nevertheless, the fact that this change has occurred not once but many times in Amphibia as well as in other vertebrates throws considerable light on the origin of certain somatic characters.

This point of view may be made clearer by further illustration. In the evolution of the Dusky Salamanders, Desmognathus, from the large *D. quadra-maculatus* to the small *D. fuscus ochrophaeus* and *D. fuscus carolinensis*, the male exhibits an increasing tendency to lose its vomerine teeth in adult life and to reduce the anterior part of the parasphenoid tooth patches. *Leurognathus marmorata intermedia*, which has been derived from *D. quadra-*

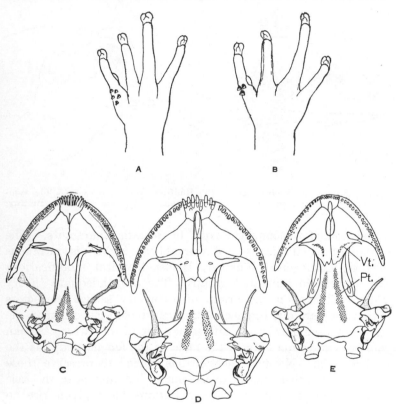

Fig. 44.—The reappearance of male characters in both sexes of other species. The nuptial spines, usually characteristic of the male frog, occur in the female *Crossodactylus gaudichaudii* (*A*) nearly as well developed as in the male (*B*). The vomerine teeth are lacking in the male *Desmognathus fuscus* (*D*) but present in the female (*E*). In the related *Leurognathus marmorata marmorata* (*C*) both sexes lack vomerine teeth. The skulls are viewed ventrally, the forelimbs dorsally. *Pt.*, parasphenoid teeth patches; *Vt.*, vomerine teeth.

maculatus, has the vomerine teeth absent in the males like the more advanced species of Desmognathus. In *L. m. marmorata* this loss occurs in both sexes and is called a "specific character" (Fig. 44). The loss might be considered an adaptation to aquatic life except that the terrestrial *D. f. carolinensis* and the aquatic *L. m. intermedia* both show the initial stage in tooth loss. Again,

it has recently been shown that the males of some and possibly
all species of Eurycea hypertrophy the teeth in both jaws from
short bicuspid teeth, characteristic of most metamorphosed
Amphibia, to elongate monocuspid ones (Fig. 45). It had

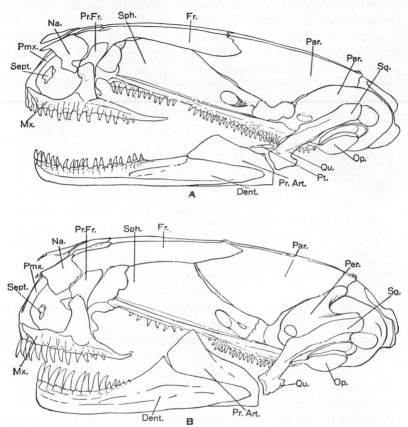

Fig. 45.—Secondary sex differences in the skull, especially in the teeth, of the
two-lined salamander *Eurycea bislineata bislineata*. *A*. Female. *B*. Male.
Dent., dentary; *Fr.*, frontal; *Mx.*, maxillary; *Na.*, nasal; *Op.*, operculum; *Par.*,
parietal; *Per.*, periotic; *Pmx.*, premaxillary; *Pr.Art.*, prearticular; *Pr.Fr.*, prefrontal; *Pt.*, pterygoid vestige; *Qu.*, quadrate; *Sept.*, septomaxilla; *Sph.*, sphenethmoid; *Sq.* squamosal.

previously been pointed out that the males of most plethodontids
have the premaxillary teeth elongate, monocuspid, and directed
more or less forward (Fig. 46). A possible use for the latter
modification was found in courtship of *Eurycea bislineata* (Noble,
1929) where during the initial stage the male rubs the female

with his snout.   No males, however, opened their mouths during
any phase of the courtship and no biting was observed even in
cases where courting pairs were crowded together in a small
aquarium.   Hence the elongate maxillary and dentary teeth of
Eurycea seemed to have no specific function.   In the related
Gyrinophilus no sexual differences in dentition appear.   In
G. porphyriticus, the purple salamander, the teeth are all bicuspid.
In the closely related *G. danielsi*, however, the teeth of both jaws
are elongate and monocuspid.   There is no evidence that these
two species of Gyrinophilus differ essentially in feeding habits,
and yet there is nearly as much difference in their dentition as
between the two sexes of Eurycea.   If the elongation of the

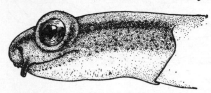

teeth in the latter is merely
due to "neutral" genes which
happen to be sex-linked or
sex-limited, the occurrence of
a similar modification in both
sexes of *G. danielsi* would
seem to be due to similar
genes which, however, have
avoided this linkage.   An
apparent difference is nevertheless to be found in the

FIG. 46.—The male *Manculus quad-
ridigitatus* has the naso-labial grooves
of each side extended into a cirrus.   As
in many other plethodontids, the premaxillary teeth are elongated, directed
forward, and exposed during the breeding season.

genesis of the teeth, since those of the male Eurycea fluctuate
with the season and are apparently under the control of the
sex hormone, while those of Gyrinophilus are not known to be
influenced by hormones.

The modification of the teeth of vertebrates is generally
believed to be closely correlated with changes in food habits.
Nevertheless, the most extreme types of dental modification in
Amphibia fail to show this correlation.   Many cases of dental
change in the evolution of the frogs resemble those of urodeles.
For example, in the ranid *Dimorphognathus africanus* (Fig. 40B)
the premaxillary and maxillary teeth in the female are of moderate length and bicuspid; those of the male are long and monocuspid as in Eurycea.   True teeth are lacking in the lower jaw
of Dimorphognathus as in all other ranid frogs, but this species
has hypertrophied the margins of the prearticular bone into a
series of pseudoteeth (Noble, 1922; Fig. 3).   The similarity of
this sexual modification of teeth with that of Eurycea extends
even to a certain seasonal fluctuation in the form of the teeth in

the upper jaw.   No male frogs are known to fight with their teeth for the possession of the female, nor do rubbing movements of the jaws as in Hydromantes (Fig. 47) play any part in courtship so far as is known.   Hence, as in the case of Eurycea, a functional significance for the dental hypertrophy is doubtful. Nevertheless, the same apparent changes in linkage seen in the plethodontids occur in frogs.   In the neotropical Hemiphractus and Amphodus, the dorsal margin of the prearticular is hypertrophied into a row of pseudoteeth in both sexes.   Hemiphractus

FIG. 47.—The elongated teeth in the upper jaw of the male *Hydromantes platycephalus* apparently serve as stimulating organs during courtship.   The males of other species of the genus rub the females with their chin and teeth during this period.

goes farther than Dimorphognathus in the development of excess bony growths, for its whole skull has become evolved in a grotesque casque of secondary dermal bone.

The exact form of the tooth varies with the species in both frogs and urodeles, although tooth characters have been rarely used in defining species.   The hypertrophy of the teeth is not always correlated first with one sex and later with both.   In Ceratophrys the smaller species have bicuspid teeth in both sexes; the larger, monocuspid elongate ones.   In young specimens of the large species such as *C. dorsata*, the teeth arise as monocuspid structures.   A similar loss of one cusp, apparently the outer, occurs in the phylogeny of Aneides; the smaller species, *aeneus*, having bicuspid teeth in both jaws for a long period, the larger, *lugubris*, developing many monocuspid teeth directly. On the other hand, many large species of both frogs and salamanders have bicuspid teeth, and small species, such as *Leptopelis brevirostris* and *Phrynopsis usumbarae* as well as various pipids, have elongate monocuspid ones, showing that there is no correlation between body size and tooth form throughout the Salientia.

Although dental modifications may or may not be sex-linked, the question arises: Do structures well known to be functional in the male ever appear in the female of another species where they cannot possibly have these functions? The best-known peculiarity of the male frog is the cluster of asperities which appear on his thumb during the breeding season. These organs serve to maintain the grip of the male on a struggling female and consequently would have no use in the latter sex. Nevertheless, in *Crossodactylus gaudichaudii* conspicuous black spines appear on the thumb of the female and while they are usually not quite so large as those on the male they are frequently more numerous (Fig. 44A). Similarly, a large frog from Okinawa Island was taxonomically isolated from the related species of Rana by creating for it the name "Babina" merely because the female frequently has its dagger-like prepollex as well developed as in the breeding male. These cases of the appearance of male characters in the female are directly comparable to the development of horns in the female caribou. Characters which are sex-linked or sex-limited in one group need not be so in another.

Discontinuous Evolution.—One of the striking features of the secondary sexual characters of Amphibia is the way apparently useful modifications are given up once they have been acquired. For example, the male *Desmognathus phoca* has not only larger maxillary teeth than the female but the lingual cusp is directed posteriorly. Such a modification would apparently assist the male in holding his grip on struggling prey. In the more advanced *D. fuscus carolinensis*, however, the maxillary teeth are broadened and the elongate cusp has been given up. Further, in a local race of *D. f. carolinensis* which has been given the subspecific name of *imitator*, the maxillary teeth of the male may revert to the form of *D. phoca*. The Plethodontidae exhibit other instances of the same "shuffling of characters." The primitive Eurycea has monocuspid premaxillary teeth as previously described. In the terrestrial Plethodon, a more advanced type, the males of the larger species fail to show this modification. In the small *P. cinereus* which was apparently derived from one of the larger species (Dunn, 1926) the character has reappeared again although on a different plan, for while the tooth is elongated, the outer cusp is longer than the inner. Batrachoseps and Hemidactylium, which were apparently both derived from Plethodon, have redeveloped the character in its typical form. Some western species of Plethodon have the teeth monocuspid but directed only slightly forward. If we assume that the larger species of Plethodon represent the primitive condition for the genus, both Batrachoseps and Hemidactylium may be described as having redeveloped a secondary sexual character found in Eurycea.

Many of the secondary sexual characters of Amphibia, especially modifications of the tooth form, skin texture, body proportions, frontal enlargements, appendage form and length, body coloration, and habits find close analogies in the sexual modification of fish. Further, many fish and reptiles show the change of a character from a sex-linked or limited one to a character of both sexes. Familiar examples may be found in the horns of Chameleons which in some species occur only in the male; in others, in both sexes, although the utility in either sex is very doubtful (Hilzheimer, 1913). Some mammals have horns in one sex and others in both and again the value of these structures in the struggle for existence has been doubted by competent mammalogists. The theories of Cunningham (1908) and Champy (1924) fail when one attempts to trace the phylogeny of secondary sexual characters; further, the experimental evidence lends little support to their views (Morgan, 1919). Secondary sexual characters apparently owe their origin to gene mutations; those characters which happen to be useful in the breeding process are retained by natural selection. As in the case of many specific characters, a parallel change may occur in a not closely related group; further, many characters seem to have no function but when not harmful have been retained in association with more useful mutations. Since the same character may appear in one sex of one species and in both sexes of another, the utility of such a character in courtship or mating becomes doubtful. On the other hand, such a change in linkage presents further evidence that many specific characters have arisen without relation to definite functions. Since Darwin's time, characters have been scrutinized with regard to their survival value. Where naturalists have failed to find such values, they have assumed that the data were merely incomplete. Genetical studies have shown that a single mutation of a gene may affect various parts of an animal's body, producing changes in certain organs which render these more efficient while they render others less important in survival. The genes, moreover, are transmitted together in groups. Hence, any mutation of great survival value might be transmitted with a number of genes which produce distinctive modifications but neutral ones in the struggle for existence. It is important to consider these neutral characters, for upon a change of environment or habit they may become highly adaptive. Amphibia in both their secondary sexual and somatic characters are preadapted by gene mutations to new conditions of living many of which conditions are never realized by any particular species.

References

APPELROT, S., 1930: Sex and seasonal variations in excitability of the cardio-inhibitory mechanism of frogs and toads, *Amer. Jour. Phys.*, XCV, 242–249.

BOULENGER, G. A., 1897: "The Tailless Batrachians of Europe," Part I, *London Ray Soc.*

————, 1912: On some tree-frogs allied to Hyla caerulea with remarks on noteworthy sexual characters in the family Hylidae, *Zool. Jahrb. Suppl.*, 15, I, 211–218.

CHAMPY, CH., 1924: "Les caractères sexuels considérés comme phénomènes de developpement et dans leurs rapports avec l'hormone sexuelle," Paris.

CHAUVIN, MARIE VON, 1883: Die Art der Fortpflanzung des Proteus anguineus, *Zeitschr. Wiss. Zool.*, XXXVIII, 671–685.

CREW, F. A. E., 1927: "The Genetics of Sexuality in Animals," Cambridge Univ. Press.

CUNNINGHAM, J. T., 1908: The heredity of secondary sexual characters in relation to hormones, a theory of the heredity of somatogenic characters, *Arch. Entw. Mech.*, XXVI, 372–428.

DAUVART, A., 1924: Ein bis jetzt unbekanntes zyklisches Geschlechtsmerkmal der Batrachier; Saisonvariation des Vorderextremitätenskelettes des Frosches, *Arch. mikr. Anat. Entw.*, CIII, 504–516.

DUNN, E. R., 1924: Some Panamanian frogs, *Occ. Papers Mus. Zool.*, Univ. Mich., No. 151.

————, 1926: "The Salamanders of the Family Plethodontidae," Smith College, Northampton, Mass.

FISHER, A. O., 1905: Marked differences between the skin of the male and that of the female frog, *Proc. Ass. Amer. Anat.*, 18th Session, XIV, inserted in *Amer. Jour. Anat.*, IV.

GAULE, J., 1900: Über die geschlechtliche Differenz der Muskeln bei Fröschen, *Arch. ges. Physiol.*, LXXXIII, 83–88.

HARMS, Jürgen W., 1926: "Körper und Keimzellen," Berlin.

HILZHEIMER, M., 1913: "Handbuch der Biologie der Wirbeltiere," Stuttgart.

KAHN, R. H., 1919: Ein neues Geschlechtsmerkmal bei den Fröschen, seine anatomische Grundlage und seine biologische Bedeutung, *Zool. Anz.*, L, 166–169.

KANDLER, RUDOLF, 1924: Die sexuelle Ausgestaltung der Vorderextremität der anuren Amphibien, *Jena. Zeitschr.*, LX, 176–240, 2 pls.

KLIER, A., 1926: Die Art- und Geschlechtsunterschiede am Becken und Ober- und Unterarmknochen bei Rana temporaria und Rana esculenta, *Zeitschr. Anat. Entw.*, LXXX, 669–703.

KLINGELHÖFFER, W., 1930: "Terrarienkunde," Lief. 13 and 14, Stuttgart.

KOMINE, S., 1924: Metabolic activities of the nervous system; On the regular seasonal changes in the relative weight and the sex difference of the central nervous system of Rana nigromaculata, *Sci. Rep. Tohoku Imp. Univ. Sendai.*, Japan Biol. Ser. I, No. I, 51–74.

KYLE, HARRY M., 1926: "The Biology of Fishes," New York.

LEEUWEN, W. D. VAN, 1907: Über die Aufnahme der Spermatophoren bei Salamandra maculosa Laur, *Zool. Anz.*, XXXI, 649–653.

LEYDIG, F., 1892: Integument brünstiger Fische und Amphibien, *Biol. Zentralb.*, XII, 205–221.

MERTENS, ROBERT, 1928: Zur Naturgeschichte der europäischen Unken (Bombina), *Zeitschr. Morph. Ökol*, XI, 613–623.

———, 1929: Herpetologische Mitteilungen, XXIII–XXV, *Zool. Anz.*, LXXXVI, 58–68.

MORGAN, T. H., 1919: The genetic and operative evidence relating to secondary sexual characters, *Carnegie Inst. Wash. Pub.*, No. 285.

———, 1926: "The Theory of the Gene," Yale Univ. Press, New Haven.

NAKAMURA, T., 1927: Étude anatomo-comparitive, embryologique et embryo-mécanique de la papille cloacale des Tritons, *Bull. Biol. France et Belgique*, LXI, 333–357.

NOBLE, G. K., 1922: The phylogeny of the Salientia; I, The osteology and thigh musculature; their bearing on classification and phylogeny, *Bull. Amer. Mus. Nat. Hist.*, XLVI, 1–87.

———, 1925: The integumentary pulmonary and cardiac modifications correlated with increased cutaneous respiration in the Amphibia: a solution of the "hairy frog" problem, *Jour. Morph. Physiol.*, XL, 341–416.

———, 1929: The relation of courtship to the secondary sexual characters of the two-lined salamander, Eurycea bislineata, *Amer. Mus. Novit.*, No. 362.

NOBLE, G. K., and E. J. FARRIS, 1929: The method of sex recognition in the wood frog, Rana sylvatica, *Amer. Mus. Novit.*, No. 363.

POPE, C. H., 1931: Notes on amphibians from Fukien, Hainan and other parts of China, *Bull. Amer. Mus. Nat. Hist.*, in press.

PYCRAFT, W. P., 1914: "The Courtship of Animals," 2d ed., London.

ROSE, WALTER, 1929: "Veld and Vlei: An Account of South African Frogs, Toads, Lizards, Snakes and Tortoises," Cape Town.

SALLER, K., 1927: Die Geschlechtsverschiedenheit am Skelett von Rana temporaria, *Arch. Entw. Mech.*, CX, 450–527.

STORER, TRACY I., 1925: A synopsis of the Amphibia of California, *Univ. Calif. Pub. Zool.*, XXVII, 1–342, 18 pls.

UEKI, T., 1930: On the sexual differences in the newt Diemictylus pyrrhogaster (Boie), *Sci. Rep.*, Tohoku Imp. Univ., Sendai (4) V, 133–152.

YUNGE, E., 1907: Des variations de la longeur de l'intestin chez la Grenouille, *Compt. rend. Acad. Sci. Paris*, CXLV, 1306–1308.

ZEPP, P., 1923: Beiträge zur vergleichenden Untersuchung der heimischen Froscharten, *Zeitschr. Anat. Entw.*, LXIX, 84–180.

CHAPTER VI

THE INTEGUMENT

Amphibians are provided with a soft, moist skin which, except for that of the caecilians, is devoid of scales. The fish ancestors of the Amphibia possessed scales and these were retained in many of the first tetrapods. Some microsaurs possessed scales over most of their body, and the caecilians seem to have inherited this condition directly from them. Within the caecilian group a reduction of the scalation has occurred, some genera retaining scales only on the back and others lacking them entirely. The scales of caecilians are small, averaging about 1.5 mm. in diameter. They are hidden under the skin and not visible but, when revealed by a needle, are found to resemble in form and sculpture one of the types of scales found among the labyrinthodonts. In some fish, scales are formed late in development, while in branchiosaurs and caecilians they do not appear until the time of metamorphosis.

A few extinct types, notably the labyrinthodont Dissorophus, had bony plates along the back. A secondary deposit of bone occurs in the skin of the head or back in various modern Salientia, especially in burrowing pelobatids, bufonids, and hylids. As most frogs use their hind legs and not their head in burrowing, it has been claimed that the bony casque may act as a plug to the burrow. A similar bony deposit has been found in species which are not known to burrow, however, and no satisfactory explanation has been given of either the origin or the function of these bony deposits. The modification reaches its extreme in the diminutive Brachycephalus, where the dorsal plate fuses with the underlying neural spines, and in the grotesque Triprion, where the bony growth distorts the face in an extraordinary manner.

The integument is far more than a wrapping around the body; it is an organ of many functions. During early embryonic life the integument is represented merely by the ectoderm. Cilia develop on its outer surface and these serve to pass a current of fluid continuously over the embryo. The direction of beat is

130

determined very early and is continued even when the ectoderm is isolated from the underlying tissues (Twitty, 1928).

Unicellular Glands.—Shortly before hatching, a series of unicellular glands appear on the snout of tadpoles and probably all urodele larvae. They may extend along the back of some frog embryos (Saguchi, 1915). In Xenopus (Bles, 1906), Alytes

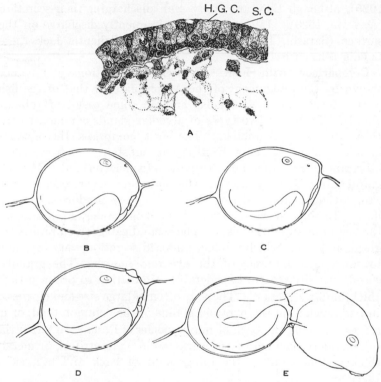

Fig. 48.—The hatching of Alytes, the midwife toad. As in the case of other Salientia, the tadpole escapes from the egg by digesting its way out. *A*. Section of the frontal organ or digesting glands just before hatching. *B–E*., Several stages in the hatching process; *H.G.C.*, hatching gland cell; *S.C.*, supporting cell.

(Noble, 1926), the axolotl (Wintrebert, 1928), and *Ambystoma opacum* (Noble and Brady, 1930), it has been shown that these glands function in producing a secretion which digests the egg capsule and frees the embryos. It is due to the early development of these unicellular glands (Fig. 48) that some frog tadpoles hatch in a very immature condition.

Before the larva hatches, more or less of the ectoderm has developed two layers of cells and is now designated as epidermis. At the same time it has become closely attached below to a membranous corium, or dermis, of mesodermic origin. The epidermis of urodeles develops a series of large, glandlike cells (the Leydig cells), which seem homologous with the clavate cells of fishes and which may serve to ward off infection (Wilder, 1925), although they are rarely seen discharging their secretion (Dawson, 1920). In caecilians they frequently discharge on the surface (Sarasin, 1887). The tadpoles of Salientia lack these Leydig cells entirely.

Comparison with Fish.—The chief evolutionary advance shown by the integument of the Amphibia over that of the fish is the development of alveolar and, in some cases, of tubular glands. There are two types of alveolar glands common to the three orders of Amphibia. The first comprises the mucous glands, which secrete a transparent substance to serve as a lubricant in the water and to keep the skin moist on land. Mucous glands are widely spread over the body and never reach a large size, although under slight stimulation they produce a copious flow. In some species, as the Slimy Salamander, *P. glutinosus,* the secretion may be sticky. The second category embraces the granular glands, which produce an acrid secretion, very injurious to mucous membranes of the eye and mouth. The granular glands usually require considerable stimulation to produce their thick, milky secretion. They are often of large size and clustered in pads such as in the paratoid glands of the common toad, or in ridges, as along the back of many species of Rana. In terrestrial salamanders they may form warts, as in Tylototriton, or merely thickened portions of the integument of back and tail, as in Plethodon.

It has been claimed that mucous and granular glands are merely different growth stages of one type of gland. Blut Proteus develops only mucous glands, and various tadpones such as those of Ascaphus may develop granular glands alone. Further, there are marked differences in the histological structure of the two glands (Dawson, 1920), the secretion of the mucous glands staining with basic dyes, and never assuming the form of granules, while the secretion of the granular glands stains readily with plasma dyes and has a granular appearance (Fig. 49). Both glands develop from the epidermis and in many species do not appear until shortly before metamorphosis. The granular glands become surrounded by a muscular sheath of epidermal origin, while the mucous glands in various species remain without this cover. Both lie, for the most part, in the corium which during development increases in thickness and differentiates into three layers, the inner and outer layer being more compact than the middle one. Besides glands, connective tissue, and blood vessels, there is considerable smooth muscle in the corium.

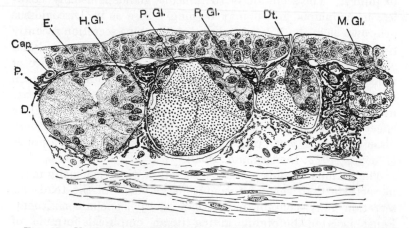

FIG. 49.—Vertical section of the skin from the dorsal surface of the tail base of *Plethodon cinereus* showing three types of skin glands. *Cap.*, capillary; *D.*, dermis; *Dt.*, duct of exhausted granular or poison gland; *E.*, epidermis; *H.Gl.*, hedonic gland (cut to one side of main axis); *M.Gl.*, mucous gland; *P.*, melanophore; *P.Gl.*, poison gland; *R.Gl.*, developing poison gland.

Poison Glands.—The granular glands of Amphibia protect their owner from being devoured by many possible enemies. The western newt, although terrestrial for a large part of the year, is rarely eaten by either birds or mammals (Storer, 1925). The poisonous properties of the glands have been studied critically, especially in European and South American Salientia (Phisalix, 1922), but these properties do not always protect many toads and salamanders from being eaten by snakes or even by other Amphibia. Secretion from both the mucous and the granular glands of many species is poisonous. Phisalix (1918) found that the mucus of *Hydromantes italicus* when injected into a frog was more poisonous than the secretion of the granular glands. Nevertheless, the chief function of the mucous glands is to keep the skin moist, while that of the granular type is to protect the possessor against being devoured. Toads, or other Amphibia, cannot give warts and usually their secretions have no effect on the unprotected hand. The West Indian *Hyla vasta* and the African *Phrynomerus bifasciala* have been found under certain circumstances temporarily to inflame the hands of the collector. Both of these species produce great quantities of milky secretion.

Mucous glands of Amphibia function on the least excitation, while the milky secretion of the granular glands requires pressure or injury. The secretion of the mucous glands is usually colorless in Amphibia, but it may be mauve rose as in Discoglossus or brown as in the Mexican axolotl. The blue secretion recently reported in a West Indian Eleutherodactylus (Dunn, 1926) apparently came from mucous glands. The toxic substance of mucous glands seems independent of the amount of mucin released. The mucous secretions of Proteus and Siren are innocuous, while that of many newts and frogs has an irritating effect on eyes or nostrils when brought near them and a very disastrous result when injected into the digestive tract of animals (Phisalix, 1922; Biedermann, 1930).

The granular glands produce a secretion which is usually much more toxic than that of the mucous glands. In the toad this secretion may contain more than one poisonous constituent. Faust isolated bufotalin, giving it an empirical formula of $C_{34}H_{46}O_{10}$. Bufotalin appears to be an oxidation product of bufonin, a weaker poison, which apparently conditions the milky appearance of the gland secretion. Abel and Macht (1912) described bufogin, assigning to it the formula $C_{18}H_{24}O_4$. Both bufotalin and bufogin resemble digitalis in increasing the tonicity of the heart, eventually leading to its stoppage. Administration of the secretion of the granular glands of toads to the stomachs of higher vertebrates causes nausea, a weakening of respiration, and muscular paralysis. The secretion brought in contact with the eye produces a serious inflammation.

The poisonous secretions of salamanders have also been analyzed chemically. Three alkaloids have been extracted from the granular glands of Salamandra. Samandarin, with the formula $C_{26}H_{40}N_2O$, affects the respiratory centers in the central nervous system of dogs, but it is apparently not so abundant in *S. salamandra* as another weaker alkaloid which has been given the name "samandaridin." The poison from the granular glands of *Salamandra atra* differs from that of *S. salamandra* and is called "samandatrin." These alkaloids have the same effect as the natural poison.

Toad skins are used as medicine by the Chinese, and their therapeutic value may not be wholly psychological. Abel and Macht discovered adrenalin in the paratoid glands of the toad. Apparently adrenalin was not secreted as such by the gland, but resulted from a chemical change within the mature secretion (Shipley and Wislocki, 1915). It is, nevertheless, remarkable to find adrenalin in an external secretion.

Species differ enormously in the virulence of their poison. It has been noted (Wright, 1914) that the common Pickerel Frog, *R. palustris*, will frequently kill other species of frogs carried home in the same jar with it. Many of the most brightly colored species, especially those marked with yellow and red, have been found to be highly poisonous, but bright colors are not always linked with virulent secretions. Brazil and Vellard (1926) found that the dull-colored *Ceratophrys americana* has a virulent poison, while the gaudy *C. dorsata* has innocuous skin secretions.

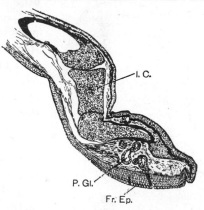

FIG. 50.—Diagram of a longitudinal section of the toe of a tree frog, showing the tree-climbing mechanism. *Fr.Ep.*, friction surface of pad with its wedge-shaped superficial cells; *I.C.*, intercalary cartilage; *P.Gl.*, friction pad gland.

The large *Leptodactylus pentadactylus* has bright thighs, but it lacks the highly poisonous secretions of the drab-colored *Bufo marinus*. The latter species produces one of the most virulent poisons known among the Amphibia, one that frequently kills dogs which have not learned to leave the toad alone. Whether or not because of this poison, the Marine Toad is almost ubiquitous in the American tropics.

Some species of the neotropical brachycephalid toad, Dendrobates, are bright green or pink, spotted with a dark tone. Their secretions are used by Indians of Colombia as a source of poison for their arrows. Whether these species are more poisonous than other less conspicuous forms of the same genus is unknown. Gadow (1901) points out that toads of this genus are used to rub on the growing feathers of parrots to change them from green to yellow.

Other Glands.—The mucous glands have apparently given rise to a number of hypertrophied and often tubular glands of special functions. Of these, the best known are the glands on the thumbs or chests of various male Salientia during the breeding season. Their secretion is more granular than that of ordinary mucous glands and helps the male to maintain by adhesion his grip on the female. The toes of tree frogs are equipped with pads which are not suction devices, as frequently stated, but elaborate friction and adhesion mechanisms (Fig. 50). The superficial cells of the epidermis are more or less free one from the other and project as so many short bristles against the substratum. The pad is supplied with a complex series of tubular glands which pour their adhesive secretion on the surface of the pad.

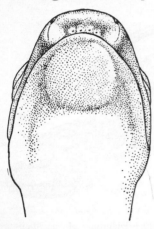

FIG. 51.—The glandular area on the chin, the hypertrophied naso-labial glands, and the elongated premaxillary teeth are characteristic of the males of several plethodontid salamanders including *Oedipus adspersa*, viewed here from the ventral surface.

Mucous glands have apparently given rise during phylogeny to another type of gland of totally different functions. The male Plethodontidae develop glands having a slightly granular secretion which apparently serves to attract the female. A patch of these glands on the chin usually becomes enlarged to form a conspicuous pad (Fig. 51).

The Plethodontidae are characterized by a naso-labial groove which serves to free the nostril from water (Wilder, 1906). This groove is flushed by a battery of tubular and frequently branched glands which seem to represent merely a ventral extension of the glandular area surrounding the nostril orifice of the species (Fig. 52). The latter cluster of glands keeps the nostrils of Amphibia free from water and dirt.

Odors.—Many frogs and salamanders have distinctive odors. The Mink Frog, *Rana septentrionalis*, receives its local name from its odor. The Marsupial Frog, *Gastrotheca monticola*, has a peculiar pungent smell, also reminiscent of that of a mink. It is noteworthy that while the two pelobatids Pelodytes and Pelobates, have the odor of onions (Boulenger 1911), the obviously unrelated *Salamandra salamandra* and *Bufo vulgaris* are both reported to smell like vanilla. The vanilla odor in *Hydromantes*

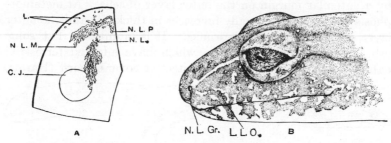

Fig. 52.—The naso-labial glands of plethodontid salamanders. The naso-labial groove is a glandular furrow which serves to free the nostrils from water in the plethodontid salamanders. The head of the Purple Salamander, *Gyrinophilus porphyriticus* (*B*), shows both naso-labial groove and lateral line organs. On the left the skin (*A*) of the head of *Desmognathus fuscus* has been removed together with the naso-labial glands and is viewed from the under surface. *C.J.*, conjunctiva; *L.*, labial glands; *L.L.O.*, lateral-line organ; *N.L.*, naso-labial glands; *N.L.Gr.*, naso-labial groove; *N.L.M.*, cut end of tubule which lies in the groove of the maxillary bone; *N.L.P.*, tubule of naso-labial gland within the premaxillary foramen. (*A*, *after Whipple*.)

italicus is produced by the granular glands (Phisalix, 1918). The odor of *Hydromantes genei* is a sweetish, penetrating odor which arises from these salamanders even when they are not handled. All odors appear to arise from either the secretions of the granular or mucous glands. Odors have not been reported from tadpoles or salamander larvae, and in most of these the glands do not become functional until shortly before metamorphosis. The mature tadpoles of *Rana heckscheri*, however, have a peculiar sweetish odor. On the other hand, it is highly probable that odors undetectable by our olfactory mechanisms are present in Amphibia and play an important rôle in the economy of some species. The secretions of the hedonic glands of newts and plethodontid salamanders have no recognizable odor and yet they seem to function in holding the attention of the female during courtship. At the height of the courtship, one species of plethodontid will not court with another, and since the male has been observed to nose the female before rejecting her, specific qualities of the skin secretions of the female are apparently recognizable by the male (Noble and Brady, 1930). No distinctive glands are present in the integument of the female and hence it is, apparently, the odor of the ordinary skin glands which must be acceptable to male plethodontids before they will begin the courtship.

Horny Growths.—The epidermis during larval life is protected by a cuticular margin on the outer layer of cells. At metamorphosis the epidermis usually increases in thickness and the outer layer of cells flattens and cornifies. It is interesting that some fish, such as Periophthalmus, which have adopted terrestrial habits should have developed a protective cover of horn (Harms,

Fig. 53.—The larva of *Onychodactylus japonicus*, showing modification of the limbs for mountain-brook life. The tips of the digits are equipped with recurved claws and the broad fin occurs on the post-axial margin of the limbs.

1929). The metamorphosis of the epidermis in Amphibia is not induced by drying as one might expect (Wilder, 1925), but is regulated by the thyroid hormone. Siren and Cryptobranchus, which are considered larval types, have succeeded in metamorphosing their integument but not all of their other structures. They thus remain aquatic forms although equipped with a thickened epidermis, having the superficial layer cornified.

A cornification of limited portions of the epidermis occurs in various larvae in a highly adaptive manner. The digit tips of various mountain-brook species of hynobiids, ambystomids, and plethodontids are covered with thickened and partly horny epidermal caps. In Onychodactylus larvae (Fig. 53) these cornifications are extended into sharp claws which have a great resemblance to those of lizards. Claws have been described in certain fossil Amphibia, but they are undoubtedly a new invention within the Hynobiidae. Pointed clawlike caps cover the digit tips of the swamp-dwelling Siren as well as the tips of the three inner toes of the African pond frogs of the family Pipidae. The main part of the suction disc on the ventral surface of Staurois tadpoles is covered with tubercles which have a cornified margin. Most frog tadpoles are provided with a battery of horny teeth which function as rasping organs (Fig. 54). Some tree-frog tadpoles which pass their larval life in water basins formed by the soft leaves of bromeliads exhibit a great reduction of the teeth, while various plankton feeders among the tadpoles have no horny teeth at all. Friction is well known to induce cornifications on the hand of man, but the importance of the mechanical factor in the development of tadpole teeth is by no means clear (Noble, 1929).

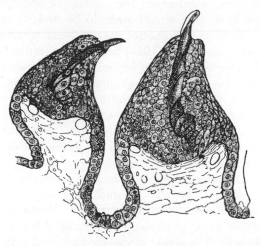

Fig. 54.—Larval teeth of a Spade-foot Toad. A section of the two tooth-rows of *Scaphiopus holbrookii*, showing modification of single cells to produce individual teeth.

Adult Amphibia frequently produce horny papillae over their heads or backs. In the males of many frogs and a few salamanders, these papillae may form patches on the thumbs, arms, chest, or even throat. The evolutionary history of these growths is discussed above with those of other secondary sexual characters. The epidermis of metamorphosed Amphibia is provided with a series of flask cells which hold the horny layer to the underlying sheets of epidermal cells. At the time of skin shedding they release a secretion and withdraw from the horny layer (Muhse, 1909; Dennert, 1924). Only the superficial layer of cornified epidermal cells is shed at this time.

Molt.—Molting occurs periodically in metamorphosed Amphibia at varying intervals, frequently a month or more apart. The process may require a few hours or more than a day.

Springer (1909) found in the case of the newt that the greater the quantity of beef fed the individual the more frequent the shedding. There may be a relation between the rate of growth and the number of molts, but in view of the fact that starving newts also molt the stretching of the epidermis cannot be the primary cause of molt. Irritating agents frequently induce the molting of salamanders. Since molting occurs on all surfaces of the body at one time, even when the irritation is restricted to a limited area, some mechanism for correlating the simultaneous action of the flask cells would seem to be present in the skin. The mechanism once set in action may induce a series of molts in rapid succession, as Wilder (1925) has shown. Since the number of cell layers in the epidermis of any one species varies only within narrow limits, the molting mechanism would seem to induce cell division in the deeper epidermal layers. Ruzicka (1917) and Adolph and Collins (1925) have presented evidence that the correlating mechanism was a chemical one. Since hypophysectomy prevents molting and leads to the development of a thick, horny layer in both toads and salamanders, molting would seem to be under hormonal control. The skin shedding of metamorphosis is produced by the thyroid hormone (Chap. XIII). Thyroidectomy of adult newts (Adams and Richards, 1929) has the same effect as hypophysectomy, namely the piling up of cornified epidermal layers. Since thyroid grafts in the newt induce molting while anterior pituitary grafts have no effect when the thyroid has been removed, it would seem that secretions of the thyroid play an important part in the normal molting of this species (Adams, Richards, and Kuder, 1930) and apparently in Amphibia in general.

Many terrestrial and some aquatic frogs and salamanders eat the shed skin. The swallowing is begun before the skin is fully shed and the movements of throat and forelimbs assist in peeling off the old skin, that of the limbs being turned inside out in the process.

Skin as a Respiratory Organ.—Aquatic and forest-dwelling frogs and toads tend to have a smoother skin than species living in drier situations. There are, however, many exceptions to this rule, some of the thoroughly aquatic pipid toads having a rougher skin than many desert bufonids. In general, burrowing Salientia, such as Scaphiopus, Rhinophrynus, and Cacopus, have thinner and smoother skins than their epigean relatives. Smooth, thin skins undoubtedly facilitate cutaneous respiration, but they are, of course, more subject to desiccation than thicker, more cornified ones. Some species of Bufo evaporate water through their skins as rapidly as Rana (Adolph, 1930), and in no amphibian does the skin retard evaporation to the extent found in the majority of reptiles.

Amphibia with reduced lungs, and therefore dependent to a large extent upon cutaneous respiration, have either a very thin epidermis or have capillaries penetrating it until they assume a position near the surface. Some frogs during metamorphosis have a temporary penetration of capillaries into the epidermis to tide them over this critical period of adjustment to land life (Maurer, 1898). The Cryptobranchidae have moderately well-developed lungs but they prefer to use the highly vascular skin folds of their bodies as veritable gills, for the capillary diverticula in these folds penetrate almost to the surface of the thick epidermis and afford ideal conditions for cutaneous respiration. Typhlonectes, the only thoroughly aquatic caecilian, exhibits a similar vascularization of the epidermis.

Pigmentation.—The Amphibia are often attractively garbed in colors as bright as those of birds or reptiles. Although diffuse pigments may occur in the tissue of some Amphibia, most of their varied colors are produced by different arrangements of three kinds of pigment cells: the melanophores, the lipophores, and the guanophores. Black or brown results from a predominance of melanophores, yellow or red from the lipophores, and white from the guanophores. Blue and green are produced by various combinations of these cells.

Colors may be chemical, structural, or a combination of both. The brilliant green on the back of many tree frogs is due to such a combination (Fig. 55). The epidermis of the skin from this region is translucent, acting merely as a protective cover to the corium with its battery of chromatophores. The lipophores lie directly under the epidermis and are filled with a yellow, fatty material in the form of fine drops or granules (Schmidt, 1920). Beneath the lipophores are the guanophores, cells packed with crystals of guanine, a substance allied to uric acid. The guanophores in turn are underlaid by the melanophores or dark pigment cells. When light falls upon the skin, it makes it appear green, for the rays of short wave length are reflected back by the crystals of guanine, those of greater length being absorbed by the black background of melanophores. The guanophores, if freed of their lipophore cover, would appear blue for the same reason that the sky appears blue, namely because of the diffraction of light by small suspended particles. The rays at the blue end of the spectrum are more scattered than the rays of greater length. The scattered rays include not only blue but also some green, indigo, and violet. In passing back through the yellow color screen formed by the lipophores, the blue, indigo, and violet rays are absorbed and the green alone allowed to pass. Frogs thus appear green because, of the light which falls upon their skin, only the green rays escape absorption.

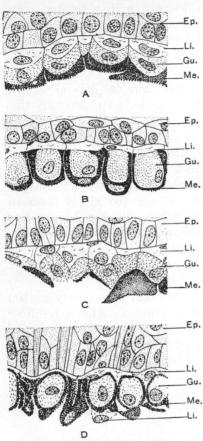

FIG. 55.—Diagrammatic section of the skin of a tree frog during color change. *A*. Bright green. The lipophores are arranged over the guanophores and the melanophores are partly expanded. *B*. Dark green. The guanophores are cylindrical and are nearly surrounded by the melanophores. *C*. Lemon yellow. Lipophores and guanophores irregularly arranged and the melanophores are greatly contracted. *D*. Gray. The lipophores are greatly flattened and some are squeezed between the guanophores. The latter are completely surrounded by the melanophores. *Ep.*, epidermis; *Gu.*, guanophores; *Li.*, lipophores; *Me.*, melanophores. (*After Schmidt.*)

Blue is a rare color in Amphibia but it occurs as a variation in *Rana clamitans* and normally in various other frogs. It is due to the same mechanism as green except that the lipophores are absent and the short blue, with some green, indigo, and violet rays, are reflected without the yellow screen to modify the result.

Red is also not a common color in Amphibia. Red and yellow pigments are very closely allied and are produced by the same cell, the lipophore. Some specimens of *Salamandra salamandra* or *Ambystoma maculatum* may possess red instead of the usual yellow spots, for within a single individual some lipophores may assume a red tone without any change occurring in the others. There is, however, an alcohol-insoluble red pigment in the skin of some frogs (Ballowitz, 1930) which may prove to be chemically different from the pigment of lipophores. Cells which bear this pigment, so-called "allophores," are found also in fish and reptiles and may possibly represent a fourth type of pigment cell. The red specimens of Wood Frog and the yellow *Triturus cristatus* which have been found in nature owe their color apparently to an inherited defect in melanophore production. A more complete failure to develop pigment leads to albinism, reported in many different groups of Amphibia.

Color Change.—Many tree frogs rival the chameleons in their ability to change their color rapidly. Such changes are induced

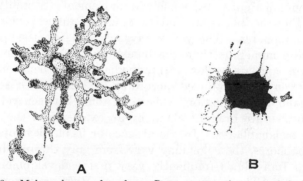

A   B

Fig. 56.—Melanophores of a frog, *Rana temporaria*, expanded (*A*) and contracted (*B*). The processes are not contracted but the pigment is withdrawn into the body of the cell. (*After Hewer, Proc. Roy. Soc. London*, 1923.)

by alterations of the form of the chromatophores or plastic pigment cells (Fig. 56). When the green skin darkens, the melanophores stream pigment into fine processes which extend between and around the guanophores. It has been frequently claimed that no such processes exist in the contracted melanophore but that the cell extends pseudopodia filled with pigment into preexisting spaces between the guanophores and lipophores. Although the young melanophore in the developing frog or salamander may change its shape, Amoeba fashion, as it migrates, with advancing age the melanophore apparently loses this activity until nothing remains but streaming movements within the extended pseudopodia. It seems clear from the work of Schmidt (1919), Schnakenbeck (1922), and others that a darkening is produced by a migration of pigmented cytoplasm within the mature melanophore and that fine, unpigmented processes are maintained even in the contracted melanophore. When the melanin has reached its furthest extension, the skin of this region appears black. In areas where the melanophores are numerous and crowded closely together, a permanent black spot is produced. We may, therefore, distinguish between pigment patterns due to the localization of pigment cells and pigment tones or rarely patterns due to the change in shape of the pigment cells under various external or internal influences.

Many tree frogs can change from green to yellow; the melanophores become fully contracted and fail to give the guanophores the necessary black background to permit them to show any considerable amount of blue. The lipophores change their relative position apparently by amoeboid movement (Schmidt, 1920) until they lie between, and in a few instances even below, the guanophores. The yellow rays reflected from the lipophores are more numerous than the blue from the guanophores, and the skin appears yellow. Intermediate tones between yellow and green are produced according to the degree to which the guanophores function, while color tones between yellow and dark brown are brought about by an extension of the melanin in the melanophores. In the absence or feeble development of the lipophores, the color may vary from gray through bluish to black. Individuals frequently vary in the development of the lipophores. Thus, some specimens of *Hyla versicolor* readily change from green to nearly black, while others vary from ash gray to nearly the same tone without being able to assume the green color. Most Amphibia can darken or lighten their general body tone but few have the ability to undergo the rapid changes of color found in some tree frogs. When the guanophores and lipophores are branched, as in *Rana esculenta* (Schmidt, 1921), the color is more diffuse.

Color change is induced by a great variety of factors, both external and internal. Low temperature in most Amphibia causes an expansion of the melanophores and hence a darkening of the skin; high temperatures induce a contraction, and a lightening. Desiccation and increased illumination have the same effect as high temperature, while humidity and darkness produce the opposite results. In some Amphibia, such as the South American frog, *Leptodactylus ocellatus*, the effect of light is induced through the intermediary of the eyes, for blinded animals fail to respond to increased illumination (Houssay and Ungar, 1925). In *Rana pipiens* the eyes of both tadpole and adult are the chief receptors of light stimuli affecting the coloration, but, in addition, the skin responds directly to the stimulation of light (Kropp, 1927), as in some lizards. In the urodeles the importance of the eye in color change varies with the species and with age. In very young Ambystoma larvae, as well as in Necturus of all ages, the skin darkens in the light and pales in the dark. With increasing age in Ambystoma larvae, and hence with increasing function of the eyes, the reverse change in coloration occurs on exposure to light on an indifferent background. Blinded larvae of this age react as young larvae (Laurens, 1917). Salamander larvae reared in aquaria with dark bottoms develop a dark coloration, because their eyes, like those of most vertebrates capable of color change, bring about an expansion of the melanophores. The impulses originate in the darkened retinae and are so strong that they overcome the tendency of the darkened chromatophores in the skin to contract. The tadpoles of Xenopus expand the melanophores of their tail fin when placed in the dark and apparently because of an optic influence. Seeing black is, however, very different from being put in darkness, at least in regard to its effect on the melanophores.

The coloration of the skin of some tree frogs is influenced by tactile stimulations. The European tree frog turns dark on a rough surface and green on a smooth surface (Biedermann, 1926). Thus, either the sight or the feel of pale, smooth leaves may bring an adaptive change in the color. Many Amphibia both in the field (Hargitt, 1912) and in the laboratory undergo erratic changes of color which cannot be correlated with any external factor but are apparently attributable to internal causes. An insufficient supply of oxygen brings about a contraction of the melanophores and hence respiratory disturbances would have some effect on the coloration.

The mechanisms controlling the expansion and contraction of the pigment cells vary with the species. In some species of Rana it would seem to be the secretion of the *pars intermedia* of the pituitary gland (Smith, 1920; Swingle, 1921) which brings about an expansion of the melanophores and its absence, a contraction.   The secretion of the adrenal organs, however, induces a rapid contraction of the dermal melanophores, although an expansion of the retinal pigment cells, and probably this secretion functions at times of intense excitement.   In *Rana pipiens*, the slow adaptive responses of the chromatophores have been attributed to the direct action of light.   The very rapid wavelike changes along the backs of some tree frogs such as *H. goughi* (Boulenger, 1911) can be due only to nervous mechanisms.   Kropp (1927) has shown that a contraction of the melanophores is produced in *Rana pipiens* by nerve section.   Hence, while the hormone of the *pars intermedia* of the pituitary probably has the most important part to play in the control of color change, the nervous mechanisms alone can also induce changes and stimuli impinging on the integument may directly affect the chromatophores without involving nerves or hormones.   It is possible that both hormone and nerve action may produce the same response, light stimulations received through the eye being transmitted on one hand to the pituitary and on the other to the nerves in the integument controlling the form of the melanophores.   No doubt the importance of one or the other mechanism varies with the species.   It is also possible that a third type of influence may originate from the eye.   Kropp (1929) has obtained evidence that a melanophore activating substance may be produced by the eye of certain tadpoles and released directly into the blood stream.   Burrowing or aquatic frogs would not have so great a need for quick changes of dress as those arboreal species which frequent exposed situations.   Hence the mechanism controlling the chromatophore expansion would not be expected to be the same in these species.

Color Patterns.—While the ground tone of nearly all Amphibia is subject to considerable change, the white spots formed by the accumulations of guanophores and the dark patterns produced by masses of melanophores change very slowly if at all during adult life.   The patterns have repeated themselves many times in the evolution of the Amphibia.   A dark stripe on the side of head and body is found in various hynobiids, plethodontids, and salamandrids; it even appears in the pigmentless cave salamander, Proteus, when exposed to light (Werner, 1892).   Werner showed that the patterns of the various subspecies of *Salamandra salamandra* of Europe were repeated in certain species of Oedipus and Eurycea of the New World.   I found that in a few hundred *Desmognathus fuscus carolinensis* collected in a single locality, the patterns of several species in other genera of plethodontids were represented. The varieties in this collection might have been arranged to show progressive change in pattern in various directions, but such series would no doubt not represent the true order of appearance of these patterns in phylogeny. Many frogs and toads possess a dark stripe through the eye, extending beyond the tympanum, and also another between the eyes. The pattern on the body frequently takes the form of a number of stripes or rows of spots. Werner (1892) assumes that there were originally four or six of these stripe areas in the Salientia. Centers of pigment formation have been described in the skin of birds and mammals. The number of possible patterns Amphibia may assume seems limited, for many stripes and bars appear in the same position in unrelated groups.

A study of the ontogeny of color patterns in urodeles has thrown some light on the reason for the frequency of the striped pattern in this group. Linden (1900) found in three species of European newts that a pattern of longitudinal stripes appeared even before hatching. The stripes were apparently correlated with the development of the main blood vessels under the skin. The longitudinal stripes were in some species gradually changed into spots, the transformation beginning at the posterior end of the body and moving forward and spreading from the dorsal surface to the ventral. There was thus a close parallel between the ontogeny of the color pattern of these newts and that of the European lizards, as described in the classical studies of Eimer (1881).

Eycleshymer (1906) followed the migration of the melanophores of Necturus from their origin in the mesenchyme to their final position in the dermis and epidermis. He noted a tendency for these pigment cells to aggregate along the large cutaneous veins. A similar migration and aggregation has been reported for some of the melanophores of the minnow, Fundulus, by Stockard (1915); and Zenneck (1894) has noticed the importance of similar early localizations of pigment in building up the pattern of a snake. Haecker (1918), from a study of the development of the melanophores in the axolotl, concluded that pigment was laid down in centers of active skin growth. It is possible that skin best supplied with blood might grow fastest. Subsequent observations (Sluiter, 1920) have not attempted to distinguish between regions of rapid growth and regions of maximum blood supply.   The striped pattern of many adult salamanders may be considered a retention of the early larval pattern.   In frogs a somewhat similar pattern may first appear at metamorphosis, but whether or not it is correlated with regions of active skin growth has not been determined.

The pigmented sides of many salamander larvae bear three rows of light spots.   In the center of each is usually located a lateral-line sense organ (Fig. 57).   In many plethodontid larvae the light area is devoid of pigment, but in certain salamandrids lipophores may be clustered in these areas.   In some adult

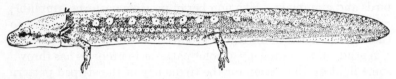

FIG. 57.—Larva of the two-lined salamander, *Eurycea bislineata*, showing the relation of the color pattern to the lateral-line organs.   Each small ring within the light areas represents a lateral-line organ.

salamanders which retain the lateral-line organs, guanophores may come to occupy the same position.   Thus, the lateral-line organs frequently have an effect on controlling the color pattern, since melanophores fail to develop near them (Noble, 1927).

Whatever might be the causes of melanophore localization, it may be noted that melanin is often produced in regions of high metabolism.   The more active hemisphere of frogs eggs is usually pigmented, although when eggs contain much yolk they may be devoid of pigmentation.   Faris (1924) found that pigment was produced in the embryo of Ambystoma in regions of rapid differentiation rather than of cell proliferation.   Melanin is produced by the oxidation of tyrosin or similar chromogen base, which is presumably, as in the case of the former, a product of protein metabolism.   The transformation is produced under the influence of a tyrosinase or similar oxidizing ferment.   A tyrosinase has been described in the skin of various Amphibia (Gessard, 1904) as well as in the frog's egg.

Banta and Gortner (1913) found that dilute solutions of tyrosin produced a darkening of the integument of *Eurycea bislineata*. Pernitzsch (1913) and Haecker (1918) noted that the difference between the albino and a pigmented axolotl was not merely a matter of failure to produce this substance in the albino.   They observed that the melanophores of the albino were smaller and grew very much more slowly than those of typical specimens. Pawlas (1925) found, however, that injecting an extract of pigmented axolotl skin into an albino axolotl would induce the development of a pattern. It thus seems that certain parts of the integument are regions of pigment formation as well as of accumulation. In many salamanders these regions are the sides of the body where cutaneous respiration is at a maximum. Possibly the greater supply of oxygen of the flanks would facilitate the production of melanin in this area. All patterns are not correlated with blood vessels. Further, some patterns are determined before they appear as pigmented areas. Lindeman (1929) found that transplanting the skin from the back to the tail of a tadpole before metamorphosis did not prevent the typical pattern from appearing in this piece of skin at the time of metamorphosis. Similarly, Reis (1930) found that larval skin transplanted on a different part of the body of the adult salamander metamorphosed and developed the color pattern it would have had in its normal position after metamorphosis. Thus, patterns are determined in the larval skin before there is any visible accumulation of melanophores. The nature of the hereditary mechanism determining these patterns has been discussed in a previous chapter (page 19).

Influence of the Environment on Pigmentation.—Under the stimulation of light the young of the cave salamanders, Typhlotriton and Proteus, will develop an extensive pigmentation of their integument. On the other hand, densely pigmented larvae, if reared in the dark, do not necessarily carry any marked effect of this sojourn into their adult life (Herbst, 1924; Banta, 1912). Although pattern, as shown from the work of Lindeman and of Reis, appears to be early localized by hereditary factors, the degree of development of the color may be influenced in some cases by light. Herbst and Ascher (1927) showed that the yellow pigment on the ventral surface of the recently metamorphosed *Salamandra salamandra* could be greatly increased by illuminating the animals from below. It would seem that if salamanders could expose their ventral surfaces to the light, patterns would appear which were previously unknown in these species. In such cases the light would not be producing a new pattern but merely bringing into view patterns potentially present but not previously realized because of the lack of light. It would also

seem probable that the degree of pigmentation of the upper surface of a salamander might be a function of the amount of exposure
to light.   Babak (1912) found that the increase and spread of
the melanophores were dependent on the form of the cells, the
expanded ones developing more rapidly than the contracted ones.
In the light, Typhlotriton expands its melanophores, while in
the dark, it contracts them.   Poorly pigmented tadpoles have
been reported from clay water, and possibly the absence of light
may have hindered their development.   Although light is not
necessary for the activation of the tyrosinase reaction, its absence
in certain cases might delay the oxidation.

Pogonowska (1914) found that sodium chloride increased the
formation of black pigment in *Salamandra salamandra* while it

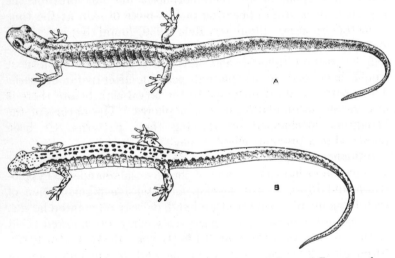

Fig. 58.—Melanism in salamanders: *A*. Melanistic specimen of *Eurycea melano-
pleura*.   *B*. Typical coloration of the same species.

reduced the development of lipophores, and Taniguchi (1929)
has reported a similar effect of common salt on the melanophores
of Hynobius.   A mineral mixture added to the diet of beef-
muscle-fed Ambystoma larvae enormously increased the intensity of pigmentation (Patch, in press).   Fatty foods may hinder
the development of the black-pigment cells (Johnson, 1913).
Wolterstorff (1927) showed that feeding white worms, Enchytraei, to the red-bellied salamander, *Triturus pyrrhogaster*, would
prevent the red colors from developing.   Similarly, *Triturus*

alpestris reared on Enchytraei and pale copepods develops a white instead of a yellow abdominal color. Tornier (1907) reported that Pelobates larvae raised on a meat diet became intensely dark, in striking contrast to tadpoles of the same species given a vegetable diet. No doubt some of the color variation found within a species in nature may be attributed directly to diet. Field studies have not yet, however, given evidence of such a correlation. Many herpetologists have reported melanistic Amphibia (Fig. 58) living side by side with typically colored individuals of the same species (Werner, 1930). Hence most melanism is apparently due to genetic and not to environmental factors. Nevertheless, several external factors are able to influence the development of pigment. Among these factors are the type of food the individuals happen to eat. Salts increase the amount of dark pigmentation, fats decrease it. Further the amount of light available during ontogeny may have an even more profound effect on the elaboration of pigment.

The internal environment produced by the hormones has also an influence on the development of the pigmentation. In the absence of the pituitary hormone new pigment is not formed (Pérédelsky and Blacher, 1929). Woronzowa (1929) found that implanting pituitary tissue into the albino race of axolotl would cause the development of pigment. It is thus evident that the skin of the white axolotl has potentialities to form normal dark coloration and that these potentialities may be realized if enough pituitary hormone is present.

Significance of Color.—The skin screens the underlying tissues from excessive visible and ultra-violet light by its horny layer and chiefly by its pigment. A sudden exposure of the stomach of a frog to ultra-violet rays brings about its contraction (Hill, 1926). The lipophores, as well as the guanophores and melanophores, act as a screen (Krüger and Kern, 1924). Many tree frogs, Hyla and Centronella, with translucent bodies have their viscera well protected by a covering of guanophores around the peritoneal cavity, and some tadpoles which habitually swim with their snouts directly under the surface film are protected by an accumulation of guanophores on the snout (Eggert, 1929). The melanophores have an equally important function as heat regulators, transforming light into heat. The melanophores of the retina have still another function, permitting rays from only one direction to reach the sensitive rods and cones, thus increasing enormously the efficiency of vision. With the marshaling of the pigment cells into patterns, a further significance was developed, for frequently such patterns are highly concealing.

The coloration of most Amphibia seems in keeping with their surroundings. Bright-green tree frogs, such as *Hyla andersoni*, remain for long periods on leafy trees; grey ones, such as *H. arenicolor*, on rocks. The wood frog, *Rana sylvatica*, resembles the brown leaves among which it sometimes hops. The pond-dwelling ranas usually lack the spots and stripes of those, such as *R. pipiens*, which frequent meadows. Nevertheless, it is common experience to find Amphibia of very different color pattern living side by side. It is difficult to consider the red color of Pseudo-triton or the yellow of Eurycea as protective. Rather, these tints are like those of the leaves in the fall—beautiful but without value.

Some of the gaudy patterns of Amphibia may be concealing, functioning according to the well-known camouflage principle of attracting the attention to them and diverting it away from the outline of the animal. Thus, the bright, median stripe of some specimens of *Plethodon cinereus* or *Acris gryllus* may assist in the concealing process. But, one naturally asks, if these stripes are of such importance, why do not all specimens of these species have them? In Ambystoma, many species (*maculatum*, *opacum*, *annulatum*, etc.) are brightly marked, but others in the genus which seem to have the same habits (*jeffersonianum*, *texanum*, etc.) lack the bright spots. Still others, as *A. tigrinum*, differ in both brightness and size of the markings in specimens from different parts of the continent. Hence, the importance of these patterns as protective devices seems not extensive.

A number of Salientia have specialized in developing bright colors on their groins, thighs, or other surfaces which are concealed by the legs when the frog is at rest. It has been assumed that the sudden flashing of these colors at the moment of leaping would dazzle the pursuer. Familiar examples of such "flash colors" are found on the thighs of *Hyla versicolor*, the groins of various species of Dendrobates or Phyllobates. *A priori*, these would seem to afford some of the best cases of protective colora-tion, but field observations as to their dazzling ability are lacking.

A number of Salientia, particularly South American bufonids and certain brevicipitids, have eyelike spots on the groins (Fig. 59). These have been assumed to function, as the ocelli in the wings of certain butterflies, in attracting the attention of the enemy toward them and away from the more essential head region of the frog. Such speculations afford interesting hypotheses to be critically studied by field students. All the intermediates between eyelike spots and black inguinal blotches exist among these frogs. The frequency with which these eye spots are repeated in unrelated groups gives the impression that they must have some important, even though still unknown, function.

Parallelism in the development of color pattern is a frequent phenomenon in Amphibia. *Plethodon glutinosus* and *Ambystoma jeffersonianum* resemble each other so closely that they are often confused. Various species of Hyla, Polypedates, and Leptopelis have almost identical patterns. If convergent evolution due to mimicry is assumed to account for the first-mentioned species, one might ask why does the same pattern appear in *Aneides*

Fig. 59.—The color pattern of *Mantipus ocellatus* resembles a face directed posteriorly. Eye spots occur in various unrelated groups of Salientia.

flavipunctatus of the West Coast. It seems far more likely that the integument of Amphibia is limited in the number of possible patterns which it is able to assume and hence the repetition of various patterns during evolution.

It has been sometimes assumed that color patterns serve as recognition marks in the various groups of vertebrates. As most Amphibia lead solitary lives except during the breeding season, such marks would function only during a short period. The bright colors of the males of some newts may serve to attract the attention of the females, but mechanisms other than color pattern function in sex recognition of most Amphibia.

References

ADAMS, A. E., and LEAH RICHARDS, 1929: The effect of thyroidectomy in Triturus viridescens, *Anat. Rec.*, XLIV, 222.

ADAMS, A. E., L. RICHARDS, and A. KUDER, 1930: The relations of the thyroid and pituitary glands to moulting in Triturus viridescens, *Science*, LXXII, 323–324.

ADOLPH, E. F., 1930: Living water, *Quart. Rev. Biol.*, V, 51–67.

ADOLPH, E. F., and H. H. COLLINS, 1925: Molting in an amphibian, Diemyctylus, *Jour. Morph.*, XL, 575–591.

ABEL, J., and D. MACHT., 1912: Two crystalline pharmacological agents from the tropical Bufo agua, *Jour. Pharm. & Exp. Therap.*, III, 319–377.

BABÁK, EDWARD, 1912: Über den Einfluss des Nervensystems auf die Pigmentbildung, *Zentralbl. Physiol.*, XXV, 1061–66.

BALLOWITZ, E., 1930: Über das Vorkommen alkoholbeständiger Rotzellen ("Allophoren" W. J. Schmidt) in der Haut einheimischer Amphibien, *Zeitschr. mikr. Anat. Forsch.*, XIX, 277–84, 2 pls.

BANTA, A. M., 1912: Experiments with the influence of darkness upon pigment development in amphibian larvae, *Science N. S.* XXXV, 460.

BANTA, A. M., and R. A. GORTNER, 1913: Induced modifications in pigment development in Spelerpes larvae (Preliminary paper); *Ohio Naturalist*, XIII, 49–55.

BIEDERMANN, W., 1926: Vergleichende Physiologie des Integuments der Wirbeltiere, I. Die Histophysiologie der typischen Hautgewebe, *Erg. Biol.*, I, 1–342.

————, 1930: Vergleichende Physiologie des Integuments der Wirbeltiere. V. Die Hautsekretion, *Erg. Biol.*, VI, 426–558.

BLES, E. J., 1906: The life history of Xenopus laevis Daud., *Trans. Roy. Soc. Edinburgh.*, XLI, 789–821, 4 pls.

BOULENGER, G. A., 1910: "Les batraciens et principalement ceux d'Europe," Paris.

BOULENGER, E. G., 1911: On a new tree-frog from Trinidad, living in the Society's gardens, *Proc. Zool. Soc. London*, 1911. II, 1082–1083, 1 pl.

BRAZIL, V., and J. VELLARD, 1926: Contribution à l'étude des batraciens, *Mem. Inst. Butantan*, III, 7–70.

DAWSON, A. B., 1920: The integument of Necturus maculosus, *Jour. Morph.*, XXXI, 487–577, 6 pls.

DENNERT, W., 1924: Über den Bau und die Rückbildung des Flossensaums bei den Urodelen, *Zeitschr. Anat. Entw.* LXXII, 407–462.

DUNN, E. R., 1926: The frogs of Jamaica, *Proc. Boston Soc. Nat. Hist.*, XXXVIII, 111–130, 2 pls.

EGGERT, B., 1929: Über den weissen Schnauzenfleck der Kaulquappe des javanischen Flugfrosches Rhacophorus leucomystax Gravh, *Zool. Anz.* LXXXIV, 180–189.

EIMER, G. H. THEODOR, 1881: "Über das Varüeren der Mauereidechse," Berlin.

EYCLESHYMER, A. C., 1906: The development of chromatophores in Necturus, *Amer. Jour. Anat.*, V, 309–313.

FARIS, HARVEY S., 1924: A study of pigment in embryos of Amblystoma, *Anat. Rec.*, XXVII, 63–76.

GADOW, HANS, 1901: "Amphibia and Reptiles," *Cambridge Nat. Hist.*, VIII.

GESSARD, M. C., 1904: Sur deux phénomènes de coloration dus à la tyrosinase, *Compt. rend. Soc. Biol.*, LVI, 285–286.

HAECKER, V., 1918: "Entwicklungsgeschichtliche Eigenschaftsanalyse (Phänogenetik)," Jena.

HARGITT, C. W., 1912: Behavior and color changes of tree frogs, *Jour. Anim. Behav.*, II, 51–78.

HARMS, J. W., 1929: Die Realisation von Genen und die consecutive Adaption; I, Phasen in der Differenzierung der Anlagenkomplexe und die Frage der Landtierwerdung, *Zeitschr. Wiss. Zool.*, CXXXIII, 211–397, 5 pls.

HERBST, C., 1924: Beiträge zur Entwicklungsphysiologie der Färbung und Zeichnung der Tiere; II, Die Weiterzucht der Tiere in gelber und schwarzer Umgebung, *Arch. Mikr. Anat. Entw.*, CII, 130–167

HERBST, C., and ASCHER, F., 1927: Beiträge zur Entwicklungsphysiologie der Färbung und Zeichnung der Tiere; III, Der Einfluss der Beleuchtung von unten auf das Farbkleid des Feuersalamanders, *Arch. Entw. Mech.*, CXII, 1–60.

HILL, L., 1926: The biological action of light, *Ann. Rep. Smithson. Inst.* for 1925, 327–336.

HOUSSAY, B. A., and J. UNGAR, 1925: Facteurs qui règlent la coloration de Leptodactylus ocellatus, *Compt. rend. Soc. Biol.*, XCIII, 259–260.

JOHNSON, M. E., 1913: The control of pigment formation in amphibian larvae, *Univ. Calif. Pub. Zool.*, XI, 53–88.

KROPP, B., 1927: The control of the melanophores in the frog, *Jour. Exp. Zool.*, XLIX, 289–318.

KROPP, B., 1929: The melanophore activator of the eye, *Proc. Nat. Acad. Sci.*, XV, 693–694.

KRÜIGER, PAUL and H. KERN, 1924: Die physikalische und physiologische Bedeutung des Pigmentes bei Amphibien und Reptilien, *Arch. ges. Physiol.*, CCII, 119–138.

LAURENS, H., 1917: The reactions of the melanophores of Amblystoma tigrinum to light and darkness, *Jour. Exp. Zool.*, XXIII, 195–205.

LINDEMAN, V. F., 1929: Integumentary pigmentation in the frog, Rana pipiens, during metamorphosis, with especial reference to tail-skin histolysis, *Physiol. Zool.*, II, 255–268.

LINDEN, MARIA VON, 1900: Die ontogenetische Entwicklung der Zeichnung unserer einheimischen Molche, *Biol. Zentralbl.*, XX, 144–167, 226–241.

MAURER, F., 1898: Die Vaskularisirung der Epidermis bei anuren Amphibien zur Zeit der Metamorphose, *Morph. Jahrb.*, XXVI, 330–336.

MUHSE, EFFA FUNK, 1909: The cutaneous glands of the common toads, *Amer. Jour. Anat.*, IX, 321–359, 7 pls.

NOBLE, G. K., 1926: The hatching process in Alytes, Eleutherodactylus and other amphibians, *Amer. Mus. Novit.*, No. 229, 1–7.

———, 1927: The plethodontid salamanders: Some aspects of their evolution, *Amer. Mus. Novit.*, No. 249, 1–26.

———, 1929: The adaptive modifications of the arboreal tadpoles of Hoplophryne and the torrent tadpoles of Staurois, *Bull. Amer. Mus. Nat. Hist.*, LVIII, No. 7.

NOBLE, G. K., and M. K. BRADY, 1930: "The Courtship of the Plethodontid Salamanders," Copeia, N. Y., 52–54.

PAWLAS, T., 1925: La formation du pigment noir dans la peau d'axolotls albiniques, sous l'influence d'excitations artificielles, Bull. Int. Acad. Polon. Cracovie, 1925, Series B, 651–672, 1 pl.

PÉRÉDELSKY, A. A., and L. J. BLACHER, 1929: Le sort de la mélanine dans la peau des amphibiens hypophysectomisées, Biol. Gen., V, 395–398.

PERNITZSCH, F., 1913: Zur Analyse der Rassenmerkmale der Axolotl, I. Die Pigmentierung junger Larven, Arch. Mikr. Anat., LXXXII, Abt. I, 148–205, 3 pls.

PHISALIX, M., 1918: Les venins cutanés du Spelerpes fuscus Gray, Bull. Mus. Hist. Nat. Paris, XXIV, 92–96.

———, 1922: "Animaux Venimeux et Venins," Paris, II, 1–843, 17 pls.

POGONOWSKA, IRENA, 1914: Über den Einfluss chemischer Faktoren auf die Farbveränderung des Feuersalamanders, 1. Mitteilung: Einfluss von Kochsalzlösung, Arch. Entw. Mech., XXXIX, 352–361.

REIS, K., 1930: Untersuchungen über das Verhalten der Transplantate larvaler Amphibienhaut auf Larven und auf erwachsene Amphibien, mit besonderer Berucksichtigung der Metamorphose, Arch. Entw. Mech., CXXII, 494–545.

RUZICKA, V., 1917: Beschleunigung der Häutung (bei Tritonen) durch Hunger, Arch. Entw. Mech., XLII, 671–710.

SARASIN, P. & F., 1887: "Ergebnisse naturwissenschaftlicher Forschungen auf Ceylon in den Jahren, 1884–86, II," Wiesbaden, 1887, 94, 11 pls.

SAGUCHI, S., 1915: Über Sekretionserscheinungen an den Epidermiszellen vom Amphibienlarven nebst Beiträgen zur Frage nach der physiologischen Degeneration der Zellen, Mitt. med. Fac. Tokyo, XIV, 299–415, 4 pls.

SCHMIDT, W. J., 1919: Vollzieht sich Ballung und Expansion des Pigmentes in den Melanophoren von Rana nach Art amöboider Bewegungen oder durch intrazelluläre Körnchenströmung? Biol. Zentralbl., XXXIX, 140–194.

———, 1920: Über das Verhalten der verschiedenartigen Chromatophoren beim Farbenwechsel des Laubfrosches, Arch. mikr. Anat., XCIII, Abt. I, 414–455, 2 pl.

———, 1921: Über die Xantholeukosomen von Rana esculenta, Jena. Zeitschr., LVII (N. S. 50), 219–228, 1 pl.

SCHNAKENBECK, W., 1922: Zur Analyse der Rassenmerkmale der Axolotl II.   Die Entstehung und das Schicksal der epidermalen Pigmentträger, Zeitschr. Indukt. Abstamm. Vererb., XXVII, 178–226.

SHIPLEY, P. G., and G. B. WISLOCKI, 1915: The histology of the poison glands of Bufo agua and its bearing upon the formation of epinephrin within the glands, Contrib. Embryol. Carnegie Inst. Wash., III, 71–90, 2 pl.

SLUITER, C. P., 1920: Rhythmical skin-growth and skin-design in amphibians and reptiles, Amsterdam Proc. Sci. K. Akad. Wet., XXII, 954–961.

SMITH, P. E., 1920: The pigmentary growth and endocrine disturbances induced in the anuran tadpole by the early ablation of the pars buccalis of the hypophysis, Amer. Anat. Mem., No. 11.

SPRINGER, A., 1909: A study of growth in the salamander Diemyctylus viridescens, *Jour. Exp. Zool.*, VI, 1–68.

STOCKARD, C. R., 1915: A study of wandering mesenchymal cells on the living yolk-sac and their developmental products: chromatophores, vascular endothelium and blood cells, *Amer. Jour. Anat.*, XVIII, 525–594.

STORER, T. I., 1925: A synopsis of the Amphibia of California, *Univ. Calif. Pub. Zool.*, XXVII, 1–342, 18 pls.

SWINGLE, W. W., 1921: The relation between the pars intermedia of the hypophysis to pigmentation changes in anuran larvae, *Jour. Exp. Zool.*, XXXIV, 119–141, 2 pls.

TANIGUCHI T., 1929: Über die Ernährung der mit verschiedenen Nahrungsmitteln gefütterten Amphibienlarven, *Fol. Anat. Jap*, VII, 113–136.

TORNIER, GUSTAV, 1907: Nachweis über das Entstehen von Albinismus, Melanismus und Neotenie bei Fröschen: Ein neuer Beitrag zur Biotechnik, *Zool. Anz.*, XXXII, 284–288.

TWITTY, V. C., 1928: Experimental studies on the ciliary action of amphibian embryos, *Jour. Exp. Zool.*, L, 319–344.

WERNER, FRANZ, 1892: Untersuchungen über die Zeichnung der Wirbelthiere, *Zool. Jahrb. Syst.*, VI, (1892), 155–229; VII, (1894), 365–410, 3 pls.

———,1930: Über das Vorkommen von Unter- und Überpigmentierung bei niederen Wirbeltieren, *Zool. Jahrb. Syst.*, LIX, 647–662.

WILDER, I. WHIPPLE, 1906: The naso-labial groove of lungless salamanders, *Biol. Bull.*, XI, 1–26.

———, 1925: "The Morphology of Amphibian Metamorphosis," Smith College, Northampton, Mass.

WINTREBERT, P., 1928: L'éclosion par digestion de la coque chez les poissons, les amphibiens et les céphalopodes dibranchiaux décapodes, *Compt. rend. Ass. Anat.*, XXIII (Prague), 496–503.

WOLTERSTORFF, W., 1927: Umfärbung bei Triton (Cynops) pyrrhogaster (Boie), dem japanischen Feuerbauchmolch, *Blätt Aquar-Terrar. Kde*, XXXVIII, 484.

WORONZOWA, MARIE A., 1929: Morphogenetische Analyse der Färbung bei weissen Axolotln, *Arch. Entw. Mech.*, CXV, 93–109.

WRIGHT, A. H., 1914: North American Anura: life-histories of the Anura of Ithaca, New York, *Carnegie Inst. Wash. Pub.*, No. 197, 21 pls.

ZENNECK, J., 1894: Die Anlage der Zeichnung und deren physiologische Ursachen beim Ringelnatterembryo, *Zeitschr. Wiss. Zool.*, LVIII, 364–393, 1 pl.

CHAPTER VII

THE RESPIRATORY SYSTEM

Oxygen required by the tissues for their metabolism is supplied by the blood. A constant refurnishing of the haemoglobin with oxygen is demanded if the animal is to live, for cessation of oxidation results in an accumulation of carbonic, lactic, and other acids in the tissues, paralyzing and eventually killing the cells. Carbon dioxide, which in solution gives carbonic acid, is the chief product of oxidation in the tissues. Since the concentration of carbon dioxide is greater in the tissues than in the blood, while that of oxygen is less, an interchange of these gases occurs by diffusion. The aeration of the blood is described as external respiration; the exchange of gases between blood and cells is distinguished by the term "internal respiration."

Since an absorption of oxygen by the blood, as well as the elimination of carbon dioxide, may occur on almost any part of the body where a thin, moist membrane overlies a capillary net, a large part of the integument of Amphibia functions in respiratory exchange. In most species the lining of the mouth is very vascular and serves for buccopharyngeal respiration. The major rôle in respiration, however, is played by the gills of the larvae and by the lungs of the adult. The primitive fish were well supplied with scales or bony plates in the integument. These, while affording protection to the animal, tended to limit the respiratory surface of the body and to necessitate the development of gills and lungs as the chief respiratory structures even in the most primitive forms.

The oxygen and carbon dioxide of the blood are not only in solution but also in chemical combination which may be readily broken down to give off the gases. Hence, respiration involves not only diffusion but also a number of complex chemical transformations. Most of the oxygen is carried in the blood combined with haemoglobin, while the carbon dioxide is transported largely in the form of bicarbonates. On the respiratory surfaces the haemoglobin in the red blood cells is oxidized to oxyhaemoglobin, which being more acid than haemoglobin tends to break up the bicarbonates and drive the carbon dioxide out of the blood stream. The loss of the carbon dioxide in turn lowers the acidity of the blood and facilitates the oxidation of the haemoglobin again. Thus, in the body tissues the accumulation of carbon dioxide favors the liberation of oxygen from oxyhaemoglobin by increasing the acidity. Further, the reduction of oxyhaemoglobin facilitates the taking on of carbon dioxide by the blood. In short, each chemical transformation on the respiratory surfaces or in the deeper tissues favors the one to follow.

Haemoglobin is chemically different in each species of animal. Its ability to carry and to unload oxygen varies with the species. The affinity of frog haemoglobin for oxygen is much lower than that of man. Hence at the same temperature human blood takes on much more oxygen than frog blood. At the low temperature ordinarily characteristic of Amphibia (15°C.), however, the oxyhaemoglobin of the frog is able to give up its load of oxygen as readily as human oxyhaemoglobin will dissociate at a much higher temperature (37°C.; Macela and Seliskar, 1925). In regard to its affinity for carbon dioxide, the blood of the bullfrog as compared with mammals binds a comparatively high amount (Wastl and Seliskar, 1925) but is unable to regulate its alkalinity as effectively as mammalian blood does.

Gills.—The gills of Amphibia are found only in the larvae and in those adult urodeles which fail to metamorphose. They sprout from the side of the neck in the branchial region which is pierced by a series of clefts. In the Gymnophiona the first cleft of the series remains open for only a short time during embryonic life. It forms a spiracle homologous with that of sharks, Polypterus, and a few other fish. In all other Amphibia the entodermal pouch forming the spiracle never breaks through to the outside but either produces a Eustachian tube, as in most Salientia, or disappears. There are four branchial clefts behind this pouch in most frogs and salamanders, but in the caecilians a fifth also occurs (Marcus, 1908). This is very probably the retention of a primitive feature, for Edgeworth (1920) has noted the development of the fifth pouch in the primitive Hynobius and Cryptobranchus.

There early develops in the pharyngeal wall, alternately with the clefts, a series of cartilaginous bars which form the hyobranchial apparatus. The cartilage between spiracle and the first branchial cleft becomes the hyoid; the following cartilages, the branchial arches. In caecilians there may be five of these branchial arches in the embryo (Fig. 60), while in all other Amphibia four is the maximum number and there may be less. The reduction in the number of arches is not always correlated with differences in habitat. The brook-dwelling Desmognathus possesses four branchial arches and some species of Eurycea, three. Branchial arches have been described in various fossil Amphibia such as Dwinasaurus, Archegosaurus, and Lysorophus, but they were not known to be more than four in number. The adult caecilians have at most four functional branchial arches, and hence the fifth may never have been a distinct arch in the adults of any Amphibia.

In the larvae of urodeles and caecilians the gills arise from a portion of the outer surface of the first three branchial arches. In the tadpoles of Salientia similar gills appear early in development and in some species they may become greatly elongated (Chap. III). In the Marsupial Frog, Gastrotheca, the two anterior pairs of external gills may form enormous bell-shaped structures which function as vascular wrappings completely surrounding the embryo. In most frog tadpoles the external gills do not attain the size or complexity of these structures in urodeles.

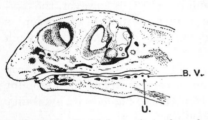

Fig. 60.—Sagittal section through the head of the caecilian, *Hypogeophis rostratus*, showing the branchial arches in cross-section. Caecilians are remarkable in retaining the fifth branchial arch. *B.V.*, fifth branchial arch; *U.*, ultimobranchial body. (*After Marcus.*)

Further, they are soon covered over by the operculum, a fold of integument which grows back from the hyoid arch. They are then replaced by rows of shorter gill processes, which grow from the anterior and posterior margins of the same arches and also from the anterior edge of the fourth branchial arch. These are often considered internal gills, homologous with the ordinary gills of fish, in contradistinction to the early formed gills, which are called "external" and homologized with the larval gills of crossopterygians and dipnoans. Except for their point of origin, there is very little difference between external and internal gills. The tissues entering into their formation are probably the same (Greil, 1906; Jacobshagen, 1921). Amphibia have specialized in the elaboration of the external gill which was an inheritance from the larvae and not from the adults of their piscine ancestors.

Relation of Gill Form to Function.—The fully developed form of the external gills of the various species of Amphibia is closely correlated with the functional needs of the larvae. This was shown in the discussion of their life history. The reduction of

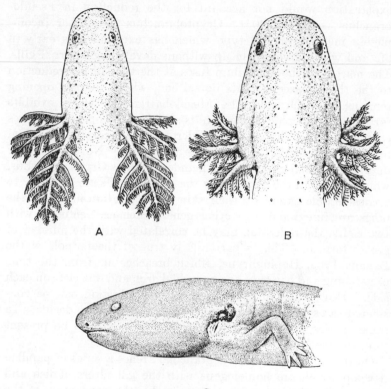

Fig. 61.—Head and gill form in *Pseudobranchus striatus* (*A*) and *Siren lacertina* (*B*), drawn from living specimens approximately six inches in total length. Young *Siren lacertina* (*C*) after treatment with 1 to 1,000 solution of iodothyrine. The branchiae are entirely lost, although their position is indicated by a densely pigmented swelling. Drawn from a formalin-fixed specimen, the lateral-line organs obscure, not indicated.

the gill clefts may also have a functional significance. For example, Siren, with four branchial arches, has the first three clefts open in the mature animal, while the closely related Pseudobranchus, which unlike Siren is a burrowing salamander, has the same number of arches, but only the second cleft remains open

(Fig. 61). On the other hand, in another burrowing type, Amphiuma, with four branchial arches and only one cleft, that between the third and fourth arches, the closure of the arches may be considered a metamorphic change partly completed. This seems probable, for Amphiuma shows other metamorphic changes such as the loss of gills early in larval life, but such an explanation would not account for the reduction in Pseudobranchus (see page 103). Cryptobranchus is another incompletely metamorphosed type which has external gills early in life and which gives them up without developing internal gills. The margin of the operculum fuses at the time of gill reduction to the throat, except at its dorsal end, where a single opening remains on each side. In Megalobatrachus, which exhibits further metamorphic changes in its skeleton, the operculum fuses completely, and this so-called "derotreme" lacks the branchial fenestrae supposed to characterize the group. No urodele ever develops internal gills, and salamanders such as Cryptobranchus, which remain in the water after the external gills are lost, rely to a considerable extent on their skin for respiration although the lungs are functional. In other genera such as Necturus, with two clefts, the reduction may be correlated with the number of arches formed. This is particularly true of the tadpole of the Banana Frog, Hoplophryne, which breathes air from the time of hatching and has only one branchial arch and one cleft on each side. How many of these instances of reduction can be considered cases of partial metamorphoses is difficult to decide. In some species, more arch-forming material seems to be present from the first.

On the concave side of the branchial arches a series of papillae develop which are homologous with the gill filters of fish and which serve the same function, namely, the prevention of the escape of food through the gill clefts. They seem to have been bony structures in some branchiosaurs. The short internal gills of Salientia are protected from the outside by an operculum as in fish. In the Salientia, however, this is not a bony cover but merely a fold which grows backward from the hyoid arch over the gills and fuses with the integument of the abdomen except for a small opening, the so-called "spiracle," which may be medial (discoglossids, brevicipitids, etc.) or sinistral (most Salientia). Rarely there is left a small opening on each side (pipids). In this way a branchial chamber is formed which freely communicates with the one of the opposite side by a broad channel ventral to the pericardium.

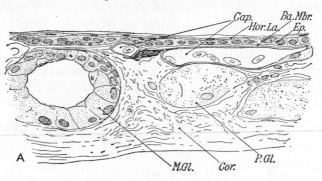

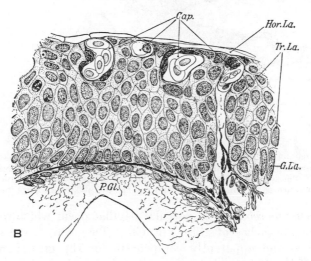

Fig. 62.—Skin capillaries. The efficiency of cutaneous respiration is increased in the Plethodontidae by the thinning of the epidermis over the superficial capillaries. In the Cryptobranchidae and certain other salamanders the capillaries penetrate the epidermis to a position very near the surface. *A. Desmognathus quadra-maculatus. B. Cryptobranchus alleganiensis. Ba.Mbr.*, basal membrane; *Cap.*, capillary; *Ep.*, epidermis; *G.La.*, germinal layer; *Hor.La.*, horny layer; *M.Gl.*, mucous gland; *P.Gl.*, poison gland; *Tr.La.*, transitional layer of epidermis; *Cor.*, corium.

Integument in Respiration.—The integument of the body of Amphibia, although it is often highly vascular and has important respiratory functions, is rarely thrown into processes resembling gills. The folds along the body of Cryptobranchus are considerably vascularized, the capillaries penetrating almost to the outer surface of the epidermis (Fig. 62).   These folds are often waved back and forth by the submerged animal in a manner suggesting the gill movements of such forms as Necturus.   Similar body folds occur in the aquatic Andean frog, Batrachophrynus.   The larva of Xenopus is provided with a pair of long vascular barbels which have been credited with primarily tactile and not respiratory functions (Nikitin, 1925).   Only in the "Hairy Frog" of Africa,

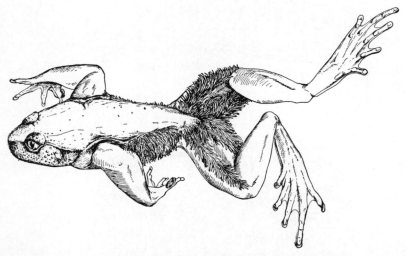

Fig. 63.—The 'Hairy Frog' *Astylosternus robustus* receives its name from the thick growth of vascular villosities which develop in the male during the breeding season.   These are respiratory organs which compensate for the reduced lungs of this species at the time of the year when the metabolism of frogs increases.

Astylosternus robustus do vascular papillae occur which resemble the finer branches of gills (Fig. 63).   These are found only in the male and apparently compensate for the greatly reduced lungs of this frog.   Their elaboration during the breeding season is to be explained by the increased metabolism during this season and the need for oxygen by the very muscular males.   The villosities which occur on the thighs and flanks resemble those which develop on the hind limbs of the brooding male, Lepidosiren, where they assist this fish to secure sufficient oxygen without leaving the egg burrow.

Lungs.—Gills and integumental filaments occur only in aquatic forms.   On land the villosities would stick together and would greatly reduce the respiratory area.   Those that remained exposed would dry due to the absence of glands and would soon lose their respiratory function. The respiratory organs of terrestrial vertebrates are the lungs. These arose in phylogeny long before the land was invaded. They are found today in both dipnoans and crossopterygians, and it seems probable that crossopterygian fish closely allied to the ancestors of Amphibia

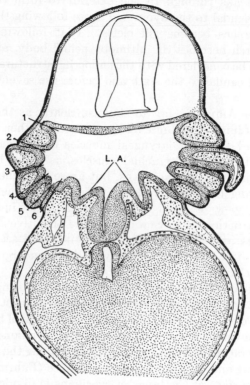

FIG. 64.—Frontal section of a larva of the midwife toad, Alytes, showing the resemblance of the lung rudiments to branchial pouches. *L.A.*, lung anlagen. Visceral pouches numbered. (*After Makuschok.*)

had paired air sacs of the same form as lungs (Barrell, 1916). Further, both air bladders and lungs arise from entodermal pockets of the pharynx which are serially homologous to the pockets which break through to form the gill clefts. That lungs are branchial pouches and not mere intestinal diverticula which have taken over secondarily a respiratory function is well shown by their development (Fig. 64) in the more primitive Amphibia and especially by the Gymnophiona as described by Marcus

(1908, 1922).   In the embryo of Hypogeophis, Marcus identifies nine visceral arches homologous to those in primitive fish.   The first forms the cartilage of the jaws, the second that of the hyoid, the third to seventh inclusive, the branchial arches, the eighth a process on the larynx, and the ninth the bulk of this structure. The entodermal pouch, which pushes out between hyoid and jawbone, breaks through to the exterior to form the spiracle. The pouch caudal to the hyoid and those following the first four branchial arches become gill clefts.   That following the fifth branchial arch becomes the ultimobranchial body, an epithelial structure to be considered with the endocrine structures, while the pouch lying caudal to the sixth and before the seventh develops into lung.

The other Amphibia fail to show as clearly as the caecilians the origin of lungs from branchial pouches.   Further, Edgeworth (1920) found that the laryngeal muscles of salamanders were not split off from the branchial muscles, as might be expected from the conditions in caecilians, but arose from the splanchnic layer covering the digestive tract.   Edgeworth, therefore, supported the view of Greil and others that the lungs are not branchial structures.   In view of the more primitive arrangement of the clefts and arches in caecilians, it would seem that the musculature of the urodele larynx had undergone various secondary changes.

The lungs of caecilians are specialized in that usually the left is rudimentary.   The same reduction occurs in most snakes and seems to be correlated with the elongate body form of both groups. Another convergence occurs in the aquatic Typhlonectes, which develops a tracheal lung or respiratory area along the passageway between lung and pharynx as in some snakes (Fuhrmann, 1914). The inner surface of the lungs of caecilians is divided by a network of blood vessels, connective tissue, and smooth muscle which form alveoli.   In the terrestrial Salientia such as Bufo, these chambers are small and numerous, and the septa branch, forming additional chambers (Fig. 65).   The septa are highly vascular and clothed with a thin epithelium except along their inner edges where ciliate and mucous cells are abundant covering bundles of smooth muscle.   In many aquatic urodeles which practice extensive cutaneous and buccopharyngeal respiration the lungs are poorly vascularized and alveoli are not formed.   This is true of some newts and especially the perennibranchs Proteus and Necturus. Simplicity of lung structure may be either a larval feature or a result of secondary degeneration in the Amphibia; it is not a primitivism.

The same holds true for the fishes which seem to have evolved poorly vascularized swim bladders out of lungs. As in newts, these are used as hydrostatic organs but in most teleosts are further modified in that only one sac develops, and this may sprout from the dorsal instead of the ventral side of the digestive tract. The further modification of the swim bladder in teleosts

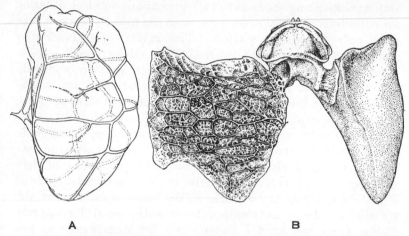

A   B

Fig. 65.—Comparison of the lungs of two Salientia. *Ascaphus truei* (*A*), living in cold mountain streams, relies chiefly on cutaneous respiration, and its lungs are greatly reduced both in size and in vascularity. *Bufo marinus* (*B*), being terrestrial and having a thick epidermis, has need of large, well-vascularized lungs. In *A* only the left lung is shown and this is greatly enlarged. In *B* the right lung is open to show the alveolar structure of its inner surface (*after Marcus*).

is very extensive and has no parallel in Amphibia, excepting in the case of its reduction and loss.

Salamanders are the only vertebrates above the fish which have succeeded in dispensing with their lungs. All plethodontids lack lungs, and various ambystomids and salamandrids exhibit reductions which lead to rudiments only 5 mm. long in Rhyacotriton and 2 mm. in Salamandrina. All Amphibia practice cutaneous respiration and most of them buccopharyngeal respiration in either the air or water. Still, the lungs have not merely dwindled away because other respiratory systems were functioning. The lungs when well developed act as hydrostatic organs, and hence no salamanders inhabiti monguntain brooks, where there would be frequent need of hiding under rocks to avoid the current, have the lungs so extensive as typical pond species. A parallel reduction occurs in the swim bladders of mountain-brook fish. The water of mountain brooks being cool, well-oxygenated, and running gives maximum possibilities for cutaneous respiration. Nevertheless, in all Amphibia which undergo a reduction of the lungs, the capillaries either penetrate into the epidermis to facilitate cutaneous respiration or the epidermis remains thin over the superficial skin capillaries (Noble, 1925). The cool, wet crannies along the banks of streams afford an ideal situation for cutaneous respiration on land, since gas interchange can take place only if the skin is moist. This habitat was invaded by plethodontids which had evolved from stream-dwelling salamandrids. The ancestral plethodontids had apparently already lost their lungs, as modern species show at most the barest indication of a lung vestige during development (Mekeel, 1926). Other salamanders, by increasing the efficiency of cutaneous respiration in the same way as stream salamanders, were able to survive with reduced lungs in suitable situations without ever having gone through a typical stream life in the course of their phylogeny. This is highly probable in the case of Salamandrina and the European Alpine Salamander, *Salamandra atra*. Cold, by slowing down metabolism, reduces the need for oxygen. Hence, frogs can survive under water for long periods at low temperatures but will quickly die if the temperature is raised. Cold seems to have been an important factor in permitting lung reduction in Ascaphus (Fig. 65*A*), since other stream-dwelling frogs in warmer waters have larger lungs. There are thus various factors which have made possible the reduction and loss of lungs in Amphibia (Noble, 1929). In the fishes, also, the hydrostatic organ was lost under a variety of conditions.

Larynx.—The lungs of Amphibia arise from a median evagination from the ventral wall of the pharynx. This becomes the laryngeal sac which opens by the glottis into the pharynx. It is very short in most Salientia, but in the Pipidae, where the lungs are important hydrostatic organs, the sac is carried posteriorly to form a trachea and this again divides into two tubes, the bronchi, which finally lead to the lungs. Pipa is further remarkable in showing a very complete infiltration of the lungs by cartilage. This strengthens the septa and other supporting structures and even forms projections extending into the lumen

(Marcus, 1927). Cranially the cartilages tend to form rings or plates which support the bronchial tubes and trachea. The caecilians, also, exhibit an infiltration of the lungs by cartilage (Marcus, 1927), which may, therefore, be a primitive feature of the Amphibia. The urodeles, in correlation with their elongate body form, usually possess a distinct trachea. This is longest in Amphiuma and Siren, which possess tracheal cartilages homologous with those of caecilians. The cartilages which support the larynx have a different origin from those of the lungs and bronchus and are always present whether or not there is

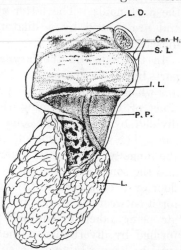

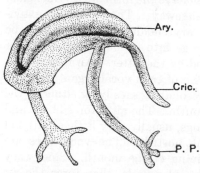

Fig. 66.—Laryngeal cartilages of a Spade-foot Toad, *Scaphiopus holbrookii*, viewed from the right side. *Ary.*, arytenoid; *Cric.*, cricoid; *P.P.*, pulmonary process.

Fig. 67.—Vocal cords of male Bullfrog, *Rana catesbeiana;* sagittal section of the larynx viewed from within. *Car. H.*, cartilaginous body of hyoid; *I.L.*, inferior vocal ligament; *L.*, left lung; *L.O.*, laryngeal orifice; *P.P.*, pulmonary process of cricoid; *S.L.*, superior vocal ligament.

any cartilage in the pulmonary structures. As discussed above, the laryngeal cartilages arise from the branchial arches, the sixth and seventh, *i.e.*, the eighth and ninth visceral, being the arches in caecilians and apparently also in other Amphibia, taking part in their formation. The last arch, which is much the larger, forms a cartilaginous bar on each side of the larynx. This may fuse in caecilians above the larynx with its mate of the opposite side. In most urodeles and all frogs the cartilage of each side splits into an anterior arytenoid and a posterior cricoid cartilage. In the Salientia the arytenoids usually form a pair of spoon-shaped cartilages lying in a narrow ring, the cricoids, which may or may not be fused (Fig. 66). These lie between the thyroid processes of the hyoid and usually send a pair of hook-shaped processes around the bases of the lungs (Fig. 67). In some frogs the tips of the hooks may be fused in the midline tending to obscure further the original bilateral origin of the laryngeal cartilages. The more anterior pair of branchial bars which take part in the formation of the skeleton of the larynx have been shown by Marcus (1922) to form merely a pair of processes on the arytenoids. The latter guard the entrance to the trachea and are moved by a dilator and usually several constrictor muscles.

In the Salientia the laryngeal chamber is divided into two parts by the vocal organs. These have the form of two thickened lips which extend across the passageway. They represent extensions of the tissue lining the arytenoids. Each lip may be divided by a groove in some frogs into an outer and an inner rim. The vocal cords are formed by the latter. Air forced from the lungs sets the elastic inner rim of each vocal organ vibrating and the sound is reinforced by resonating sacs lying either in the floor or at each corner of the mouth. The air is forced back and forth between vocal sacs and lungs, usually very little additional air being taken in through the nostrils. The vocal sacs are formed by diverticula of the lining of the mouth. Since they usually lie just above the subhyoid muscle, they force the air back into the lungs chiefly by the action of this muscle. In many species the diverticula fuse in the midline to form a median throat sac capable of great distention. It is because the vocal mechanism represents a closed system that frogs can call when under water. The larynx is usually very much larger in the male than the female, and the latter lacks vocal pouches. As there is no true larynx at all in fishes, the Amphibia have made a considerable advance not only in the development of this structure with its cartilages but also in producing a trachea and bronchus including their cartilaginous skeleton.

Ways of Respiration.—The Amphibia possess several respiratory mechanisms. These, however, are not available to all species, and, further, a complication occurs in that the mechanisms of the larva are usually replaced by others during adult life. The ontogenetic sequence of mechanisms shows little relation to the phylogenetic sequence, except in the case of the perennibranchs which have retained or elaborated the larval organization. In the larvae of the more primitive salamanders such as the newt, movements of the branchial apparatus bring water in through the nostrils and out through the gill clefts, but in some species cilia play an important part in maintaining this respiratory current. The external gills are equipped with muscles which give them independent though limited motion. The lower jaw also functions as a force pump driving water from the partly open mouth out through the clefts or nares. The same mechanism is found in tadpoles except that the gills are covered by an operculum and are devoid of muscles. Many tadpoles and urodele larvae increase the efficiency of this apparatus by developing valves about the internal nares; these prevent a backflow of water through the nasal chamber. Since the buccal cavity is highly vascular in larval Amphibia, some gaseous exchange takes place through the walls. Most larvae enjoy not only branchial but also some buccopharyngeal and cutaneous respiration in the water. As the larvae develop they rise to the surface and snap for air. The air bubbles function in the gaseous exchange within the buccal cavity. In many salamanders and frogs the lungs become functional during larval life and the air bubble snatched from the surface is pressed back through the glottis into the lungs. Some tadpoles, however, such as those of Bufo may fail to develop functional lungs until after metamorphosis has occurred. Some urodele larvae respond quickly to lack of oxygen by increased respiratory movements (Babak, 1921) and hence must have well-developed nervous centers of respiratory control, analogous, if not homologous, to those of higher vertebrates. There is considerable variation in the respiratory mechanisms of the various species of Amphibia, but primitively the larvae would seem to practice buccopharyngeal, pulmonary, and cutaneous respiration.

Urodeles and Salientia lose their gills on metamorphosis but the other respiratory mechanisms of the larvae are transmitted to the adult and further elaborated. In the air the mouth is held tightly closed. The lips are formed to fit firmly together and in some species a muscle is developed in the upper lip assuring by its tension a close union of the jaws (Bruner, 1902). Air is sucked in and forced out of the nares by a rhythmical lowering of the floor of the mouth. Smooth muscles develop about the external nares of the metamorphosed urodele better to control the respiratory currents. There are two dilators and a constrictor. Bruner (1896) has shown that the latter contracts whenever the nostrils are moistened. In the water the nares are closed but most urodeles in this situation resume their larval habits of buccopharyngeal respiration and water is taken in and expelled from the mouth.

Apparently the smooth muscle equipment of the external nares was found inadequate for the needs of the Salientia, and they seized upon a unique way of utilizing the quick-moving striated jaw and throat muscles for effecting a closing of the nares. A tubercle was formed on the anterior angle of the lower jaw and this, supported by the small mento-Meckelian bones underlying it, was made available as a wedge. When, either by a contraction of the submental muscle or by a slight forward movement of the lower jaw, the tubercle is carried upward, it pushes apart the two premaxillary bones and this in turn effects a closing of the nostrils by carrying mesially the prenasal superior process of the nasal cartilage (Gaupp, 1896). Though rudimentary smooth muscles of the urodele nares are present in Salientia, they apparently play no part in the occlusion of the nostril (Bruner, 1902), except in such forms as Xenopus having fused premaxillaries.

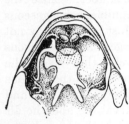

FIG. 68.—A secondary mechanism for closing the nasal chamber of frogs. Roof of the mouth of *Rana esculenta* on which is schematically projected the hyoid and the anterior end of the omosternum. A process of the hyoid fits into the internal nares when the hyoid is raised. (*After Willem.*)

In both urodeles and Salientia the rhythmical throat movements of buccopharyngeal respiration are interrupted by a deeper lowering of the throat. At the height of this movement the nares are closed, the glottis opened, and the air streams from the lungs into the buccal cavity. Immediately the throat muscles are vigorously contracted and the mixed air is forced back into the lungs through the open glottis. After one or more of these expiratory and inspiratory movements the glottis is closed again, the nares opened, and the shallower movements of buccopharyngeal ventilation continue. There is some specific variation in the exact moment that the nares are closed. If they are retained open too long, as in some aquatic salamanders, a secondary snapping of air is necessary to provide enough air in the buccopharyngeal chamber to fill the lungs properly. The efficiency of this mechanism is further increased in some Salientia such as Pelobates by using the anterior processes of the hyoids as plugs (Fig. 68) for the internal nares during the period that the lungs are being emptied and filled (Willem, 1924). Some of these differences in the respiratory mechanisms of adult Amphibia would seem to be correlated with habitat differences. Newts rising to the surface can probably fill their throats more quickly through the mouth than through the nostrils. Pelobates and other burrowing Salientia are continually subjecting their muscles to strains which would make an extra guard on the respiratory outlets an advantage.

Lunglessness.—The modification of the adult mechanism reaches its extreme in those urodeles which have reduced or entirely lost their lungs. The conditions under which these are lost have been discussed above, and it was noted that in these forms the efficiency of cutaneous respiration was increased either by the penetration of capillaries into the epidermis or the thinning of the epidermis over the superficial capillaries. The efficiency of buccopharyngeal respiration is increased not only by a vascularization of the epithelium but also by an increase in the rate of the throat movements of buccopharyngeal respiration. These movements in such lungless salamanders as *Aneides lugubris* may reach the remarkable rate of 120 to 180 vibrations a minute (Ritter and Miller, 1899). Some lungless salamanders such as *Pseudotriton ruber* are primarily aquatic, and one might imagine that buccopharyngeal respiration in the water would be as active as on land. It is surprising to find that this is not the case and that these species take no water into their mouths when submerged (Noble, 1925). This is the more unexpected in that Salamandrina, which has greatly reduced lungs and is primarily terrestrial, is able to practice aquatic buccopharyngeal respiration (Bruner, 1896).

The buccopharyngeal respiration of lungless salamanders is ample proof that this is a distinct mode of respiration taken over from larval life and not primarily a means of facilitating the flow of blood in the lungs, as Keith (1904) maintains. The pulmonary circulation of Amphibia is retarded by the pulmonary pressure which, thanks to the character of the respiratory apparatus, is always greater than that of the atmosphere. Nevertheless, this pressure is not detrimental to pulmonary circulation.

Comparison with Other Vertebrates.—The respiratory mechanisms of the larval Amphibia have considerable structural and functional resemblance to those of fish, but those of the adult show little approach to the conditions in other tetrapods. The reason is to be found in the reduction or loss of the ribs in modern Amphibia. The respiratory mechanism of reptiles is a suction apparatus with the ribs pulling the air into the lungs where the pressure is less than that of the atmosphere and then forcing it out again. Some fossil Amphibia, having longer ribs than modern species, may have had the beginnings of this mechanism.

Marcus (1923) sees in the respiration of caecilians a mechanism intermediate between that of fish and reptiles. This may represent the primitive inheritance of Amphibia. The ribs do not function in either inspiration or expiration of caecilians, but the laryngeal cartilages which are serially homologous to branchial arches are forced back and pressed together when air is taken into the glottis in much the same way that branchial arches of the fish are retracted during a swallowing movement. In frogs and urodeles there may be also some movement of the larynx in respiration but in the position of rest the larynx is forward in caecilians and reptiles while it is backwardly situated in frogs. The caecilians take air into the buccal cavity as in other Amphibia. In these forms, however, inspiration includes not only a lifting of the floor of the mouth but also a backward movement of the closed glottis. The small mouths of caecilians may be ample justification for their not elaborating the buccal movements found in other forms. The laryngeal movements, however, seem a primitive feature which was handed on with further modification to reptiles.

In both fish and amphibians the efficiency of cutaneous respiration is frequently increased by structural changes in the integument. In any one individual there is a considerable variation in the respiratory quotient at different times of the year. Dolk and Postma (1927), in extending the earlier work of Krogh (1910), have shown that there is an almost constant intake of oxygen through the skin of frogs throughout the year, a slight rise occurring only during the spawning season. Further, the skin releases more carbon dioxide than the lungs and shows considerable variation, with the greatest drop occurring in winter. The oxygen absorption through the lungs varies with the season, reaching a peak during the breeding period. Krogh (1904, 1910) suggested that the rate of oxygen consumption might be dependent on the rate of blood flow through the lungs, which in turn would be regulated by the vasomotor system. Bastert (1929) has shown that there exists a vasomotor control over the pulmonary vascular supply, which, between certain limits, rations out the oxygen from the lungs and sends a constant supply of oxygen to the tissues. This mechanism functions only when the central nervous system is intact. When the central nervous system is destroyed, the oxygen supply to the tissues varies with the oxygen pressure and follows the ordinary laws of gas diffusion. The integument is able to make no such change in oxygen consumption even though the increased metabolism of the breeding season makes an increased demand for oxygen at this time. Where increased efficiency of cutaneous respiration is imperative, for example in species which have reduced their lungs, a change in the structure of the integument occurs to make this increase possible. Apparently no regulatory variations are possible here as in the lungs.

Respiratory Responses.—In salamanders with reduced lungs, the buccopharyngeal as well as the cutaneous respiration increases in importance. Lapicque and Petetin (1910) found that Euproctus immersed in vaseline succumbed in 24 hours, while it remained normal with its buccal cavity obstructed. Hence, in this species with reduced lungs, cutaneous respiration is more important than buccopharyngeal. Probably less aquatic species will show more dependence on buccopharyngeal respiration, for in these animals the rate of the throat movements increases. The buccopharyngeal movements of frogs are far more regular than their pulmonary movements, which may be suspended entirely as during hibernation. A change in the rate of the throat movements has frequently been used as an indication that the frog is aware of certain sensory stimulations. Sudden illumination, moving images, mechanical vibrations, spontaneous movements of the body, temperature change, and various other factors will induce a change in the rate of the buccopharyngeal respiration of the frog. Cole and Allison (1929) have shown that higher rates due to an increase in the illumination or to moving images gradually decrease to the original rate, indicating an adaptation to the new conditions. Since blinded frogs do not show such a response, the eyes, and possibly the photochemical changes in the eyes, have some relation to these changes.

Popow and Wagner (1928) studied the effect of nutritive fluids on the pharyngeal movements of the isolated head of the frog. Increasing the carbon dioxide content of the fluid induced a marked increase in the respiratory movements. Apparently the carbon dioxide, by making the blood more acid, increased the rate of respiration, as it is assumed to do in the intact animal. The nervous centers controlling the respiration probably involve several parts of the brain (Chap. XV). Stewart (1923) found that removing the cerebral hemispheres of Necturus induced an increased rate of gill movement. Apparently the hemispheres inhibit the normal gill movements. Impulses from the medulla by way of the vagus nerves keep the lungs of Cryptobranchus, and presumably of other salamanders also, in a state of relaxation. A destruction of the nerve fibers induces a hypertonic state of the lungs (Luckhardt and Carlson, 1921). The section of the vagus in reptiles seems to have the opposite effect, but in these animals the vagus control has not been adequately investigated. Apparently these sharply contrasted methods of nervous control of the lungs in reptiles and modern Amphibia are correlated with their different methods of respiration.

References

BABÀK, E., 1921: Die Mechanik und Innervation der Atmung, Winterstein's "Handb. vergl. Physiol." Pt. 2, 706–810.

BARRELL, J., 1916: Influence of Silurian and Devonian climates on the rise of air-breathing vertebrates, Bull. Geol. Soc. Amer., XXVII, 387–436.

BASTERT, C., 1929: Über die Regulierung des Sauerstoffverbrauches aus der Lunge der Frösche im Hinblick auf ihr Tauchvermögen, Zeitschr. vergl. Physiol., IX, 212–218.

BRUNER, H. L., 1896: Ein neuer Muskelapparat zum Schliessen und Öffnen der Nasenlöcher bei den Salamandriden, Arch. Anat. Physiol., Anat. Abt., 1896.   395–412, 1 pl.

―――, 1902: The smooth facial muscles of Anura and Salamandrina, a contribution to the anatomy and physiology of the respiratory mechanism of the amphibians, Morph. Jahrb. XXIX, 317–359, 2 pl.

COLE, W. H., and J. B. ALLISON, 1929: The pharyngeal breathing rate of the frog as related to temperature and other factors, Jour. Exp. Zool., LIII, 411–420.

DOLK, H. E., and N. POSTMA, 1927: Über die Haut- und die Lungenatmung von Rana temporaria, Zeitschr. vergl. Physiol. V, 417–444.

EDGEWORTH, F. H., 1920: On the development of the hypobranchial and laryngeal muscles in Amphibia, Jour. Anat., LIV, 125–162, 15 pls.

EKMAN, G., 1913: Experimentelle Untersuchungen über die Entwicklung der Kiemenregion (Kiemenfäden und Kiemenspalten) einiger anuren Amphibien, Morph. Jahrb., XLVII, 419–452.

FUHRMANN, O., 1914: Le genre Typhlonectes, *Neuchâtel Mem. Soc. Sci. Nat.*, V, 112–138.

GAUPP, E., 1896: Zur Lehre von dem Athmungsmechanismus beim Frosch, *Arch. Anat. Physiol., Anat. Abt.*, 1896, 239–268.

GREIL, A., 1906: Über die Homologie der Anamnierkiemen. *Anat. Anz.*, XXVIII, 256–272.

HARRISON, ROSS G., 1921: Experiments on the development of the gills in the amphibian embryo, *Biol. Bull.* XLI, 156–170.

JACOBSHAGEN, E., 1921: Die Homologie der Wirbeltierkiemen, *Jena. Zeitschr.*, LVII, 87–142, 2 pls.

KEITH, A., 1904: Respiration in Frogs, *Nature*, LXIX, 511–512.

KROGH, A., 1904: On the cutaneous and pulmonary respiration of the frog, *Skand. Arch. Physiol.*, XV, 328.

———, 1910: On the mechanism of the gas exchange in the lungs, *Skand. Arch. Physiol.*, XXIII, 248.

LAPICQUE, L., et J. PETETIN, 1910: Sur la respiration d'un batracien urodèle sans poumons, Euproctus montanus, *Compt. rend. Soc. Biol.*, LXIX, 84–86.

LUCKHARDT, A. B., and A. J. CARLSON, 1921: Studies on the visceral sensory nervous system; 6. Lung automatism and lung reflexes in Cryptobranchus with further notes on the physiology of the lung of Necturus, *Amer. Jour. Physiol.*, LV, 212–222.

MACELA, T., and A. SELIŠKAR, 1925: The influence of temperature on the equilibrium between oxygen and haemoglobin of various forms of life, *Jour. Physiol.*, LX, 428–442.

MARCUS, H., 1908: Beiträge zur Kenntnis der Gymnophionen; I. Über das Schlundspaltengebiet, *Arch. Mikr. Anat.*, LXXI, 695–744, 4 pls.

———, 1922: Der Kehlkopf bei Hypogeophis, *Anat. Anz. Ergheft.*, LV, 188–202.

———, 1923: Beiträge zur Kenntnis der Gymnophionen; VI. Über den Übergang von der Wasser- zur Luftatmung mit besonderer Berücksichtigung des Atemmechanismus von Hypogeophis, *Zeitschr. Anat. Entw.*, LXIX, 328–343.

———, 1927: Lungenstudien, *Morph. Jahrb.*, LVIII, 100–121.

MEKEEL, A. GRACE, 1926: A pulmonary vestige in the lungless salamanders, *Anat. Rec.*, XXXIV, 141.

NIKITIN, B., 1925: Some particularities in the development of the vascular system of Xenopus, *Bull. Soc. Natur. Moscow, Sec. Biol.*, N. S. XXXIV, 305–308.

NOBLE, G. K., 1925: The integumentary, pulmonary and cardiac modifications correlated with increased cutaneous respiration in the Amphibia; A solution of the "hairy frog" problem, *Jour. Morph. Physiol.*, XL, 341–416.

———, 1929: The adaptive modifications of the arboreal tadpoles of Hoplophryne and the torrent tadpoles of Staurois, *Bull. Amer. Mus. Nat. Hist.*, LVIII, Art. VII, 291–334.

POPOW, N. A., and L. B. WAGNER, 1928: Zur Frage nach dem Einfluss der Kohlensäure auf das Atmungszentrum des Frosches, *Zeitschr. vergl. Physiol.*, VIII, 89–98.

RITTER, WILLIAM E., and LOYE MILLER, 1899: A contribution to the life history of Autodax lugubris Hallow., a Californian salamander, *Amer. Naturalist*, XXXIII, 691–704.

STEWART, G. N., 1923: The gill movements in one of the perennibranchiate urodela (Necturus maculatus) and their relation to the central nervous system, *Amer. Jour. Physiol.*, LXVI, 288–296.

WASTL, H., and A. SELIŠKAR, 1925: Observations on the combination of CO_2 in the blood of the bullfrog (Rana catesbiana), *Jour. Physiol.*, LX, 264–268.

WILLEM, L., 1924: Recherches sur la respiration aérienne des amphibiens. *Bull. Acad. Roy. Belgique. Cl. Sci.*, X, 31–47.

CHAPTER VIII

THE CIRCULATORY SYSTEM

Food absorbed by the digestive system is carried by the fluids of either the blood or lymph channels to all parts of the body. Blood owes its color to the protein pigment haemoglobin which is present in the red blood cells. Haemoglobin possesses the property of absorbing oxygen where it is plentiful and releasing it again in regions poor in this commodity. The blood, therefore, although having important nutritive functions, is the chief medium for the transportation of oxygen throughout the body. Lymph differs from blood in lacking the red blood corpuscles and specializes in feeding and cleansing the tissues of the body. Blood and lymph also transport the phagocytic cells, which destroy infectious bacteria and carry away the fragments of cell decomposition to the organs where they are eliminated. In brief, the circulatory system carries the materials necessary for metabolism to the cells of the body and transports the waste products from them to the excretory organs. It also carries the hormones, or chemical "messengers," from the endocrine organs to the body tissues and serves to equilibrate the water content, thus preventing the rapid drying of exposed parts.

Blood Corpuscles.—The fluid portion of the blood is the plasma. It contains a high percentage of water, various proteins, salts, sugars, and fats as well as oxygen and the products of metabolism. The cellular elements of the circulating blood include the erythrocytes or red cells, the thrombocytes or spindle cells, the leucocytes or white cells. The latter includes the lymphocytes, the monocytes, and three categories of granulocytes. Of special interest in Amphibia are the plasmocytes resulting from the fragmentation of the red blood cells and hence not considered an additional type. The plasma of Amphibia, on account of the low body temperature, is a far more efficient carrier of oxygen than that of mammals (Barcroft, 1924), since more oxygen goes into solution at lower temperatures. Nevertheless, most of the oxygen needed by the tissues is brought to them by the erythrocytes. The efficiency of the haemoglobin as a carrier of oxygen varies with the species due to chemical differences in their haemoglobin (Chap. VII).

The red blood cell of Amphibia is an elliptical disc sometimes bulging in the center where the oval nucleus occurs (Fig. 69*A*). It varies in size from approximately 70 microns for the greatest diameter in Amphiuma to 18 microns in Bombina (Ponder, 1924). Amphiuma may claim the distinction of having the largest erythrocytes of any animal. Those of some other perennibranchs are only 7 or 10 microns smaller. This difference between the size of the erythrocytes of perennibranchs and those of other

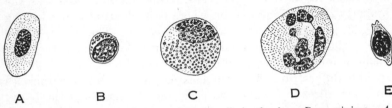

A   B   C   D   E

FIG. 69.—The principal types of blood cells in the frog, *Rana pipiens*. *A.* Normal erythrocyte. *B.* Small lymphocyte. *C.* Eosinophilic leucocyte. *D.* Polymorphonuclear leucocyte. *E.* Thrombocyte. *(After Jordan.)*

Amphibia extends to all the cells of their bodies and, from observations of Smith (1925), would seem to be closely correlated with the lower metabolic rate of these forms. The number of erythrocytes varies from nearly 700,000 per cubic millimeter in *Hyla arborea* (Heesen, 1924) to 56,633 in Necturus and 36,000 in Proteus (Ponder, 1924). In any species the number is subject to considerable variation, it being greatest just before spawning and lowest just after sexual activity. Aquatic forms tend to have a lower count than terrestrial forms (Heesen, 1924). This occurs apparently because the blood of aquatic forms is more subject to dilution. Food, temperature, and disease affect the number, and there is also a pronounced sexual difference in some species at least, the male having the greater number of erythrocytes. In case of the frog, the life of any one erythrocyte is probably not over 100 days (Jordan and Speidel, 1925). Nevertheless, this is considerably longer than in higher forms. In man the average life of an erythrocyte is 10 days. The red blood cells are removed from the blood stream by the liver and spleen, especially by the Kupffer cells in the former organ. These cells protrude into the blood vessels and capture passing erythrocytes before they disintegrate.

In higher vertebrates there is found both an increase in number of erythrocytes over that of Amphibia and a diminution in their size. There is also an increase in the amount of blood as compared with the living weight (Frase, 1930). The smaller the red blood cell the greater is the surface of exposure in any quantity of blood. The nucleus, which has nothing to do with the absorption of oxygen, is finally eliminated in the mammals, and the Amphibia are noteworthy in showing at various stages a similar progressive change. In terrestrial Salientia and Caudata

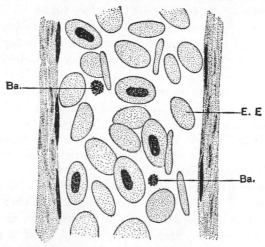

Fig. 70.—Optical section of a blood vessel of Batrachoseps showing enucleated erythrocytes and basophilic plastids. *Ba.*, basophilic plastids; *E.E.*, enucleated erythrocytes. (*After Emmel.*)

as well as in some aquatic forms, there is a fragmentation or enucleation of some of the red blood cells. In *Rana temporaria* this fragmentation has the appearance of the splitting off of small portions of the cytoplasm (Beyer, 1921). In Bufo the fragmented portions are larger, while in Bombina they may be larger than the nucleated portion. In some urodeles there is so little cytoplasm remaining with the nucleus that the latter has the appearance of being extruded from the cells as in the development of erythrocytes in the mammalian embryo. The fragmentation reaches its extreme in Batrachoseps (Fig. 70) where more than 90 per cent of the red blood cells are enucleated

(Emmel, 1924).   Further, all stages of enucleation may be found in the circulating blood.   This change is not correlated merely with terrestrialism.   *Aneides lugubris* and *Plethodon cinereus* have only 2.3 per cent of the blood so altered.   The difference occurs in both the adults and the embryos, and Emmel has suggested that the great increase of enucleated red blood cells in Batrachoseps has been conditioned by the abbreviation of the gills of the embryo and the reduced vascularity of the integument of the adult.   It may well be, however, that the change in the respiratory efficiency of the blood of Batrachoseps preceded the alteration of gill form, for an hypertrophy of the gills may be readily effected during the ontogeny of many urodeles by merely decreasing the available oxygen (Drastich, 1925).

The thrombocytes or spindle cells resemble erythrocytes but are smaller and have pointed ends, a granular endoplasm, and clear ectoplasm (Fig. 69E).   They are very unstable and when brought in contact with foreign substances break down, releasing a substance which acts on certain plasma proteins in the presence of blood calcium to form an insoluble clot or coagulation.   In this process the insoluble fibrin is formed from the protein fibrinogen and blood corpuscles become entangled in the resulting gel to form the clot.   In many lungless salamanders and especially in Batrachoseps, the thrombocytes are frequently fragmented and resemble the blood platelets of mammals both structurally and functionally (Emmel, 1925).   There are also present in Batrachoseps basophilic plasmocytes arising from basophilic leucocytes.   Spindle cells do not occur in mammals, and the blood platelets which are so important in preventing excessive bleeding arise from a different type of mother cell.

Phagocytosis.—The lymphocytes, monocytes, and granulocytes are less abundant in the blood than the erythrocytes and thrombocytes.   Further, they vary much more in size and form.   The lymphocytes are nucleated blood cells with a large nucleus and a comparatively small amount of non-granular cytoplasm.   The small lymphocytes are often found associated with rapidly growing tissues and it has been suggested that they may have growth stimulating properties (Jordan and Speidel, 1923).   The large lymphocytes specialized for phagocytosis are called "monocytes."   The so-called "macrophages," cells which wander by amoeboid movement through the tissues, devouring bacteria, cell débris, or other injurious material, are merely enlarged monocytes in action outside the blood stream. By injecting cream into the living tadpole's tail, Clark and Clark (1928) witnessed the migration of monocytes through capillary walls to phagocytose the fat globules. They get out of the capillaries by squeezing their way between the epithelial cells of the capillary wall. The injection of bacteria causes an increase in the monocytes in the blood, and Pentimalli (1909) concluded that the amphibian normally responds to bacterial infection by increasing the production of monocytes.

Some of the granulocytes also have phagocytic functions. The neutrophiles, which have a finely granular cytoplasm unlike the other leucocytes, induce the breakdown of worn tissue, while the macrophages carry away the débris. The eosinophiles (Fig. 69C), which may be identified by their large eosin-staining granules, are found commonly along the digestive tract and may have functions similar to the neutrophiles. As the granulocytes mature, their nuclei assume very irregular forms and may even divide into several parts. Granulocytes, like the monocytes, are not confined to the blood vessels but may migrate into any of the tissues of the body or may even make their way carrying their phagocytosed material to the outside of the body by wandering out on mucous and epidermal surfaces (Claypole, 1893). Jordan and Speidel (1923a) suggest that the eosinophiles which pass through the intestinal epithelium and disintegrate among the fecal contents of the tract may have an immunizing function against the intestinal bacteria. Most leucocytes which escape from the blood vessels are returned to them again by way of lymphatic vessels.

Origin of Blood Corpuscles.—The blood corpuscles all arise from a single type of cell indistinguishable from the lymphocyte of the circulating blood but located for the most part in the kidney of the tadpoles (Jordan and Speidel, 1923a) and in the spleen of adult frogs such as *Rana pipiens*. Only for a short period in the spring, when the metabolic rate is high, does the bone marrow form the locus for blood histogenesis as in the case of mammals. In the more terrestrial *Rana temporaria*, however, with its higher metabolism, the bone marrow has the same function found in mammals (Maximow, 1910). Jordan and Speidel (1923) suggest that the shift of the primary center of blood cell formation from the kidney in fish to the bone marrow in mammals is correlated with an increase in the metabolic rate during phylogeny.   The Amphibia are of interest in showing during ontogeny the whole range of possible loci.   Some species may have different areas for red blood cell and for granulocyte genesis.   Thus, Jordan and Speidel (1924) found that in the newt the spleen was the sole organ for erythrocyte and thrombocyte formation, while the granulocytes were generated in outer portions of the liver.   Since the mother cell is the same in both sites, it would seem that an environmental factor, possibly different degrees of vascularization, determined the final form assumed by the blood cell.

There are various masses of lymphoidal tissue in the bodies of Amphibia.   The more conspicuous are located anterior to the clavicles of frogs or between skin and muscle near the girdles of burrowing species.   During the spring these produce both lymphocytes and leucocytes but appear to store fat at other seasons (von Braunmühl, 1926).   Accumulations of lymphocytes in the connective tissue and overlying epithelium of the lingual region occur in both frogs and urodeles.   These may be described as tonsils (Kingsbury, 1912; Myers, 1928).   In the urodeles they occur in front of the glottis, near the articulation of the jaws and under the tongue.   In the Salientia they are of more variable occurrence, the sublingual tonsil being the most constant. They usually do not appear until metamorphosis, although in Bufo they may develop before metamorphosis is complete.   The Amphibia are the lowest group of vertebrates in which tonsils occur, the lymphocyte accumulations in the fish being too diffuse to be called tonsils.   In these loci lymphocytes and leucocytes increase by fission.   The amphibian tonsils are, thus, defense stations from which hosts of phagocytosing cells may be mobolized for an attack against bacteria or protozoan invaders of mouth and lungs.   Red blood cells of Amphibia are also able to undergo multiplication in the blood stream by mitosis (Dawson, 1928).

Blood Vessels.—The blood vessels as well as the first blood cells originate from mesoderm.   In large-yolked species such as Desmognathus, discontinuous thickenings of mesoderm, the blood islands, join to form the vessels (Hilton 1913).   In smaller-yolked forms as Ambystoma, or even in some large-yolked forms as Megalobatrachus, the area may be more continuous and ventral on the yolk.   Goss (1928) found that cutting away the blood island from the ventral surface of Ambystoma embryos did not prevent the development of the blood vessels but that these grew without any red blood cells. Federici (1926) obtained similar results on removing the median ventral blood island of frog tadpoles. Hence the blood vessels arise from a different primordium than the erythrocytes. The early embryonic vessels are formed independently of the molding influence of flowing blood, but very soon in development the mechanical effect of the circulating fluid becomes evident. Clark (1918) found that destroying the hearts of tadpoles prevented a development of the vessels beyond an embryonic stage. It would seem that the full elaboration of the blood vessels may be a functional matter dependent chiefly on the blood pressure within and the available space without the vessels. In Ambystoma the early differentiation of brain and pronephros seems to stimulate the development of the vascular system in these regions at this stage, the chief function of the vessels being the elimination of injurious products of metabolism (Moore, 1915). Nevertheless, the larger vessels continue to develop according to a definite plan whatever be the mechanical factors regulating this scheme.

The larger blood vessels of the urodele embryo follow closely the primitive vertebrate plan. There is a subintestinal vessel which may be divided anteriorly by the yolk into two omphalo-mesenterics. A cardinal vein appears on each side in the body wall associated with each pronephros and grows posteriorly to send branches to the caudal or posterior extension of the subintestinal vessel (Grodzinski, 1924). At its anterior end the subintestinal sends a series of vessels around the gut between the gill slits. These join on each side and after uniting to form a single vessel are continued posteriorly as the dorsal aorta. The latter gives off intersegmental branches to the body wall and others supply the gut. The heart, which develops very early in the subintestinal vessel, pumps the blood through the aortic arches (the vessels between the gill slits) and back along the dorsal aorta to supply body wall and gut. The circuit is completed along the gut by way of the subintestinal vessel and along the body wall by the postcardinals. The cardinals extend across the body cavity to form the *ducti Cuvierii* entering the heart on each side. The subintestinal is further modified by the growth of the liver which develops as a glandular outgrowth across the path of the vessel.

The veins which arise out of this ground plan of embryonic vessels are the conduits leading blood to the heart. They are equipped with valves which prevent the backflow of the blood. The arrangement in urodeles is very similar to that of lung fishes, and here functional covergence may have produced the structural resemblance. The postcardinals are present in the larvae of urodeles and frogs but are usually replaced in the adult by the *vena cava posterior*, a new formation first found in dipnoans and lying, unlike the subintestinal vessel, dorsal to the gut. In the adult Ascaphus and Bombina, as well as in some adult urodeles, both postcardinals and the posterior *vena cava* occur together. The latter vessel functions alone in dipnoans, which are thus more advanced in this regard than many Amphibia. The posterior portions of the postcardinals are modified to form a renal portal system. In Amphibia this system collects blood from the tail and limbs and sends it to a capillary plexus in the kidneys. Some of the blood from the hind limbs is returned to the heart by way of the abdominal veins which are paired vessels associated with the cardinals in the body wall of sharks, and which represent the primitive route for returning blood from the hind limbs to the heart. In Amphibia the abdominal vessels are fused to form a single conspicuous vessel running along the ventral surface of the abdominal cavity and emptying, not into the cardinal veins as in fish, but into the hepatic portal vein. Blood from the legs must pass, therefore, through either the renal or the hepatic strainer; it cannot pass directly to the heart without sifting through a capillary net. The anterior cardinals are less modified in Amphibia. They receive blood from the internal and external jugulars as in fish. Dipnoans, with their well-developed lungs, have anticipated the Amphibia in developing a pulmonary vein returning blood directly to the heart, but Amphibia have specialized for respiration in another direction as well. They have developed a pair of large veins under the skin of the body to assist in cutaneous respiration.

The blood vessels leading away from the heart are the arteries. They differ from most veins in having muscular walls, which are present, however, in the largest veins. A short distance from the heart the main vessel, the anterior part of the subintestinal, divides and sends paired branches to the dorsal side of the gut by the only route available, namely, by the tissue between the gill clefts or pouches. The resulting aortic arches may be four in Amphibia, although two more anterior to these are indicated in the embryo. In many adult urodeles and all Salientia the fifth of these six arches dwindles away. In the Salientia the third and sixth arches lose their connection with the dorsal aorta, only the fourth remaining as the so-called "systemic arch." In the caecilians two aortic arches occur. The arteries leading cranially from the third arch are the external and internal carotids. The sixth arch sends a pulmonary artery to the lungs, as well as a branch to the pharynx. In the lungless salamanders the pulmonary artery is lost but the arch remains to supply the pharynx with blood in need of oxygenation. The sixth arch also gives rise to a cutaneous artery which sends several branches to the skin where much of the respiration of all Amphibia takes place. When gills appear during the larval life of most Amphibia, a direct connection between ventral and dorsal aorta remains at the base of each gill. With the loss of the gills at metamorphosis this connecting channel, the original aortic arch, is further developed. The segmental arteries of the body are decreased in number in Salientia, apparently in correlation with the modified metamerism. There are various differences between the blood vessels of the pelvis of frogs and salamanders. Some of these are correlated with the loss of the tail in the frog. The arteries and veins in a typical urodele are shown in Fig. 71 A and B. Necturus, the species figured, differs from the above description chiefly in the aortic arches. The sixth, with its pulmonary artery appears to be part of the fifth which is well developed while most of the sixth has been lost in the adult in correlation with the failure of the last branchial cartilage to develop (see p. 102).

Heart.—With the development of lungs in the piscine ancestors of Amphibia, it became necessary, in order to secure the maximum efficiency from these organs, to separate those blood channels in need of oxygen from those already supplied with it by the lungs. Some dipnoans partly succeeded in accomplishing this necessary advance by forming an incomplete separation of the two halves of the single piscine auricle, the left auricle for the blood received from the lungs and the right for that from the body. The division of the two blood streams was continued in the ventral aorta by the formation there of another incomplete partition, the spiral valve. This same plan of separation is taken over and further developed in Amphibia with well-developed lungs.

The heart, which may be considered a modified portion of the subintestinal vessel equipped with striated branching muscle fibers of a type not found elsewhere in the body, has the form

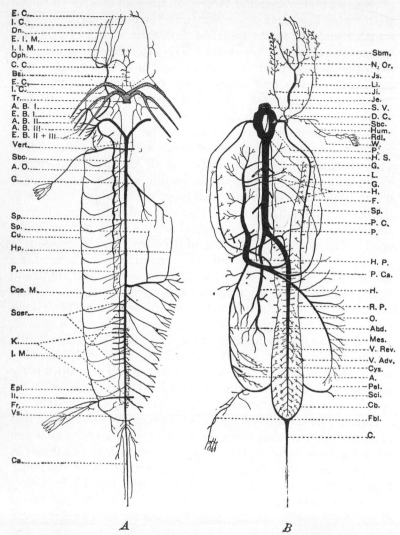

E. C.
I. C.
Dn.
E. I. M.
I. I. M.
Oph.
C. C.
Bs.
E. C.
I. C.
Tr.
A. B. I.
E. B. I.
A. B. II.
A. B. III.
E. B. II + III.
Vert.
Sbc.
A. O.
G.

Sp.
Sp.
Cu.
Hp.

P.

Coe. M.

Sper.

K.

I. M.

Epi.
Il.
Fr.
Vs.

Ca.

Sbm.
N. Or.
Js.
Li.
Ji.
Je.
S. V.
D. C.
Sbc.
Hum.
Rdl.
W.
P.
H. S.
G.
L.
G.
H.
F.
Sp.
P. C.
P.

H. P.
P. Ca.

H.

R. P.
O.
Abd.
Mes.
V. Rev.
V. Adv.
Cys.
A.
Pel.
Sci.
Cb.

Fbl.

C.

A   *B*

Fig. 71.—The vascular system of *Necturus maculosus*. *A.* Arterial system, left arm and leg omitted. Ventral aorta and its branches shaded, systemic arteries in solid line. *B.* Venous system, viewed ventrally with liver turned to the right side. Right arm and left leg omitted. (*After Miller.*) Arterial system: *A.B.I.*, first afferent branchial artery; *A.B.II.*, second afferent branchial artery; *A.B.III.*, third afferent branchial artery; *A.O.*, dorsal aorta; *Bs.*, basilar; *Ca.*, caudal aorta; *C.C.*, cerebral carotid; *Coe.M.*, coeliaco-mesenteric; *Cu.*, cutaneous; *E.B.I.*, first efferent branchial artery; *E.B.II.*, second efferent branchial artery; *E.B.III.*, third efferent branchial artery; *E.C.*, external carotid; *E.I.M.*, external inferior maxillary; *Epi.*, epigastric; *Fr.*, femoral; *G.*, gastric; *Hp.*, hepatic; *I.C.*, internal carotid; *I.I.M.*, internal inferior maxillary; *Il.*, iliac;

of a tube folded on itself S-fashion. The upper half of the S is the thin-walled receiving part of the heart; the ventral, the muscular propelling section. The blood is prevented from flowing backward by valves, one set placed near the entrance to the heart, a second between the two main parts, and a third in a double series in the ventral aorta leading away from it. The receiving portion of the heart is provided as in fishes with a *sinus venosus* which joins the ducts of Cuvier and merges anteriorly into the atrium. The latter is divided into two auricles completely separated in frogs and older urodele larvae by a thin septum of endothelium and connective tissue. The *sinus venosus* empties into the right auricle and the pulmonary vein into the left. In adult urodeles with well-developed lungs a few minute perforations appear in this membrane, but, as shown by injecting ink into the living heart, these small holes do not permit an observable mixture of arterial and venous blood (Noble, 1925). The propelling part of the heart, the ventricle, is not divided by a septum, but its chamber is crossed by many muscular strands which tend to hold blood received from the left auricle separate from that received from the right (Fig. 72). The ventral aorta or *conus arteriosus* is furnished with striated muscles and hence may be considered a part of the heart. Its caudal section or pylangium is more muscular than the cranial portion or synangium. Two to four semilunar valves that are directed forward guard the entrance to the pylangium, while the same number of similar valves are found at its cranial end at the beginning of the synangium. One of the latter valves in frogs and in most adult urodeles with well-developed lungs is extended caudally in the form of a spiral for more or less the entire length of the pylangium. This valve has important functions in separating arterial from venous blood as they are forced out from the ventricle.

I.M., inferior mesenteries; *K.*, renal; *On.*, orbito-nasal; *Oph.*, ophthalmic; *P.*, pulmonary; *Sbc.*, subclavian; *Sp.*, splenic branch of gastric; *Sp.'*, splenic; *Sper.*, spermatics; *Tr.*, truncus arteriosus; *Vert.*, vertebral; *Vs.*, vesical. Venous system: *A.*, anal; *Abd.*, abdominal; *C.*, caudal; *Cb.*, branch of caudal forming renal portal; *Cys.*, cystic; *D.C.*, duct of Cuvier; *F.*, Fallopian; *Fbl.*, tibial; *G.*, branches from stomach to hepatic; *H.*, hepatic; *H.P.*, hepatic portal; *H.S.*, hepatic sinus; *Hum.*, humeral; *Je.*, external jugular; *Ji.*, internal jugular; *Js.*, jugular sinus; *L.*, lateral; *Li.*, lingual; *Mes.*, mesenteric; *N.Or.*, naso-orbital, *O.*, ovarian; *P.*, pulmonary; *P.C.*, posterior cardinal; *P.Ca.*, post caval; *Pel.*, pelvic; *Rdl.*, radial; *R.P.*, renal portal (letters placed just above anastomosis with posterior cardinal); *Sbc.*, subclavian; *Sbm.*, submaxillary; *Sci.*, femoral; *Sp.*, splenic; *S.V.*, sinus venosus; *V.Adv.*, venae advehentes; *V.Rev.*, venae revehentes; *W.*, ulnar.

The oxygenated blood received from the lungs is squeezed from the left auricle into the left and caudal part of the ventricle. The blood that is poor in oxygen is forced from the right auricle a moment before the blood is sent from the left and tends to remain on the right side of the ventricle, being held in this position by the many muscular strands. Since the conus springs from this half of the ventricle, this poorly oxygenated blood is forced out first into the pylangium when the ventricle contracts.

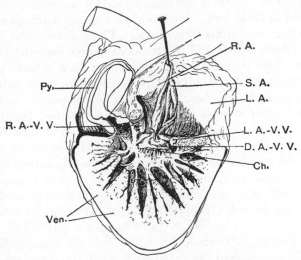

Fig. 72.—Heart of *Rana catesbeiana*, frontal section, showing the septa which prevent the mixing of the arterial and venous blood in the ventricle. *Ch.*, chorda; tendinea; *D.A.-V.V.*, dorsal auriculo-ventricular valve; *L.A.*, left auricle, *L.A.-V.V.*, left auriculo-ventricular valve; *Py.*, pylangium; *R.A.*, right auricle, *R.A.-V.V.*, right auriculo-ventricular valve; *S.A.*, auricular septum; *Vent.*, ventricle. (*After Benninghoff.*)

The blood makes its way into the nearest openings and into those vessels offering the least resistance. These are the openings into the sixth or pulmonary arches, which because of their short circuit, are free from the resistance of accumulated blood. In salamanders the openings to the pulmonary arch lie directly cephalad of the synangial valves, but in frogs the two pulmonary arches unite to form a single vessel which opens into the pylangium just caudal of the synangial valves. This position, nearer the source of supply, is a more favorable one for securing the first blood passed through the pylangium. As the blood is squirted into the pylangium, the latter contracts, bringing the free margin of the spiral valve against its wall and forcing the blood received during the latter part of the contraction to flow along only the ventral surface of the valve and hence to the more ventrally situated vessels in the synangium (Fig. 73A). This blood, which comes from the ventricle last, is the oxygenated blood from the

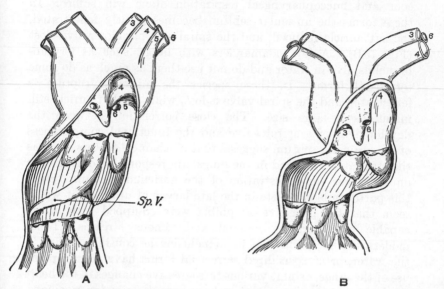

Fig. 73.—The *conus arteriosus* of two salamanders opened along the left side and turned back to show the valves. *A. Ambystoma maculatum. B. Plethodon glutinosus. Sp.V.,* spiral valve.

left auricle and it is directed into the carotid and systemic arches by the spiral valve. In Rana, the spiral valve completely shuts off from the pulmonary arch the systemic flow of blood; but in the salamanders, where the openings from all the arches lie in the synangium, it would seem that some mixture must occur. Nevertheless, the directive action of the spiral valve is such that ink injected into the left auricle is found to be carried only to the ventral part of the truncus, from the point where the anterior arches arise.

A further device for making sure that the oxygenated blood be carried to the head of Amphibia is the development of a so-called "carotid gland" at the point on the third arch where the internal and external carotids take origin. This structure is not a gland at all but merely a spongy enlargement of the arch which offers further resistance to the blood and steadies the pressure by continuing to contract between beats.   There is also a *valvula para-doxa* near this point which may equalize the flow of blood in the two carotids (Subba Rau, 1924).

Modifications of the Heart.—Many salamanders undergo a reduction of their lungs, for they live in situations where cutaneous and buccopharyngeal respiration alone will suffice.   In these forms the auricular septum becomes greatly fenestrated, the left auricle reduced, and the spiral and paradox valves lost (Fig. 73B).   A few salamanders with lungs, such as Crypto-branchus, live in water and do not use them as much as do some terrestrial forms.   In these species the auricular septum is fenestrated and the spiral valve is lost, while the left auricle still maintains a large size.   The close correlation between the development of a spiral valve and the functional completeness of the auricular septum suggests that mechanical factors, such as the stagnation of blood in the lungs, are responsible during each ontogeny for the fenestration of the auricular septum.   Since this partition is complete in the late larvae of urodeles, it would seem that the primitive Amphibia were equipped with hearts capable of separating arterial and venous streams.   Those modern urodeles, which as permanent larvae continue to live in the water, or as specialized terrestrial forms have given up the use of the lungs, exhibit various retrogressive changes in the heart mechanism.   Similar conditions have been described in caecilians. These Amphibia may be compared to the human fetus which, unable to use its lungs, maintains a foramen between right and left auricles, serving to equilibrate the pressures of the two blood streams.

Although the heart has the form of a twisted tube, it does not owe this character solely to the pressure of adjacent tissue, such as the Cuvierian ducts behind and the aortic arches in front.   If the heart rudiment is removed from a frog embryo and cultured in Ringer's solution, it may grow into a twisted, pulsating organ (Ekman, 1924) which, however, has not a typical form.   Transplanting a heart rudiment into the tissues of a second frog embryo in such a way that it taps the blood supply will give a "parasite" heart of enormous size while the host's own heart especially the ventricle, dwindles.   Thus function may have an important effect on the size of the heart or its parts, although only a little on its general form (Stöhr, 1925, 1926).   Salamanders of great length but only moderate girth, such as Siren and Amphiuma, have increased the heart capacity by the development of a series of pendulent extensions of the auricles (Fig. 74) and the same maintains in the small, but very slim Pseudobranchus.

Function of the Heart.—The primary function of the heart is to force blood into the arteries against the pressure caused by the tonic contraction of the smooth muscle fibers of the arteries and arterioles. The difficulty is increased by the friction within these vessels and capillaries as well as by the viscosity of the blood due chiefly to the relative amount of protein held in colloidal solution in the blood. The blood pressure maintained by the heart must be higher than that of the osmotic pressure of the plasma proteins in order to permit the filtration of urine through the glomeruli of the kidney. In the frog the systolic pressure of the heart is about three times the osmotic pressure of the colloids (Bieter and Scott, 1928).

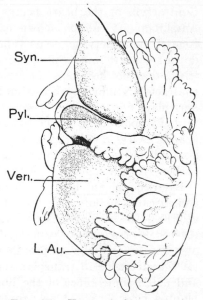

FIG. 74.—Heart of *Siren lacertina.* Numerous finger-like processes greatly increase the volume of the auricles. *L.Au.*, left auricle; *Pyl.*, pylangium; *Syn.*, synangium; *Ven.*, ventricle.

The output of blood by the heart must be sufficient to insure an adequate supply of food and oxygen for the tissues of the body. The blood flow in the capillaries, because of their larger total area, is much slower than in the larger vessels, thus allowing greater opportunity for gas exchange and other functions of the blood to take place. The heart output is determined in part, by the stroke volume of blood but chiefly by the rate of pulsation. The latter is regulated principally by the vagus which inhibits the heart rate and by the sympathetic impulses which accelerate it. Kräupl (1927) has demonstrated the cardio-accelerator effects upon stimulation of the isolated sympathetic trunk, after cutting the vagus connection to the heart. The rate is affected by temperature, gradually increasing with each rise up to a certain maximum but with a greater increase between 10 to 35°C. than between lower temperatures (Inukai, 1925). The slowing in heart rate during cooling is partly compensated for by a reflex increase in the stroke volume (Schulz, 1906) which tends to maintain the heart output despite a decrease in heart rate.

Any living tissue after excitation shows a refractory period during which it is not excitable. This period is much longer in heart than in skeletal muscle and gives it a rhythmic beat. Contraction of the heart begins at the sino-auricular node in Amphibia. It can be shown experimentally that cooling the zone of union between sinus venosus and right auricle will slow down the heart rate, while cooling the surface of auricles or ventricles does not have this effect. Although all heart muscles will contract rhythmically on stimulation, the tissue of the sino-auricular node is especially sensitive and comparatively rapid in rate of response. If the heart is removed without the sinus, the beating is less rapid than when the sinus is left attached to the isolated heart. Hence the sino-auricular node is the "pace maker" for the remainder of the heart.

Even though the heart is normally regulated by nervous control, it can function independent of innervation. Further, each species seems to have its own rate of pulsation. The heart of *Ambystoma tigrinum* transplanted into *A. maculatum* retained its own rate in this new environment (Copenhaver, 1927). Weiss (1927) succeeded in transplanting the hearts of adult Bombina and noted some effect of the host upon the beat of the transplanted heart before a new innervation was established. This he interpreted as due to a hormone. The recent work of Copenhaver (1930) indicates that the sinus has not only important functions in controlling the rate of heart beat in Ambystoma but may also influence the specific tempo of the beat. The posterior part of the heart of *A. tigrinum* may be transplanted into *A. maculatum* in such a way that it will combine with the anterior part of the heart of the latter species. In such cases the posterior part not only dominates the anterior part by acting as a general pace maker, but it also imposes its own specific rate upon the heart parts of the host species.

Blood pressure is increased by a constriction of the arterioles and capillaries. Stimulation of the medulla of the frog causes a strong constriction of the arterioles of the webs between the toes (Bikeles and Zbyszewski, 1918). There are also vasoconstrictors in the spinal cord. Besides the nerves, hormones may affect the constriction of the peripheral vessels. Pituitrin, the hormone of the posterior lobe of the pituitary gland, as well as adrenalin induces a constriction of the vessels.

Lymphatic System.—Besides the arteries and veins, there is another system of channels extending throughout the body of Amphibia. These are the lymphatics, which collect the blood which seeps through the walls of the capillaries and return it to the veins. Such blood is devoid of erythrocytes and is, therefore, colorless, but it contains most of the other ingredients of blood. It is called "lymph."

The lymphatic vessels may arise by sprouting from embryonic blood channels in very much the same way as arteries and veins arise from these plexes, or they may be formed from mesenchyme independently of preexisting channels (Kampmeier, 1922). Although the lymphatics closely resemble the blood vessels in their origin, they differ in that they frequently widen out to form great sinuses and make connections with the large pericardial and peritoneal cavities. Unlike blood vessels the lymphatics of the intestine absorb fat and are known as "lacteals." The lymph vessels of urodeles form two main systems: one running parallel to the aorta and emptying into the subclavian vein of each side, another lying superficially under the skin and carrying the lymph chiefly to the postcardinals and cutaneous veins. The lymphatics of the Salientia are remarkable in forming large sinuses under the skin, the function of which may be to prevent a rapid drying of the skin. The lymph in these channels flows towards the heart and it is pumped into the veins by a series of lymph hearts. In the caecilians there may be over 200 of these hearts lying flat under the skin intersegmentally and forcing the lymph into intersegmental veins (Marcus, 1908). Each heart, which is a simple sac of endothelium encircled by a network of striated muscle and a sheath of connective tissue, receives lymph from several lymph vessels. Valves prevent the flow of blood from the veins into the lymphatics. In urodele larvae there may be a series of similar hearts along the body emptying into the large cutaneous vein. In tadpoles there is a pair of lymph hearts emptying into the third intersegmental vein (Fig. 75) and several others along the tail. Grodzinski (1925) correlates this reduction with the poor development of the large cutaneous veins in the tadpole. In adult Salientia there is usually a single pair, the anterior pair of the tadpole, emptying into the vertebral vein, and a caudal pair, one on either side of the coccyx, pumping the lymph into a branch of the ischiadic vein. These hearts may be readily observed by removing the skin from the end of the coccyx.

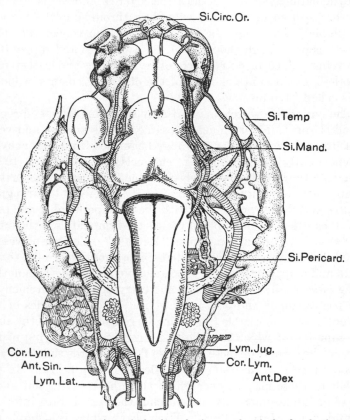

Fig. 75.—Reconstruction of the lymphatic vessels of the head of a toad tadpole showing their relation to the larger blood vessels. *Cor.Lym.Ant.Dex.*, right anterior lymph heart; *Cor.Lym.Ant.Sin.*, left anterior lymph heart; *Lym. Jug.*, lymphatica jugularis; *Lym.Lat.*, lymphatica lateralis; *Si.Circ.Or.*, circumoral division of sinus maxillaris primigenius; *Si.Mand.*, mandibular division; *Si.Pericard.*, pericardial division; *Si.Temp.*, temporal division. (*After Kampmeier.*)

Their beating is independent of that of the heart or of the other lymph hearts. It is, nevertheless, under nervous control since cutting away the spinal cord destroys the beat. The lymph heart tissue is thus neither structurally nor functionally similar to heart tissue (Brücke and Umrath, 1930). The number of lymph hearts varies with the species. In the primitive Ascaphus there may be three pairs of lymph hearts near the coccyx, and some brevicipitids and pipids may have two or three pairs. Even Rana, which is usually described as having only one pair of posterior lymph hearts, may have this one divided into three pairs (Jolly and Lieure, 1929).

The amount of lymph flowing through the four small lymph hearts of frogs is very remarkable. Isyama (1924) estimated that the entire blood plasma goes through these portals fifty times a day. This speed of lymph circulation, much greater than in mammals, is a consequence of the greater permeability of the blood vessels in Amphibia (Conklin, 1930). It demands, moreover, a mechanism of the rapid return of the lymph to the blood vessels in order that the blood volume be not seriously lowered. The lymph heart system of Amphibia is well developed as an adaptation to meet the exigencies of a rapid turnover of lymph. If the hearts become clogged or otherwise fail, the frog soon becomes edematous and dies because of the isolation of valuable constituents of the blood in the lymph spaces.

The lymphatics may have special functions to perform. At times of injury those near the wound gather up extravasated erythrocytes lying near the lymphatic capillaries. The erythrocytes seem to exert a specific attraction on the endothelium of the lymphatic capillaries which send out sprouts for a distance as great as 76 microns and gather up the red blood cells, finally to return them to the veins intact (Clark and Clark, 1925). If the erythrocytes are further away than this distance, or remain there over 12 hours, the wandering macrophages phagocytose them.

References

BARCROFT, J., 1924: The significance of hemoglobin, *Physiol. Rev.*, IV, 329–351.

BEYER, W., 1921: Über kernlose rote Blutkörperchen bei Amphibien, *Jena. Zeitschr.*, LVII, 491–511.

BIETER, R. N., and F. H. SCOTT, 1928: Blood pressure and blood protein determinations in the frog, *Proc. Soc. Exp. Biol. and Med.*, XXV, 832.

BIKELES, G., and L. ZBYSZEWSKI, 1918: Über den Einfluss einer Reizung der Oblongatagegend mittels Wechselströme auf die Vasomotoren beim Frosche, *Zentralbl. Physiol.*, XXXII, 377–378.

BRAUNMÜHL, A. VON, 1926: Über einige myelo-lymphoide und lympho-epitheliale Organe der Anuren, *Zeitschr. Mikr. Anat. Forsch.*, IV, 635–688.

BRUCKE, E. T., and K. UMRATH, 1930: Über die Aktionsströme des Lymphherzens und seiner Nerven, *Arch. Ges. Physiol.*, CCXXIV, 631–639.

CLARK, E. R., 1918: Studies on the growth of blood-vessels in the tail of the frog larva by observation and experiment on the living animal, *Amer. Jour. Anat.*, XXIII, 37–88.

CLARK, E. R., and E. L. CLARK, 1925: On the fate of the extruded erythrocytes, *Anat. Rec.*, XXIX, 352–353.

———, 1928: The relation between the monocytes of the blood and the tissue macrophages in living amphibian larvae, *Anat. Rec.*, XXXVIII, 8.

CLAYPOLE, EDITH J., 1893: The blood of Necturus and Cryptobranchus, *Proc. Amer. Micr. Soc.*, XV, 39–76, 6 pl.

CONKLIN, R. E., 1930: The formation and circulation of lymph in the frog; II. Blood volume and pressure, *Amer. Jour. Phys.*, XCV, 91–97.

COPENHAVER, W. M., 1927: Results of heteroplastic transplantations of the heart rudiment in Amblystoma embryos, *Proc. Nat. Acad. Sci. Wash.*, XIII, 484–488.

———, 1930: Results of heteroplastic transplantation of anterior and posterior parts of the heart rudiment in Amblystoma embryos, *Jour. Exp. Zool.*, LV, 293–318.

DAWSON, A. B., 1928: Changes in form (including direct division, cytoplasmic segmentation, and nuclear extrusion) of the erythrocytes of Necturus in plasma, *Amer. Jour. Anat.*, XLII, 139–154.

DRASTICH, L., 1925: Über das Leben der Salamandralarven bei hohem und niedrigem Sauerstoffpartialdruck, *Zeitschr. vergl. Physiol.*, II, 632–657.

EKMAN, GUNNAR, 1924: Neue experimentelle Beiträge zur frühesten Entwicklung des Amphibienherzens, *Comment. Biol. Soc. Sci. Fennica*, I, 1–26, 1 pl.

EMMEL, VICTOR E., 1924: Studies on the non-nucleated elements of the blood. 2. The occurrence and genesis of non-nucleated erythrocytes or erythroplastids in vertebrates other than mammals, *Amer. Jour. Anat.*, XXX, 347–405.

———, 1925: Studies on the non-nucleated cytoplasmic elements of the blood. 3. Leucoplastids or non-nucleated leucocytic derivatives in vertebrates other than mammals, *Amer. Jour. Anat.*, XXXV, 31–62.

FEDERICI, E., 1926: Recherches expérimentales sur les potentialités de l'îlot sanguin chez l'embryon de Rana fusca, *Arch. Biol.*, XXXVI, 465–487.

FRASE, W., 1930: Zellengrösse als Leistungsfaktor der Haustiere, *Der Naturforscher*, VII. 221–224.

GOSS, CHARLES M., 1928: Experimental removal of the blood island of Amblystoma punctatum embryo, *Jour. Exp. Zool.*, LII, 45–64.

GRODZINSKI, Z., 1924: Über die Entwicklung der Gefässe des Dotterdarmes bei Urodelen, *Bull. Int. Acad. Polon. Sci. Let. Cracovie*, Ser. B, 1924, 57–67, 1 pl.

———, 1925: Weitere Untersuchungen über die Blutgefässentwicklung bei Urodelen, *Bull. Int. Acad. Polon. Sci. Let. Cracovie*, Ser. B, 1925, 195–209, 1 pl.

HEESEN, WILHELM, 1924: Über die Zahlenverhältnisse der roten und weissen Blutkörper der heimischen Amphibien im Wechsel der Jahreszeiten, *Zeitschr. vergl. Physiol.*, I, 500–516.

HILTON, W. A., 1913: The development of the blood and the transformation of some of the early vitelline vessels in Amphibia, *Jour. Morph.*, XXIV, 339–382.

INUKAI, T., 1925: Über den Einfluss der Temperatur auf die Pulsationzahl bei den Amphibienlarven und Vogelembryonen, *Japan Jour. Zool.*, I, 67–75.

ISAYAMA, SUNAO, 1924: Über die Geschwindigkeit des Flüssigkeitsaustausches zwischen Blut und Gewebe, *Zeitschr. Biol.*, LXXXII, 101–106.

JOLLY, J., and LIEURE, C., 1929: Sur les coeurs lymphatiques des Anoures, *Compt. rend. Soc. Biol. Paris.*, CI, 1063–1066.

JORDAN, H. E., and C. C. SPEIDEL, 1923: Blood cell formation and destruction in relation to the mechanism of thyroid accelerated metamorphoses in the larval frog, *Jour. Exp. Med.*, XXXVIII, 529–541.

———, 1923a: Studies on lymphocytes; I. Effects of splenectomy, experimental hemorrhage and a hemolytic toxin in the frog, *Amer. Jour. Anat.*, XXXII, 155–188, 5 pl.

———, 1924: Studies on lymphocytes; III. Granulocytopoieses in the salamander with special reference to the monophyletic theory of blood cell origin, *Amer. Jour. Anat.*, XXXIII, 483–505, 2 pls.

———, 1925: Studies on lymphocytes; IV. Further observations upon the hemopoietic effects of splenectomy in frogs, *Jour. Morph.*, XL, 461–477.

KAMPMEIER, O. F., 1922: The development of the anterior lymphatics and lymph hearts in anuran embryos, *Amer. Jour. Anat.*, XXX, 61–131.

KINGSBURY, B. F., 1912: Amphibian tonsils, *Anat. Anz.*, XLII, 593–612.

KRÄUPL, F., 1927: Über reine Reizung der Förderungsnerven am Froschherzen, *Arch. ges. Physiol.*, CCXVII, 327–342.

MARCUS, H., 1908: Beiträge zur Kenntnis der Gymnophionen; II. Über intersegmentale Lymphherzen nebst Bemerkungen über das Lymphsystem, *Morph. Jahrb.*, XXXVIII, 590–607, 1 pl.

MAXIMOW, A., 1910: Über embryonale Entwickelung der Blutzellen bei Selachiern und Amphibien, *Anat. Anz. Ergheft.*, XXXVII, 64–70.

MOORE, JULIA S., 1915: The growth of the vascular system as it is correlated with the development of function in the embryos of Amblystoma, *Anat. Rec.*, IX, 109–111.

MYERS, M. A., 1928: A study of the tonsillar developments in the lingual region of anurans, *Jour. Morph. Physiol.*, XLV, 399–433.

NOBLE, G. K., 1925: The integumentary, pulmonary, and cardiac modifications correlated with increased cutaneous respiration in the Amphibia: A solution of the "hairy frog" problem, *Jour. Morph. Physiol.*, XL, 341–416.

PENTIMALLI, F., 1909: Über die Zahlverhältnisse der weissen Blutkörperchen bei den Amphibien in verschiedenen Zuständen, *Int. Monatsschr. Anat. Physiol.*, XXVI, 206–222.

PONDER, ERIC, 1924: The erythrocyte and the action of simple haemolysins, *Biol. Monog. and Manuals*, II, Edinburgh.

SCHULZ, N., 1906: Studien über das Verhalten des Blutdruckes von Rana esculenta unter den verschiedenen äusseren Bedingungen, insbesondere bei verschiedener Körpertemperatur, *Arch. ges. Physiol.*, CXV, 386–445, 6 pl.

SMITH, H. M., 1925: Cell size and metabolic activity in Amphibia, *Biol. Bull.*, XLVIII, 347–378.

STOHR, P., JR., 1925: Zur Entstehung der Herzform, *Anat. Anz. Ergheft.*, LX, 105–112.

———, 1926: Zwei neue experimentelle Resultate zur Herzentwicklung bei Amphibien, *Anat. Anz. Ergheft.*, LXI, 151–153.

SUBBA RAU, A., 1924: Observations on the anatomy of the heart, lungs and related parts of Ceratophrys, *Jour. Anat. London*, LVIII, 306–327.

WEISS, P., 1927: Herztransplantation an erwachsenen Amphibien, *Arch. ges. Physiol.*, CCXVII, 299–307.

CHAPTER IX

THE DIGESTIVE SYSTEM

Life on land necessitated a profound change in the anterior portion of the digestive tract. A tongue for the seizing and swallowing of food developed to meet the new conditions of life. As shown in the ontogeny, this structure was formed by the addition of a glandular fold anterior and lateral to the piscine tongue rudiment. Fishes lack multicellular glands in the mouth, but the first tetrapods, to judge from the fenestrae in the palates of labyrinthodonts, were equipped with a glandular mass behind the premaxillaries. In Salientia and Caudata this gland opens by one or more ducts in the roof of the mouth. Many Salientia

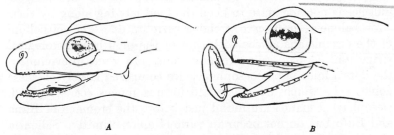

Fig. 76.—Two types of tongue form in plethodontid salamanders. In *Desmognathus fuscus* (*A*) the tongue is attached in front, while in *Eurycea bislineata* (*B*) it is free all round and capable of projection well beyond the mouth.

have, in addition, a glandular mass in the palatine region (Cohn, 1910). It is apparently this mass which has extended in Breviceps to cover the greater part of the roof of the mouth. The chief function of all these glands would seem to be to render the tongue more adhesive. Most Salientia have the tongue attached by resistent tissue to the front angle of the jaws and capable of projection only by flapping the posterior part over and beyond the anterior. A few frogs in different parts of the world have succeeded in freeing the anterior attachment, and many of the common urodeles have the tongue in the shape of a mushroom, capable of projection several times the length of the head (Fig.

76). It is remarkable that this boletoid tongue is found in such moderately aquatic types as the Red Salamander (Pseudotriton) and yet is lacking in the terrestrial Plethodon. Thoroughly aquatic Salientia tend to reduce the tongue, and both this structure and the intermaxillary gland are lacking in the Pipidae.

The lining of the mouth differs from skin chiefly in possessing numerous mucous or goblet cells and in lacking subepithelial mucous glands and pigment. Taste buds are present on tongue and palate. Cilia are present on these regions in terrestrial Amphibia but are lacking in larvae and in throughly aquatic types such as Leurognathus. They are especially active in the vicinity of the intermaxillary gland outlets. Unlike the cilia covering the body of the embryo, they appear to be under sympathetic control (McDonald, Leisure, and Lenneman, 1928).

The oesophagus is frequently separated from the mouth cavity by a fold. Its lining is thrown into a number of more or less persistent longitudinal folds and is ciliated. The presence of cilia suggests that the peristaltic action of the oesophageal muscles is not adequate to keep the food moving along by their efforts alone as in the case of higher vertebrates. The epithelium of the oesophagus agrees with that of the mouth in histological structure. Goblet cells are numerous. In some brevicipitids the dorsal folds of the oesophagus are composed largely of these goblet cells which are massed to form a mucus secreting pad. Oesophageal glands are found just before the stomach of Rana and Bufo but do not occur in various more primitive Salientia or in certain urodeles (Kingsbury, 1894). They are pepsin-secreting structures and may be considered modified stomach glands (Bensley, 1900).

Stomach.—The stomach is not sharply marked off from the oesophagus. Both are provided with an outer longitudinal and an inner circular layer of smooth muscles. Within this *muscularis* and separated from it by a well-vascularized layer of connective tissue is another outer sheath of longitudinal muscle fibers and an inner, of circular fibers. These form the *muscularis mucosae*, a thin layer of muscle lying directly adjacent to the glandular lining of the stomach. The muscles function in passing the food posteriorly and in mixing it with gastric juice in the stomach. If disagreeable substances are swallowed, a frog is able to reverse this action and turn the stomach inside out, until it bulges far outside the mouth. The stomach usually lies to the left of the midline and is curved with the convex side toward the left. It is held in place by two folds of the peritoneum (Fig. 77). Its lining or mucosa consists of a simple, columnar epithelium on which there empty great numbers of small glands. Those at the oesophageal end of the stomach consist of a long neck of the same structure as the surface epithelium, a few large and transparent mucous cells, and one or more diverticula of cells having a granular cyptoplasm (Fig. 78). The latter cells apparently secrete both pepsin-producing granules and hydrochloric acid. In mammals two different types of cells perform these functions. The glands near the pylorus are comparable to the necks of the other glands. Large mucous cells are occasionally found at the bottom of the pyloric glands giving further evidence of this homology. The stomach of Amphibia serves to alter both physically and chemically the food swallowed; it functions also as a place of food storage. Food may be available only at irregular intervals and many frogs are able to expand their stomachs enormously when filling them on these occasions.

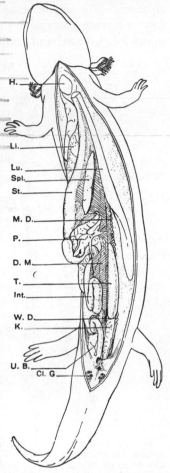

FIG. 77.—Viscera of *Necturus maculosus*. *Cl.G.*, cloacal glands; *D.M.*, dorsal mesentery; *H.*, heart; *Int.*, intestine; *K.*, kidney; *Li.*, liver; *Lu.*, lung; *M.D.*, Müllerian duct; *P.* pancreas; *Spl.*, spleen; *St.*, stomach; *T.*, testis; *U.B.*, urinary bladder; *W.D.*, Wolffian duct. (*Modified from Cope.*)

Intestines.—The intestine in Amphibia is a tube of nearly uniform width except posteriorly where it widens to form the large intestine. It is nearly straight in some caecilians and only slightly folded in Siren and Proteus. Increase in length reaches its extreme stage in the common Rana tadpoles, where the small intestine is coiled in watch-spring fashion. The intestine possesses the same longitudinal and circular muscle layers as the stomach. Its mucosa consists of columnar and goblet cells, the former having absorptive functions. The mucosa is thrown into many longitudinal and transverse folds which like the villi of the

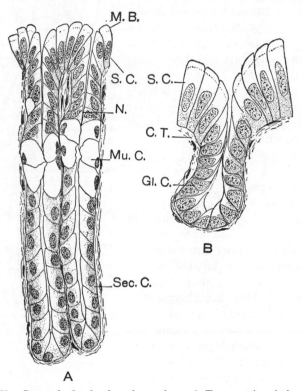

FIG. 78.—Stomach glands of a salamander. *A.* Two gastric tubules from the middle region of the stomach of *Necturus maculosus.* *B.* Section through a pyloric-gland tubule. *C.T.,* connective tissue; *Gl.C.,* gland cells; *M.B.,* mucigenous border of surface cells; *Mu.C.,* mucous cells; *N.,* neck of the gland; *S.C.,* surface cells of the stomach; *Sec.C.,* secreting cells of the fundus of the gland. *(After Kingsbury.)*

mammalian intestine afford a greater absorptive surface. The cross-folds delay the passage of food, and Jacobshagen (1915) believes their arrangement may have some systematic value. Urodeles but no frogs have glands between the folds of the small intestine. They resemble the pyloric glands of the stomach, although ducts may be absent (Goldsmith and Beams, 1929). The small intestine is sharply marked off from the stomach by the pyloric constriction. In higher Salientia it is equally well demarcated from the large intestine by a valve or ring fold. The large intestine usually presents a differentiation into two parts, an anterior larger reservoir for feces and a posterior more muscular part. A slight asymmetrical enlargement of this anterior section has been considered in some frogs and urodeles to represent a rudimentary caecum (Crofts, 1925). It is covered with lymphoidal tissue.

Glandular Outgrowths.—Associated with the anterior part of the small intestine are the liver and the pancreas, the two glandular outgrowths of the embryonic midgut common to all vertebrates. The liver develops very early in Rana by the formation of a cavity in the vitelline mass. A diverticulum is produced from the antero-ventral margin of the cavity (Weber, 1903) and develops into a compound tubular gland. The cavity and proximal portion of the gland are transformed into a hepatic duct. A gall bladder is formed as a reservoir for the secretion of the gland. The pancreas arises near the liver in the form of three outgrowths from the intestinal wall, which soon fuse to form a single structure. The distal portions of the outgrowths form glands of the tubular or acinous type; the proximal portion, the ducts. In urodeles two of the ducts empty into the intestine, the anterior behind the pylorus and a posterior in association with the hepatic duct. In Salientia the more anterior duct is lost (Göppert, 1891). Of especial interest are a series of cell aggregations between the tubular glands of the pancreas; these are the islets of Langerhans. They develop without ducts and produce a secretion which is passed directly into the blood stream. Intestine, liver, and pancreas are covered with peritoneum which lines the body cavity and forms the mesenteries which hold the organs in place.

Digestion.—Food is needed for growth and repair, also for energy to perform the daily round of activities. The simple chemical elements cannot be used for food. They must be first combined into molecules often of extreme complexity. The compounds—proteins, carbohydrates, and fats—constitute foods. Certain salts, water, and apparently vitamines are also indispensable. Adult Amphibia live largely on insects or other invertebrate prey and hence their food is rich in proteins. These perform the definite function of renewing the worn-out tissues of the animal and when digested may be resynthesized to form carbohydrates. The latter are stored in the organism mainly in the form of the insoluble substance glycogen. The glycogen, when needed, is converted into some form of sugar (mostly glucose) which on oxidation is the greatest source of energy in all animals. Starvation in Amphibia as well as in man quickly leads to the depletion of the carbohydrate stores. Hence the energy for the fasts, which are perhaps not rare in Amphibia, must be furnished by the fat reserve or by the tissue protein. Since fat is stored in practically a pure form, while protein is not, the storage of energy in the form of fat is much more economical than in the form of protein. Nevertheless, Amphibia are lean animals and never have learned the trick of developing the great stores of fatty tissue seen in birds and mammals. Perhaps cold-blooded animals, with their low metabolism, have no need of these stores of potential energy, or perhaps one of the reasons for their never becoming warm-blooded is the leanness of their bodies.

Digestion in Amphibia follows, on the whole, the typical vertebrate pattern known to us in our own bodies, however, with certain modifications. An insect seized by a frog is quickly swallowed, the small teeth crushing it only to a small extent and the secretions of the mouth serving merely as a lubricant. Digestion first begins in the stomach where the gastric glands secrete hydrochloric acid and also an enzyme, pepsin, which acts solely on the proteins transforming them into substances of smaller molecular weight. A second enzyme, rennin, has been shown by Kingsbury (1894) to be present in the stomach of Necturus, but as no Amphibian normally drinks milk on which this enzyme is well known to act in mammals, its function in Amphibia is obscure.

The partly digested food rendered acid by the gastric juice is passed on to the intestine. The intestinal glands activated by this acid produce a substance secretin, which is released not into the intestine but into the blood. On reaching the pancreas, secretin causes the pancreas to pour forth its highly alkaline secretion which stops the action of pepsin but initiates a second series of digestive processes. This pancreatic juice contains three additional enzymes. The most important for the carnivorous diet of Amphibia is trypsin which is secreted in an inactive form, trypsinogen, but is rendered active by a substance secreted by the intestinal wall. It continues the protein digestion begun in the stomach and carries it well on toward the final products of this digestion chiefly to the peptone stage. The other two enzymes are an amylase, which changes starches into sugars, and a lipase, which causes a splitting of the fats into fatty acid and glycerol. The liver secretes bile, which renders the fats more readily attacked by the lipase. Finally, the intestinal juice produced by the mucosa of the intestinal walls contains enzymes which complete the process of digestion. Of these the most important is erepsin which acts on the peptones and thus completes the work begun by the pepsin and trypsin of liberating the amino-acids from the proteins.

The secretion of the liver contains no digestive enzymes. The liver, which occupies such a large part of the body cavity, is not primarily an organ of digestion. It is concerned chiefly in the further elaboration of the fatty substances, in the storage of glycogen, in the formation of urea, and finally in the destruction of the red blood corpuscles. The importance of the liver as a place of fat storage in cold-blooded forms is particularly emphasized during hibernation and in the early spring mating season, (Buddenbrock, 1928; Berg, 1924), since fat can be most rapidly mobilized from this organ. By determining the ratio of carbon dioxide produced to the oxygen utilized during respiration, it is possible to analyze the nature of the oxidation processes occurring at any one time. If this respiratory quotient—the volume of carbon dioxide given off divided by the volume of oxygen absorbed—is higher than 0.80, carbohydrate is being oxydized in excess of protein and fat, while a quotient less than 0.80 indicates that fat oxidation predominates. Dolk and Postma (1927) by the use of this method have demonstrated that the hibernating frog uses its fat and not its glycogen reserves.

Absorption and Assimilation.—The products of digestion are absorbed by the walls of the intestine. The amino-acids are gathered up by the mesenteric veins and transported to those portions of the body where they are needed for building up the tissues. Here they are reconverted into the proteins. Those amino-acids which are not required for building are broken down by the liver. The nitrogenous part is excreted as urea while the remainder is formed into carbohydrates which supply energy to the organism. The amino-acids and sugars are passed by the intestinal epithelium into the capillaries, while the products of fat digestion seem to be usually transmitted to the lymph vessels. The sugars that are not used as an immediate source of energy are stored in the form of glycogen or animal starch. Proteins cannot be stored as such, but after they are deaminized the remainder may be converted into glycogen. Various tissues, especially the muscles, store glycogen, but the liver serves as the general depot. The latter releases carbohydrates to the blood in the form of glucose as it is required. In the fall, before hibernation, the liver of some frogs may be more than twice as large as in early summer, due chiefly to the increased storage of glycogen. The fats, not used at once by the tissues, are stored chiefly in the liver and the adipose body, the latter being a modification of the genital tract found just anterior to the gonads. Some frogs have a conspicuous fat body just anterior to the clavicles, and various narrow-mouthed toads have small, fat bodies under the skin. In salamanders large accumulations of fat are usually to be found in the tail. In Proteus, fatty tissue forms a thin sheet under the skin (Maurer, 1911). By means of vital dyes, Hadjioloff located a number of small deposits of fat about the heart and in the pelvic region of various European frogs. Apparently it is an accumulation of fat which gives the greenish color to the bones of some of the more translucent species of tree frog, for Hadjioloff found considerable fat in the bone marrow of the frogs he studied.

The more indigestible food is retained for a time in the large intestine which is enlarged anteriorly. Such an enlargement of the intestinal tract first makes its appearance in Amphibia. It would seem to serve not only as the last region of food absorption in the gut but also as a storage place for the feces. At intervals the excreta are passed out through the cloacal orifice to the outside.

The waste products of growth and repair of the tissues are released into the blood stream in the form of urea, carbon dioxide, water, and various soluble products of protein metabolism. The carbon dioxide is eliminated from the body by the organs of respiration. The other waste products are collected from the blood by the kidneys. The liver also serves as an organ of elimination of nitrogenous waste products. These are passed with the bile into the intestine and are excreted with the feces.

Modifications of Digestive Tract.—The absorbing surface of the digestive tract is increased in Amphibia not by the formation of pyloric caeca or spiral valves, as in fish, but merely by an increase in length.   Great length without great bulk is secured by the narrowing of the tube and its twisting into a compact spiral. Most frog tadpoles feed largely on water plants and like other vegetarians require a maximum amount of absorbing surface. The winding of the intestine is not in one plane but extends ventrally as the spiral becomes narrower.   There are usually two and a half to three loops, but as each loop is double, the winding seems more extensive.   A few tadpoles living in the confined space between the leaves of bromeliads or banana plants feed to a considerable extent on frog eggs.   Their intestines do not have the characteristic watch-spring form of most tadpoles but are short and resemble the intestines of the adult frog in lacking a spiral.   The more carnivorous tadpoles, such as those of *Ceratophrys dorsata*, have a shorter digestive tract than herbivorous forms.

It is probable that many of these differences in length and form of the intestines of tadpoles is due to the character of the food during each ontogeny (Fig. 79).   In view of the experiments of

A   **B**

Fɪɢ. 79.—Effect of food on the intestine of tadpoles.   *A*. Intestine of a tadpole reared on a plant diet.   *B*. Intestine of another reared on an animal diet.   (*After Babak.*)

Yung (1904, 1905), the mechanical effect of bulky food would seem to be greater than the chemical effect of plant tissues on the digestive tract of the tadpole.   The experiments of Babák (1905, 1911) suggest that the chemical factor may also play a part in controlling the length of the digestive tract.

The environment affects the digestive processes of Amphibia directly.   Müller (1922) has shown that the digestive action of the frog pepsin increases with rising temperature reaching an optimum at 40°C., a temperature at which few frogs will survive. Thus the optimum conditions for digestion are not the best temperatures for the health of the frogs.

Amphibia are able to withstand long fasts.   Tadpoles may live for months without food.   This would seem to be due to their ability to feed on bacteria or other small particles in the water

(Bock, 1925; Krizenecky and Petrov, 1926). Nevertheless, some urodeles such as Proteus, which are not known to have this ability, have been kept for over a year without food. Axolotls have been reported to live 650 days without food (St. Hiller, 1929). During this time they lost 81 per cent of their initial weight. Although Amphibia with their low metabolic rate might be expected to withstand longer fasts than warm-blooded animals, their ability to live for months on their own tissues is remarkable for active vertebrates.

References

BABÁK, E., 1905: Über die morphogenetische Reaktion des Darmkanals der Froschlarve auf Muskelproteine verschiedener Tierklassen, *Beitr. Chem. Physiol.*, VII, 323–330.

————, 1911: Über das Wachstum des Körpers bei der Fütterung mit arteigenen und artfremden Proteinen *Zentralbl. Physiol.*, XXV, 437–441.

BENSLEY, R. R., 1900: The oesophageal glands of Urodela, *Biol. Bull.*, II, 87–104.

BERG, W., 1924: Über funktionelle Leberzellstrukturen; III, Periodische Veränderungen im Fettgehalt der Leberzellen des im Winter hungernden Salamanders und ihre Ursachen, *Zeitschr. Mikr. Anat. Forsch.*, I, 245–296, 2 pls.

BOCK, FRIEDRICH, 1925: Weiterer Beitrag zur Frage der Ernährung von Amphibienlarven durch im Wasser Gelöste Nährstoffe, *Zool. Anz.*, LXIV, 261–276.

BUDDENBROCK, W. VON, 1928: "Grundriss der vergleichenden Physiologie," Berlin.

COHN, L., 1910: Zur Kenntnis der Munddrüsen einiger Anuren, *Zool. Jahrb. Suppl.*, XII, 719–724.

CROFTS, DORIS R., 1925: The comparative morphology of the caecal gland (rectal gland) of selachian fishes, with some reference to the morphology and physiology of the similar intestinal appendage throughout Ichthyopsida and Sauropsida, *Proc. Zool. Soc. London*, 1925, 101–188.

GOLDSMITH, J. B., and H. W. BEAMS, 1929: A study of the intestinal glands of some urodeles, *Trans. Amer. Micr. Soc.*, XLVIII, 292–301, 2 pls.

GÖPPERT, E., 1891: Die Entwicklung und das spätere Verhalten des Pancreas der Amphibien, *Morph. Jahrb.*, XVII, 100–122, 1 pl.

HADJIOLOFF, A., 1930: Recherches sur le tissue adipeux chez les poissons et la grenouille, *Bull. Hist. appl. physiol. path. tech. micros.*, VII, 8–20.

JACOBSHAGEN, E., 1915: Zur Morphologie des Oberflächenreliefs der Rumpfdarmschleimhaut der Amphibien, *Jena. Zeitschr.*, LIII, 663–716.

KINGSBURY, B. F., 1894: The histological structure of the enteron of Necturus maculatus, *Proc. Amer. Micr. Soc.*, XVI, 19–65.

KRIZENECKY, J., and I. PETROV, 1926: Weitere Untersuchungen über das Wachstum beim absoluten Hungern, *Arch. Entw. Mech.*, CVII, 299–313.

MCDONALD, J. F., C. E. LEISURE, and E. E. LENNEMAN, 1928: Newly discovered controls of ciliary activity, *Amer. Jour. Physiol.*, LXXXV, 395.

MAURER, F., 1911: Die ventrale Rumpfmuskulatur von Menobranchus, Menopoma und Amphiuma, verglichen mit den gleichen Muskeln anderer Urodelen, *Jena. Zeitschr.*, XLVII, 1–40.

MÜLLER, H., 1922: Bestehen Unterschiede in der Pepsinverdauung des Frosches und der Warmblüter? *Arch. Ges. Physiol.*, CXCII, 214–224.

ST. HILLER, M., 1929: L'influence du jeûne sur la régénération chez l'axolotl, *Bull. Int. Acad. Polon. Sci. Let.*, 1928, 191–216.

WEBER, A., 1903: L'origine des glandes annexes de l'intestin moyen chez les vertébrés, *Arch. Anat. Micr.*, V, 487–727, pls. 17–27.

YUNG, E., 1904: De l'influence du régime alimentaire sur la longueur de l'intestin chez les larves de Rana esculenta, *Compt. rend. Acad. Sci. Paris*, CXXXIX, 749–751.

————, 1905: De l'influence de l'alimentation sur la longueur de l'intestin; Expériences sur les larves de Rana esculenta, *Compt. rend. 6me Congr. int. Zool. Berne*, 297–314.

CHAPTER X

THE SKELETON

In a preceding chapter we have traced the emergence of the first tetrapods from their fish ancestors and have seen that after vertebrate life became established on land it reverted not once but many times to the aquatic habitat and that this occurred frequently long before the first modern Amphibia appeared. The skeleton of the early Amphibia shows reductions and other specializations for which there cannot always be found a close environmental correlation. In other words, the skeleton might be considered as something quite independent of the environment changing progressively because of inherent capacities or restrictions. Certain trends of evolution became established and were apparently automatically carried through to an extreme specialization. The same phenomenon is seen to a lesser extent among modern Amphibia, for the families of Salientia may have arboreal, aquatic, or fossorial members with the family characters well defined. It is, therefore, important to isolate as far as possible the slow, progressive changes from the more rapid and adaptive ones. This may be accomplished best by describing the progressive changes in the skeletal elements or, in other words, by reviewing briefly the history of the various parts of the skeleton.

Skull.—The skull of the first tetrapods resembled closely that of their fish ancestors and differed from that of modern Amphibia in the greater number of skull elements, in the greater extent of ossification of the chondocranium or cartilaginous brain case, and in its shape, the early tetrapod skull being high as in most fishes and in all Sauropsida instead of flattened as in modern Amphibia. A thick interorbital septum was present, and the brain lay above the septum.

The skull of the Embolomeri agreed closely with that of the osteolepid fishes. The number and arrangement of the elements forming the skull roof were very similar. In both fish and Amphibia the lateral-line canals were present and crossed the same bones: namely, the lacrimal, prefrontal, jugal, postorbital, postfrontal, supra, and intertemporals. The spiracle had, apparently, become replaced by a tympanum, for the spiracular notch of Osteolepis had the same relation to the skull bones as the otic notch of the Embolomeri (Watson, 1926). The palate of fish and Amphibia agreed in most details. The interpterygoid vacuities were small, and large labyrinthodont teeth were present in both fish and tetrapods. Since internal nares were present in the osteolepids, the latter apparently breathed in the manner of Amphibia. The lower jaw of the Embolomeri was identical with that of the Osteolepidae and differed strikingly from that of modern Amphibia in the large number of bones of which it was composed. It was sheathed outwardly by the dentary and surangular, mesially by three coronoids and a prearticular, ventrally by two splenials and the angular. Only dentary and one other element are invariably present in modern forms, as will be seen below. The dentary and coronoids carried large teeth which were replaced alternately like those in the upper jaw. A shagreening of small teeth was present on the coronoids and prearticulars of some forms.

The chief difference between the skulls of osteolepids and of Embolomeri was to be found in the brain case. The basioccipital condyles of both were single, and the basisphenoids had basipterygoid processes with which the epipterygoids articulated. Posterior to this basisphenoid, as shown in Fig. 2, a large part of the floor of the brain case, or *basis cranii*, of the osteolepids remained unossified. Although the osteolepids may not have been the immediate ancestors of the tetrapods, the resemblance in skull roof, jaws, and palates are so close that we may consider them as having the ancestral type of fish skull from which the amphibian skull was derived.

Progressive Modification of the Skull.—With the origin of the Embolomeri, the highly complex skull inherited from the fishes began to undergo a progressive fenestration. The bones apparently tended to segregate along lines of greatest stress. A second change was the apparent shortening of the skull, for while the Embolomeri retained 12 cranial nerves, the more advanced labyrinthodonts show a gradual shifting posteriorly of the hypoglossal fenestra until in the stereospondyls the hypoglossal nerves lay posterior to the skull as in the case of modern Amphibia. Most reptiles and all mammals have retained the primitive number of 12 cranial nerves within the skull. It is clear, therefore, that the heads of modern Amphibia differ from those of the first tetrapods and of the higher modern forms in that they contain three fewer somites. This loss has been largely in the occipital or "vertebral" part of the skull. Just as any of the posterior vertebrae of a frog are apparently able to produce sacral diapophyses when properly stimulated by the presence of the ilium, so any one of these three or four skull vertebrae is apparently able to produce exoccipitals or basioccipitals if the head size demands it. The homology of the occipital elements lies not so much in their somites of origin as in their mutual relationship and their phylogenetic origin.

Another fundamental change in the evolution of the skull within the labyrinthodonts was its gradual flattening, the trabeculae of the higher types being no longer squeezed together. As a result, the forebrain was dropped lower and lower in the brain case until finally it came to rest on the dorsal surface of the parasphenoid. This progressive flattening reached its extreme in certain stereospondyls and in the aquatic Salientia and Caudata, although all along the line aquatic forms were frequently more flattened than terrestrial ones.

In the evolution of the Labyrinthodontia, and to a certain extent of the other orders of Amphibia, there was a progressive weakening of ossification. Basioccipital, basisphenoid, and supraoccipital became reduced in the Labyrinthodontia and have disappeared entirely in the modern Amphibia. Stadtmüller (1929) has described a separate ossification in the brain case of *Triturus alpestris*, however, which he interprets as a basioccipital. In this way, the original single condyle of the fishes was progressively modified into a tripartite and later into a bipartite condylar surface.   Withdrawal of the basioccipital in the reptile series leads to exactly the same result, in the promammals to the production of a pair of widely separated condyles like those of modern Amphibia.   This is a striking example of convergence, that is, of similar changes in unrelated forms.

Accompanying these major changes, there were a number of minor ones, some destined to produce characteristic structures in the modern forms. The pineal foramen which occurred between the frontals of the osteolepids shifted back to between the parietals in the first tetrapods and finally disappeared entirely. In the reptiles it was retained even to recent times in some forms. The loss of elements in the skull roof was closely correlated with an increase in the size of the eye, and the reduction of the elements in the temporal region gave greater freedom to the temporal muscles. Thus, the solid domelike skull roof of the Embolomeri was restricted enormously during evolution until in the frogs only the premaxillary, maxillary, septomaxillary, nasal, quadratojugal, squamosal, frontal, and parietal bones are left. The urodeles are more primitive than the frogs in retaining in some species both lacrimals and prefrontals in addition to these other elements. Further, the frontals and parietals of each side are free from one another, not fused as in frogs. In some frogs, such as Xenopus, the fronto-parietals of each side may be more or less fused posteriorly with one another. The quadratojugal appears as a separate element in the urodeles only during ontogeny. Probably temporal muscles were largely responsible for the cleaning off of surface bones from the temporal region of the skull of modern Amphibia. In some urodeles the temporal muscles extend beyond the skull and attach to the cervical vertebrae.

The cartilage bones of the brain case, as stated above, also undergo both degeneration and loss during the phylogeny of the Amphibia. The anterior wall of the ear capsule ossifies as a prootic in most frogs and some salamanders, while a separate center of ossification, the opisthotic, appears in the posterior wall of this capsule in Ambystoma, Necturus, Siren, and a few other urodeles. The ossification from the prootic extends posteriorly, while that of the exoccipital spreads into the posterior wall of the ear capsule in most Amphibia. In higher urodeles and in frogs a separate opisthotic never appears, while in the Plethodontidae neither prootic, opisthotic, nor exoccipitals form separate ossifications even in the larvae. This is a specialization away from the labyrinthodont condition. The exoccipitals and prootics frequently fuse in Salientia and in some pipids the combined bones of the two sides may fuse to form a single element. In most Salientia and Caudata the interorbital walls of the brain case ossify to form a sphenethmoid on each side. In some species, especially in burrowing types, the ethmoid may also ossify and fuse with the sphenethmoid. Slow-moving aquatic Amphibia have their brain cases least ossified; burrowing types have them usually the most ossified.

Modification of the Palate.—Progressive changes in the palate region went forward even more rapidly than those on the roof of the skull or in the brain case. Most conspicuous of these changes was the increase in size of the interpterygoid vacuities and the corresponding reduction in width of the pterygoids. The pterygoids within the Labyrinthodontia lost their connection with the basipterygoid processes and in the advanced types were supported by the parasphenoid. The dorsal processes of the pterygoids in modern Amphibia fuse with the ear capsule, while the ventral processes may either fuse with the base of the ear capsule or articulate with it by a joint, the old basipterygoid joint. Primitively the pterygoid cartilage extended far forward, fusing with the nasal capsule, and this condition still maintains in frogs and in some primitive salamanders. In the Plethodontidae the bony pterygoid which forms around the cartilaginous element may either be missing entirely or represented by a small nodule of bone. In Xenopus the posterior mesial borders of the pterygoids grow caudally over the Eustachian tubes which extend across the roof of the throat to open by a single orifice into the pharynx. They thus form a bony protection to the tubes. The ectopterygoid, a very primitive element which is lost early in the history of the phyllospondyls, is still retained in some caecilians such as Hypogeophis. As this element never appears even as a rudiment in frogs and salamanders, it may be considered further evidence that the groups are not closely related.

The palates of modern Amphibia are remarkable in the variability of the bones which occur there. The palatine, for example, may or may not be present within a single genus of frogs. The urodeles are peculiar in that the prevomers and palatines fuse (at least in part during metamorphosis), and the combined structure grows rapidly in a caudal direction in various families. In the salamandrids (Fig. 80) two dentigerous processes of the combined prevomers and palatine are carried back along side of the parasphenoid, while in the plethodontids (Fig. 81), which have been derived from the salamandrids, these two processes overlie the parasphenoid and form a patch of tooth-bearing bone. The prevomers may entirely disappear in some frogs, while in others, such as Bombina, they fuse to form a single element. In Xenopus this fusion is correlated with the reduction of the intermaxillary gland. The latter structure is useless in Amphibia feeding under water, since their tongues have no need of its sticky secretion. The palates of most frogs appear strikingly different from those of urodeles. This is chiefly due to the long maxillae

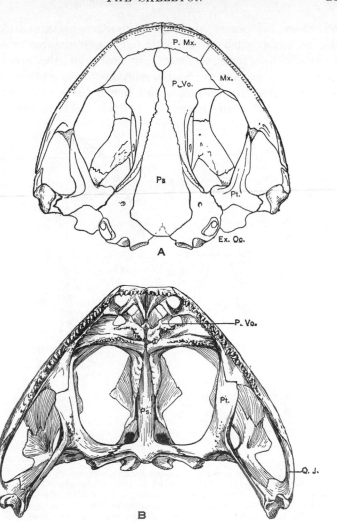

Fig. 80.—Palates of a salamander and a frog showing the fundamental
resemblances in skull structure. The chief difference is that in the salamander,
Tylototriton verrucosus (*A*), the prevomers have grown back along either side of
the parasphenoid, while in the frog, *Rana adspersa* (*B*), these bones retain their
primitive position. Frogs are also primitive in retaining their quadratojugal
which is lost as a separate element in the urodeles. The triradiate pterygoid is
an inheritance from Carboniferous ancestors. *Ex. Oc.*, exoccipital; *Mx.*, *maxilla;*
P.Mx., premaxilla; *Ps.*, parasphenoid; *Pt.*, pterygoid; *P.Vo.*, prevomer bearing
the vomerine teeth; *Q.J.*, quadratojugal.

and short prevomers of frogs. Primitive salamandrids with long maxillae, such as Tylototriton, have palates which are essentially like those of frogs (Fig. 80). On the other hand, Ascaphus, some species of Scaphiopus, and various other Salientia may lack the quadratojugal and hence have a skull outline resembling that of the salamandrid, Pachytriton, closely.

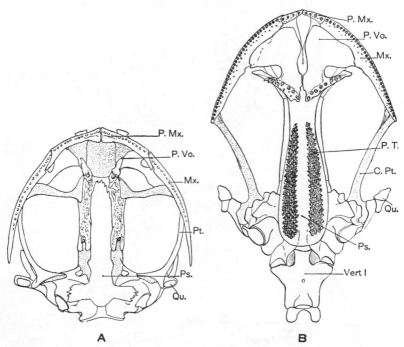

A   B

Fig. 81.—Palates of a frog and a salamander with reduced maxillae. In most salamanders the maxillae fail to reach the quadrate and a quadratojugal is missing. In some frogs, such as *Ascaphus truei* (A), the same condition maintains. Salamanders also specialize in the backward growth of the vomerine bones. In the plethodontids, the posterior processes of these may become separated as the two dentigerous patches shown in *Plethodon glutinosus* (B). *C.Pt.*, cartilaginous pterygoid; *Mx.*, maxilla; *P.Mx.*, premaxilla; *Ps.*, parasphenoid; *Pt.*, pterygoid; *P.T.*, palatine tooth patches; *P.Vo.*, prevomer; *Qu.*, quadrate; *Vert.I.*, first vertebra.

With the flattening of the skull and the widening of the interpterygoid vacuities, the pterygoid underwent considerable change in form. A row of bones which formed a dorsal cover to the palatoquadrate bar of osteolepids and probably represented the metapterygoid and mesopterygoid of teleosts was reduced in the first tetrapods to a single bone. This bone articulated with the basipterygoid process and extended dorsally separating the various branches of the fifth cranial nerve. It was handed on in nearly this form to the reptiles where as the epipterygoid or columella cranii, it is a characteristic element of the lacertilian skull. In the cynodont ancestors of the mammals the epipterygoid became greatly broadened and finally incorporated into the skull of mammals as the alisphenoid (Gregory and Noble, 1924). The epipterygoid was not destined to such an important future in the amphibian series. In the labyrinthodonts it grew larger and developed a process which gained attachment at the prootic. It very soon failed to separate from the pterygoid as a distinct bone and was handed down to modern forms as an ascending

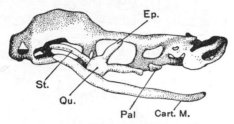

FIG. 82.—Chondrocranium of *Ichthyophis glutinosus* from a model. *Cart.M.*, Meckel's cartilage; *Ep.*, epipterygoid; *Pal.*, palatine cartilage; *St.*, stapes; *Qu.*, quadrate. (*After Winslow.*)

process on the palatoquadrate bar of the larvae (Fig. 82). It is reduced or disappears on metamorphosis in both Caudata and Salientia, and is obscured by secondary bony growths in the adult caecilians.

Changes in the Jaws.—In the development of the skull of urodeles many of the dermal bones of the mouth seem to arise in part by the fusion of the bases of the teeth. This has been interpreted as a harking back to the condition of the first bony fish in which the dermal bones were believed to have arisen by the fusion of the bases of placoid scales. There is no proof of this interpretation in the immediate fossil ancestors of the Amphibia. In the Salientia the bones arise much earlier than the teeth. It would seem that the immediate cause for the development of dermal bones from tooth bases in the Caudata was the early need for teeth and tooth supports in the young carnivorous larvae.

Perhaps the greatest reduction in the phylogeny of the amphibian skull occurred in their jaws. The Embolomeri inherited a

complex mandible of ten pieces. This number is reduced in
labyrinthodonts and branchiosaurs until the extreme condition
of only a dentary and a prearticular are left in the Salientia. In
the most primitive urodeles, the Cryptobranchoidea, there is
not only a dentary, prearticular, and articular, but also an
angular. Single coronoids occur in the larvae of most urodeles
(Fig. 83) and these may ·be cited as another example of a primitive character in these forms. The caecilians, which are primi-

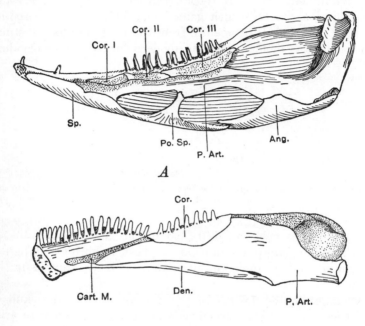

FIG. 83.—The jaw of a labyrinthodont and a urodele compared from the
lingual aspect. The jaw of the labyrinthodont contains many more bones than
the jaw of the urodele. *A. Eogyrinus attheyi (after Watson, Phil. Trans. Roy.
Soc. London, 1926). B. Necturus maculosus. Ang.,* angular; *Cart.M.,* Meckel's
cartilage; *Cor.I.,* coronoid I.; *Cor.II.,* coronoid II; *Cor.III.,* coronoid III; *Den.,*
dentary; *P.Art.,* prearticular; *Po.Sp.,* postsplenial; *Sp.,* splenial.

tive in most features of their skulls, exhibit an early fusion of the
jaw elements. Possibly coronoids are present as well as dentary,
articular, and prearticular, for many genera retain two rows of
teeth in the lower jaw even in the adult. The anterior end of
Meckel's cartilage ossifies as a pair of distinct elements in many
Salientia even in such primitive genera as Ascaphus and Alytes.

Often these symphysial bones are fused to the dentary in Salientia, and they are hardly recognizable or absent in the Pipidae. Their loss in certain species of this family is correlated with a fusion of the premaxillary bones and a modification of the respiratory mechanism characteristic of most Salientia. The symphysial bones seem to have developed in connection with the special function of the premaxillae in closing the nostrils. But it is also possible that they owe their existence as separate elements to their occurrence in the larva, where they form the definitive lower jaw. It may be noted, however, that a mental bone occurred in certain osteolepids (Watson, 1926).

Auditory Apparatus.—Another part of the skull which was closely correlated with function is the auditory apparatus and here we cannot expect to find the progressive evolution seen in some other parts of the skull. The primitive labyrinthodont as represented by Eogyrinus did not transmit the sound waves to a fenestra in the ear capsule. It had a stapes, the fish hyomandibular, but this abutted against the otic capsule. This crude mechanism was improved early in the history of the Labyrinthodontia. A *fenestra ovalis* for the proximal end of the stapes was formed in the capsule. The stapes in some labyrinthodonts, as Eryops, seems to consist of two parts, the inner, the hyomandibular; the outer, the symplectic of fishes. Some Rachitomi, Dissorhophus, and Cacops, specialized in surrounding the tympanum by a bony downward growth of the tabular. The modern Amphibia exhibit a considerable range of variation in their auditory apparatus. In many Salientia the tympanum is hidden under the skin and in a few it may disappear altogether. The stapes also may become greatly reduced, and in some forms, such as Ascaphus, it may be lost. In the urodeles the auditory apparatus is considerably modified from the primitive condition seen in some frogs and fossil Amphibia. The tympanum and middle ear are lost in all urodeles and the stapes becomes connected with the squamosal in the larvae. Here, as a result, the sound waves are transmitted to the quadrate from the lower jaw when that rests on the bottom of the pond, thence are carried to the stapes, and finally to the inner ear.

As discussed in another chapter, this apparatus is further modified in the adult. A piece of the otic capsule, the operculum, may form a footplate for the stapes in some species, but this is apparently not the primitive condition. In primitive frogs (van Seters, 1922) and in caecilians (Peter, 1898) the operculum arises free of the capsule in the membrane closing the *fenestra ovalis*. An opercular muscle stretches from the supra-scapula to the plate and is said to transmit vibrations from the forelimb to the inner ear of the metamorphosed animal. The muscle, which may be homologous with the stapedial muscle of Amniota, strongly suggests that the operculum originally belonged to a movable visceral arch (Goodrich, 1930). In which case the capsular origin of the operculum is a secondary modification. In modern urodeles fusions between operculum and stapes and between operculum and otic capsule is a matter of systematic importance (Reed, 1920; Dunn, 1922).

Although the operculum may undergo various modifications during phylogeny, other features of the urodele auditory appara-tus may be more conservative. The columella and ceratohyal of the urodeles chondrify out of a single blastema (Kingsbury and Reed, 1908). Very early the columella forms an attachment to the squamosal and not to the quadrate as in caecilians. This is very suggestive of the conditions in labyrinthodonts from which the branchiosaur ancestors of urodeles and frogs were evolved. As shown by Sushkin (1927), the columella extends not downward to the laterally placed quadrate but upward to make an articula-tion by its suprastapedial process with the parotic crest. This columella was apparently equipped with a cartilaginous outer section which was in contact with a tympanum. Its inner portion was perforated by a stapedial artery as in caecilians. Frogs approach the first tetrapods in their otic equipment more closely than the other modern Amphibia do. A special feature is the tympanic annulus, a ring of cartilage surrounding the tympanum. This develops from the quadrate and does not seem to have a homologue in the otic apparatus of fossil forms. Modifications of the otic apparatus occur chiefly in aquatic or burrowing forms. In the aquatic Pipidae the tympanum lies under the skin and the Eustachian tubes open by a common orifice in the roof of the pharynx as in crocodiles.

Visceral Skeleton.—The visceral skeleton of modern forms seems to be very erratically modified. A closer study, however, reveals certain trends of evolution which may be noted here. If we compare the loosely hung jaws of the modern fish with the firmly attached ones of the Amphibia, it would seem that an enormous change must have taken place in these structures in the transformation of fish into tetrapods. A comparison of the jaws of the embolomerous amphibian with those of the osteolepid fish shows, however, that the change was actually a slight one. In both fish and tetrapod the upper jaw was firmly attached to the anterior part of the neural cranium. Laterally it was securely held by the maxilla, while mesially the basipterygoid process formed a strong support. In both groups the posterior jaw elements were freed for other functions; namely, the transmission of sound waves to the otic capsule. A very similar but purely convergent transformation occurred again in the origin of mammals from cynodont reptiles. In these forms the dentary found a new point of articulation for the lower jaw and left the posterior jaw elements free to be changed into the otic ossicles or sound transmission device of the Mammalia.

The visceral arches of the osteolepid fish consist of the mandibular, hyoid, and five branchial arches. The jaws of osteolepid and primitive labyrinthodont were almost identical but the hyoid arch differed slightly. Here the hyomandibular had already been changed into a stapes and had not only shifted its position relative to the otic capsule but also, according to Watson (1926), had split its proximal end into two parts, the upper of which retained the original position of the hyomandibular, while the lower moved down to the position of the future *fenestra ovalis*. Such a bifid head of the stapes is seen in modern reptiles. Thus, in the stapes, as in many features of the skull, we must look to the reptiles for more primitive conditions than exist in modern Amphibia. The Salientia in retaining a tympanic membrane and long columella are far less specialized than the urodeles, but neither are so primitive in this respect as the reptiles. The columella of Rana, at least, develops independently of the hyoid. The Eustachian tube also has a specialized mode of development. Hence, again we must rely on our palaeontological rather than on our embryological record for an understanding of the origin of these structures.

Since the gill arches in the adult urodele or frog are modified by reduction and fusion, the larval branchial arches have been considered more primitive. Gill arches of larval Branchiosauria and Rachitomi approach those of larval urodeles in form. It is highly probable that all groups of Amphibia, at least above the Rachitomi, primitively passed through a larval life in the water. At least one rachitomous form, Dwinasaurus, already in Permian

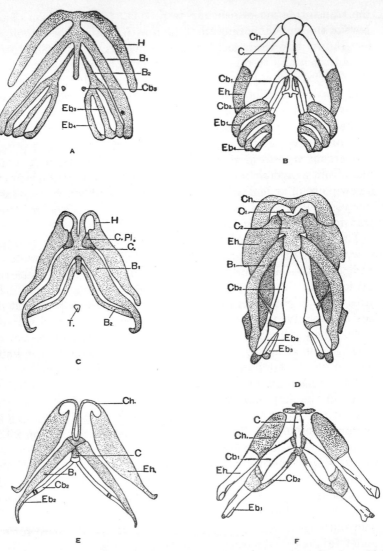

Fig. 84.—A comparison of three stages in the ontogeny of the hyobranchial skeleton of Hynobius (*A*, *C*, and *E*) with the same structure in the adults of three other urodeles. The hyobranchial skeleton of Siren (*B*) is essentially that of an early larva, while the skeleton of Megalobatrachus (*D*) represents a partly metamorphosed condition. The hyobranchial of the adult Triturus (*F*), while fully metamorphosed, is more specialized than that of the adult Hynobius. B_{1-2}, branchial arches I and II; C_{1-2}, copular series; Cb_{1-3}, ceratobranchials I to III; *Ch*, ceratohyal; *C.Pl.*, copular plate; Eb_{1-4}, epibranchials I to IV; *Eh.*, epihyal; *H*, hyoid; *T.*, os thyreoideum. (*A*, *C*, *and E after Tsusaki, B after Fukuda;* not drawn to the same scale.)

times had become neotenous. The presence of gill arches in this form is not an indication of its lowly phylogenetic position but merely a proof that almost at the base of the Amphibian stem some forms began to fail to complete their development. Gilled adults have not "secondarily returned to the water" but have failed to leave their habitat of infancy for the reason that their adult structures have failed to develop (Fig. 84). The gill arches of Dwinasaurus were of the same number and had the same arrangement as those of larval ambystomids.

The condition of the branchial arches in the metamorphosed labyrinthodont is unknown, and it is idle to speculate as to the steps by which the gill arches of the osteolepids were changed into those of the first metamorphosed tetrapods. Can we in this case resort to the embryological record as a possible guide? All larval urodeles and Salientia have from three to four branchial arches, while the metamorphosed adults have no more than two. This is correlated with the change in function, more arches being necessary to support the clefts than to give attachment to tongue muscles. At metamorphosis the posterior arches are not merely lost and the anterior ones shifted to the final position. As Smith (1920) has shown, the process involves degeneration of other parts of the visceral skeleton and the formation of much new tissue. Whether the first tetrapods on metamorphosis underwent such a revolutionary change in their branchial arches is unknown, but it is highly probable that in this case as with all other metamorphic processes, the change was originally a very gradual one.

The hyobranchial skeleton of the adult Amphibia exhibits considerable variety of form. In the hynobiid salamanders and in most frogs the hyoid arches are long and continuous with the basihyal or copula. In most urodeles the lateral portions of the hyoid arches (epihyals) are free from the basihyal, which may be carried far beyond the mouth when the tongue is protruded. In these forms the basihyal, or copula, may bear one or two pairs of cornua. Some urodeles, especially Ambystomidae, possess an arcuate bar in the floor of the pharynx connecting one pair of cornua. In many urodeles the posterior part of the copular piece of the larval hyobranchial separates on metamorphosis from the remainder of the apparatus and ossifies as a distinct *os thyreoideum* lying cephalad to the pericardium. Neither of these modifications is found in the hyobranchials of other Amphibia.

The perennibranchs possess a hyobranchial apparatus which is essentially larval, although a partial metamorphosis occurs in this structure in Megalobatrachus. Amphiuma and Necturus exhibit various reductions which do not appear to be metamorphic (Noble, 1929). The hyobranchial apparatus of the adult caecilians consists of a single hyoid and first branchial arch fused and followed by two or three separate branchial arches. This retention of the branchial arches in adult life may be considered a neotenous feature in caecilians but it may also be correlated with the poor development of the tongue musculature in this group. In the adult Salientia the hyobranchial apparatus consists of a cartilaginous plate bearing three or four pairs of processes. The most anterior pair, the hyoids, are long and slender. They extend posteriorly and make attachment to the skull, a secondary modification. The most posterior, the thyroid processes, are usually well ossified and support the larynx. Although some of this apparatus is derived from the larval hyobranchial, part of it arises *de novo*. In the Pipidae the reduction of the tongue and elaboration of the lungs and bronchus have led to the development of a boxlike hyobranchial apparatus with a loss of the hyoid (Ridewood, 1898), in at least one genus (Pipa). Other changes in the structure of the hyobranchial apparatus of adult Amphibia may have a phylogenetic rather than a functional significance. For example, the Hynobiidae retain two epibranchials after metamorphosis, while other salamanders have only one (or the barest rudiment of the second).

Laryngeal Skeleton.—The modern Amphibia have the laryngeal cartilages more or less specialized. In forms provided with a voice the laryngeal cartilages would in all probability be well developed. The presence of a tympanum in the first tetrapods suggests that they may have used their voice to attract the females as do modern frogs. A larval larynx is not necessarily a primitive one. How closely the larynx of the first tetrapods approached that of the most primitive frogs is unknown. The form of the larynx in modern Amphibia is sometimes of systematic importance as, for example, in the Pelobatidae (Beddard, 1907).

Vertebrae.—In the classification of the Labyrinthodontia, the form and composition of the vertebrae as stated in Chap. I are of primary importance. The vertebrae also present diagnostic characters for the classification of various other major groups of Amphibia, and hence their evolution may be considered in some detail. The vertebrae of some modern fish, such as Amia, are embolomerous in part, in that a single neural arch is associated with two centra in each segment. The same was true of some of the vertebrae of the crossopterygian fish, Eusthenopteron, which stood near the main line of tetrapod evolution. The development of the vertebrae in Amia shows that each is formed by the ossification and growth of four pairs of arch cartilages as well as by an ossification in the perichordal sheath. The cartilages are formed from mesenchyme which condenses in the region of greatest strain, namely the point where the myosepta, which are under muscular pull, join the relatively stiff notochord at its upper and lower surfaces. Thus on each side of the body four blocks of cartilage develop, pressed against each myoseptum at its junction with the notochord, the two anterior blocks of each side belonging to one myotome and the two posterior, to another. The four pairs of blocks together with what ossification may occur in the sheath around the notochord form the basis of a single vertebra which lies with its midpoint between two myotomes. The cartilaginous blocks, or arcualia, have been given names by Gadow. The pair lying in the posterior part of one myotome and above the notochord are the "basidorsals." The pair immediately below them are the "basiventrals." The arcualia formed in the anterior part of a myotome and above the notochord are the "interdorsals," those below them the "interventrals." Each vertebra is formed by the union of the basidorsals and basiventrals of one segment with the interdorsals and interventrals of a posterior one.

In the Embolomeri at the very base of the amphibian phylum each neural arch was provided with two centra. The anterior centrum apparently represents the basiventral which has grown dorsally and, possibly uniting with an ossification in the perichordal sheath, formed an amphicoelous disc. The posterior centrum apparently represents the interdorsal and interventral fused or united by an ossification of the perichordal sheath to form a similar disc.

In the evolution of the Labyrinthodontia a gradual weakening in the ossification of the skeleton occurred. The Rachitomi, being a step in advance over the Embolomeri, have failed to ossify the perichordal sheath of the vertebrae completely, with the result that the four arcualia (Fig 85B) or cartilaginous blocks remain more or less separate on ossification. Each basiventral side may fuse with its mate of the opposite to form a moon-shaped element which, unfortunately for the sake of

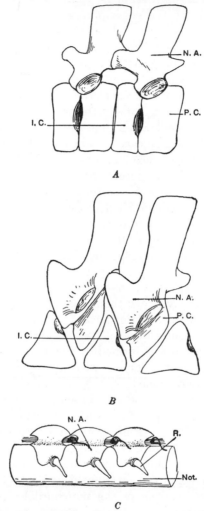

Fig. 85.—Three types of vertebrae characteristic of extinct orders of Amphibia, viewed from the left side. These types also represent stages in the progressive reduction of ossification in phylogeny: *A.* Cricotus, an embolomerous labyrinthodont. *B.* Eryops, a rachitomous labyrinthodont. *C.* Branchiosaurus, with epichordal vertebrae. (*After Whittard.*) *I.C.*, intercentrum; *N.A.*, neural arch; *Not.*, notochord; *P.C.*, pleurocentrum; *R.*, rib.

clarity, is called an "intercentrum." The interventrals, which ossify free of the other elements, are called "pleurocentra," while the interdorsals, which are of rare occurrence, are described as "dorsal pleurocentra." In the sturgeon, Acipenser, where the ossification of the skeleton is poorly developed, these four pairs of blocks remain cartilaginous and illustrate in a diagrammatic way the cartilaginous basis of the vertebrae of all back-boned animals. The vertebrae of the Rachitomi represent an ossification of these blocks. In most cases, there is, in addition, a fusion of the basiventrals and a loss of the interdorsals.

In the Stereospondyli the pleurocentra, that is, the interdorsal and interventral, are reduced or lost. It is possible that they remain cartilaginous. The single centrum of these labyrinthodonts probably includes a perichordal ossification as well as the basidorsal and basiventral, but this is only an inference based on the development of recent forms. Reptiles, which sprang from embolomerous Amphibia, have emphasized the interdorsal and interventral elements at the expense of the basidorsal and basiventral, an arrangement exactly opposite to that of the Amphibia.

In the lepospondyls and phyllospondyls it is impossible to determine how much was formed by arcualia and how much by perichordal sheath. It seems probable, however, that the interdorsal and interventral were reduced to cartilaginous rings between the centra, the latter being formed from perichordal sheath together with some contribution from the basidorsal and basiventral. This reduction of the interdorsal and interventral brings the rib to an intervertebral position, and this may be considered the primitive position for the rib in the lepospondyls. In all phyllospondyls the rib has shifted to the side of the vertebra and is attached to a well-marked transverse process. The vertebrae of frogs and salamanders agree in the extensive development of the perichordal ossification, the basidorsal and the basiventral being intimately associated with it in their ossification. Primitive frogs, the Liopelmidae, agree with primitive urodeles in that the interdorsal and interventral remain cartilaginous throughout life; the vertebrae are thus amphicoelous, as in lepospondyls and some phyllospondyls. In Ascaphus these cartilaginous rings serve to hold the vertebrae together and no joint surfaces are formed. In higher frogs and urodeles this cartilaginous ring or ball splits in such a way that most of the cartilage is either on the anterior or the posterior end of a vertebra. When the cartilage ossifies an opisthocoelous or a procoelous vertebra results, according to whether the ball is on the anterior or the posterior end of the centrum. In a few pelobatid and bufonid toads the ball ossifies but remains more or less free from the centra on either side of it. This ossification of the interdorsal and interventral cartilages is an advance in vertebral evolution not found in either lepospondyls or, at least in its typical form, in phyllospondyls. Except for this feature the vertebrae of modern Amphibia agree closely with those of these extinct orders.

The development of a vertebra does not always give a clear picture of its phylogenetic origin. Thus, in Rana the basidorsals appear but soon fuse to form two longitudinal strips along the upper surface of the notochord. A similar cartilaginous strip which develops along the ventral side of the notochord produces regular swellings. These have been homologized with fused basiventrals and interventrals. Ingrowths of the dorsal cartilaginous strips begin to constrict the notochord and the ossification beginning in them spreads round the notochord in the perichordal sheath. Cartilage, apparently representing the interdorsals, early appears intervertebrally and when it ossifies forms a ball which may remain attached to the centrum either before or after it. Most vertebrae in Rana are procoelous, that is, the ossified intervertebral cartilage remains attached to the centrum anterior to it. In the coccygeal region the three longitudinal strips of cartilage never split into distinct vertebrae but ossify to form a rodlike bone, the coccyx or urostyle.

In the primitive Discoglossidae, Pipidae and Pelobatidae, the perichordal sheath may not ossify, and when the notochord is reduced on metamorphosis, vertebrae are produced with greatly flattened centra. It seems probable that branchiosaurs had the same type of vertebrae (Fig. 85, C). The Gymnophiona, which have been found to be so primitive in various features of their skull and vertebrae, might be expected to afford a primitive type of vertebral development. Marcus and Blume (1926) have followed the development of the vertebrae of Hypogeophis. Gadow's four pairs of arcualia appear, but the basidorsal and interdorsal fuse to form the neural arch, the intervertebral cartilage which is poorly developed arising from the ventral arcualia. Even in this primitive group, cartilaginous strips appear before the arcualia and take part in their formation. Marcus and Blume have showed that similar parachordal cartilages appear in other vertebrates, although their homology with the early cartilage strips in frog vertebrae is not clear. An important feature in the ontogeny of Hypogeophis is the retention of the early embryonic metamerism in the ventral arcualia. While the basidorsal of one segment unites with the interdorsal of the succeeding to form the neural arch, the basiventral and interventral of the first segment form the ventral arch of the resulting vertebra. Possibly the Lepospondyli, with ribs intervertebrally situated, have vertebrae which developed the same way. Since this can never be determined in these fossil forms, it is impossible to say how closely the lepospondyls agree with the Gymnophiona in the composition of their vertebrae.

The number of vertebrae ranges from over 200 in some caecilians to only 6 segments in the Roraima toad, Oreophrynella, and in the African Hymenochirus of a very different family. In the latter, more than in the former, the composite nature of the sacrum is indicated by its great length. Hymenochirus is thoroughly aquatic, while Oreophrynella is terrestrial, and hence this reduction in the number of vertebrae is not correlated with a special type of habitat. The number of vertebrae may be reduced by a fusion of the first and second vertebrae as in some species of Xenopus and of Atelopus. Salientia have fewer vertebrae than Caudata. The most primitive family of frogs, the Liopelmidae, have one more presacral vertebra than any other Salientia. The pelvis may attach to any one of a great number of vertebrae. Thus, in Amphiuma there are 63 vertebrae exclusive of the caudals, while in the more primitive, shorter-bodied urodeles this number of dorsal vertebrae is usually less than 20. The increase in number of vertebrae may continue during life. In a small but fully formed *Batrachoseps attenuatus* 2.3 cm. from snout to vent, I find there are 22 dorsal vertebrae and 28 caudals, a number which approximates that found in some species of Plethodon. In an adult 4.75 cm. head and body length, there are 22 dorsals and 61 caudals. Hence, the number of tail vertebrae more than doubles during the active terrestrial life of this species. The frogs and toads are characterized by the reverse phenomenon, namely, the reduction of the tail during ontogeny. Correlated with this reduction, the caudal cartilages fuse to form a bony rod, the coccyx. In the Discoglossidae the diapophyses of the first of these coccygeal vertebrae are formed as small but discrete elements. The number of potential vertebrae taking part in the formation of the coccyx is difficult to estimate, for a separation is indicated during ontogeny in only two or three of the more anterior ones. The caudal vertebrae of urodeles are much more primitive. They are provided ventrally with a series of processes, the haemal arches. As shown by Gamble (1922), these arise like the parapophyses as a pair of processes from the basiventrals. In the trunk region the parapophyses enlarge, while in the tail region the haemapophyses dominate, the parapophyses disappearing.

The first vertebra of the column is modified for articulation with the skull. It is cup-shaped without transverse processes but with two facets for the occipital condyles. There is no atlas-axis complex as in higher vertebrates for the rotation of the head. In many Caudata there is an anteriorly directed process on the first vertebra, however, which bears a pair of additional facets. This process may represent a part of a vertebra, the neural arch of which has been lost.

Ribs.—The ribs in primitive Amphibia were long and tended to surround the body like a series of hoops. They articulated with the vertebrae as far as the middle of the tail. The ribs are genetically closely related to the various processes of the vertebrae; namely, diapophyses, parapophyses, haemapophyses, and rib bearers. Unlike these processes they usually arise in the septa at a distance from the notochord and later gain an articulation with the vertebrae. With the shifting of the horizontal muscle septum, the ribs come to lie higher on the vertebrae and thus the parapophyses may gradually change into the diapophyses. The ribs were primitively single-headed but even in some Embolomeri they have become two-headed. The lower head, or capitulum, articulates principally with the basiventral, while the upper head, or tubercle, abuts against the basidorsal. The ribs of Gymnophiona, when they first appear in ontogeny, are continuous with the vertebrae. Since the capitulum apparently is derived from the ventral arcualia, the tubercle from the dorsal arcualia, Marcus and Blume (1926) have assumed the two-headed condition of the rib primitive. The septum in which the rib rises may change its relationship to the vertebrae and hence various shiftings of the ribs have occurred during phylogeny. Thus, within the lepospondyls the vertebrae either may have the primitive intervertebral position or may articulate with diapophyses extending from the side of the arch. Both frogs and salamanders, since they arose from the typical branchiosaurs, presumably had their ribs attached to stout diapophyses. This condition is

retained in the frogs. A very similar condition is found in hynobiids and cryptobranchids. In most urodeles the ribs are two-
headed and attach lower on the side of the vertebrae than in
frogs. In a single animal, such as Necturus, the capitular head
of the ribs shifts from a parapophysis, or process from the side
of the centrum in the vertebrae of the trunk region, to a ribbearer,
a more dorsal process of the second and third vertebrae (Gamble,
1922). This division of a rib head into a capitulum and tubercle
may have originated within the Caudata. At least it is not found
in frogs and reaches its greatest development in the more specialized urodeles. The functional significance of double-headed
ribs would seem to lie in their mechanical advantage over single-
headed ones in resisting the downward pull of the viscera in
terrestrial life.

Although the ribs are long in some labyrinthodonts and lepospondyls, they never meet in the midline or take part in the formation of the sternum. In the branchiosaurs the ribs are short and
straight, and this condition is inherited by frogs and salamanders.
It is sometimes assumed that the ribs of Amphibia are duplex
structures which have arisen by the fusion of the dorsal and
ventral ribs of fishes (Naef, 1929). Although there is no reason
why the rib-forming mesenchyme may not shift its position in
the septa, there is no palaeontological proof of this fusion of
dorsal and ventral ribs in the ancestors of modern Amphibia.

In the primitive salamandrids, such as the Spanish newt,
Pleurodeles waltl, and also in its close relative, Tylototriton, the
tips of the ribs may be pointed and actually protrude through
the skin. This modification of the ribs finds a parallel in the
toes of some African frogs where the terminal phalanges protrude
through the integument. The modification in the urodeles is
believed to serve as a mode of protection.

In the more long-bodied salamanders, such as Siren and
Amphiuma, the ribs are greatly reduced in number and are
found only on the anterior vertebrae. In the Salientia the
reduction has reached an extreme; only the liopelmids and
discoglossids retain ribs in the adult, but the pipids have
ribs while larvae. These ribs in the pipid larvae later fuse
to the diapophyses of the vertebrae and are not distinguishable from them. No ribs appear as distinct ossifications in
Salientia higher than the Pipidae, although bits of cartilage
are frequently found on the ends of the diapophyses.

Abdominal Ribs.—The ventral side of the body of many Labyrinthodontia, Lepospondyli, and especially Phyllospondyli was sheathed with a coat of closely set bony rods or plates. These had various forms and sizes but they were usually arranged in a series of ∧-shaped rows, with the apexes directed forward. They are unknown in the Stereospondyli and may have been lost in other higher Labyrinthodontia. The reptiles inherited their abdominal ribs from embolomerous ancestors. The turtles fused some of them together to form part of the plastron. Sphenodon and some lizards retain them as slender rods of cartilage or bone in the ventral musculature (see Camp, 1923).

The abdominal ribs were well developed in the branchiosaur ancestors of the Caudata and Salientia. Large cartilages of much the same form as the abdominal ribs of the lizards appear in the myosepta of the *M. rectus abdominis* of Liopelma (Fig. 94). Goette found in Bombina some traces of paired cartilage formation in the ventral musculature which, according to Gegenbaur, might correspond to the ventral sections of true ribs. The abdominal ribs, however, have no ontogenetic nor phylogenetic relationship to the true ribs. They are dermal elements similar to the interclavicle in origin. The development of these slips of cartilage in the Liopelmidae and Discoglossidae has not been studied. In their adult condition they appear to be remnants of the abdominal basket of the branchiosaurs. Similar pieces of cartilage have been described in Necturus, but in no urodele are they so well developed as in Liopelma.

Pectoral Girdle.—The pectoral girdles of frogs and salamanders appear very different, although they both were derived from the same type originally. The Embolomeri inherited a girdle almost exactly like that of their fish ancestors except that a new element, the interclavicle, was added to its ventral surface. The girdle consisted of two half rings articulating in the midventral line with the interclavicle. The bulk of each half ring was formed by a single element, the scapula or scapulo-coracoid, for in the higher Amphibia there are two centers of ossification in this element. On the anterior edge of the scapulo-coracoid were a clavicle and a cleithrum as in fish. In the most primitive Embolomeri there were also a supracleithrum and a post-temporal attaching the clavicle to the skull.

Within the Labyrinthodontia there occurred an increase in the size of the scapulo-coracoid element at the expense of the dermal

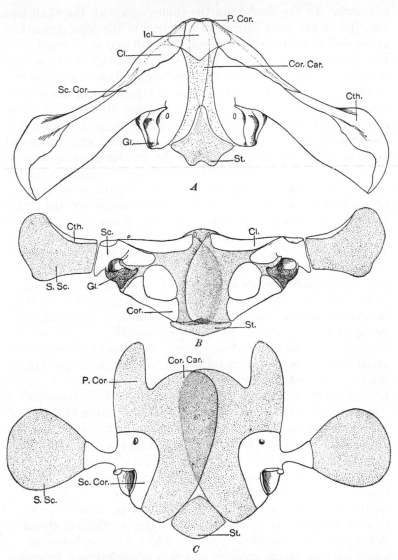

FIG. 86.—The pectoral girdles of three orders of Amphibia showing a progressive loss in the bony elements and an increase in cartilage. *A.* Eryops, a labyrinthodont (*after Miner*). *B.* Ascaphus, a primitive frog. *C. Ambystoma jeffersonianum*, a salamander. *Cl,* clavicle; *Cor.,* coracoid; *Cor.Car.,* coracoid cartilage; *Cth.,* cleithrum; *Gl.,* glenoid; *Icl.,* interclavicle; *P.Cor.,* procoracoid; *S.Sc.,* suprascapula; *Sc.,* scapula; *Sc.Cor.,* scapulo-coracoid; *St.* sternum.

elements.   In the Rachitomi the connection with the skull was
lost, but in the more terrestrial members of the same group the
girdle shifted so near to the base of the skull that there could have
been little movement of the neck.   The formation of the double
occipital condyle further strengthened the skull against side movements.   In the more advanced labyrinthodonts of undoubted
aquatic habits there occurred a broadening of the ventral elements.   The loss of the clavicle, interclavicle, and cleithrum in
the urodeles (Fig. 86) may have been correlated with continued
aquatic habits, possibly also with the greater development of
movement in the forelimbs.   The branchiosaurs afford a valuable
clue to the origin of the distinctive features of the pectoral girdle
of modern Amphibia.   Not only their coracoids but the entire
glenoid region was unossified.   They still retain a very narrow
clavicle and cleithrum and usually a small interclavicle while
specializing in the development of a broad cartilaginous coracoid.
The urodeles merely extend this condition one step further; they
lost the dermal elements and further broadened the coracoid.

The primitive Salientia approach the branchiosaurs even more
closely in the form of their pectoral girdle, the chief difference
being that the posterior part of the coracoid cartilage became
ossified as a distinct piece, while the glenoid extended its
ossification into the procoracoid region in some forms (Liopelmidae).   The main part of the cartilaginous ventral plate of the
branchiosaurs remained unossified anteriorly to form the so-called
"procoracoid cartilage" (Fig. 86).   It is interesting to note that
two salamanders, Siren and Pseudobranchus, have also developed
an ossification in the posterior half of the coracoid plate.   This
must be considered a change parallel to that of frogs.   The dorsal
end of the scapula frequently calcifies in Salientia, and it may
ossify as a suprascapula, which is not to be confused with the
cleithrum in the same region.   Urodeles are peculiar in the great
dilation of the coracoid cartilage and in the extension of the anterior process, the so-called "procoracoid."   The two halves of the
girdle overlap in the midline and this is doubtless a primitive
inheritance.

Within the Salientia many modifications of the pectoral girdle
take place.   In various families the two halves may fuse in the
midline (Fig. 87), forming the firmisternal type of girdle as
distinguished from the more primitive arciferal type where the
two halves merely overlap.   Within a single family, the Brevici-

pitidae, both clavicle and procoracoid may become lost entirely. An anterior extension of the procoracoid cartilage in the midline frequently splits off to form a distinct element which may become ossified. This is the so-called "omosternum," which in some families, especially in the Polypedatidae and African Ranidae, may become widely forked posteriorly. The sternum is a cartilaginous plate in primitive frogs, and since a sternum is never found among the fossilized remains of branchiosaurs and labyrinthodonts, it may have been represented by a cartilaginous piece in these ancestral groups as well. In primitive frogs the sternum resembles the abdominal ribs but possesses anteriorly two leaves fitting between the coracoid cartilages. In the higher Salientia these leaves are lost and the diverging processes of the sternum fuse to form a single plate which in the many advanced types may become ossified. The sternum of the discoglossids resembles that of urodeles, while that of many higher Salientia is specialized not only by calcifying or ossifying but also by assuming a plate or rodlike form. The narrow, bony sternum of Rana represents the extreme condition of this modification.

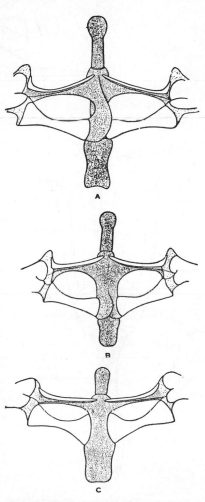

Fig. 87.—The pectoral girdles of three neotropical frogs showing the change from the arciferal to the firmisternal type. *A. Eleutherodactylus bransfordii. B. Sminthillus limbatus. C. Rhinoderma darwinii.*

Pelvic Girdle.—The pelvis of the primitive Embolomeri was a distinct advance over the condition found in any fish. It was

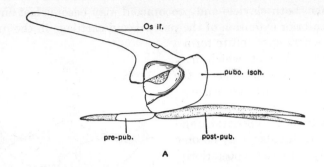

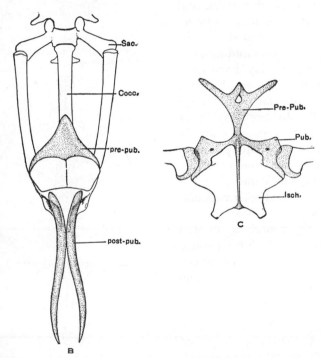

Fig. 88.—The pelvis of a frog and that of a salamander compared. *A*. Pelvis of *Ascaphus truei* viewed laterally. *B*. Same seen from below. *C*. Ventral aspect of pelvis of *Tylototriton verrucosus*. A prepubis occurs in both. In the salamander the pubis is cartilaginous, while in the frog it is fused with the ischium. *Cocc.*, coccyx; *Isch.*, ischium; *Os.il.*, ilium; *post-pub.*, postpubis; *pre-pub.* prepubis; *Pub.*, pubis; *pubo.isch.*, puboischium; *Sac.*, sacrum.

a triradiate structure on each side with a long ilium, a short ischium and pubis meeting in the acetabulum (Fig. 88*A*). The more terrestrial labyrinthodonts had all three elements well ossified, and such a girdle was handed on to the reptiles as a primitive inheritance. Within the Embolomeri various changes

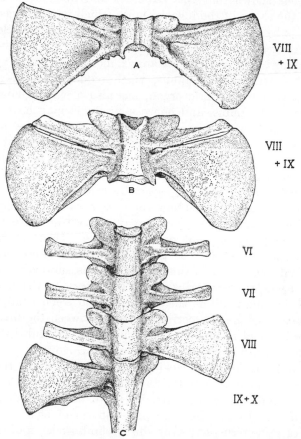

VIII + IX

VIII + IX

VI

VII

VIII

IX + X

Fig. 89.—Variation in the sacrum of *Atelopus varius*. A single vertebra, the ninth, usually forms the sacrum, but others may fuse with it.

occurred. Watson (1926) has shown that Diplovertebron retained a cartilaginous pubis, and this condition was handed on to the branchiosaurs and to modern frogs and salamanders. Amphibia never have the large obturator foramen characteristic of the pelvis of reptiles, nor do they usually ossify the pubis. In the Salientia the pelvis is greatly compressed, and in some species the pubis is calcified, or even ossified. The cartilaginous pubis is, however, the primitive inheritance of both frogs and salamanders.

Many aquatic urodeles have developed a Y-shaped cartilage attached to the anterior end of the pubis (Fig. 88C). Whipple (1906) has shown that this structure and its muscles serve to control the shape of the inflated lungs which in these species act largely as hydrostatic organs. Contraction of the muscles pulls the cartilages dorsally, forcing the air anteriorly into the lungs and making the head end of the animal more buoyant. It may be noted, however, that Ascaphus, which frequents streams and has no need of a hydrostatic organ, has also a cartilaginous plate anterior to the pubis, and hence a prepubis may have been a primitive character of modern Amphibia. Ascaphus has also developed a pair of rodlike cartilages lying on the ventral surface of the pubis of the male and serving as a support for the copulatory apparatus which is unique in this frog.

The pelvis of Salientia is especially characterized by its long ilia which make a ligamentous connection with the diapophyses of the sacral vertebrae. There may be two or three of these pairs of diapophyses, but one is the rule. In some Salientia these diapophyses may be greatly expanded (Fig. 89). The functional significance of this modification is, however, not clear. In the urodeles, sacral ribs afford a support to the ilia. The pelvis is lacking in Siren, the caecilians, and some lepospondyls.

Limbs.—The general correspondence between the fins of fish and the limbs of tetrapods is obvious, but the detailed record of how the former were converted during Devonian or Silurian times into the latter is lacking. Anatomists have, therefore, come from time to time to the rescue of the evolutionist and have advanced many ingenious theories as to how fins might have changed into legs. Thus the fin supports of sharks, of lung fishes, of Polypterus, and even the forelimb skeleton of the very young salamander larva have been taken by the advocates of one or the other theory as a basis for further modifications. The difficulty with all these theories is that they are based on modern forms, and where any palaeontological evidence is available this should be considered first to the exclusion of all other data.

The skeletons of the forelimbs of only a few generalized crossopterygians are known. These consist of a proximal humerus and two distal elements which may be called "radius" and "ulna." Distal to the latter are a series of elements too numerous to be homologized with definite digits. The most radical change in the evolution of the fish paddle into the forelimb of tetrapods must have been in the reduction of elements in this distal row. The fundamental plan of humerus, radius, ulna, and a series of digits was marked out in the skeleton of the fish paddle long before the tetrapods evolved (Fig. 90).

Embolomeri might have been expected to show the most primitive type of tetrapod limb. Watson (1926) has shown

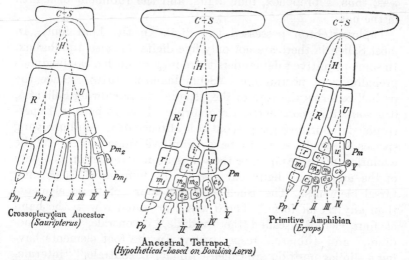

Fig. 90.—Diagram of the evolution of the carpus: $c.$, centrale; c_{1-5}, carpalia; C-S, scapulo-coracoid, H, humerus; $i.$, intermedium; m_{1-5}, medialia; Pp, prepollex; Pm, postminimus; r, radiale; R, radius; u, ulnare; U, ulna. (*After Gregory, Miner and Noble.*)

that Diplovertebron agreed with the oldest reptiles in having five well-developed fingers and toes. On the other hand, Gregory, Miner, and Noble (1923) found evidence of a prepollex in the rachitomous Eryops, and although four well-developed digits were present, there was space for cartilaginous pieces which might represent a fifth and a sixth digit. It might be argued that the short thumb of Diplovertebron represents the prepollex of modern Amphibia, but Steiner (1921) found that in Bombina five digits were present in the blastema of the hand as well as the prepollex. The prepollex has also been described in the embryo of reptiles (Steiner, 1922). Thus there can be no doubt that the original hand consisted of a prepollex as well as five digits and possibly also a cartilaginous rudiment of a sixth digit. In all Amphibia above the Embolomeri, only four functional digits are known, although some fossil types, to judge from the tracks, may have had a supporting ray on the inner side, namely, the prepollex. In frogs and toads the prepollex is often enlarged in the male to serve as a gripping organ during amplexus. A bony prepollex is, moreover, present in some salamanders such as *Ambystoma opacum*. The inheritance of modern Amphibia was, thus, a prepollex, four digits, and the rudiment of a fifth in the hand.

Diplovertebron possessed five digits in the hind foot. In most Salientia there are not only five digits but also a prehallux. In some primitive salamanders there may be both a cartilaginous prehallux and postminimus (Schmalhausen, 1910). Since the prehallux forms the core of the "spade" in burrowing Salientia, it is sometimes considered a neomorph. It is, to be sure, hypertrophied in burrowing types, but as it also occurs in non-burrowing species it would seem to be a primitive inheritance. In the evolution of the Amphibia there has been a reduction not only of the number of digits but also in the number of carpal and tarsal elements. The Rachitomi had more of these elements than any recent form. There was a proximal row in the hand of four elements called the "radiale," "centrale," "intermedium," and "ulnare," respectively. In the foot elements having a similar position are called "tibiale," "centrale," "intermedium," and "fibulare." Distal to this proximal row in hand and foot, there was, respectively, a row of three carpal and three tarsal elements, called "medialia" by Schmalhausen. Distal to these were five carpalia in the hand and five tarsalia in the foot. There was, therefore, an almost exact correspondence between the elements in the primitive carpus and those of the primitive tarsus.

The carpus and tarsus of modern Amphibia differ from those of Rachitomi in exhibiting various fusions. The primitive salamanders approached most closely to the original condition. Schmalhausen (1917) found that the tarsus in Ranodon differed from that of Trematops only in that tarsalia I and II are fused. In the Salientia marked changes have occurred in all three rows of elements and also in the long bones of the legs. Radius and ulna are no longer separate but fused to form a single bone in each forelimb, and the fused tibia and fibula form a single bone in each hind limb. The tarsus of the frogs is distinctive in the elongation of the tibiale and fibulare and in the loss or fusion of most of the other elements except a few tarsalia. The primitive families retain three tarsalia, the more advanced only two. The elongation of the proximal segment of the tarsus may be an adaptation for jumping, and the reduction of the distal elements may be a consequence of this elongation. The tibiale and fibulare may be fused together at their two ends in some Salientia, while in Pelodytes they are united for their entire length. The Salientia, which are more primitive than Caudata in most details of the skeleton, have specialized considerably away from the primitive condition in their single lower limb bones and in their reduced carpus and tarsus. Discoglossidae and Pelobatidae exhibit fewer fusions than the higher Salientia (Ridewood and Howes, 1888). The carpalia III and IV, for example, are usually free instead of fused to the mediale III. The medialia are always more or less fused to other carpal elements in all Salientia, and the intermedium of urodeles never appears in the group as a separate element.

Diplovertebron had a phalangeal formula of 2, 3, 3, 3, 4 in the forelimb. This formula is unique, and Watson (1926) suggests that it has arisen by reduction from the primitive reptilian formula which was presumably found in the most primitive Embolomeri (whose appendages are unknown). It may be assumed that the most primitive tetrapods had a formula of 2, 3, 4, 5, 4. The number 2, 2, 3, 4, 3, is retained in the feet of most labyrinthodonts, at least one branchiosaur, and most Salientia. The labyrinthodont Trematops and the lepospondyl Hylonomus, etc., have been credited with 2, 3, 4, 4, 3, phalanges in the foot. Most urodeles have 2 (1), 2, 3, 3, 2 phalanges in the foot and 2 (1), 2, 3, 2, in the hand. Eryops had the same number of hand phalanges, but most branchiosaurs and the Salientia usually have 2, 2, 3, 3 phalanges. One branchiosaur, however, has the typical urodele number. One group of species of Ambystoma have redeveloped an extra phalanx in the fourth toe, and their formula reads 2, 2, 3, 4, 2 (Cope, 1889). Whether or not this be considered a case of atavism, it is interesting to note that the Salientia in spite of their specialized tarsus approach nearer to their branchiosaur ancestors in number of hind limb phalanges than do the Caudata.

Reduction in the length of the lateral digits or the complete loss of the same occurs in both Salientia and Caudata. Many of these reductions have a systematic value as discussed in another chapter. Where losses occur, the tarsal or carpal elements are reduced apparently by fusion. In Proteus and Amphiuma with three digits in the forelimbs, the carpus may be reduced to three elements (Kingsley, 1925). On the other hand, increase in length may lead to a multiplication of parts. Thus, the prehallux of *Rana hexadactyla* may be divided into three segments.

Skeleton of Modern Amphibia.—In conclusion, it may be emphasized that the Salientia, the Caudata, and the Gymnophiona represent three lines of evolution, each of which retains primitive characters of its own. The Salientia exhibit various primitive characters in their skull, pectoral girdle, and digits, while the Caudata are obviously nearer the ancestral stock in the character of their lower jaws, ribs, pelvis, carpus, and tarsus. The Gymnophiona, although highly specialized for fossorial life, exhibit such primitive features as an ectopterygoid and epipterygoid, both lost or greatly reduced by the adults of the other orders. Thus, it cannot be said that the skeleton as a whole, of frog, salamander, or caecilian is more primitive than that of the other Amphibia. Another general conclusion which may be derived from the above review is that homology must be based upon the phylogenetic and not the embryological origin of a structure. The limbs, sacrum, occiput, and many other parts of the skeleton may be derived from different somites in different groups of Amphibia. Nevertheless, if structures in different groups can be demonstrated to have arisen from the same structure in a common ancestor, they may be considered homologous. Apparently, organ-forming materials may become distributed in different somites in the course of phylogeny. We shall refer to this subject again in the following chapter.

References

BEDDARD, F. E., 1907: Notes upon the anatomy of a species of frog of the genus Megalophrys, with reference to other genera of Batrachia, *Proc. Zool. Soc. London*, 1907, 324.

CAMP, C. L., 1923: Classification of the lizards, *Bull. Amer. Mus. Nat. Hist.*, XLVIII, Art. XI.

COPE, E. D., 1889: The Batrachia of North America, *Bull. U. S. Nat. Mus.*, No. 34.

DUNN, E. R., 1922: The sound-transmitting apparatus of salamanders and the phylogeny of the Caudata, *Amer. Naturalist*, LVI, 418–427.

EDGEWORTH, F. H., 1920: On the development of the hypobranchial and laryngeal muscles of Amphibia, *Jour. Anat.*, LIV., 125–162.

GAMBLE, D. L., 1922: The morphology of the ribs and transverse processes in Necturus maculatus, *Jour. Morph.*, XXXVI, 537–566.

GOODRICH, E. S., 1930: "Studies on the Structure and Development of Vertebrates," London.

GREGORY, W. K., R. W. MINER, and G. K. NOBLE, 1923: The carpus of Eryops and the structure of the primitive chiropterygium, *Bull. Amer. Mus. Nat. Hist.*, XLVIII, 279–288.

GREGORY, W. K., and G. K. NOBLE, 1924: The origin of the mammalian alisphenoid bone, *Jour. Morph. Physiol.*, XXXIX, 435–463.

KINGSBURY, B. F., and H. D. REED, 1909: The columella auris in Amphibia, *Jour. Morph.*, XX, 549–628, 10 pls.

KINGSLEY, J. S., 1925: "The Vertebrate Skeleton," New York.

MARCUS, H., and W. BLUME, 1926: Über Wirbel und Rippen bei Hypogeophis nebst Bemerkungen über Torpedo, *Zeitschr. Anat. Entw.*, LXXX, 1–78.

NAEF, A., 1929: Notizen zur Morphologie und Stammesgeschichte der Wirbeltiere; 15. Dreissig Thesen über Wirbelsäule und Rippen insbesondere bei den Tetrapoden, *Zool. Jahrb. Anat. Abt.*, L, 581–600.

NOBLE, G. K., 1929: Further observations on the life-history of the newt, Triturus viridescens, *Amer. Mus. Novit.*, No. 348.

PETER, K., 1898: Die Entwicklung und funktionelle Gestaltung des Schädels von Ichthyophis glutinosus, *Morph. Jahrb.*, XXV, 555–628, pls. 19–21.

REED, H. D., 1920: The morphology of the sound-transmitting apparatus in caudate Amphibia and its phylogenetic significance, *Jour. Morph.*, XXXIII, 325–375.

RIDEWOOD, W. G., 1898: On the structure and development of the hyobranchial skeleton and larynx in Xenopus and Pipa; with remarks on the affinities of the Aglossa, *Jour. Linn. Soc.*, XXVI, 53–128, pls. VIII–XI.

———, and G. B. HOWES, 1888: On the carpus and tarsus of the Anura, *Proc. Zool. Soc. London*, 141–182.

SCHMALHAUSEN, J. J., 1910: Die Entwickelung des Extremitätenskelettes von Salamandrella Kayserlingii, *Anat. Anz.*, XXXVII, 431–446.

———, 1917: On the extremities of Ranidens sibiricus Kessl, *Rev. Zool. Russe*, II, 129–135.

SETERS, W. H. VAN, 1922: Le développement du chondrocrâne d'Alytes obstetricans avant la metamorphose, *Arch. de Biol.*, XXXII, 373–491, pls. 8–9.

SMITH, LOUISE, 1920: The hyobranchial apparatus of Spelerpes bislineatus, *Jour. Morph.*, XXXIII, 527–550.

STADTMÜLLER, FRANZ, 1929: Studien am Urodelenschädel; II. Nachweis eines Basioccipitale bei einem rezenten Amphibium (Triton alpestris), *Zeitschr. Anat. Entw.*, XC, 144–152.

STEINER, H., 1921: Hand und Fuss der Amphibien, ein Beitrag zur Extremitätenfrage, *Anat. Anz.*, LIII, 513–542.

STEINER, H., 1922: Die ontogenetische und phylogenetische Entwicklung des Vogelflügelskelettes, *Acta Zoologica*, III, 307–360.

SUSHKIN, P. P., 1927: On the modifications of the mandibular and hyoid arches and their relations to the brain case in the early Tetrapoda, *Pal. Zeitschr.*, VIII, 263–321.

WATSON, D. M. S., 1926: The evolution and origin of the Amphibia, *Phil. Trans. Roy. Soc. London*, Ser. B, CCXIV, 189–257.

———, 1926a: The Carboniferous Amphibia of Scotland, *Palaeontologica Hungarica*, I, 221–252, 3 pls.

WHIPPLE, INEZ L., 1906: The ypsiloid apparatus of urodeles, *Biol. Bull.*, X, 255–297.

CHAPTER XI

THE MUSCULAR SYSTEM

The Amphibia exhibit many modes of locomotion: the aquatic urodeles have retained some of the swimming movements of fish; the frogs have specialized in leaping and have lost the tail; many burrowing Salientia must be content with walking, as they are too short-legged to leap; finally, a few salamanders and many frogs have become arboreal and can successfully clamber up the trunks of trees. As in other animals, nearly all movement in the Amphibia is produced by muscles. These are of two kinds: the involuntary, non-striated muscle derived from the mesenchyme (rarely from ectoderm) and found in the walls of digestive tracts, viscera, blood vessels, etc., and the voluntary, striated muscle arising from the myotomes and serving for the movement of limbs and body wall as well as for the attachment of many skeletal elements to one another. The muscles of the gill arches and jaws arise from mesenchyme in the wall of the pharynx, but they become striated and voluntary and are spoken of as visceral in contradistinction to the somatic voluntary muscles of myotome origin. The heart muscles are also of mesenchyme origin. They become striped but remain involuntary in action. Further, they have a distinctive branching or anastomosis of fibers not found in other muscular tissue. It is thus possible to classify muscles in several ways: according to their origin from mesenchyme (visceral) or myotomes (locomotor and body muscles), according to function (voluntary and involuntary), according to their structure (smooth or striated), according to their innervation (facial, etc.). None of these classifications has proved thoroughly satisfactory, since in all cases there is a certain intergradation between the types. For example, limb muscles may arise from myotomes in sharks but apparently from mesenchyme in Amphibia. Muscle movement is caused by the contraction of either the muscle cell itself or the contractile myofibrils within the cell or group of cells. The voluntary muscles are much more rapid in their action than the involuntary muscles. They owe their speed of action to their myofibrils which are striated, that is have alternate light and dark transverse segments unlike the myofibrils of smooth muscle.

Although all muscles are under nervous control of impulses from the central nervous system, visceral muscles may respond directly to stretching by contracting. Further they may maintain a state of contraction once obtained without further nervous stimulation. In this they stand in contrast to the skeletal muscles which owe a sustained contraction to rapidly recurring stimuli. With the onset of fatigue the skeletal muscles relax. The heart continues its contractions when removed and placed in suitable fluid; it is thus an independently functioning organ whose activity is merely influenced by sympathetic and parasympathetic impulses. Its rhythmic activity is due to the refractory period following each contraction during which the heart cells are incapable of excitation. Since the duration of this refractory period differs with the species, the isolated hearts of different species of Amphibia beat at different rates.

The form and arrangement of the muscles are very closely correlated with function. The skeleton is merely a trestle work for the muscles which frequently may shape the form of the bones. Since the skeleton usually affords the best evidence of a species relationship, it is of interest to examine not only the correlation between bone and muscle form but also the phylogenetic changes in the muscle system as a whole, since the latter no doubt has left its stamp upon the skeleton. The muscles of the frog are frequently used in physiological studies and the names applied to the separate elements are largely borrowed from human anatomy without sufficient evidence as to the homology of the parts. The muscular system of the frog has been derived from that of a primitive amphibian ground plan which is not yet known in all its details. Some of the more obvious features of this plan may be discussed with relation to the evolution of the Amphibia.

The muscular system of vertebrates was originally segmentally arranged with a pair of spinal or cranial nerves to each segment. Connective tissue sheets, or myocommata, separated the respective segments, and in Amphibia where muscles, such as the *rectus abdominis*, are built out of components from several segments, the myocommata may still remain as evidence of this primitive segmentation. The innervation is the best evidence of the homology of a muscle, for the original nerve supply tends to follow a muscle throughout the various migrations it may have made during phylogeny. Transplantation experiments have shown that this relation between nerve and muscle is not a fundamental one, since limbs transplanted into a foreign position may pick up a new nerve supply from the spinal nerves of its new environment (Detwiler, 1920; Mangold, 1929). Further, just as the pelvis or the occiput may be formed from different somites in labyrinthodonts and frogs and yet be considered homologous structures, so the limb muscles, together with their nerve supply, may have arisen in these two groups from different somites but are nevertheless considered homologous.

Body Muscles.—The somatic muscles derived from the myotomes give rise to the trunk muscles and in other groups after modification to the limb muscles, while in the gill region they are squeezed into an epibranchial and a hypobranchial mass by the visceral muscles, and produce there merely part of the throat and neck muscles. Primitively in vertebrates the muscle fibers extended from myocomma to myocomma and only the fibers nearest the vertebrae gained an attachment to the axial skeleton. In fishes the somatic muscles are already sharply divided, by a horizontal myoseptum or connective tissue plate, into a dorsal epaxial mass—the definitive back muscles, and a ventral hypaxial mass—the body wall, the lower portion of the tail musculature-and the ventral throat muscles. The epaxial muscles are inner vated by dorsal branches, the hypaxial by ventral branches of the spinal nerves. In fishes the epaxial muscles are greater in volume than the hypaxial and serve with the latter to bend the body from side to side in swimming. In Amphibia, the epaxial muscles are reduced, and correlated with this, the horizontal septum together with the transverse processes of the ribs are pushed to a higher level on the side of the vertebral column. Less dependence on the epaxial (dorsal) muscles occurs during locomotion, until in frogs the epaxial muscles serve to bend the vertebral column dorsally instead of laterally (Fig. 91). The hypaxial muscles, also, show marked changes in correlation with terrestrial life. This is far greater in the body wall, which serves for supporting the viscera and for respiratory movements, than in the tail, which still functions in locomotion. With the reduction of their locomotory functions, the hypaxial (ventral) muscles give rise to a subvertebral system which comes to underlie the vertebrae and ribs. Before considering the modifications of the hypaxial (ventral) system in detail, some further reference may be made to the epaxial musculature, since the frogs with their short bodies and leaping movements have molded this epaxial (dorsal) musculature in correlation with their distinctive habits.

In urodeles the epaxial muscle mass is divided by myocommata into the same number of segments as there are vertebrae. Most of the muscle fibers run from myocomma to myocomma as in fish, but these septa show little of the folding so characteristic of the dorsal muscles of swift-swimming fish. Proximally each myocomma makes a firm attachment to a single vertebra in adult Amphibia, although in some larvae the proximal attachment extends to several vertebrae, a piscine condition and one apparently correlated with the elastic and poorly jointed vertebral column. The muscle fibers adjacent to the vertebrae are more or less attached to them, forming short intersegmental bundles. In the Salientia this deep muscle formation is carried much farther, and definitive *Mm. intertransversarii* and *interneurales* between the transverse processes and the neural arches, respectively, may be distinguished in the more advanced

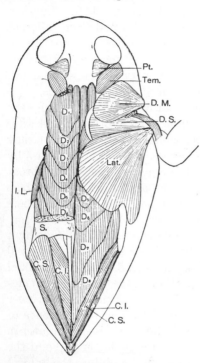

FIG. 91.—Dorsal body musculature of *Bombina maxima*. *C.I.*, Coccygeo-iliacus; *C.S.*, coccygeo-sacralis, D_{1-8}, longissimus dorsi, successive segments; *D.M.*, depressor mandibulae; *D.S.*, dorsalis scapulae; *I.L.*, ileolumbaris; *Lat.*, latissimus dorsi; *Pt.*, pterygoideus; *S.*, sacral diapophyses; *Tem.*, temporalis.

groups where they have split from the primitive *M. dorsalis trunci* mass. Further, a lateral *ileolumbaris* is present on each side in frogs of several families. The overlying muscle fibers, while more or less fused in Ascaphus, become free of these intervertebral muscles in Discoglossus and in most frogs form a long muscle extending from head to coccyx, the *M. longissimus dorsi*. Although V-shaped myocommata are retained, they make little or no attachment to the vertebrae (Fig. 91). These superficial epaxial muscle fibers of frogs have practically given up their original function of lateral bending but have assumed new functions of holding up the head in leaping and of bending the body sharply upward in a so-called "warning" attitude (Chap. XVI).

Although both urodeles and Salientia have very short necks, many species are capable of bringing the head to a lateral position nearly at right angles to the main axis of the body. Such a movement is facilitated by a division of the anterior part of the *M. dorsalis trunci* into several muscle bundles which

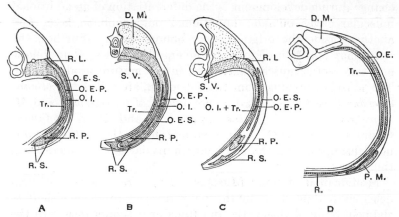

Fig. 92.—A comparison of the ventral body musculature of various Amphibia. Schematic cross-sections through the middle of the body. *A*. Triturus, larva. *B*. Triturus, adult. *C*. Salamandra, adult. *D*. Rana, adult. *D.M.*, back musculature; *O.E.*, M. obliquus externus abdominis; *O.E.P.*, M. obliquus externus profundus; *O.E.S.*, M. obliquus externus superficialis; *O.I.*, M. obliquus internus; *P.M.*, M. pectoralis; *R.*, M. rectus abdominis; *R.L.*, rectus lateralis; *R.P.*, rectus profundus; *R.S.*, rectus superficialis; *S.V.*, subvertebralis; *Tr.*, transversus. (*After Maurer.*)

extend to the skull. In the newt there are three of these muscle heads, an apparent fourth being the temporalis, a visceral jaw muscle which extends to the neural spine of the first vertebra of many urodeles and is especially well developed in the species of Desmognathus.

The hypaxial musculature of the early urodele larva approaches the condition in fish. Myocommata are present and the fibers instead of running longitudinally, as assumed for the primitive vertebrate, are arranged into two layers of oblique fibers, the outer running ventroposteriorly and the inner, dorsoanteriorly, that is, in the opposite direction. These are the *Mm. obliquus externus* and *internus*, while the medioventral fibers which retain the primitive longitudinal direction form the *M. rectus abdominis*. There develops in some aquatic larvae such as those of the newt a muscle bundle just below the horizontal septum which appears to be homologous with the *M. rectus lateralis* an important swimming muscle of many teleosts (Versluys, 1927). As the larva develops, the hypaxial muscles differentiate further from the fish condition until at metamorphosis radical changes frequently occur (Fig. 92). The first change during development is the differentiation of an additional muscular layer outside the original outer oblique layer and another inside the original inner oblique layer. Further, the *rectus* may also split off an outer layer. In this way four oblique and two rectus muscles may arise in the mature urodele larva. The muscles, reading from the outside in, are called *M. obliquus externus superficialis, M. o. e. profundus, M. o. internus,* and *M. transversus,* also *M. rectus superficialis* and *M. r. profundus* (Maurer, 1892, 1911). At metamorphosis the *rectus lateralis* may disappear and the secondary hypaxial muscles increase in thickness.

Modification of Body Muscles.—The various genera of urodeles show differences in the body muscles for which there is claimed both phylogenetic and functional significance. In the terrestrial Salamandra there are four muscle layers forming the body wall of the larva, but the *M. o. internus* and the *M. transversus* fuse together during metamorphosis. On the other hand, in the aquatic Cryptobranchus the *Mm. o. e. superficialis* and *profundus* are fused or possibly never separate, the conditions in the early larvae being unknown. In the different genera of urodeles the superficial *rectus* shows various degrees of freedom from the *profundus* and the latter from the primary *obliquus externus* and *internus* of its origin. Failure of the *M. rectus profundus* to separate from the latter may be considered a larval condition retained by the perennibranchs. The condition is, however, found in a few metamorphosed types such as the newt (Fig. 92*B*). A progressive change found developed to various degrees in the different groups of urodeles is the loss of the myocommata in the body muscles. In Amphiuma, for example, this loss of segmentation occurs in both the *M. o. e. superficialis* and the *M. transversus.* In the case of the former it might be correlated with the digging habits of the species. The loss of the myocommata frees the muscle layers from adjacent integument or muscle and makes possible independent action. There are, in brief, two tendencies of urodele evolution found in these body muscles: first, reduction in number of layers; and second, loss of metameric structure.

In the Salientia these tendencies are carried nearly to completion. The primary oblique muscles form a single sheet as in very young but not older urodele larvae (Maurer, 1895). Further, this combined *obliquus externus* and *internus* is replaced just before metamorphosis by the secondary *M. obliquus externus superficialis* and *M. transversus*. The *M. rectus abdominis* develops in the tadpole as a single muscle and remains undivided in the adult frog. The myocommata are not formed in the first two muscles and only the *rectus* retains the original segmentation.

While the reduction of the number of muscles in the body wall may be traced from the axolotl to the frog, there remains to be considered what the primitive condition may have been in Amphibia. Reptiles, although terrestrial, exhibit no reduction of hypaxial muscle layers. On the contrary, in addition to the four muscle layers forming the body wall of the newt, they have two additional layers associated with the ribs. Since the branchiosaur ancestors of frogs and salamanders had short ribs, they presumably possessed no such development of the hypaxial muscles as is found in modern reptiles. The reduction of the primary hypaxial muscles at metamorphosis in the Salientia would apparently be correlated with the absence of the ribs rather than with the assumption of terrestrial life. We may conclude that four layers of muscle formed the body wall of the primitive amphibian larva, and that the two primary or central layers were reduced in correlation with the degeneration of the ribs in the metamorphosed adult.

The hypaxial muscles of the tail retain the primitive metamerism, and the muscle fibers run longitudinally between the myocommata. In the pelvic region two muscle bundles gain an insertion on the hind limb of each side and assume important functions in walking. Many urodeles, both aquatic and terrestrial forms, are able to use their tails as prehensile organs, but as the tip is merely moved to the side, no fundamental changes of musculature, such as is found in the chameleon's tail, for example, are made in this appendage.

Ventral Throat Musculature.—The *rectus abdominis* is continued forward into the throat region by the *sternohyoideus* or *abdominohyoideus* of urodeles. The latter muscle is part of the hypaxial system, but its union with the *rectus* is apparently secondary, since the labyrinthodonts had a better developed pectoral girdle than modern urodeles, and this would have separated the two muscles (Miner, 1925). The condition in Salientia where

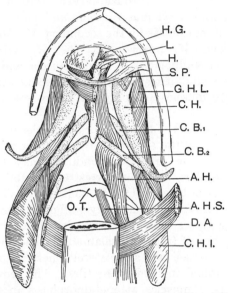

Fig. 93.—Dissection of the hyobranchial muscles of the adult *Eurycea bislineata*, dorsal view. The dorsal surface of the tongue has been partly removed and the posterior edge entirely so, to show underlying muscles. *A.H.*, abdominohyoideus; *A.H.S.*, abdominohyoideus ventral slip; *C.B.₁₋₂*, ceratobranchial I and II; *C.H.*, ceratohyal; *C.H.I.*, ceratohyoideus internus; *D.A.*, depressores arcuum; *G.H.L.*, geniohyoideus lateralis; *H.*, horn of copula; *H.G.*, hyoglossus; *L.*, lingual cartilage; *O.T.*, os thyreoideum; *S.P.*, suprapeduncularis. (*After Smith.*)

the muscles are separate, although sometimes overlapping, is more primitive. The sternohyoid is continued to the lower jaw by the same tongue muscles in both frogs and urodeles. The *geniohyoideus* extends from hyoid to the anterior margin of the lower jaw, while a median bundle of muscle fibers extends to the floor of the mouth and forms the bulk of the superficial tongue muscles (Fig. 93). The detailed arrangement of these muscles varies with the group of Amphibia considered (Gaupp, 1896; Drüner, 1902, 1904), and in the perennibranch urodeles the conditions may be more larval than primitive. In some urodeles and frogs the lateral portion of the *sternohyoideus* may form a distinct *omohyoideus* as in higher vertebrates.

Forelimb Muscles.—The forelimbs of the earliest tetrapods were held more or less at right angles to the body and the

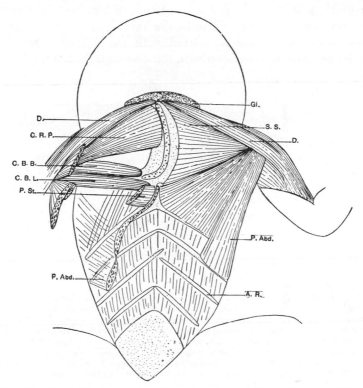

Fig. 94.—Ventral body muscles of Liopelma showing the cartilaginous abdominal ribs which occur in this primitive frog. *A.R.*, abdominal ribs; *C.B.B.*, coracobrachialis brevis; *C.B.L.*, coracobrachialis longus; *C.R.P.*, coracoradialis proprius; *D.*, deltoideus; *Gl.*, lymphoidal gland, *P.Abd.*, pectoralis abdominalis; *P.St.*, pectoralis sternalis; *S.S.*, supracoracoideus.

sharply bent forearms supported the weight. The humerus was advanced and the forearm extended, or the humerus brought posteriorly and the forearm flexed. The musculature of the forelimb, as far as it may be judged by the form of the limb and girdle, consisted of a ventrolateral and a dorsomedial group of muscles, which Romer (1924) has homologized with the muscle masses found one on either side of the anterior fins of fish.

The hind limbs also were held astraddle when at rest, and a dorsal and a ventral group of muscles could be inferred in the early tetrapods. The limb muscles have presumably split from the hypaxial musculature during phylogeny, but modern Amphibia show no evidence of such origin in their ontogeny (Lewis, 1910; Rylkoff, 1924). The musculature of fore- and hind limbs was not alike in detail even in the most primitive tetrapods. Such a difference was correlated with the different structure of the pectoral as compared with the pelvic girdle inherited from

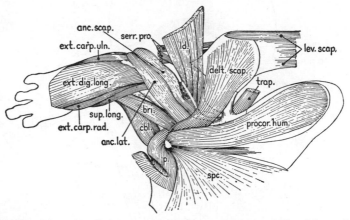

Fig. 95.—Dissection of the arm and shoulder musculature of Megalobatrachus. *anc.lat.*, M. anconeus lateralis; *anc.scap.*, M. anconeus scapularis; *bri.*, M. brachialis inferior; *cbl.*, M. coracobrachialis longus; *delt.scap.*, M. deltoides scapularis-dorsalis scapulae; *ext.carp.rad.*, M. extensor carpi radialis; *ext.carp.uln.*, M. extensor carpi ulnaris; *ext.dig.long.*, M. extensor digitorum longus; *lev. scap.*, M. levator scapulae; *ld.*, M. latissimus dorsi; *p.*, M. pectoralis; *procor.hum.*, M. procoracohumeralis; *serr.pro.*, M. serratus profundus; *spc.*, M. supracoracoideus; *sup. long.*, M. supinator longus; *trap.*, M. trapezius. (*After Miner.*)

fish. Further, the forelimbs were early used to raise the body, while the hind limbs pushed it forward. In correlation with this functional difference, the elbow joint formed in the forelimbs tended to be directed backward like that of modern Amphibia, while the knee joint gave a better purchase when directed forward. This functional difference, continued in phylogeny, affected the distal segments least and a great similarity may still be found in the distal muscles of the fore- and hind limbs of modern salamanders such as Necturus (Wilder, 1908). Although the pelvic girdle very early in the history of the first tetrapods gained a firm attachment to the vertebral column, the pectoral girdle, apparently in correlation with the requirements of respiration, did not succeed in the amphibian series in securing a similar support. Hence, the forelimb muscles in Amphibia spread dorsally and ventrally over the body, the *pectoralis* group of each side meeting ventrally in the midline in many species (Fig. 94), while in some aquatic and burrowing types which use their forelimbs to a considerable extent, one of the dorsal muscles (*M. latissimus dorsi*) came to cover a considerable part of the back. Although some hypaxial muscles attach to the pelvis and femur, these are tail muscles which utilize the swing of the caudal appendage to pull the legs posteriorly, and they may be sharply contrasted to the several powerful hypaxial muscles which extend from the ribs, transverse processes or skull, to give support to the pectoral girdle. The chief muscle masses which originally attached to the cleithrum and scapula of labyrinthodonts extend mainly to the suprascapula of modern Amphibia, a *levator* group forming an anterior mass and a *serratus* group forming a posterior one (Fig. 95). The musculatures of the fore- and hind limbs do agree, however, in being formed of short, deep muscles extending over one limb joint and of long, more superficially placed muscles reaching over two or more limb segments.

Comparison of Frog and Salamander.—A detailed comparison of the limb muscles of the various groups of Amphibia lies beyond the scope of the present discussion. Still, the proximal limb muscles of common frogs and salamanders seem at first glance so very different in the two groups that the similarity of plan may be emphasized here. If the skin from the chest and upper arm of such a primitive frog as Ascaphus or Liopelma be peeled back and the muscles compared with those from the same region in Megalobatrachus or other primitive urodele, a remarkable resemblance will be noted. The urodeles have lost the dermal shoulder girdle, and the long slip of muscle found in the frogs, running from the ventral surface of the head of the humerus to the mesial end of the clavicle and called by Anthony and Vallois (1914) *episterno-cleido-humeralis longus*, has disappeared unless it is represented by a muscle carried forward on the anteriorly directed procoracoid cartilage of salamanders. Except for this difference, the number and arrangement of the muscles covering the ventral surface of the pectoral girdle of frogs and urodeles are the same. Beginning at the anterior end there is a *supracoracoideus* covering *coracoradialis proprius* and inserting on the ventral process of the humerus. The latter deep-lying muscle is continued in all frogs and many salamanders as a tendon hidden among the muscles of the upper arm to the radius, which accounts for its name. Superficially covering the chest a broad *pectoralis* muscle lies immediately caudal to the *supracoracoideus* and with the latter covers two *coracobrachialis* muscles which extend between humerus and coracoid (Fig. 94). All of these muscles belong to the ventrolateral muscle mass in the earliest tetrapods and in their fish ancestors. The muscles on the flexor aspect of the forearm and hand of Amphibia also are part of this mass. It would hardly be inferred from a superficial examination of modern Amphibia that the *dorsalis scapulae*, originating on the suprascapula and inserting on the ventral process of the humerus, also belonged to this ventrolateral group. In the earliest Amphibia the cleithrum formed the anterior border of the coracoscapula, and the *dorsalis scapulae* was part of a *deltoideus* mass which had a broad seat of origin along this dermal element (Miner, 1925). With the reduction of the cleithrum in frogs the *deltoideus* was split into two or more masses, one of which formed the *dorsalis scapulae*, another the *episterno-cleido-humeralis longus* (= *deltoides clavicularis*) of frogs, some fibers remaining in the original central position marked by the acromion process and forming the *acromio-cleido-episterno-humeralis* of Anthony and Vallois. In urodeles the cleithrum has been lost entirely and the only evidence of the former continuity of the *dorsalis scapulae* and the *procoracohumeralis* is their common innervation.

The pectoral musculature has undergone some modification in the phylogeny of both frogs and salamanders. All Pelobatidae, as far as known, have the *episterno-cleido-humeralis longus* fused with the *supracoracoideus*, and the caudal part of the latter muscle retains the primitiveness of Discoglossidae in remaining a single muscle instead of splitting off a *supracoracoideus profundus* as in many Bufonidae (Noble, 1926). The pectoral musculature of Rana is highly specialized but not so much so as in the case of many Brevicipitidae which have lost the clavicle and procoracoid and piled the pectoral muscles close together. The *pectoralis* is usually split into a sternal and an abdominal portion in Salientia. The latter may extend to the thighs in some species of frogs.

The muscles of the dorsomedial group show far less specialization than those of the ventrolateral group, and not only are frogs and salamanders alike in regard to the general form and arrangement of the several muscles comprising this series, but the homologous muscles in reptiles and mammals may be recognized from their positions relative to the bones and to one another. Beginning at the proximal end of the series a *latissimus dorsi* is found in both frog and salamander originating from a broad base on the dorsal fascia immediately caudal to the *dorsalis scapulae* and narrowing to its insertion on the head of the humerus or its capsules. Hidden from view by more laterally placed muscles, the *subcoracoscapularis* is the second muscle of the series. It runs from the posterior margin of scapula and coracoid to the medial process of the humerus. Its head of origin is thrust between two of the heads of the *anconeus* or *triceps*, the third muscle of the series to consider. The latter is the large muscle covering the dorsal side of the upper arm. It originates from four heads on the scapula, coracoid, and humerus which merge into a single muscle inserting on the ulna. Obviously this is the chief muscle for extending the lower arm. The more distal muscles on the extensor surface of forearm and hand are the final part of the dorsomedial series. A part of the lower-arm muscles arises from the humerus, the extensor muscles from the ectepicondyle. These work in opposition to the flexor muscles which arise from the entepicondyle and cover the ventral surface of the arm and hand. In primitive tetrapods with their heavy bodies and broad trackways these distal condyles of the humerus were greatly expanded. The muscles serving for the movement of hand and fingers have been considered by Gaupp, 1896; Ribbing, 1907; Miner, 1925; and others. In general, during both ontogeny and phylogeny there is a reduction of the short muscles of this region and their functional replacement by the longer muscles. The same maintains for the evolution of the muscles of the feet.

Hind Limb Musculature.—The musculature of the hind limb may be considered briefly. The pelvis of frogs is short and narrow, that of urodeles longer and flatter. This has a marked effect upon the arrangement of the proximal muscles especially as viewed from the ventral surface after removing the skin. Nevertheless, when the musculatures of primitive frogs and urodeles are compared, a general agreement of plan will be recognized which may be taken as evidence that the two groups arose from ancestors having a common type of musculature (Fig. 96). It is this common plan which must be compared with the hind-limb musculature of higher vertebrates in deducing homologies; the mammalian names given to the muscles of the specialized Rana are for the most part erroneous (Noble, 1922, Table 1).

If we compare the muscles on the ventral surface of the thigh of such primitive genera as Ascaphus and Rhyacotriton, a considerable resemblance will be noted (Fig. 96), the chief differences being that some of the same muscles which are dorsally arranged in the salamander cover the anterior portion of the thigh of the frog and that the two muscles extending between thigh and tail of the salamander are not visible, for they have been carried dorsally by the reduction of the tail. Anteriorly on the ventral surface of the thigh of salamanders is a *pubotibialis* overlying a deep *puboischiofemoralis internus*. Their innervations as well as their origins and insertions show that these muscles are homologous with the so-called ventral head of the *adductor magnus* and the deep-lying *pectineus* of frogs, respectively. Two large muscles caudal to the *pubotibialis* and forming the bulk of the muscles covering the ventral surface of the thigh, the *pubois-chiofemoralis externus* and the *puboischiotibialis*, are homologous to the muscles having a similar position in the frog, the first to the dorsal head of the *adductor magnus* and the second to a single muscle which represents the combined *sartorius* and *semitendino-sus* of higher Salientia. Some reference is made to these muscles, for the changes which take place in the ventral thigh musculature are often diagnostic of higher groups (Noble, 1922, 1926). The most posterior thigh muscle in Rhyacotriton, the *ischioflexorius*, appears to be a dorsal muscle and in the frogs it is represented by the *semimembranosus*, a large muscle on the dorsal side of the femur. A part of this *ischioflexorius*, however, forms a distinct muscle or pair of them on the posterior margin of the thigh in the Salientia. This is the *gracilis major* and its separate slip, the *gracilis minor*. Obviously the urodele names, expressing as they do the origins and insertions of each muscle, are more adequate than the names in common use for the frog muscles. The literature available concerning the muscles of frogs employs for the most part the latter names, and hence both have been indicated in the present brief comparison.

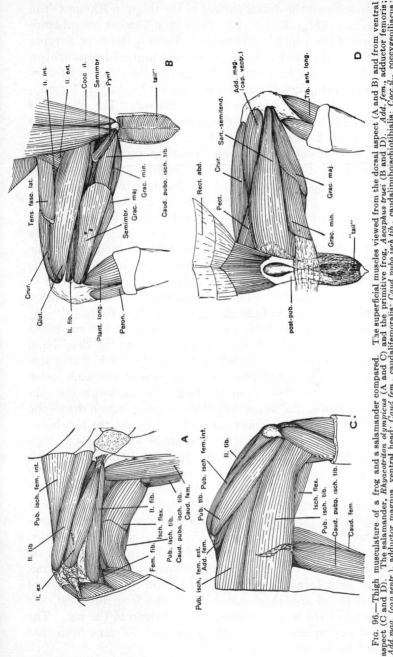

Fig. 96.—Thigh musculature of a frog and a salamander compared. The superficial muscles viewed from the dorsal aspect (A and B) and from ventral aspect (C and D). The salamander, *Rhyacotriton olympicus* (A and C) and the primitive frog, *Ascaphus truei* (B and D). *Add.fem.*, adductor femoris; *Add.mag.* (*cap.ventr.*), adductor magnus, ventral head; *Caud.fem.*, caudalifemoralis; *Caud.pubo.isch.tib.*, caudalipuboischiotibialis; *Cocc.ii.*, coccygeoiliacus; *Crur.*, cruralis; *Fem.fib.*, femorofibularis; *Glut.*, glutaeus; *Grac.maj.*, gracilis major; *Grac.min.*, gracilis minor; *Il.ext.*, ilioextensorius; *Il.fib.*, iliofibularis; *Il.tib.*, iliotibialis; *Il.int.*, iliscus internus; *Isch.flex.*, ischioflexorius; *Pect.*, pectineus; *Peron.*, peroneus; *Plant.long.*, plantaris longus; *Post-pub.*, postpubis; *Pub.isch.fem.ext.*, puboischiofemoralis externus; *Pub.isch.fem.int.*, puboischiofemoralis internus; *Pub.isch.tib.*, puboischiotibialis; *Pub.tib.*, pubotibialis; *Pyrif.*, pyriformis; *Rect.abd.*, rectus abdominis; *Sart.semiten.*, sartorio-semitendinosus; *Semimbr.*, semimembranosus; *Tens.fasc.lat.*, tensor fasciae latae; *Tib.ant.long.*, tibialis anticus longus.

The muscles on the dorsal surface of the thigh in Rhyacotriton and Ascaphus (Figs. 96*A* and *B*) show even a closer resemblance than those of the ventral surfaces do. There is the same number of elements and these have nearly the same mutual relationships. The ilium is carried far forward in frogs and the *puboischiofemoralis internus* forming the anterior margin of the thigh in Rhyacotriton is pulled out into an *iliacus externus*. The *iliotibialis* has shortened in Ascaphus and it remains so in all higher frogs where it is called the *tensor fasciae latae*. The two "tail-wagging" muscles, *caudalipubofemoralis* and *caudalipuboischiotibialis*, are both present, although very small in the frog and extending to the coccyx. The first masquerades under the name of *pyriformis* in the frog, but as this muscle is apparently homologous with the *pyriformis* of mammals it may well be substituted for the *caudalipubofemoralis* of salamanders as well. The remaining muscles on the dorsal surfaces of the two thighs offer no difficulty. The *ilioextensorius* is obviously homologous with the combined *cruralis* and *glutaeus*, which are, however, very much more powerful in frog than in salamander. The *iliofibularis* is homologous with a muscle of the same name in frogs. The *ischioflexorius* has already been stated to be the homologous equivalent of the combined *semimembranosus* and *gracilis*. A small part of the deep-lying *iliofemoralis* shows on the dorsal surface of the thigh of Rhyacotriton, and this is homologous with a muscle of the same name covered by the *iliofibularis* in the frog. In mammals the *iliofemoralis* becomes the important *glutaeus* group which draws the chief trochanter of the femur forward and hence the leg backward in running. The other deep muscles of the frog's thigh need not be mentioned, although they are homologous with muscles in the urodele and have undergone certain changes in the evolution of the various groups. Homology is determined by the origin and insertion of a muscle, its relation to adjacent muscles, and its innervation in a natural series of forms. Function is no criterion of homology even in related groups. Thus, the *ilioextensorius* carries the knee dorsally in salamanders on contraction, while the homologous *cruralis* and *glutaeus* in frogs bring the knee forward and extend the lower leg. If the flexors on the back of the thigh are tense in the frog, however, the contraction of the same muscle causes a flexion of the leg. The action of any muscle when working alone is different from that produced by several acting together.

Visceral Muscles.—In the discussion of the forelimb musculature no reference was made to a conspicuous muscle, the *trapezius*, arising from skull or dorsal fascia and inserting on the scapula. This is one of the visceral muscles which forced the epaxial muscles dorsally, the hypaxial, ventrally, in reaching their superficial position on the side of the neck. The other visceral muscles include the jaw, hyoid, and gill muscles. In fact, with the exception of the tongue, eye, and some medioventral throat muscles, all the musculature of the head is visceral. In the larvae of urodeles and frogs there are a superficial constrictor of the branchial arches and a deep-lying set of levators, marginales, and other slips controlling the movements of the gill arches. A similar superficial constrictor and a deeper series of short muscles derived from it occur in fishes, some of which possess also a *trapezius* inserting on the shoulder girdle. At metamorphosis with the disappearance of the gill arches, all of these visceral muscles dwindle away except the *trapezius*, which retains its original position relative to the pectoral girdle. In the frog, however, the series of *levatores arcuum* are retained as a group of *petrohyoidei* extending from skull to hyoid plate and serving to raise the hyoid apparatus and carry it forward.

The hyoid arch primitively in fish is surrounded by a constrictor belonging to the same series as the more posterior constrictors. In Amphibia this constrictor is divided by the hyoid into a pair of dorsal muscles which develop as the *depressor mandibulae* or mouth-opening muscles, while the ventral portions of the same pair of muscles join in the midline to form a muscle which is more or less distinct in both urodeles and frogs. These constrictors of the hyoid are innervated by the *facialis* nerve, while the more posterior visceral muscles are supplied by the *glossopharyngeus* and *vagus*. The *depressor mandibulae* may arise entirely from the skull or have a second, more posterior part in many Salientia arising from the suprascapula.

The constrictors of the jaws are innervated by the *trigeminus* and hence are readily distinguishable from the hyoid constrictors which may encroach upon their territory ventrally. The jaw constrictors were split early in the phylogeny of the vertebrates into three pairs of muscles, of which the *adductor mandibulae* is the most important. These adductors are divided into two or more parts in Amphibia (Lubosch, 1914). The *temporalis* inserts on the coronoid process of the lower jaw and extends back to a point of origin on the first cervical vertebra of many urodeles (Dubecq, 1925) but mainly to the cranial roof in frogs. The *pterygoideus* extends from the pterygoid or side of the brain case and inserts on the lower jaw. In the Salientia two slips of the *temporalis* make separate attachment to the squamosal or quadratojugal and are called "masseters" in allusion to a possible homology with the masseters of mammals. The changes in shape and distribution of these *adductor mandibulae* muscles are closely correlated with the shape of the skull.

The ventral segments of the constrictors of the jaws unite to form the submaxillary or superficial throat muscles of Amphibia. An anterior portion is differentiated in frogs to raise the mento-Meckelian bones at the anterior angle of the lower jaw and is called the *submentalis*. The various natural groups of Amphibia often show differences in their visceral musculature (Drüner, 1902, 1904; Smith, 1920; Edgeworth, 1923) of systematic value. The phylogenetic change in the hyoid and other bony structures of Amphibia is closely correlated with changes in their musculature.

References

ANTHONY R., and H. VALLOIS, 1914: Sur la signification des éléments ventraux de la ceinture scapulaire chez les batraciens, *Bibl. Anat.*, XXIV, 218–276.

DETWILER, S., 1920: Experiments on the transplantation of limbs in Amblystoma; The formation of nerve plexuses and the function of limbs, *Jour. Exp. Zool.*, XXXI, 117–169.

DRÜNER, L., 1902: Studien zur Anatomie der Zungenbein-Kiemenbogen und Kehlkopfmuskeln der Urodelen, I. Teil, *Zool. Jahrb. Anat. Abt.*, XV, 435–622, pls. 25–31.

———, 1904: Studien zur Anatomie der Zungenbein-Kiemenbogen und Kehlkopfmuskeln der Urodelen, II Teil, *Zool. Jahrb. Anat. Abt.*, XIX, 361–690, 12 pls.

DUBECQ, J., 1925: Constitution du muscle temporal chez les amphibiens urodèles: signification morphologique de ce muscle, *Compt. rend. Soc. Biol.*, XCIII, 1523.

EDGEWORTH, F. H., 1923: On the larval hyobranchial skeleton and musculature of Cryptobranchus, Menopoma and Ellipsoglossa, *Jour. Anat.*, LVII, 97–105.

GAUPP, E., 1896: "Ecker's and Wiedersheim's Anatomie des Frosches," Braunschweig.

LEWIS, WARREN H., 1910: The relation of the myotomes to the ventrolateral musculature and to the anterior limbs in Amblystoma, *Anat. Rec.*, IV, 183–190.

LUBOSCH, W., 1914: Vergleichende Anatomie der Kaumuskeln der Wirbeltiere, in fünf Teilen, I Teil: Die Kaumuskeln der Amphibien, *Jena. Zeitschr.*, LIII, 51–188, 5 pls.

MANGOLD, O., 1929: Das Determinationsproblem; II. Die paarigen Extremitäten der Wirbeltiere in der Entwicklung, *Erg. Biol.*, V, 290–404.

MAURER, F., 1892: Der Aufbau und die Entwicklung der ventralen Rumpfmuskulatur bei den urodelen Amphibien und deren Beziehungen zu den gleichen Muskeln der Selachier und Teleostier, *Morph. Jahrb.*, XVIII, 76–179.

———, 1895: Die ventrale Rumpfmuskulatur der anuren Amphibien, *Morph. Jahrb.*, XXII, 225–263.

———, 1911: Die ventrale Rumpfmuskulatur von Menobranchus, Menopoma und Amphiuma, verglichen mit den gleichen Muskeln anderer Urodelen, *Jena. Zeitschr.*, XLVII, 1–40.

MINER, ROY WALDO, 1925: The pectoral limb of Eryops and other primitive tetrapods, *Bull. Amer. Mus. Nat. Hist.*, LI, 145–312.

NOBLE, G. K., 1922: The phylogeny of the Salientia; I. The osteology and the thigh musculature; their bearing on classification and phylogeny, *Bull. Amer. Mus. Nat. Hist.*, XLVI, 1–87, pls. 1–XXIII.

———, 1926: An analysis of the remarkable cases of distribution among the Amphibia, with descriptions of new genera, *Amer. Mus. Novit.*, No. 212.

RIBBING, L., 1907: Die distale Armmuskulatur der Amphibien, Reptilien und Säugetiere, *Zool. Jahrb.*, XXIII, 587–683, 2 Taf.

ROMER, A. S., 1924: Pectoral limb musculature and shoulder-girdle structure in fish and tetrapods, *Anat. Rec.*, XXVII, 119–143.

RYLKOFF, HELENE (WORONESCH), 1924: Die Entwicklung der Schultermuskeln bei urodelen Amphibien, *Zeitschr. Wiss. Zool.*, CXXII, 116–171.

SMITH, LOUISE, 1920: The hyobranchial apparatus of Spelerpes bislineatus, *Jour. Morph.*, XXXIII, 527–583.

VERSLUYS, J. J., E. W. IHLE, and P. N. VAN KAMPEN, 1927: "Vergleichende Anatomie der Wirbeltiere," Berlin.

WILDER, H. H., 1908: The limb muscles of Necturus, and their bearing upon the question of limb homology, (*Amer. Soc. Zool.*), *Science*, n. s., XXVII, 493–494.

CHAPTER XII

THE UROGENITAL SYSTEM

The excretory and reproductive systems, although originally separate as in most invertebrates, are so closely associated in vertebrates, including Amphibia, that they may be considered together. The waste products of metabolism must be removed from the tissues of the body if the animal is to live. They are swept from the tissues by the blood and especially by the lymph, then carried to those parts of the body where they may be discharged. Lungs and skin both throw off carbon dioxide and water as metabolic products. The skin may also dispose of some salts and possibly some urea. The latter, $(NH_2)_2CO$, is a white, crystalline compound, soluble in water. It is a product of protein metabolism and is formed in most vertebrates in the liver by the conversion of nitrogen from protein combustion. From the liver the urea passes into the blood and is eventually eliminated chiefly by the kidneys. Foreign substances in the blood, both organic and inorganic, may also be removed by the kidneys. In birds and terrestrial reptiles nitrogen is excreted largely as uric acid, in a semi-solid form. This is apparently an adaptation toward economy of water and seems to have arisen under arid environmental conditions such as have been assumed to have confronted the early reptiles. Although the formation of urea is believed to be restricted to the liver, Gottschalk and Nonennbruch (1923) found that the urea content of liverless frogs remained the same as that of normal frogs after the injection of amino-acids. This has led Buddenbrock (1928) to suggest that the method of forming urea in the blood directly from ammonia may be the more primitive one, perhaps characteristic of all Anamnia.

Urogenital Organs.—The kidneys in vertebrates may have been primitively a pair of narrow elongate bodies extending the whole length of the body cavity, a condition which is approached among Amphibia by Ascaphus and the caecilians. These kidneys were formed by a series of segmentally arranged tubules resem-

266

bling roughly the sweat glands of mammals, and, like them, they are excretory organs. The anterior part of such a kidney rudiment theoretically, if not actually present, develops in most lower vertebrates into a functional organ, the pronephros, before the posterior section, the mesonephros, differentiates. The former is the typical kidney of the young larvae, and in forms such as Eleutherodactylus, which hatch from the capsules as metamorphosed individuals, it shows a very early degeneration. In other Amphibia it functions up to the time of independent feeding or a little later.

Both pronephros and mesonephros arise from the mesomere, a portion of the mesoderm lying between the myotomes and the non-segmented lateral plates of the embryo (Fig. 97). In urodeles two or three or at most four segments (Megalobatrachus,

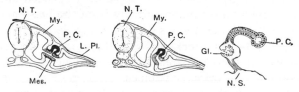

Fig. 97.—Diagram of the development of the pronephric canal. *Gl.*, glomerulus; *L.Pl.*, lateral plate; *P.C.*, pronephric canal; *Mes.*, mesomere; *My.*, myotome, *N.S.*, nephrostome; *N.T.*, neural tube. (*After Felix.*)

Mibayashi, 1928) of this mesomere give rise to tubules, usually one to each segment. These collectively form the pronephros. The tubules open proximally into the body cavity in the form of nephrostomes, while distally their ends bend caudally and fuse to form a common pronephric duct. This grows posteriorly immediately under the ectoderm and finally fuses with the cloaca. In Salientia, as in most urodeles, only two or three tubules enter into the formation of the pronephros, while in caecilians the number involved is from 10 to 13. In the wall of the body cavity of the larva, adjacent to the proximal openings or nephrostomes of the pronephric tubules, a series of branches from the dorsal aorta push out a fold of the peritoneum to form a sinus, the glomus, which serves as the arterial blood supply. In some forms, at least, these blood vessels are originally metamerically laid down as in the case of the tubules. The blood is carried away by the postcardinal veins which form a plexus about the tubules.

The mesonephric tubules arise in the same way as do those of the pronephros, but in growing distally they frequently fuse with the common pronephric duct. Their proximal ends form a series of nephrostomes or openings into the body cavity similar to those of the pronephros. Vessels from the dorsal aorta push in between the tubules to form a vascular pocket or glomerulus in the wall of each tubule instead of uniting to produce a plexus within the body cavity as in the case of the pronephros. The mesonephric tubules arise in a strictly metameric order in cae-cilians, Amphiuma, and some others, but in most Salientia and urodeles secondary tubules early develop and obscure this arrangement. In urodeles the secondary tubules are derived by budding from the primary ones after they have attained a functional state. In some Salientia such as *Rana temporaria* the whole process of differentiation is apparently speeded up, for the secondary tubules arise independently from the blastema (Gray, 1930). The collecting tubules which form outlets for the secondary tubules arise as short, straight ducts with only abortive enlargements at their proximal ends as evidence of their phylogenetic origin from primary tubules. The mass of mesonephric tubules forms an elongate organ on the dorsal surface of the body cavity. In Rana this kidney may include over 5,000 glomeruli (Hayman, 1928), although 2,000 is the average. In perennibranchs and derotremes the mesonephric kidneys project into the body cavity and are surrounded on both sides by peritoneum.

Each tubule (Fig. 98) in the mature kidney, or mesonephros, of both urodeles and frogs exhibits typically certain structurally different parts which may be homologized with similar parts of the tubules of the mammalian kidney, a metanephros. The nephrostomes on the ventral surface of the kidney open into a short ciliated neck which connects with a similarly ciliated tubule extending to an enlarged chamber, the glomerular capsule. One part of this chamber is invaginated by a rete of arterioles, the glomerulus, which with its capsule is called a "renal corpuscle." The first segment of the tubule which arises from the capsule is ciliated as stated above. Distal to this first segment, the tubule widens out into a long convoluted part lined with cells having a glandular appearance. This is the proximal convoluted portion of the tubule. It runs dorsally in most Amphibia, usually to the upper portion of the kidney where it joins a second ciliated part. This part is sometimes designated as the narrow segment of the tubule, although it may be as wide as all the other segments except the proximal ciliated one. It corresponds in position to Henle's loop of the mammalian kidney, and although it may extend ventrally again it has neither the great length nor the characteristic form of this important part of the metanephric tubule of the mammalian kidney. There follows on this segment the fourth or distal convoluted portion of the tubule. It is joined by a short junctional segment with

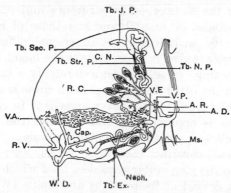

Fig. 98.—Diagrammatic section of the kidney of *Necturus maculosus* to show the form of a typical tubule and its relation to the blood supply. *A.D.*, dorsal aorta; *A.R.*, renal artery; *Cap.*, capillary; *C.N.*, ciliated neck; *Ms.*, mesentery; *Neph.*, nephrostome; *R.C.*, renal (Malpighian) corpuscle; *R.V.*, renal portal vein; *Tb.Ex.*, outer tubule; *Tb.J.P.*, junctional part of renal tubule; *Tb.N.P.*, narrow part of renal tubule; *Tb.Sec.P.*, proximal convoluted part of renal tubule (secretory part in pelvic kidney); *Tb.Str.P.*, distal convoluted part of renal tubule (striated part in pelvic kidney); *V.A.*, afferent renal vein; *V.E.*, efferent renal vein; *V.P.*, vena cava posterior; *W.D.*, Wolffian duct. (*After Chase.*)

a connecting tubule which in some frogs extends transversely across the kidney to make an outlet to the Wolffian duct. These five parts of the tubule may be seen in Fig. 98.

Many tubules of both urodele and frog kidney lack a nephrostome and hence have given up all direct connection with the coelom. In higher vertebrates, those with a metanephric kidney, nephrostomes are given up entirely. One modification of the nephrostome is found only in the Salientia. In many, but not all, of these the nephrostomal segment of the tubule joins with nephric veins (Sweet, 1908). Originally the nephrostomes discharged into the tubules waste fluids secreted through the walls of the peritoneum, but within the Amphibia apparently with the increasing use of the peritoneal cavity as a lymphatic chamber these same nephrostomes became conduits for circulatory fluids. This offers a good example of structures assuming totally new functions during phylogeny without changing to any great extent their original character. It may be further noted that in *Rana temporaria*, at least (Gray, 1930), the nephrostomal funnels arise independently of the tubules, and hence the frog shows in its development no evidence of the ancient use of these structures as essential parts of the excretory system.

Function of the Kidney.—The structural differences between the kidney tubules of amphibians and those of mammals are closely correlated with important functional differences. The mammalian urine is always hypertonic to the blood, *i.e.*, possesses a higher percentage of solids and accordingly a higher osmotic pressure. On the other hand, amphibian urine is usually hypotonic to the blood or at least never exceeds it in concentration. This difference is apparently correlated with the absence of a typical Henle's loop in the amphibian tubules. Through the thin membrane covering each glomerulus, there apparently filters out into the glomerular capsule a fluid which is essentially blood plasma devoid of its proteins and lipins (Walker, 1930). The tubules show a selective function in reabsorbing useful substances especially sodium chloride and glucose and in transmitting them back to the blood stream (Liang, 1929). Dyes have been frequently injected into the vascular system of frogs with a view to demonstrating the part of the tubule which eliminates such foreign substances. It appears that the glomerulus may eliminate certain dyes and the tubule others (Kuki, 1929). Bensley and Steen (1928) found by the use of dyes that the distal convoluted segment of the frog's renal tubule had resorptive functions, while the proximal section, although taking up the dye from the blood, excreted it into the tubule lumen in a more dilute solution. According to these authors, this process of secretion is present even when there is no circulation in the renal corpuscles. Bieter and Hirschfelder (1929), on the other hand, have stressed the rapidity with which dye may be eliminated by the glomeruli as contrasted with the slower elimination by the tubule. In brief, the tubule plays a most important rôle in reabsorption, while the glomerulus, with its thin cover of cells, may be looked upon as a mechanism for flushing the tubule.

In salt-water fish and reptiles which must conserve their water, the glomerulus may be poorly developed or even, as in some of the former, absent entirely.

In spite of the dilute character of frogs' urine, certain of its constituents are very much more concentrated than in either blood or capsular fluid. This has been shown to be the case for urea (Przylecki, 1922), where the concentration may be as great as seventy-four times (Crane, 1927). In comparison with mammalian urine, however, phosphates are far less efficiently concentrated in the amphibian kidney, and chlorides and bicarbonates not at all (Crane, 1927). Crane suggests that the concentration of urea is probably due to a selective secretory function of the tubules, and this author points out that this may be a primitive mechanism which is lost higher in the evolutionary scale. Throughout the vertebrate series the glomerulus remains as the primary outlet for water.

Frogs and toads excrete proportionately much more urine per day at ordinary temperature than man. While man excretes about one-fiftieth of his weight per day, the frog excretes about one-third (Adolph, 1927). Like most essential processes in Amphibia, the rate of excretion is dependent on environmental temperature. During the winter, kidney function is almost entirely suspended. This is apparently not due, however, to the slowing down uniformly of all the processes of excretion. Oliver and Eshref (1929) have shown that there is an increase in resorptive functions of the tubules during the winter months. In *Rana pipiens* an increase in temperature of 10°C. increases the rate of water passage through the skin 2.3 times (Adolph, 1930). At any one temperature the water is absorbed through the skin at a rather constant rate (Adolph, 1927) and does not vary with the area of skin exposed. The water is excreted by the kidneys at the same rate and hence the concentration of body fluids does not change essentially. The frog thus regulates its fluid content at the point of output and not at the point of intake. The blood pressure has an important control over the amount of urine eliminated, since the blood plasma apparently passes through the glomeruli by filtration, not by secretion. In salamanders the destruction of one kidney, either mesonephros or pronephros (Howland, 1920), results in a compensatory hypertrophy of the kidney of the opposite side. It would seem that in this case the amount of water absorbed remained the same as before the operation and that the one remaining kidney grew to do the work of two.

In brief, the work of the kidney is not purely excretory, that is, the elimination of waste products of metabolism. The kidney has regulatory functions as well. By allowing the passage of certain substances to the exterior, and in the retention of others, the kidney is of the greatest importance in maintaining the characteristic constancy in composition of the body fluids. Amphibia are continually absorbing water through their skin, and, further, they take less sodium chloride in their food than mammals. Hence, the materials eliminated are different in the two groups. In mammals water is saved and the salts excreted, while in Amphibia the reverse maintains to a large degree. Further, with the less efficient regulatory mechanism of the amphibian kidney, the bladder (to be discussed below) functions not merely as a receptacle for urine. Since the bladder is permeable to water, there is an absorption by the tissues of water from the bladder under conditions of dehydration until the osmotic equilibrium with the blood is again attained (Steen, 1929).

One modification of the amphibian kidney requires further mention, for it has apparently considerable phylogenetic significance. The mesonephric tubules of caecilians exhibit a type of modification not found in other Amphibia but one which was taken up and elaborated by the more advanced vertebrates. While in some Salientia and Caudata the collecting ducts of the mesonephros are primary tubules which usually extend to the common pronephric duct to gain exit to the outside, in the caecilians the posterior part of this duct sends out branches to the tubules of the kidney before they grow out. In higher vertebrates these ureters are reduced in number until in some mammals only a single one is formed. Caecilians thus show the first step in the origin of the true ureter of higher vertebrates.

Reproductive System.—The ducts of the kidneys are modified in Amphibia chiefly in correlation with the different methods of transferring the sexual products to the outside. The common pronephric duct splits in sharks to give rise to the Müllerian duct or tube for the passage of eggs to the cloaca, while the remainder, now called the "Wolffian duct," retains its original function of a discharge canal for the mesonephros. The Müllerian duct arises partly from the pronephric duct in Ambystoma but in frogs and toads has a wholly independent origin from a fusion and backward growth of two or more evaginations, which although appearing later than the pronephric tubules seem to be homologous with them. Hall (1904) has suggested that these evaginations, which lie ventral to the pronephric nephrostomes, originally possessed a secretory function which was given up when they became specialized to subserve a sexual function. The Müllerian duct develops in both sexes of most Amphibia but grows to a functional condition only under the influence of the ovary (Christensen, 1929). The Müllerian ducts usually open separately into the cloaca in most Amphibia, but in Bufo and Alytes they may unite just anteriorly to the cloaca, while in Nectophrynoides the chamber resulting from the fusion produces a bicornuate uterus in which the young develop.

The spermatozoa gain exit to the outside by way of the Wolffian duct. A series of genital cords which grow out from the tissues of the kidney to the developing testis form, at a later stage, a series of fine ducts to serve as a passageway from the testis to the mesonephros. The net is usually arranged in the form of a series of from four to nine transverse cords, the vasa efferentia, and two longitudinal ones. The first of the longitudinal cords forms the central canal extending through the length of the testis and receiving spermatozoa either from the spermatic ampullae or from branches extending to the same. The second longitudinal duct is situated close to the median border of the mesonephros and crosses the vasa efferentia. In some plethodontids this longitudinal duct is absent and the vasa efferentia run directly to the renal corpuscles of their apparent origin. In Ascaphus three or more branches of the vasa efferentia of one side are connected with the longitudinal canal of the opposite kidney, and India ink injected into the Wolffian duct of one kidney will fill the vasa efferentia and kidney tubules of the opposite side. The kidney shown in Fig. 99 has been injected in this way. It is interesting that the only other amphibian known to show a fusion of parts of the testicular nets of the two sides is the primitive salamander, *Hynobius lichenatus*, as described by Yamagiva (1924).

Primitively in both frogs and urodeles the spermatozoa were passed by a series of vasa efferentia into renal corpuscles of the mesonephros from which they made their way into the Wolffian duct and cloaca. In some of the most primitive of living urodeles the mesonephric tubules fail to reach the Wolffian duct but extend posteriorly to empty independently into the cloaca. Yamagiva (1924) has shown this to be the condition in both sexes of Megalobatrachus and in the male Hynobius. In the

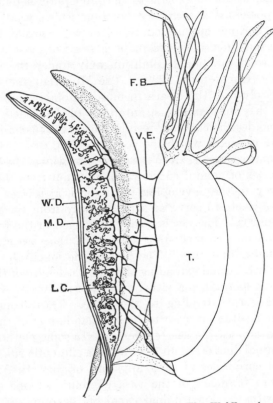

Fig. 99.—The vasa efferentia of Ascaphus. The Wolffian duct of the right kidney has been injected with ink. Transverse ducts connect the vasa efferentia of the one side with a longitudinal canal of the opposite kidney. Hence ink injected into the right Wolffian duct makes its way into the vasa efferentia of the opposite kidney. *W.D.*, Wolffian duct; *M.D.*, Müllerian duct; *V.E.*, vasa efferentia; *L.C.*, longitudinal canal; *T.* right testis; *F.B.*, fat body.

female a few of the tubules empty into the Wolffian duct, while others open into the cloaca. It is remarkable that in the closely related Onychodactylus some of the tubules of the male fuse to form a common duct opening into the cloaca, while others join the Wolffian duct. Onychodactylus has been derived from Hynobius and yet it shows a theoretically more primitive condition of these ducts. Such facts when considered in their phylogenetic perspective show that evolution has not always proceeded in a progressive manner. Possibly the more primitive condition of the mesonephric ducts of Onychodactylus may be explained as the retention of a juvenile character which is passed over in the ontogeny of Hynobius.

The testes of Amphibia are shorter than the kidneys and the vasa efferentia empty into only a limited number of the glomerular capsules. Such capsules are usually reduced in size, and their renal corpuscles as well as their nephrostomes arc lost. The cells in the proximal convoluted portion of the tubules leading from these capsules become ciliated in some forms such as Necturus (Chase, 1923), while the distal convoluted portion of the same tubules becomes very wide. In some Salientia the vasa efferentia appear to empty directly into the transverse collecting tubules, apparently because the glomerular capsules have been lost and the nephric tubules shortened. Radical differences in the modification of these ducts may exist between closely related species, as, for example, between the two European frogs *Rana esculenta* and *R. fusca*. Radical changes in the mesonephric tubules transversed by spermatozoa do not lead in some Amphibia, such as Necturus, to any alteration in the form of the kidney, but in most urodeles the anterior part of the mesonephros is narrowed as if to facilitate a short passage across the kidney for the male sex products.

Both frogs and urodeles show a tendency to reduce the posterior part of the testicular net. In Necturus and Proteus, only the two anterior vasa efferentia are functional, while Chase (1923) records one specimen of the former in which only the most anterior transverse duct of the testicular net was utilized. The discoglossid toads, although primitive, show an extreme stage in this restriction of function to the anterior vasa efferentia. In the adult male Discoglossus and Alytes the first and second vasa efferentia, which alone are functional, reach the Wolffian duct by crossing entirely anterior to the kidney. Probably a portion of this duct includes one or more modified mesonephric tubules which have completely freed themselves from the rest of the kidney. The collecting tubules of the mesonephros of these genera form a common duct which resembles a ureter of higher vertebrates in serving as a duct for the kidney secretions alone, but it differs from a true ureter in not having arisen from the

Wolffian duct. In the dipnoans it is the posterior part of the testicular net which is modified to make a short circuit to the Wolffian duct. Rudiments of the testicular net appear in the females of some Amphibia, but like the Müllerian ducts in the male they never attain a functional state. In some Salientia, such as *Rana sylvatica* and Alytes, the caudal portion of the Wolffian duct of the male is enlarged to form a saccular reservoir for the spermatozoa, the *vesicula seminalis*. This would seem to permit the use of a large amount of sperm in a short time by these species.

Urinary Bladder.—The renal ducts of Amphibia are not enlarged to form reservoirs for the urine as in some fish. On the other hand, an evagination of the ventral wall of the cloaca immediately adjacent to the openings of the Wolffian duct extends forward into the abdominal cavity and functions as a urinary bladder. This bladder may be cylindrical as in Proteus or Amphiuma, bicornuate as in salamandrids and various frogs, or nearly two-lobed as in certain discoglossids (Field, 1894). It reaches its largest size in the aquatic Amphiuma and in some terrestrial species such as Hydromantes and Bufo. In the latter it would seem to function, as stated above, as a reserve supply of water to delay desiccation. The bladder is held in place by sheets of peritoneum. It is well provided with smooth muscle and is closed by a sphincter which is frequently released by frogs and toads when roughly handled. The release of the fluid from the bladder lightens the animal and facilitates its escape.

Sex and Its Modification.—In the above description of the urogenital organs various similarities between the two sexes were noted at certain stages of development. The earlier the stage selected the more difficult it becomes to distinguish between the sexes. In fact, for a considerable period the gonads and associated structures of the two sexes are identical except for assumed differences in the chromatin material which are often not demonstrable cytologically. Sex is, nevertheless, determined very early. During the maturation of the germ cells, sex differences may be seen in the chromosomes of the developing sex products (Fig. 8). Two kinds of germ cells occur in the male of some species of Rana, one male-determining, the other female-determining, but in the toad only one kind has been demonstrated (Brambell, 1930). Iriki (1930) was unable to distinguish a heteromorphic sex chromosome in *Hyla arborea japonica* and concluded that the male tree frog was homozygous in respect to sex. Whether there are two kinds of sperm cells in the male or two kinds of eggs in the female, sex is, nevertheless, determined at the time of fertilization by genetic factors carried by the chromosomes of the uniting germ cells. Once the sex has been established, environmental factors may intervene to reverse the result completely and permit the opposite sex to come to full development.

The germ cells when first distinguishable are found in the entoderm of Salientia and some urodeles (Bounoure, 1925) but in the mesoderm of other urodeles (Humphrey, 1929). In *Rana sylvatica* at the time of hatching they form a median ridge above the mesentery. Witschi (1929) has traced the history of these cells. At the time the external gills are being reduced the ridge divides into two rows of germ cells, the future gonads. A series of cells migrate from the blastema of the mesonephros and enter the gonads. These are the rete cords which come to occupy a central position in the undifferentiated gonad while the germ cells form the cortex. Sex is first distinguishable when the germ cells migrate from their more peripheral position and become surrounded by rete cells which are to form the seminiferous tubules of the male. In the female the germ cells transform into ovocytes and eggs without losing their position in the cortex. At about the time of metamorphosis some rete cells in the male form the vasa efferentia connecting the seminiferous tubules with the mesonephros, while in the female they are transformed into the ovarian sacs without extending to the kidney. Witschi concluded from this and earlier studies that the rete cords in the center of the gonad contain the male differentiating system. If it becomes active it causes the germ cells to migrate from the cortex into the medulla of the gonad and to transform into spermatogonia. If it is not active, other substances in the cortex and presumably in the follicle cells transform the germ cells into ovogonia. Witschi (1929) subjected Wood Frog tadpoles to high temperatures and produced either males or females transforming into males, but he obtained no typical females. In this case heat had apparently destroyed or inhibited the female determining substance in the cortex, releasing a compensatory growth of the medulla and its subsequent differentiation into rete and seminiferous tubules. Piquet (1930) has confirmed Witschi and has shown that high temperatures would tend to change genetic females into males. In both *Rana temporaria*

and *Bufo vulgaris* a temperature of 25° produces a very high
excess of males.   A temperature of 20° is neutral in the toad but
has a slight masculinizing effect in the frog.

In the toad the reversal of sex has apparently been accomplished but under different conditions.   In the tadpole of Bufo,
the anterior portion of each gonad becomes enlarged and in the
adult, forms the Bidder's organ, a structure which has been
frequently compared to a rudimentary ovary.   Harms (1926)
and Ponse (1926) found that removing the testes caused the

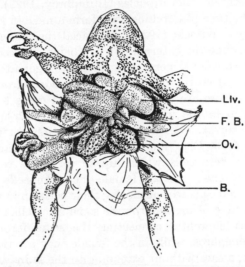

FIG. 100.—Sex reversal in a toad.   Three and a half months after removing
the testes of the adult toad, part of the Bidder's organ has developed into an
ovary.   *B.*, urinary bladder; *F.B.*, fat body; *Liv.*, liver; *Ov.*, rudimentary ovary.
(*After Harms.*)

Bidder's organ to develop into a functional ovary (Fig. 100)
If Bufo is assumed to be hermaphroditic, this would not be a
case of sex reversal but merely a growth of the ovary after the
inhibitory effect of the testes was removed (Ponse, 1927).   The
cells of Bidder's organ, however, have the appearance of indifferent germ cells which, although potential sperm, are transformed
into ova by the conditions of the experiment.

Sex reversal has also been accomplished in salamanders in a
more decisive manner.   Burns (1925) joined pairs of Ambystoma
together at an early stage before sex differences in the gonads were
visible.   When the salamanders developed, the sex of the mem-

bers of each pair was always the same. As it was very unlikely this could have come about through the chance selection of individuals of the same sex, a sex reversal would seem to have occurred in some instances. Humphrey (1929*a*) implanted the preprimordium of the gonad of one sex into the embryo of another after removing the corresponding gonad preprimordium from the latter and found that it usually differentiated according to the sex determination of the donor. Later a modification or sex reversal of the graft or host gonad may be effected. When an ovary or testis of similar size and species developed together in an animal it was always the ovary which suffered modification. A hormone from the testis apparently exerted an inhibitory influence on the growth of the ovarian cortex very similar to the

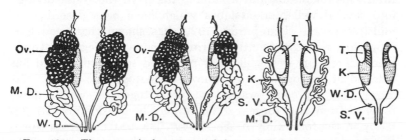

Fig. 101.—The urogenital systems of four adult frogs, *Rana temporaria*, representing stages in the transformation of females into males. *K.*, kidney; *M.D.*, Müllerian duct; *Ov.*, ovary; *S.V.*, seminal vesicle; *T.*, testis; *W.D.*, Wolffian duct. (*After Witschi.*)

action of heat in the case of the Wood Frog, and further changes in the male direction were a result of the cessation of cortical activity. If the gonad developed from a male donor was small in size or retarded in development, it was not able to dominate the ovary, but on the other hand, it underwent a partial sex reversal. It would thus seem that there are both male and female determining substances in the developing gonads. Amphibia pass through an indifferent and apparently later a bisexual state before genetic factors give the ascendency to the tissues which shape the germ cells into either ova or sperm. Up to a certain stage various environmental factors can reverse this dominance, and gonads of the opposite sex will develop. This shift of balance is not, however, transmitted to the next generation. Female frogs which have changed into males (Fig. 101), when mated with normal females produce only female offspring (Crew,

1921). The genetic constitution of the germinal material is not changed, although its expression in any one generation may be modified.

Segmentation of the Gonads.—The gonads of frogs shortly after the penetration of the rete cords exhibit a certain lobulation which has been considered evidence of a primitive metamerism perhaps harking back to the first vertebrates which presumably had metamerically divided body cavity and gonads. The suggestion is rendered the more probable in that the testes of caecilians are divided into a series of segments connected by the central longitudinal canal. Other elongate-bodied Amphibia, such as Siren and Amphiuma, have the testis undivided and hence the segmentation is not merely a consequence of body form. Many plethodontids and salamandrids have the testis divided into several well marked lobes which have been described as multiple testes. Humphrey (1922) has shown that each lobe represents a center of active spermatogenesis, the region between lobes merely an area which has produced spermatozoa and has delayed in the formation of a new spermatogenetic cycle. The lobes thus represent waves of spermatogenesis which move forward from year to year. There may be considerable irregularity in the formation of the lobes. The testes of frogs sometimes exhibit a certain gonomery during their ontogeny. This has no relation to the lobulation of the urodele testis but may be reminiscent of the caecilian condition. The lobulation in urodeles apparently has no phylogenetic significance, but it is interesting that only two closely related families of salamanders should have developed this type of testicular modification.

Fat Bodies.—The gonads of Amphibia have certain nutriment requirements which are often violated under laboratory conditions. Inanition prevents sexual differentiation in immature animals and causes degeneration of the mature germ cells in the adult. Amphibia are provided with conspicuous paired fat bodies as a reserve supply of nutriment for the gonads. The fat bodies in urodeles are usually in the form of a pair of bands enveloped in folds of peritoneum and lying parallel to the kidneys between them and the gonad. In the Salientia the fat bodies are fingerlike structures situated at the anterior end of the gonad. In the caecilians they are more extensive than in other Amphibia and form a series of lobes parallel to the genital organs. In both frogs and toads the fat bodies are known to arise from the anterior part of the developing gonad, although this has been denied by some investigators (Kennel, 1913). They reach their maximum size in the fall before hibernation and their minimum size after egg laying. Partial castration causes the fat bodies to hypertrophy (Dubois, 1927). Removal of the fat bodies causes a degeneration of the sexual products, the most advanced stages degenerating first (Adams and Rae, 1929). The fat bodies are therefore necessary for maintaining the health and normal development of the gonads.

Ovulation.—The eggs lie in the cortex of the ovary and each egg during the growth period is surrounded by a layer of follicle cells which is enclosed by a vascular network. A thin vitelline membrane covers the surface of the mature egg. This membrane is duplex, an outer portion, the zona pellucida, having been produced by the follicle cells (Fig. 102) and an inner portion, the zona radiata, by the egg itself. The eggs project into the lumen of the ovary, and the outer surface of the latter is covered with peritoneum.

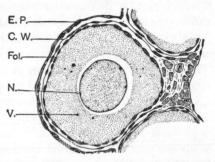

Fig. 102.—A developing ovocyte of Cryptobranchus. A section through the ovarian wall of a 26 cm. specimen. *C.W.*, cyst wall; *E.P.*, inner epithelial membrane of the ovarian wall; *Fol.*, follicle cell; *N.*, nucleolus; *V.*, vitelline body. (*After Smith.*)

During the breeding season each egg breaks through the wall of the ovary at the point where its stalk joins the ovarian epithelium. A small hole appears in the peritoneum and the egg in squeezing through this aperture may be forced into an hourglass shape (Smith, 1916). The egg when free in the peritoneal cavity is said to be carried to the open mouths of the Müllerian ducts by ciliary action. Smith (1916) finds few cilia present in either *Rana pipiens* or Cryptobranchus, however, and it seems possible that eggs are forced into the oviducts partly by suction; the mouths of the oviducts being attached to the pericardium would gape open at each heart beat. The movements of the female would also tend to squeeze the eggs through the outlet. Fertilization in some salamanders takes place near the mouth of the oviduct, the egg having thrown off the polar bodies while within the ovary or peritoneal cavity. Weber (1922) suggests that the fertilization of the eggs of *Salamandra atra* may occur in the peritoneal cavity and that the death of the eggs which reach the oviduct last may be due to excessive polyspermy, for as many as 200 spermatozoa may be found in a single egg destined to degenerate.

The eggs are propelled through the oviducts by the action of cilia. The oviducts are lined with either mucus-producing cells as in the newt or with tube-shaped glands as in Rana. The cilia usually lie on the summits of ridges which run more or less the length of the oviduct. As the eggs progress they become covered with mucus or similar gelatinous material. In most Amphibia the distribution of the glands or mucous cells is not uniform throughout the oviduct, and, as shown by Lebrun (1891), the anterior, middle, and posterior regions of the oviduct may differ considerably in muscular, glandular, and ciliary equipment. Further, the glandular tubules in the anterior part of the oviduct may differ in length or character from those in the posterior part. This structural differentiation of the oviduct is reflected in the egg capsules which may be as many as three well-defined ones, aside from the vitelline membrane. Where the eggs pass continuously through the oviduct as in Bufo, the outer capsule may be a string of uniform width; if the eggs are held in the posterior part of the oviduct and finally ejected rapidly, the spawn may form a clump surrounded by a single saclike capsule. It is remarkable that such apparently trivial differences are frequently uniform throughout natural groups of species and may be used as a ready means of identification. The egg sacs of the Hynobiidae, for example, cannot be confused with those of other salamanders.

There is some evidence that mucus may be secreted without the direct contact of the egg (Wetzel, 1908). Frogs have been found with egg capsules but no eggs in one of the oviducts (Voss, 1927). Further, some species, such as the tree frog, Phyllomedusa, normally lay empty egg capsules which may be used in the construction of its "nest." Frogs that build "foam nests" may produce gelatinous nest material before the eggs are laid, and *Limnodynastes tasmaniensis* has been described as building one foam nest entirely without eggs (Klingelhoffer 1930).

The gelatinous capsules of the eggs swell enormously when brought in contact with water, and frogs which have been prevented from laying have been described as bursting from the rapid imbibition of water by the uterine eggs (Nussbaum, 1908).

Fertilization.—Fertilization is external in most frogs; only two genera are known to impregnate the eggs within the oviducts. On the other hand, all salamanders except the primitive Hynobiidae and Cryptobranchidae (apparently the Sirenidae as well) produce spermatophores, which are usually picked up by the female, although they may be transmitted directly into her cloaca. It is interesting to trace the evolution of the sperm-receiving mechanisms of the female, for it follows closely the phylogenetic order. In Ascaphus, one of the most primitive frogs, the cloaca is extended into a highly vascular tube which may be bent forward by the contraction of the *rectus abdominis*. The tip of this copulatory organ is inserted into the cloaca of the female during amplexus, and the oviducts become well provided with spermatozoa which make their way between the mucous folds, there being no special organ for receiving them. The Gymnophiona also practice internal fertilization and for this purpose are provided with a muscular extension of the cloaca which, as in the case of the "tail" of Ascaphus, may bear horny spines, these being visible only when the organ is fully everted. (Fig. 154C). Unlike Ascaphus, the male caecilians withdraw their cloacal extensions entirely within the vent when not in use, a special retractor muscle making this possible. Caecilians agree with Ascaphus and differ from urodeles in lacking a spermatheca or sac in the female cloaca for reception of the sperm.

Structure of the Cloaca.—The spermatophore of the salamanders is produced by the combined action of two sets of glands: the pelvic gland lying in the roof and sometimes in the upper portion of the cloaca of the male, and the cloacal glands which cover the walls of the cloaca and are most conspicuous on the sides where they form rows of papillae or in some species villosities. In the posterior corner of the cloaca there empties a third set of glands, the abdominal, which receive their name from the fact that in some species of salamandrids they extend forward over the roof of the cloaca into the abdominal cavity. The abdominal glands may empty outside of the cloaca on small papillae as in some newts (Heidenhain, 1892), or on a low papilla on either side of the posterior corner of the cloaca as in *Plethodon cinereus*. Since these glands may or may not empty within the cloacal lips they seem to play no part in spermatophore formation but apparently serve to stimulate the female during courtship.

In the cloaca of the female salamander all three sets of glands may appear, although here they have different functions. The

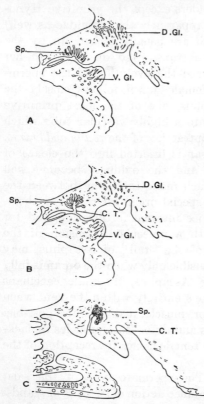

pelvic gland serves as a reservoir for the spermatozoa which migrate from the disintegrating spermatophore held between the lips of the cloaca to these tubules in the roof of the cloaca (Noble and Weber, 1929). The cloacal glands which are present in all ambystomids, salamandrids, and primitive plethodontids, may play some part in egg-capsule formation. The abdominal glands are also developed in female newts. They are present in Ambystoma, Necturus, and Eurycea, although apparently rudimentary and non-functional. Their homologies with the male glands have been established by transplanting a testis into the body of the female. The spermatheca in the newt then changes into the pelvic gland, the rudimentary abdominal glands into a functional organ (Beaumont, 1928). It is interesting that in Desmognathus, where neither abdominal nor cloacal glands are present even as rudiments in the female, the same operation causes these two glands to sprout *de novo* from the undifferentiated epithelium of the cloaca of the adult female (Noble and Pope, 1929).

FIG. 103.—Diagrammatic sagittal section of the cloacas of three salamanders to show the evolution of the spermatheca. Anterior end on the left. (*Based on data from Kingsbury and from Dieckmann.*) *A.* Necturus. Spermatheca tubules numerous and opening on the roof of the cloaca. *B.* Ambystoma. Tubules less numerous and opening into a common duct. *C.* Desmognathus. Showing further reduction and modification of the tubules, also loss of dorsal and ventral glands. *C.T.*, common tube of spermatheca; *D.Gl.*, dorsal gland; *Sp.*, spermatheca; *V.Gl.*, ventral gland.

Thus, even in the higher plethodontids the abdominal and cloacal glands are potentially present although unrepresented by visible rudiments.

Evolution of the Spermatheca.—The spermatheca, or modified pelvic gland of the female, undergoes a progressive change during phylogeny. In the salamandrids and Necturus, it is represented by numerous tubules which empty like the pelvic gland of the male on the roof of the cloaca. In the ambystomid Rhyacotriton, the area on which some of these tubules empty is evaginated from the roof of the cloaca as a shallow pocket. In the Plethodontidae this pocket has become a duct into which a number of tubules empty. Each of the latter ends blindly in a saccular enlargement, in which the spermatozoa come to rest. The more specialized and terrestrial plethodontids exhibit a reduction in number of the spermathecal tubules emptying into the common duct (Fig. 103). The only exception to this progressive change in cloacal apparatus within the Plethodontidae is found in the Four-toed Salamander, Hemidactylium. This species fails to develop a central tube and moreover retains a rudiment of the abdominal gland of the female. Nevertheless, its tubules are only 3 or 4 (Dieckmann, 1927) instead of 15 to 25 as in primitive plethodontids, and it lacks the cloacal gland rudiment which is present in the female of Gyrinophilus and Eurycea. Hence the cloaca of Hemidactylium may be considered a further specialization rather than a retention of a primitive type.

In the evolution of the common tube out of a diverticulum of the roof of the cloaca, not all of the pelvic gland tubules were involved. Transplanting a testis into the adult female Desmognathus causes some pelvic gland tubules to sprout *de novo* from the epithelium of the roof of the cloaca. It is interesting that the abdominal and cloacal glands which are closely controlled by the testicular hormones in Desmognathus should appear in both sexes in more primitive salamanders. This subject will be considered further in the discussion of the endocrine organs.

Identification of Sex.—The different glandular equipment of the cloacas of the two sexes of most salamanders permits their ready identification without dissection. The papillae within the cloacal lips of the male are replaced by smooth folds in the female (Fig. 104). The abdominal gland or its papillae are often visible in the male. The spermatheca is usually heavily pigmented even in the cave salamander, Typhlomolge. Hence a salamander with smooth or folded cloacal walls without papillae but with a dark pigment spot in the roof of the cloaca is a female. Some female plethodontids, especially Plethodon, have a small papilla

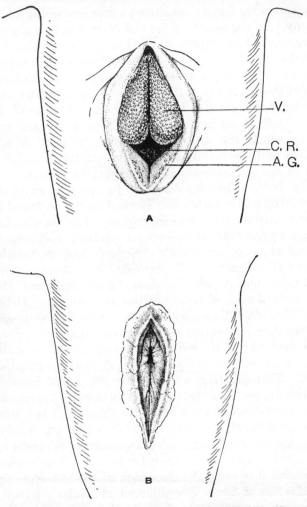

Fig. 104.—The cloacal orifice of a male (*A*) and a female (*B*) salamander, *Desmognathus fuscus*, showing the villosities which serve to distinguish the males of most species of salamanders from the opposite sex. *A.G.*, abdominal gland; *C.R.*, cloacal roof, region of pelvic gland; *V.*, villosities of the cloacal glands.

which projects from the roof of the cloaca, obscuring the view of the spermatheca. Males are identifiable not only by their papillose cloacas but by their secondary sexual characters. There are sexual differences also in the cloacas of the hynobiids and cryptobranchids which have a simpler glandular equipment than the salamanders producing spermatophores. The pelvic gland has been compared with the prostate of mammals. Its secretion, which may be readily observed in the living animal, is white, and serves to hold the spermatozoa together in a clump on the top of a gelatinous base produced by the cloacal glands. From its position the pelvic gland may be homologous to the prostate, although it has different functions. The enlarged glands within the cloacas of Salientia may possibly be homologized with the pelvic glands, although their function is not definitely known. In the Salientia sex may be identified by the presence of the secondary sexual characters discussed in Chap. V.

References

ADAMS, A. E., and E. E. RAE, 1929: An experimental study of the fat-bodies in Triturus (Diemyctylus) viridescens, *Anat. Rec.*, XLI, 181–204, 1 pl.

ADOLPH, E. F., 1927: The excretion of water by the kidneys of frogs, *Amer. Jour. Physiol.*, LXXXI, 315–324.

——, 1930: Living water, *Quart. Rev. Biol.*, V, 51–67.

BEAUMONT, J. DE, 1928: Modifications de l'appareil uro-genital du Triton cristatus femelle après greffe de testicules, *Compt. rend. Soc. Biol.*, XCVIII, 563–564.

BENSLEY, R. R., and W. BROOKS STEEN, 1928: The functions of the differentiated segments of the uriniferous tubule, *Amer. Jour. Anat.*, XLI, 75–96.

BIETER, R. N., and A. D. HIRSCHFELDER, 1929: The rôle of the glomeruli as the preferential route for excretion of phenolsulphonephthalein in the frog's kidney, *Amer. Jour. Physiol.*, XCI, 178–200.

BOUNOURE, L., 1925: L'origine des gonocytes et l'évolution de la première ébauche génitale chez les batraciens, *Ann. Sci. Nat. Zool.*, VIII, 201–278.

BRAMBELL, F. W. ROGERS, 1930: "The Development of Sex in Vertebrates," New York.

BUDDENBROCK, W. VON, 1928: "Grundriss der vergleichenden Physiologie," Berlin.

BURNS, ROBERT K., 1925: The sex of parobiotic twins in Amphibia, *Jour. Exp. Zool.*, XLII, 31–77, 6 pls.

CHASE, SAMUEL W., 1923: The mesonephros and urogenital ducts of Necturus maculosus Rafinesque, *Jour. Morph.*, XXXVII, 457–531.

CHRISTENSEN, K., 1929: Effect of castration on the oviduct in males and females of Rana pipiens, *Proc. Soc. Exp. Biol. Med.*, XXVI, 652–653.

CRANE, M. M., 1927: Observations on the function of the frog's kidney, *Amer. Jour. Physiol.*, LXXXI, 232–243.

CREW, F. A. E., 1921: Sex reversal in frogs and toads. A review of the recorded cases of abnormality of the reproductive system and an account of a breeding experiment, *Jour Gen.*, XI, 141–181.

DIECKMANN, J. M., 1927: The cloaca and spermatheca of Hemidactylium scutatum, *Biol. Bull.*, LIII, 281–285.

DUBOIS, A. M., 1927: Les corrélations physiologiques entre les glandes génitales et les corps jaunes chez les batraciens, *Rev. Suisse Zool.*, XXXIV, 499–581.

FIELD, H. H., 1894: Morphologie de la vessie chez les batraciens, *Bull. Soc. Zool. France*, XIX, 20–22.

GOTTSCHALK A., and W. NONNENBRUCH, 1923: Die Bedeutung der Leber für die Harnstoffbildung, *Arch. exp. Path.*, XCIX, 261.

GRAY, P., 1930: The development of the amphibian kidney. Part I. The development of the mesonephros of Rana temporaria, *Quart. Jour. Micr. Sci.*, LXXIII, 507–546, pls. 27–31.

HAAN, I., and A. BAKKER, 1924: Renal function in summer frogs and winter frogs, *Jour. Physiol.*, LIX, 129–137.

HALL, R. W., 1904: The development of the mesonephros and the Müllerian ducts in Amphibia, *Bull. Mus. Comp. Zool. Harvard*, XLV, 31–125, 8 pls.

HARMS, JÜRGEN W., 1926: "Körper und Keimzellen," Berlin.

HAYMAN, J. M., 1928: Notes on the arrangement of blood vessels within the frog's kidney together with some measurements of blood pressure in the renal portal and renal veins, *Amer. Jour. Physiol.*, LXXXVI, 331–339.

HEIDENHAIN, M., 1892: Notiz betreffend eine rudimentäre Drüse bei den Weibchen der einheimischen Tritonen, *Anat. Anz.*, VII, 432–435.

HOWLAND, R. B., 1920: Experiments on the effect of removal of the pronephros of Amblystoma punctatum, *Jour. Exp. Zool.*, XXXII, 355–395.

HUMPHREY, R. R., 1922: The multiple testis in urodeles, *Biol. Bull.*, XLIII, 45–67.

———, 1929: The early position of the primordial germ cells in urodeles: evidence from experimental studies, *Anat. Rec.*, XLII, 301–314.

———, 1929a: Studies on sex reversal in Amblystoma; II. Sex differentiation and modification following orthotopic implantation of a gonadic pre-primordium, *Jour. Exp. Zool.*, LIII, 171–221, 4 pls.

IRIKI, S., 1930: Studies on amphibian chromosomes; 1. On the chromosomes of Hyla arborea japonica Guenther, *Mem. Coll. Sci. Kyoto Imp. Univ.*, (B) V, 1–18, 2 pls.

KENNEL, PIERRE VON, 1913: Les corps adipolymphoïdes des batraciens, *Ann. Sci. Nat. Zool.*, 9th Ser., XVII, 219–254.

KLINGELHÖFFER, W., 1930: Terrarienkunde, Lief. 15–16. Stuttgart.

KUKI, S., 1929: The ratio of the elimination of the dyes from both the glomeruli and tubules, *Proc. Imp. Acad. Tokyo*, V, 393–395.

LEBRUN, H., 1891: Recherches sur l'appareil génital femelle de quelques batraciens indigènes, *La Cellule*, VII, 417–484, 6 pls.

LIANG, T. J., 1929: Über die Harnbildung in der Froschniere XVIII Mitt; Über die Bedingungen der sekretorischen Abscheidung in den 2. Abschnitten, *Pflugers Arch.*, CCXXII, 271–286.

MIBAYASHI, R., 1928: Über die Entwickelung des Vornierensystems beim Riesensalamander, *Zeitschr. Anat. Entw.*, LXXXVIII, 88–111.

NOBLE, G. K., and S. H. POPE, 1929: The modification of the cloaca and teeth of the adult salamander, Desmognathus, by testicular transplants and by castration, *Brit. Jour. Exp. Biol.*, VI, No. 4, 399–411, 2 pls.

NOBLE, G. K., and J. A. WEBER, 1929: The spermatophores of Desmognathus and other plethodontid salamanders, *Amer. Mus. Novit.*, No. 351.

NUSSBAUM, M., 1908: Zur Mechanik der Eiablage bei Rana fusca und Rana esculenta, *Arch. ges. Physiol.*, CXXIV, 100–111.

OLIVER, J., and S. ESHREF, 1929: A mechanism of conservation in the kidneys of the winter frog, *Jour. Exp. Med.*, L, 601–615.

PIQUET, J., 1930: Determination du sexe chez les batraciens en fonction de la temperature, *Rev. Suisse Zool.*, XXXVII, 173–281, 1 pl.

PONSE, K., 1926: Changement expérimental du sexe et intersexualité chez le crapaud (nouveaux résultats), *Compt. rend. Soc. Physiol. Hist. Nat. Genève*, XLIII, 19–22.

———, 1927: L'évolution de l'organe de Bidder et la sexualité chez le crapaud, *Rev. Suisse Zool.*, XXXIV, 217–220.

PRZYLECKI, J., 1922: L'échange de l'eau et des sels chez les amphibiens, *Arch. Int. Physiol.*, XIX, 148–159.

RICHARDS, A. N., and CARL F. SCHMIDT, 1924: A description of the glomerular circulation in the frog's kidney and observations concerning the action of adrenalin and various other substances upon it, *Amer. Jour. Physiol.*, LXXI, 178–208.

SMITH, B. G., 1916: The process of ovulation in Amphibia, *Mich. Acad. Sci. 18th Ann. Rep.*, 102–105.

STEEN, W. BROOKS, 1929: On the permeability of the frog's bladder to water, *Anat. Rec.*, XLIII, 215–220.

SWEET, GEORGINA, 1908: The anatomy of some Australian Amphibia; Part I. A. The openings of the nephrostomes from the coelom; B. The connection of the vasa efferentia with the kidney, *Proc. Roy. Soc. Victoria*, N. S., XX, 222–249, 2 pls.

VOSS, H., 1927: Wodurch wird die Bildung der Gallerthüllen des Froscheies im Eileiter ausgelöst? *S. B. naturf. Ges. Rostock* (3), I, 81–83.

WALKER, A. M., 1930: Comparisons of total molecular concentration of glomerular urine and blood plasma from the frog and from *Necturus*, *Jour. Biol. Chem.*, LXXXVII, 499–522.

WEBER, A., 1922: La fécondation chez la salamandre alpestre, *Compt. rend. Ass. Anat.*, XVII, 322–329.

WETZEL, G., 1908: Der Wassergehalt des fertigen Froscheies und der Mechanismus der Bildung seiner Hülle im Eileiter, *Arch. Entw. Mech.*, XXVI, 651–661.

WHITE, H. L., 1929: The question of water reabsorption by the renal tubule and its bearing on the problem of tubular secretion, *Amer. Jour. Physiol.*, LXXXVIII, 267.

———, and F. O. SCHMITT, 1926: The site of reabsorption in the kidney tubule of Necturus, *Amer. Jour. Physiol.*, LXXVI, 483–495.

WITSCHI, EMIL, 1929: Studies on sex differentiation and sex determination in amphibians; I. Development and sexual differentiation of the gonads of Rana sylvatica; II. Sex reversal in female tadpoles of Rana sylvatica following the application of high temperature, *Jour. Exp. Zool.*, LII, 267–292, 5 pls.

YAMAGIVA, S., 1924: Das Urogenitalsystem der Urodelen, *Jour. Coll. Agr., Hok. Imp. Univ.*, XV, 37–82.

CHAPTER XIII

THE ENDOCRINE GLANDS

The coordination of the activities of the various organs of the body may be brought about either through nervous impulses transmitted along nerve tissue or by chemical substances set free in the circulation. The latter are the hormones, and the best known are produced by the endocrine glands. These glands of internal secretion are found in various parts of the body. They have frequently changed their form and character during phylogeny, and in some instances their endocrine functions seem to have been secondarily acquired. The effects of their products control many types of form and function and range from influencing the rate of development, the coloration of the skin and the growth of the secondary sexual characters to the appearance of various types of behavior. Several of the endocrine organs are duplex, having arisen from tissue of totally different origin. They are functionally closely correlated among themselves, the stimulation of one organ leading to a change in the activity of another. This phenomenon makes it especially difficult to analyze the specific functions of any one organ, for its extirpation or transplantation leads to changes in the others. The study of the internal secretions has attracted many investigators in recent years, but the functions of several of the organs are still incompletely known. Probably some tissues not united into discrete endocrine organs discharge hormones into the blood stream, there to regulate the activities of other parts of the body. A good example is the small intestine with its hormone secretin, discussed in another chapter. Again, waste products of metabolism, such as carbon dioxide, may affect the respiratory centers in the brain. As discussed in the chapter on respiration, these centers control the breathing movements of Amphibia, increasing the rate according to the need. Hormonal or parahormonal substances which are not produced by definite endocrine organs, however, are considered in other chapters.

The secretions of the endocrine organs often produce reactions similar to those accomplished by the nervous system alone. The nervous system is a more rapid and precise means of coordination, and hence where speed of response is needed, as, for example, in the color changes of certain tree frogs, the nervous component plays the more important rôle in coordination. Where continuous activity is required, however, as in digestion, circulation, or metabolism, a chemical control has decided advantages over a nervous regulation. The two systems are often closely interrelated, both stimulating the same effectors. In general, endocrine control is slow and diffused; nervous control, swift and precise. Nevertheless, the nervous system became well differentiated as a discrete system in phylogeny before the endocrine organs had evolved as definite structures.

Thyroid Gland.—The thyroid gland arises as a median outgrowth from the ventral wall of the pharynx although in the frog its tissue appears to be derived from an ingrowth of ectoderm. In Amphioxus and the Ascidians, this region is occupied by an open groove of ciliated and mucus-producing cells which serve to entrap food particles and drive them along to the intestine. In the larva of Petromyzon this structure, the endostyle, is present in a modified form, while in all higher vertebrates a homologous growth, the thyroid, early separates from the pharynx wall and develops a series of closed follicles which produce a secretion of considerable importance in controlling the metabolic level of the animal.

The thyroid was originally an unpaired structure, and this condition is still maintained in the reptiles. During ontogeny the thyroid of Amphibia becomes bilobed and the two halves usually separate to move posteriorly and laterally to their final position. In the adult frog the paired thyroids lie one on either side of the hyoid apparatus just posterior to the postero-lateral processes; in salamanders they have a more lateral position, usually being found near the external jugular veins (Fig. 105). There is, however, considerable variation in urodeles (Uhlenhuth, 1927), and accessory follicles appear in both frogs and salamanders, a median group being the most frequent. The follicles increase in size but not in number during larval life (Uhlenhuth and Karns, 1928). At the time of metamorphosis there is a marked increase in the secretory activity of the follicular cells, and this is followed by a release into the blood stream of the

colloid contained in the follicles.   During adult life the thyroid
undergoes certain cyclic changes, storing colloid in winter and
releasing it in summer (Sklower, 1925).

Thyroid and Metamorphosis.—The administration of thyroid
substance to man leads to an increased rate of metabolism, as
measured by oxygen consumption, also increased body temperature and pulse rate, emaciation, and nervousness.   The first
result is obtained with amphibian larvae on treating them with
thyroid extracts (Helff, 1926; Bělehrádek and Huxley, 1927).
The treated larvae undergo a rapid transformation into the adult
form.   The result is particularly striking in the case of such
species as *Rana catesbeiana* and *Eurycea bislineata* which normally

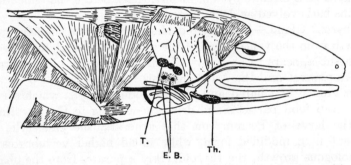

Fig. 105.—Diagram of the head of an adult Ambystoma showing position of
the thymus.   *E.B.*, epithelial bodies; *T.*, thymus; *Th.*, thyroid glands and associated blood vessels.   (*After Baldwin.*)

have a larval period extending over more than a year, since
changes begin from approximately a week to three weeks after
the treatment and are complete within the month.   A single
feeding of thyroid gland is sufficient to bring forth all the changes
of metamorphosis in the case of some species.

Metamorphosis consists of many external and internal changes
in the organization of an amphibian.   The more conspicuous
changes in salamanders include a loss of the gills and tail fin, a
shedding of the larval skin in one piece and its replacement by
the adult skin of different structure and usually color, a protrusion
of the eyeballs with the formation of lids, and finally a fusion of
the margin of the operculum to the underlying integument.
Wilder (1925) has described the many external and internal
changes of *Eurycea bislineata* at transformation, but not all of
these occur in other species of Amphibia.   The larvae of frogs

lose their tail and larval mouth parts; they also radically change the shape of their head and body. Most tadpoles develop eyelids on metamorphosing, but various pipids fail to do so. The complete reduction of the gills is evidence of metamorphosis in most salamanders but not in Siren (Noble, 1924). The limbs of urodeles appear early in development and rarely show a structural change during metamorphosis, but the rapid limb growth in the tadpoles of some Salientia may be considered a metamorphic change. Allen (1929) considers the degree of limb development in tadpoles of *Rana pipiens* an accurate criterion of the extent to which metamorphosis has advanced. Metamorphosis is a combination of changes, most of which normally take place over a short period, but in some species it may be extended over a long period or may, in fact, not occur at all. In other words, metamorphosis involves different changes in different species.

In metamorphosis there are two factors to be considered: first, the tissue undergoing the change and, second, the mechanism producing the change. Eyes (Uhlenhuth, 1917) or intestine (Sembrat, 1925) transplanted from one individual to another metamorphose synchronously with the host, but where transplant and host are of different species the transplanted tissue retains its own specific characters, those determined by its heredity. As Allen (1918) and E. R. and M. M. Hoskins (1919) first showed, tadpoles deprived of their thyroids are unable to metamorphose. Thyroid extracts have no effect upon the segmentation of the egg (Deutsch, 1924) or upon the very early larva. A certain amount of differentiation must have taken place before the thyroid hormone is able to act in the dramatic manner first described by Babák (1913) and Gudernatsch (1913). In Rana tadpoles the critical stage occurs shortly after the operculum has grown back (Romeis, 1924). In the case of some perennibranch urodeles, such as Necturus and Proteus, this critical stage never occurs; in others, notably Cryptobranchus and Siren, which metamorphose only their skin, it occurs soon after hatching. Still, in neither perennibranch nor frog tadpole is the animal's own thyroid sufficiently developed at this time to produce metamorphic changes. Cryptobranchus and Siren have large thyroids capable of inducing metamorphosis when fed to thyroidectomized axolotls (Noble, 1924), but they fail to induce a complete metamorphosis in their own bodies because most of the tissues which in other salamanders usually undergo metamorphosis here are not sensitive to the thyroid hormone.   Jensen, Swingle, and others found that thyroid substances induced no change in Proteus or Necturus, although the thyroid of the latter is capable of hastening metamorphosis when transplanted to Rana tadpoles (Swingle, 1922).   When Cryptobranchus and Siren are subjected soon after hatching to thyroid extracts or thyroxin, they shed their larval skin and assume the characteristic integument of metamorphosed salamanders.   This change normally occurs much later in the life of Cryptobranchus and Siren, and presumably takes place under the influence of the salamanders' own thyroids.   It is evidence for the fact that the skin, alone of all the tissues, which normally metamorphose in related salamanders, is in these forms sensitive to the thyroid hormone.

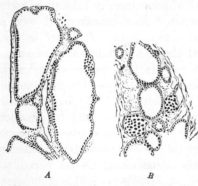

Fig. 106.—Sections of one of the thyroid glands of a normal (A) and a neotenic newt (B), *Triturus cristatus*. (*After Kuhn.*)

Neoteny.—Urodele larvae are frequently found sexually mature in nature, showing that the development of the gonads is not dependent on the thyroid hormone.   The removal of the thyroid in mammals prevents growth and leads to cretinism, but the growth of the larvae of both frogs and urodeles is unaffected by this operation.   In the perennibranch Typhlomolge the thyroid may be absent, but in view of the fact that none of the other perennibranchs fully metamorphoses after thyroid treatment it appears doubtful if neoteny in this genus can be attributed to the loss or reduction of this organ.   Blacher (1928) found that the intestine of tadpoles was stimulated to metamorphic change by weaker solutions of thyroid extracts than those necessary to produce changes in the tail, while the latter responded to weaker solutions than those required by jaws or trunk.   Fontès and Aron (1929) by using minimum doses of thyroxin showed that the skin of tadpoles was more sensitive than the tail in the species they were considering.   The quantity of thyroid hormone necessary to produce a metamorphic change varies with the kind of tissue, the age of the animal, and the species (see page 102).

Neoteny in salamanders may be due not to a deficiency of the tissues but to some factor which prevents the release of the thyroid hormone into the circulation. As long ago as 1817 Spix suspected that Proteus was the larval form of a terrestrial salamander. On his memorable voyage to Brazil he carried a series of live Proteus with him hoping that the warmer climate of the tropics would induce Proteus to metamorphose. Cold apparently inhibits the release of the hormone, for salamander larvae of species which normally metamorphose frequently fail to do so when they live at high altitudes. This is the case of the axolotl of the Rocky Mountains, the neotenous larva of *Ambystoma tigrinum*. There are other axolotls, larvae of the same or a closely related species which live in warmer waters but due to some inherited defect of the releasing mechanism remain larvae for long periods. Such is the case of a Mexican axolotl and of some tiger salamanders of New Mexico. Many newts (Fig. 106) and other salamandrids have been found to develop neotenous larvae at times. A large percentage of newts in the Woods Hole region were found to be neotenous, but whether this was due to an inherited defect of the releasing mechanism or to some environmental factor is unknown (Noble, 1929). Zondeck and Reiter (1923) found that calcium delayed the metamorphosis of tadpoles. A lack of vitamines in the diet will prevent the metamorphosis of Ambystoma larvae. Patch (1927) showed that larvae fed only Enchytraei or beef muscle failed to metamorphose. The addition of cod liver oil or yeast to the diet of the controls permitted them to metamorphose successfully. There are, also, various internal factors, such as the amount of insulin available, which inhibit metamorphosis (Gessner, 1928). Hence, the failure of a salamander to metamorphose may be due to any one of several different causes.

Iodine and Metamorphosis.—It has long been known that the thyroid gland is rich in iodine content. No other tissues of craniates, in fact, contain so high a percentage. Swingle (1919) found that iodine or its inorganic compounds administered to toad and frog tadpoles induced a precocious metamorphosis (Fig. 107), and Ingram (1929) has recently demonstrated that the subcutaneous implantation of iodine crystals in the thyroidectomized and hypophysectomized axolotl brought the same result. In nature the iodine is received with the food or possibly to a certain extent with the water, and the function of the thyroid gland is to store it in the form of a colloid secreted by the follicle cells of the gland. When the thyroid gland is removed and iodine crystals are implanted, apparently other tissues are able to elaborate an iodine compound effective in producing metamorphosis.

Kendall (1918) succeeded in isolating from the thyroid gland of mammals a single crystalline substance containing iodine and

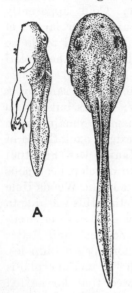

having the physiological properties of thyroid extract. This, according to Harington (1926), is an iodine derivative of parahydroxyphenyl ether of tyrosine, having the formula $C_{15}H_{11}O_4 N I_4$. The iodine is apparently necessary for the complete ossification of the skeleton, since Terry (1918) found ossification deficient in thyroidectomized tadpoles. Once metamorphosis has taken place, the tissues may still respond to the thyroid hormone, since Bělehrádek and Huxley (1927) found that oxygen consumption was almost immediately increased by injecting thyroid into the metamorphosed Ambystoma. Gayda (1924), however, was not able to find any effect of thyroid feeding on adult frogs, but as Sembrat (1925) found that larval intestines of Pelobates transplanted into the metamorphosed frog underwent a transformation, the thyroid hormone must have been circulating in the tissues of this species. Possibly Gayda's frogs were too old to respond to treatment. The thyroid hormone would seem to have an important function throughout life, but in Amphibia it is especially significant in its influence on metamorphosis.

FIG. 107.—The effect of iodine on metamorphosis. The tadpole which was fed iodotyrosine (*A*) had well begun its metamorphosis in fifteen days while the control (*B*) fed tyrosine remained a tadpole after forty-two days of treatment. (*After Swingle.*)

Pituitary Gland.—The pituitary gland of Amphibia agrees with that of teleosts in arising from a solid ingrowth of ectoderm between forebrain and foregut (Fig. 108). It loses its connection with the surface and becomes applied to the infundibulum, a ventral diverticulum of the thalamus. The ingrowth does not develop normally if the infundibulum is experimentally destroyed (Smith, 1920), while the nervous diverticulum fails to differentiate completely in the absence of the ingrowth. Hence, the two portions of the gland, the hypophysial ingrowth and the infundibulum, although of totally different origin, are mutually dependent on one another for their differentiation.

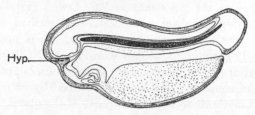

Fig. 108.—Diagrammatic median sagittal section of a young frog larva showing the hypophysial ingrowth. *Hyp.*, hypophysis.

The hypophysial ingrowth of the pituitary differentiates into three different parts: the *pars anterior, pars intermedia,* and *pars tuberalis* (Fig. 109). The first is the largest and most conspicuous portion. It lies not anterior but ventral and slightly posterior to the others, but it receives its name from the homologous part in mammals which has a more anterior position. The *pars inter-*

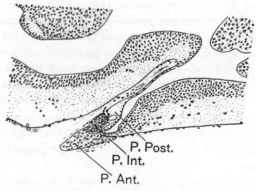

Fig. 109.—Longitudinal section of the hypophysis of the salamander, *Eurycea bislineata*. The nasal region is on the right. *P.Ant.*, anterior lobe; *P.Int.*, middle lobe; *P. Post.*, posterior or neural lobe. (*After Atwell.*)

media is less vascular than the *pars anterior* and appears whitish or opaque in the fresh animal. It lies chiefly dorsal to the pars anterior in the adult. The *pars tuberalis* develops as a pair of anteriorly directed processes on either side of the *pars anterior* (Atwell, 1921). In the Salientia they become detached at the time of metamorphosis to form separate plaques closely applied to the base of the thalamus.   In most urodeles they are retained as processes, a separation having been reported only in one of the newts (Sumi, 1926).   The *pars tuberalis* reaches its maximum size in the Plethodontidae, in a species of Plethodon, being five times as large as the *pars intermedia* (Atwell and Woodworth, 1926).   The infundibulum is sometimes described as the *pars posterior* or *pars nervosa* of the pituitary.   It is non-glandular but frequently sacculated, as, for example, in Necturus.

Pars Anterior.—The pituitary produces a number of hormones. The source of some of these has been traced by extirpation and replacement methods to particular parts of the gland.   From the work on mammals the *pars anterior* is known to produce a substance which stimulates growth.   When hypertrophy of this part of the gland takes place in man it leads to gigantism before puberty and to acromegaly after puberty.   In tadpoles removal of the pituitary results in a considerable retardation of their growth (Smith, 1920).   The restoration of the *pars anterior* alone is sufficient to induce a return to the normal growth curve (Allen, 1928), while the implantation of the intermediate and posterior lobes does not have this effect.   Allen (1925) showed that the extirpation of the pituitary stunted the growth of the limb bones especially, and the effect was greater in frog than in toad tadpoles. Frequent intraperitoneal injections of *pars anterior* extracts were found by Smith and Smith (1923) to produce tadpoles twice the volume of the controls.   Gigantism has been produced in tiger salamanders by feeding anterior lobe substance (Uhlenhuth, 1920).   The giant larvae of frogs and urodeles sometimes found in nature, however, are usually individuals which have failed to metamorphose due to the non-functioning of their thyroid apparatus and hence are individuals which have prolonged the period of larval growth.

The anterior lobe of the pituitary exerts an important control over metamorphosis by influencing the growth and development of the thyroid gland.   This has been indicated in much of the work on metamorphosis but was especially well shown recently in the case of the tadpoles of Rana and Bufo by Allen (1927).   There is no accumulation of thyroid colloid in the follicles if the anterior lobe of the pituitary is removed.   Uhlenhuth and Schwartzbach (1927) suggest that the hormone of the anterior lobe may be also the factor which induces the release of colloid from the thyroid follicles.   Various investigations have shown that the anterior lobe is unable to induce metamorphosis in larvae which have been deprived of their thyroids, but the recent work of Spaul (1930) makes it appear probable that during the later stages of larval life the anterior lobe may function independently of the thyroid in inducing metamorphosis. The extirpation of the thyroid causes an hypertrophy of both the *pars anterior* and *pars intermedia* (Larson, 1927). The thyroid would thus seem to exert normally a certain inhibitory effect on the pituitary, while it in turn receives a growth-stimulating hormone from the *pars anterior* of that organ. This stimulating hormone is apparently produced by one type of cells in the anterior pituitary, for cells of this type, the basophils, undergo a rapid increase at the onset of metamorphosis (Allen, Torreblanca, and Benjamin, 1929). Spaul and Howes (1930), however, consider the oxyphils to be more concerned in metamorphosis because the oxyphil region of the cattle pituitary is especially iactive in inducing metamorphosis.

The *pars anterior* of the pituitary not only influences the body growth and metamorphosis of amphibian larvae, but it also has a specific effect on the growth and liberation of the sex products of the adults. Daily transplants of fresh anterior pituitary hasten sexual maturity in rats (Smith 1926), and similar treatment causes *Rana pipiens*, a spring breeder, to lay its eggs in October or November (Wolf, 1929). The simple act of inserting fresh anterior lobe substance of *Eurycea bislineata* at frequent intervals, through small slits made in the chin skin of adult females of the same species, caused the latter to lay their eggs in December and January (Noble and Richards, 1930), several months before the normal breeding season. The eggs were laid in typical position attached to the under side of stones placed for that purpose in laboratory dishes. Since the females carry spermatozoa in their spermathecae at this season, the eggs develop without further assistance from the males. Wolf (1929*a*) found that male frogs are also stimulated to sexual activity by fresh pituitary substances injected into their lymph sinuses. The effect of the implants is greater in the female than in the male Bufo, however; more implants being necessary in the latter sex to induce sexual activity (Houssay, Giusti, and Gonzalez, 1929), and the same sexual difference appears to be true of some urodeles. Ablation of the anterior pituitary in the toad leads to testicular atrophy (Houssay and Giusti, 1929). From this work it would follow that the breeding-season rhythm of Amphibia is under the direct control of the hormone of the *pars anterior* of the pituitary. The hormone, in turn, may be under nervous control. It is obvious that the breeding season occurs at certain favorable seasons.

The discovery of a gonad-stimulating hormone has apparently considerable practical value to students of Amphibia, for it provides a ready means of obtaining embryological material at any time of the year.

Pars Intermedia.—The *pars intermedia* of the amphibian pituitary exerts an important control over the pigmentation. It produces a hormone which induces both an expansion of the melanophores and a contraction of the lipophores and possibly also of the guanophores. As discussed in the chapter on the integument, the pigment cells are also under nervous control and further may respond directly to light. Nevertheless, the pituitary hormone plays the chief rôle of color-tone regulator in some species of Salientia. It was known from the early work of Smith (1916) and Allen (1917) that ablation of the pituitary induced a marked bleaching of the color in tadpoles. The removal of the pituitary through the roof of the mouth is a simple operation in the large-mouthed salamanders and it leads in a few hours to the same lightening of color. Swingle (1921) showed that intraperitoneal grafts of *pars intermedia* in hypophysectomized Rana tadpoles brought a return of the original color or even a more pronounced darkening. The *pars intermedia* and *posterior* of the pituitary of cattle can also induce an expansion of the melanophores of Amphibia (Atwell, 1919; Hogben and Winton, 1922). The melanophore-expanding hormone, although apparently produced by the *pars intermedia,* is able to make its way into the *pars anterior* as well as into the *pars posterior,* for Blacher (1927) and Smith (1925) have noted pigmentary changes resulting from the injection of anterior lobe substance.

Pars Posterior.—The posterior lobe has certain specific effects which would seem to be due to more than one hormone. It has an important influence on the water equilibrium of both larva and adult. Injection of posterior lobe extracts causes an increased water intake, but repeated injections result in a loss (Bělehrádek and Huxley, 1927a). Removal of the entire pituitary in adult toads causes parts of the epidermis to form a thickened horny layer (Puente, 1927). Marx (1929) found that hypophysectomized Salamandra developed a similar pigmented horny layer. In adult salamanders of several genera I have found this development to occur chiefly on the under surface. It would seem that this alteration of the skin was correlated with a decreased water intake, for the entire integument of the hypophysectomized salamanders appears drier than that of the controls.

The removal of the whole pituitary results in a change in the tonus of the cutaneous capillaries, which become strongly dilated. Krogh (1926) suggests that the normal function of the pituitary hormones is to maintain capillary tonus. Possibly the effect of the postpituitary hormone on water regulation is produced through its effect on the capillaries of the skin or kidney. Extracts of the posterior lobe have a marked stimulating effect on the smooth muscles of the mammalian uterus, but it is doubtful if the effect is a general one on all smooth muscle (Hogben, 1927). Allen (1929a) found that implantation of the posterior lobe in adult frogs causes a contraction of the body walls lasting several days. Spaul (1930) found that extracts of the posterior lobe inhibit metamorphosis. In brief, all parts of the pituitary have functions of great importance in the life of Amphibia. The isolation of their specific autocoids, as has been accomplished in the study of the thyroid, is still a matter for experimentation.

Pancreas.—The pancreas includes, besides the enzyme-producing glands which pour their digesting fluids into the intestine by way of the pancreatic ducts, a number of clusters of epithelial cells which secrete a hormone directly into the blood stream. These cell clusters, unlike the thyroid follicles, are arranged in solid masses. They are called the "islets of Langerhans." Their hormone, insulin, regulates the amount of sugar in the blood by facilitating the assimilation of sugar by the tissues. If insulin is not present in the blood, glucose is neither oxidized nor converted into glycogen but accumulates in the blood and is excreted in the urine. Prevention of the normal functioning of the islets of Langerhans leads to the disease *diabetes* which is characterized by excessive amounts of sugar in the blood. Since the discoveries by Banting and Best in 1922, the function of insulin has been extensively investigated in mammals. Apparently, injection of insulin in Amphibia has the same effect as in mammals, if allowance is made for the lower body temperature of these forms. Huxley and Fulton (1924) showed that the

effects were hastened in frogs by increasing the temperature up
to the normal maximum, and Olmsted (1926) has noted that
temperature increase speeded up the effect of insulin in the
toad. Aron (1928) finds that the internal secretion of the
pancreas is not manifest until the time of metamorphosis, but as
the glycogen of the liver does not vary greatly in relative amount

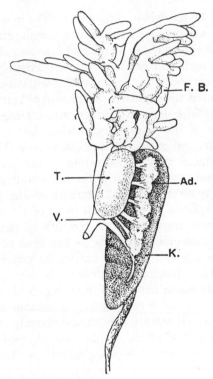

Fig. 110.—An adrenal organ of a frog. Left kidney of *Rana catesbeiana*
viewed ventrally showing the left adrenal organ, and associated structures.
Ad., adrenal organ; *F.B.*, fat body; *K.*, kidney; *T.*, testis; *V.*, postcaval vein.

during ontogeny (Goldfederowa, 1926), other tissues may be
producing insulin. Recent investigations on mammals have
shown that insulin may be found in other tissues after the destruction of the pancreas. Hence, insulin is not a specific product of
the pancreas, although it would seem to be produced chiefly
by the islets of Langerhans.

Adrenal Organs.—The adrenal organs receive their name from
their proximity to the kidneys. In Salientia they form an irregu-

lar strip of yellow tissue adherent to the ventral surface of each kidney, usually near the midline and closely associated with the renal veins (Fig. 110). In Ascaphus they lie along the inner edge of the kidneys, and this is the position of the bulk of the organs in most urodeles. The adrenal organs resemble the pituitary in being formed of two kinds of tissue of different origin and function. The interrenal tissue, distinguished by the fatty inclusions which give it the yellow color, develops from the peritoneal epithelium either between the kidneys or anterior to them near the midline. The chromaffin tissue, distinguished by its intense staining in chromic salts and the granular inclusions

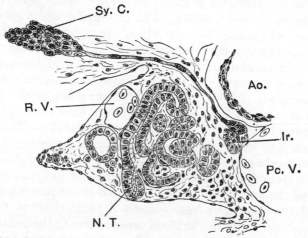

Fig. 111.—Development of the adrenal organ of Hypogeophis. *Ao.*, aorta; *Ir.*, interrenal component of adrenal organ; *N.T.*, nephric tubule; *Pc.V.*, post-caval vein; *R.V.*, renal vein; *Sy.C.*, sympathetic cells. (*After Brauer.*)

of its cells, arises from the neural tube at the time the sympathetic ganglia are being formed (Fig. 111). In the mammals the interrenal tissue forms the cortex, and the chromaffin the medulla of their adrenal organs which are here, as in other amniotes, isolated from the kidneys. In many urodeles adrenal tissue is found anterior to the kidneys in small isolated masses frequently associated with the sympathetic ganglia. In fact, chromaffin cells have been considered merely modified sympathetic cells and, like ganglia of the latter chain, they may receive sympathetic fibers directly from the cord. Urodeles have a more diffuse adrenal system than frogs or toads, but even in the latter the adrenal tissue is usually broken up into a varying number of segments (Vincent, 1898). There is more interrenal than chromaffin tissue in Amphibia. Bonnamour and Policard (1903) distinguish four kinds of cells in the adrenals of the frog. Possibly these represent different stages in the activity of the interrenal and chromaffin tissue.

The function of the interrenal tissue in Amphibia is unknown, although there is evidence in mammals that its secretions influence the growth of the gonads. Precocious sexual maturity in children has been attributed to a hypertrophy of this tissue in certain cases. The interrenal tissue may also control the elimination of the acid end products of normal metabolism through the kidneys (Swingle, 1927). The chromaffin tissue releases a hormone, adrenalin, into the blood stream which apparently has a non-specific effect of increasing the metabolism of the tissues (Martin and Armistead, 1922). Feeding of adrenal tissue to tadpoles increases their growth rate but has no effect on metamorphosis (Herwerden, 1922). Destruction of the adrenal organs in Salientia has been claimed not to have the fatal effects well known in mammals (Giusti, 1921; Gley, 1927). The tissue, however, is so widely distributed in the body cavity that its complete removal presents great difficulty. In the toad *Bufo marinus* Lascano Gonzalez (1929) has shown that some individuals which survived the operation had some adrenal tissue present. Injection of adrenalin into frogs induces a contraction of the skin melanophores and a rise in blood pressure due to the constriction of the smooth muscle of the arterioles. Apparently in Amphibia, as in mammals, adrenalin affects those organs innervated by the sympathetic neurons and stimulates them in the same way. It seems to act on the myoneural junctions rather than on the sympathetic fibers, for the same results are obtained after the fibers have been cut. The function of adrenalin in the behavior of mammals is still a disputed matter (Hogben, 1927), although there is evidence that it plays a part in some of the reflexes associated with fright, where it is probably associated essentially with the mobilization of bodily resources for the protective reactions of the animal. In Amphibia, adrenalin may have an influence on the normal metabolism by increasing the amount of glucose in the blood through stimulating the liver to discharge. Thus it increases the amount of sugar in the blood, while insulin decreases it. The release of adrenalin in the blood would seem to have some effect on pigmentation, for in some species injection of adrenalin causes a contraction of the melanophores.

Adrenalin has been isolated chemically and found to be an amine (organic base) closely related to the amino-acid, tyrosin. Various substances closely allied to adrenalin and having similar physiological effects have been synthetically produced.

Gonads.—The gonads, while primarily organs of reproduction, release hormones into the blood stream which have an important function in stimulating the growth and maintaining the development of the secondary sexual characters. The latter include a great variety of features in the Amphibia, ranging from the familiar nuptial pads of male frogs and the broad tail crests of male newts to obscure differences of teeth in salamanders and tendon structure in frogs. The secondary sexual characters include differences in red blood cell count, lung size, behavior patterns, and many other structural and physiological differences between the sexes. Some of these are discussed in a preceding chapter. The utility of many secondary sex characters is not always clear and their phylogeny presents a problem of special interest.

Castration of sexually mature male newts results in a rapid loss of the secondary sexual characters (Bresca, 1910). This change is delayed by overfeeding (Champy, 1924) and by cold (Aron, 1923). Further, only a partial regeneration of testicular tissue suffices to bring a return of the secondary sexual characters. In frogs, because of these or other modifying influences, the results of castration have not always been so marked. It seems established, however, that the testis induces and maintains the secondary sexual characters of the male. Welti (1925) and Ponse (1923) induced the development of the nuptial pad in female toads by testicular transplants, and Noble and Pope (1929) have caused blunt bicuspid premaxillary teeth characterizing the female *Desmognathus fuscus* to be replaced by elongate monocuspid ones distinctive of the male by transplanting the testes into the body of the adult female (Fig. 112). Testicular transplants also induce the development of male behavior. Brossard and Gley (1929) found that extracts made from fresh bull testes would induce the reappearance of the clasping reflex when injected into frogs.

The testicular hormone of mammals is apparently produced by the interstitial cells. In Amphibia these are stromal cells

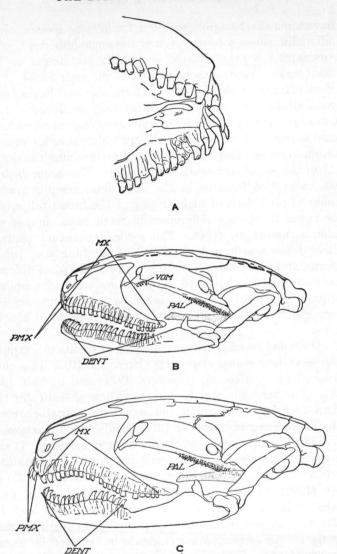

Fig. 112.—Effect of testicular hormone on the teeth of a salamander. *A*. The anterior teeth in the upper jaw of the female *Desmognathus fuscus carolinensis* 220 days after spaying and transplanting a testis. The new premaxillary teeth which have grown in, are elongate and directed forward in the form characteristic of the male. The skull of the typical female (*B*) and a male (*C*), for comparison. *DENT*, dentary teeth; *MX*, maxillary teeth; *PAL.*, palatine teeth; *PMX*, premaxillary teeth; *VOM*, vomerine teeth. (*After Noble and Pope.*)

surrounding the lobules of the testes. When the spermatozoa are released from the lobule and the Sertoli cells undergo degeneration, the stromal cells increase by mitosis, change their form, and exhibit lipoidal droplets and fuchsinophil granules in their cytoplasm. Humphrey (1925) showed that all the secondary sexual characters may be present in the male newt in which the spermatozoa had not left the lobules and in which the interstitial tissue had not yet made its appearance. It seems established from the work of Champy (1924), Humphrey (1925), and Harms (1926) that the source of the testicular hormone in Amphibia is not to be found in the interstitial cells but rather in the sperm or in the Sertoli cells.

Whether the testicular hormone be a by-product of spermatogenesis or a substance released by the Sertoli cells, it can produce its effect only on tissues which are sensitive to its action. Differences between two secondary sexual characters are due to differences between the tissues and are not accountable to the amount of hormone. Further, the development of some secondary sexual characters may be due to other factors. Nakamura (1927) found that the cloacal papilla of certain European newts could be made to develop in the female by treatment with thyroid. The latter apparently affected adversely the growth of the ovaries, and this, in turn, permitted the development of the papilla which would appear to be a specific character normally held in check by secretions of the ovary. In birds the function of the ovary in supressing the male plumage is well known. In frogs the ovary apparently controls growth of skin papillae and influences the development of the oviducts. As stated above, the growth and liberation of the sex products is under the control of a hormone from the *pars anterior* of the pituitary. Aron (1927) found that the spermatogenetic cycle of salamanders was influenced by the elimination of spermatozoa. Further, the grafting of immature testes into mature animals did not hasten the cycle.

Parathyroids and Ultimobranchial Body.—The parathyroids develop as epithelial growths from the ventral portion of the third and fourth visceral slits. They appear late in larval life, in Ambystoma apparently not until the time of metamorphosis (Baldwin, 1918). Allen (1920) found that removing the thyroid of toad tadpoles caused a marked hypertrophy of the parathyroids. There was no deposition of colloid or other histological change suggesting that the parathyroids might assume the functions of the thyroids. The parathyroids in mammals produce hormones which play an important rôle in calcium metabolism, especially by controlling the concentration of calcium salts in the blood. There is evidence that this may be true of Amphibia as well (Waggener, 1929).

The ultimobranchial body arises as an epithelial growth from the last gill pouch of each side. In urodeles that on the right side is usually lacking, although it persists in Necturus and Amphiuma. The branchial origin of the structure suggests an endocrine function but it rarely develops a colloid and shows no enlargement during metamorphosis. In the adult it lies near the truncus or larynx. Its function is unknown, although its widespread occurrence throughout most vertebrates suggests that it must have some functional significance. Wilder (1929) has described the ultimobranchial body in a large series of urodeles and because of its variability concluded that it probably had little or no physiological significance.

Thymus.—The thymus gland arises from thickenings in the dorsal portion of the visceral pouches. These thickenings become epithelioid bodies which early lose their connection with the pouches. In caecilians the first six visceral pouches of each side produce thymus buds. In some salamanders, such as Ambystoma, the first five develop buds (Baldwin, 1918) but the first two degenerate. The thymus of the adult accordingly is a three-lobed structure, presumably formed by a fusion of the three remaining buds of each side. In caecilians the first and last pair of buds degenerate and the four remaining pairs fuse to form a single element on each side. In some Salientia, according to Maurer (1906), only the first two pairs of visceral pouches take part in bud formation. The first pair degenerates and the second pair develops into the definitive thymus which in the adult lies under the skin caudal to the tympanic membrane and is partly covered by muscle. In brief, while all except the most posterior visceral pouches produce thymus tissue in the primitive Amphibia, this power is greatly restricted in some salamanders and in the Salientia.

The thymus glands, since they develop in much the same way as the parathyroids, are assumed to have endocrine functions, but these have not been clearly defined in either Amphibia or mammals. Thymus feeding has had a variable effect both on pigmentation and growth of tadpoles. The thymus is proportionately larger during larval than adult life. In mammals its persistence is associated with the retardation of sexual and bodily development. In Amphibia the thymus functions in producing lymphocytes, granulocytes, and also erythrocytes to a certain extent. Speidel (1925) found that thyroid feeding greatly stimulated the thymus of tadpoles and caused the growth of lymphoid cells and their migration into the circulation. Extirpation of the thymus in adult frogs apparently has little effect on the animal's health (Agafonow, 1927), but it would be interesting to perform the same operation during the breeding season. Riddle has shown that the operation leads to serious defects in the egg capsules of pigeons. The eggs of birds, however, are much more advanced in structure than those of frogs. The thymus may produce specific as well as general effects in birds, but none of the specific effects has been established in Amphibia.

Pineal Organ.—A well-marked pineal foramen is found in the skulls of both branchiosaurs and lepospondyls, indicating that the ancestors of modern Amphibia were equipped with a functional median eye. In some tadpoles and even in a few adult frogs the position of the pineal organ is indicated by a pigmentless, translucent spot on the forehead. The pineal arises in the embryos of both frogs and salamanders as a diverticulum of the thalamus which extends toward the integument of the forehead. The tip enlarges to produce a vesicle which in Ambystoma may assume the form of a rudimentary retina (Tilney and Warren, 1919), having both pigment and an incipient differentiation of the cells. Sense cells appear in the pineal organs of many Amphibia and there are also ganglion and supporting cells (Vialli, 1929; Kleine, 1929). In the primitive Bombina, pigment is also formed, giving further evidence of the original sensory nature of the pineal in frogs. In many species, however, these differentiations fail to appear, and the vesicle may fail to develop a well-defined lumen.

Nerve fibers usually appear in the stalk of the diverticulum connecting the vesicle with the posterior commissure, but the vesicle later becomes detached from the stalk and hence at this stage can have no sensory function. In many aquatic Amphibia (Triturus, Pipa, etc.), the vesicle is lacking. Most Amphibia are nocturnal and hence might not be expected to have great need of a median eye. It is interesting, therefore, to find that the pineal has taken over other functions. In many species, such as the cave salamander, *Hydromantes italicus*, the rudimentary vesicle is primarily a secretory organ. In species where the stalk persists, the latter also develops glandular functions. The pineal organ of Amphibia has been reported to arise from a paired diverticulum (Cameron, 1903; Riech, 1925). This is of interest, for two diverticula, each with a terminal vesicle, develop in Petromyzon. In the lizards it is the anterior one of these which forms the parietal eye, which in some of these reptiles apparently still functions as a light-receiving organ. Since the two diverticula apparently fuse during the development of Amphibia, it is not clear whether the pineal vesicle is homologous with the median eye of lizards or represents the posterior of the two elements found in Petromyzon. Whether this vesicle has any sensory functions in modern Amphibia is unknown. The presence of sense cells in the structure may be taken as evidence of some sensory function. The presence of lipoids, however, and various other secretion products in the lumen and in some of the cells (Vialli, 1929) shows that the organ has secretory functions as well. The pineal is a rudimentary organ which seems to have assumed endocrine functions.

The specific functions of the secretion of the pineal are not clearly understood in Amphibia. McCord and Allen (1921) found that feeding of pineal caused a temporary contraction of the melanophores of *Rana pipiens*. Groebbels and Kuhn (1923) confirmed the observation on another species of Rana. But as McCord and Allen failed to observe definite changes in toad tadpoles and as experiments with the pineal of urodeles have been equally inconclusive, it would seem that the pineal hormone was not an important regulator of pigmentary changes in amphibian larvae. In mammals pineal extirpation induces a precocious development of the gonads. Recently Schulze and Hölldobler (1926) have found that implantation of pieces of beef pineal in tadpoles causes an acceleration of body growth; and Addair and Chidester (1928) secured some evidence that feeding desiccated pineal organ would hasten metamorphosis. Further investigation is necessary before any specific function can be assigned to the pineal gland of Amphibia.

References

ADDAIR, J., and F. E. CHIDESTER, 1928: Pineal and metamorphosis; The influence of pineal feeding upon the rate of metamorphosis in frogs, *Endocrinology*, XII, 791–796.

AGAFONOW, F. D., 1927: Zur Physiologie der Glandula Thymus, *Arch. ges. Physiol.*, CCXVI, 682–696.

ALLEN, B. M., 1917: Effects of the extirpation of the anterior lobe of the hypophysis of Rana pipiens, *Biol. Bull.*, XXXII, 117–130.

———, 1918: The results of thyroid removal in the larvae of Rana pipiens, *Jour. Exp. Zool.*, XXIV, 499–519, 1 pl.

———, 1920: The parathyroid glands of thyroidless Bufo larvae, *Jour. Exp. Zool.*, XXX, 201–210.

———, 1925: The effects of extirpation of the thyroid and pituitary glands upon the limb development of anurans, *Jour. Exp. Zool.*, XLII, 13–30, 10 charts.

———, 1927: Influence of the hypophysis upon the thyroid gland in amphibian larvae, *Univ. Calif. Pub. Zool.*, XXXI, 53–78, 2 pl.

———, 1928: The influence of different parts of the hypophysis upon size growth of Rana tadpoles, *Physiol. Zool.*, I, 153–171.

———, 1929: The influence of the thyroid gland and hypophysis upon growth and development of amphibian larvae, *Quart. Rev. Biol.*, IV, 325–352.

———, 1929a: The functional difference between the pars intermedia and pars nervosa of the hypophysis of frog, *Proc. Soc. Exp. Biol. Med.*, XXVII, 11–13.

———, EUGENIO D. TORREBLANCA, and JOHN A. BENJAMIN, JR., 1929: A study upon the histogenesis of the pars anterior of the hypophysis of Bufo during metamorphosis, *Anat. Rec.*, XLIV, 208.

ARON, M. M., 1923: Influence de la température sur l'action de l'hormone testiculaire, *Compt. rend. Acad. Sci. Paris*, CLXXVII, 141–143.

———, 1927: Recherches sur le déterminisme du cycle spérmatogénetique chez les urodèles, *Compt. rend. Soc. Biol.*, XCVI, 269–271.

———, 1928: Corrélation fonctionelle entre la glande thyroide et le pancréas endocrine chez les larves d'amphibiens, *Compt. rend. Soc. Biol.*, XCIX, 215–217.

ATWELL, W. J., 1919: On the nature of the pigmentation changes following hypophysectomy in the frog larva, *Science, n. s.*, XLIX, 48–50.

———, 1921: The morphogenesis of the hypophysis in the tailed Amphibia, *Anat. Rec.*, XXII, 373–390.

———, and E. A. WOODWORTH, 1926: The relative volumes of the three epithelial parts of the hypophysis cerebri, *Anat. Rec.*, XXXIII, 377–385.

BABÁK, EDWARD, 1913: Einige Gedanken über die Beziehung der Metamorphose bei den Amphibien zur inneren Sekretion, *Zentralbl. Physiol.*, XXVII, 536–541.

BALDWIN, T. M., 1918: Pharyngeal derivatives of Amblystoma, *Jour. Morph.*, XXX, 605–680.

BĚLEHRÁDEK, J., and J. S. HUXLEY, 1927: Changes in oxygen consumption during metamorphosis induced by thyroid administration in the axolotl, *Jour. Physiol.*, LXIV, 267–278.

———, 1927a: The effects of pituitrin and of narcosis on water-regulation in larval and metamorphosed Amblystoma, *Brit. Jour. Exp. Biol.*, V, 89–96.

BLACHER, L. J., 1927: The role of the hypophysis and of the thyroid gland in the cutaneous pigmentary function of amphibians and fishes, *Trans. Lab. Exp. Biol. Zoopark, Moscow*, III, 37–81.

———, 1928: Materials on the mechanics of amphibian metamorphosis, *Trans. Lab. Exp. Biol. Zoopark, Moscow*, IV, 172–173.

BONNAMOUR, S., and A. POLICARD, 1903: Note histologique sur la capsule surrénale de la grenouille; Note préliminaire, *Compt. rend. Ass. Anat. 5me Sess.*, 102–104.

BRESCA, GIOVANNI, 1910: Experimentelle Untersuchungen über die sekundären Sexualcharaktere der Tritonen, *Arch. Entw. Mech.*, XXIX, 403–431.

BROSSARD, G., and PIERRE GLEY, 1929: Production expérimentale du réflexe d'embrassement de la grenouille, *Compt. rend. Soc. Biol.*, CI, 757–758.

CAMERON, J., 1903: On the origin of the pineal body as an amesial structure, deduced from the study of the development in Amphibia, *Anat. Anz.*, XXIII, 394–395.

CHAMPY, CHARLES, 1924: "Les charactères sexuels considérés comme phénomènes de développement et dans leurs rapports avec l'hormone sexuelle," Paris.

DEUTSCH, J., 1924: Über die Beeinflussung frühester Entwicklungsstufen von Amphibien durch Organsubstanzen (Thyreoidea, Thymus, Ovarium, Testis, Supraren), *Arch. mikr. Anat.*, C, 302–316.

FONTÈS, GEORGES, and MAX ARON, 1929: Mode d'action qualitative et quantitative de la thyroxine synthétique; Son influence sur la métamorphose des larves d'anoures, *Compt. rend. Soc. Biol.*, CII, 679–682.

GAYDA, T., 1924: Contribution à l'étude de la physiologie de la thyroïde dans la grenouille, *Arch. Ital. Biol.*, LXXIII, 30–38.

GESSNER, O., 1928: Weitere Beiträge zur Frage der Beeinflussung der durch Thyraden hervorgerufenen und der natürlichen Metamorphose von Amphibienlarven durch parasympathicotrop und sympathicotrop wirkende Pharmaka, *Zeitschr. Biol.*, LXXXVII, 228–238.

GIUSTI, L., 1921: Conséquences de la destruction des surrénales chez le crapaud (Bufo marinus) et la grenouille (Leptodactylus ocellatus), *Compt. rend. Soc. Biol.*, LXXXV, 30–31.

GLEY, P., 1927: Functions of the adrenals, *Endocrinology*, XI, 39–40.

GOLDFEDEROWA, A., 1926: Le glycogène au cours de l'ontogénèse de la grenouille et sous l'influence des saisons, *Compt. rend. Soc. Biol.*, XCV, 801–804.

GROEBBELS, FRANZ, and E. KUHN, 1923: Unzureichende Ernährung und Hormonwirkung; IV, Mitteilung; Der Einfluss der Zirbeldrüsen und Hodensubstanz auf Wachstum und Entwickelung von Froschlarven, *Zeitschr. Biol.*, LXXVIII 1–7.

GUDERNATSCH, J. F., 1913: Feeding experiments on tadpoles; I, The influence of specific organs given as food on growth and differentiation, *Arch. Entw. Mech.*, XXXV, 457–483, 1 pl.

HARINGTON, C. R., 1926: Chemistry of thyroxine, *Biochem. Jour.*, XX, 293–313.

HARMS, JÜRGEN W., 1926: "Körper und Keimzellen," Berlin.

HELFF, O. M., 1926: Studies on amphibian metamorphosis; II, The oxygen consumption of tadpoles undergoing precocious metamorphosis following treatment with thyroid and di-iodotyrosine, *Jour. Exp. Zool.*, XLV, 69–93.

HERWERDEN, M. A. VON, 1922: Der Einfluss der Nebennierenrinde des Rindes auf Gesundheit und Wachstum verschiedener Organismen, *Biol. Zentralb.*, XLII, 109–112.

HOGBEN, LANCELOT T., 1927: "The Comparative Physiology of Internal Secretion," Cambridge Univ. Press.

————, and F. R. WINTON, 1922: The pigmentary effector system; I. Reactions of frog's melanophores to pituitary extracts, *Proc. Roy. Soc. London*, Ser. B, XCIII, 318–329.

HOSKINS, E. R., and M. M. HOSKINS, 1919: Growth and development of Amphibia as effected by thyroidectomy, *Jour. Exp. Zool.*, XXIX, 1–70. 9 pl.

HOUSSAY, B. A., and L. GIUSTI, 1929: Le fonction de l'hypophyse et de la région infundibulo-tuberienne chez le crapaud, *Compt. rend. Soc. Biol.* CI, 935–937.

————, L. GIUSTI, and J. M. LASCANO-GONZALEZ, 1929: Hypophysentransplantation und sexuelle Reizung bei der Kröte, *Rev. Soc. Argent. Biol.*, V, 397–418.

HUMPHREY, R. R., 1925: The development of the temporary sexual characters in Diemyctylus viridescens in relation to changes within the testis, *Anat. Rec.*, XXIX, 362.

HUXLEY, J. S., and J. F. FULTON, 1924: The influence of temperature on the activity of insulin, *Nature*, CXIII, 234–235.

INGRAM, W. R., 1929: Studies on amphibian neoteny; I, The metamorphosis of the Colorado axolotl by injection of inorganic iodine, *Physiol. Zool.*, II, 149–156.

KENDALL, E. C., 1918: The active constituent of the thyroid, *Jour. Amer. Med. Ass.*, LXXI, 871.

KLEINE, AUGUST, 1929: Über die Parietalorgane bei einheimischen und ausländischen Anuren, *Jena. Zeitschr.*, XLIV, 339–376.

KROGH, A., 1926: The pituitary (posterior lobe) principle in circulating blood, *Jour. Pharm. and Exp. Therap.*, XXIX, 177–189.

LARSON, MARY ELIZABETH, 1927: The extirpation of the thyroid gland and its effects upon the hypophysis in Bufo americanus and Rana pipiens, *Sci. Bull. Univ. Kansas*, XVII, 319–330, 2 pls.

LASCANO-GONZALEZ, J. M., 1929: Le destruction des surrenales chez le crapaud, Bufo marinus (L) Schneid., *Compt. rend. Soc. Biol.*, CII, 458–459.

MARTIN, E. G., and R. B. ARMISTEAD, 1922: The influence of adrenalin on metabolism in various excised tissues, *Amer. Jour. Physiol.*, LXII, 488–495.

MARX, L., 1929: Entwicklung und Ausbildung des Farbenkleides beim Feuersalamander nach Verlust der Hypophyse, *Arch. Entw. Mech.*, CXIV, 512–548.

MAURER, F., 1906: Die Entwickelung des Darmsystems, *Hertwig's Handb. vergl. Exp. Entw. Wirbelt.*, II, Part I, 109–252.

McCord, C. P., and F. P. Allen, 1921: Evidence associating pineal gland function with alteration in pigmentation, *Jour. Exp. Zool.*, XXIII, 207–224.

Nakamura, T., 1927: Étude anatomo-comparative embryologique et embryo-mécanique de la papille cloacale des tritons, *Bull. Biol. France et Belgique*, LXI, 332–358, 3 pls.

Noble, G. K., 1924: The "retrograde metamorphosis" of the Sirenidae; Experiments on the functional activity of the thyroid of the perenni-branchs, *Anat. Rec.*, XXIX, 100.

————, 1929: Further observations on the life-history of the newt, Triturus viridescens, *Amer. Mus. Novit.*, No. 348.

————, and S. H. Pope, 1929: The modification of the cloaca and teeth of the adult salamander, Desmognathus, by testicular transplants and by castration, *Brit. Jour. Exp. Biol.*, VI, 399–411.

————, and L. B. Richards, 1930: The induction of egg-laying in the salamander, Eurycea bislineata, by pituitary transplants, *Amer. Mus. Novit.*, No. 396.

Olmsted, J. M. D., 1926: The effect of insulin on the rate of disappearance of reducing substances in toad's blood at different temperatures after injection of glucose, *Amer. Jour. Physiol.* (*Proceed.*), LXXVI, 200.

Patch, E. M., 1927: Biometric studies upon development and growth in Amblystoma punctatum and tigrinum, *Proc. Soc. Exp. Biol. Med.*, XXV, 218–219.

Ponse, K., 1923: Masculinisation d'une femelle de crapaud, *Compt. rend. Soc. Physiol. Hist. Nat. Genève*, XL, 150–152.

Puente, J. J., 1927: Modifications histologiques de la peau du crapaud hypophysectomisé, *Compt. rend. Soc. Biol.*, XCVII, 602–603.

Riech, F., 1925: Epiphyse und Paraphyse im Lebenscyclus der Anuren, *Zeitschr. vergl. Physiol.*, II, 524–570.

Romeis, B., 1924: Histologische Untersuchungen zur Analyse der Wirkung der Schilddrüsenfütterung auf Froschlarven; 2, Die Beeinflussung der Entwicklung der vorderen Extremität und des Brustschulterapparates, *Arch. mikr. Anat.*, CI, 382–436.

Schotté, O., 1926: Hypophysectomie et régéneration chez les batraciens urodeles, *Compt. rend. Soc. Physiol. Hist. Nat. Genève*, XLIII, 67–72.

Schulze, W., and Karl Hölldobler, 1926: Weitere Untersuchungen über die Wirkung inkretorischer Drüsensubstanzen auf die Morphogenie; IV, Die Zirbeldrüse, ein inkretorisches Organ mit morphogenetischer Bedeutung, *Arch. Entw. Mech.*, CVII, 605–624.

Sembrat, Kazimierz, 1925: Nouvelles recherches expérimentales sur les facteurs provoquant la métamorphose de l'intestin chez les têtards des anoures (Pelobates fuscus Laur), *Compt. rend. Soc. Biol.*, XCII, 1004–1006.

Sklower, A., 1925: Das incretorische System im Lebenscyclus der Frösche (Rana temporaria L.); I, Schilddrüse, Hypophyse, Thymus und Keimdrüsen, *Zeitschr. vergl. Physiol.*, II, 474–524.

Smith, P. E., 1916: The effect of hypophysectomy in the early embryo upon the growth and development of the frog, *Anat. Rec.*, XI, 57–64.

SMITH, P. E., 1920: The pigmentary, growth and endocrine disturbances induced in the anuran tadpole by the early ablation of the pars buccalis of the hypophysis, *Amer. Anat. Mem.*, II, 1–112, 19 pls.

———, 1925: Further evidence upon the differential response of the melanophore stimulant and the oxytocic and blood pressure autocoid of the pituitary to destructive agents, *Anat. Rec.*, XXIX, 396–397.

———, 1926: Hastening development of female genital system by daily homoplastic pituitary transplants, *Proc. Soc. Exp. Biol. Med.*, XXIV, 131–132.

———, and I. P. SMITH, 1923: The function of the lobes of the hypophysis as indicated by replacement therapy with different portions of the ox gland, *Endocrinology*, VII, 579–591.

SPAUL, E. A., 1924: Experiments on the injection of pituitary body (anterior lobe) extracts to axolotls, *Brit. Jour. Exp. Biol.*, II, 33–55.

———, 1930: On the activity of the anterior lobe pituitary, *Jour. Exp. Biol.*, VII, 49–87.

———, and N. T. HOWES, 1930: The distribution of biological activity of the anterior pituitary of the ox, *Jour. Exp. Biol.*, VII, 154–164.

SPEIDEL, C. C., 1925: The significance of changes in the thymus glands of thyroid-treated frog tadpoles, *Anat. Rec.*, XXIX, 374.

SUMI, R., 1926: Beitrag zur Morphogenese der epithelialen Hypophyse der Urodelen, *Fol. Anat. Japon.*, IV, 271–282.

SWINGLE, W. W., 1919: Iodine and the thyroid; III, The specific action of iodine in accelerating amphibian metamorphosis; IV, Quantitative experiments on iodine feeding and metamorphosis, *Jour. Gen. Physiol.*, I, 593–606; II, 161–171.

———, 1921: The relation of the pars intermedia of the hypophysis to pigmentation changes in anuran larvae, *Jour. Exp. Zool.*, XXXIV, 119–142, 2 pls.

———, 1922: Experiments on the metamorphosis of neotenous amphibians, *Jour. Exp. Zool.*, XXXVI, 397–421.

———, 1927: The functional significance of the suprarenal cortex, *Amer. Naturalist*, LXI, 132–146.

TERRY, G. S., 1918: Effects of the extirpation of the thyroid gland upon ossification in Rana pipiens, *Jour. Exp. Zool.*, XXIV, 567–587, 3 pls.

TILNEY, F., and L. F. WARREN, 1919: Morphology and evolutionary significance of the pineal body, *Amer. Anat. Mem.*, IX, 257.

UHLENHUTH, E., 1917: A further contribution to the metamorphosis of amphibian organs; The metamorphosis of grafted skin and eyes of Amblystoma punctatum, *Jour. Exp. Zool.*, XXIV, 237–302, 5 pls.

———, 1920: Experimental gigantism produced by feeding pituitary gland, *Proc. Soc. Exp. Biol. Med.*, XVIII, 11–14.

———, 1921: The internal secretions in growth and development of amphibians, *Amer. Naturalist*, LV, 193–221.

———, 1927: Die Morphologie und Physiologie der Salamander-Schilddrüse; I, Histologisch-Embryologische Untersuchung des Sekretionsprozesses in den verschiedenen Lebensperioden der Schilddrüse des Marmorsalamanders Ambystoma opacum, *Arch. Entw. Mech.*, CIX, 616–749.

UHLENHUTH, E,. and HILDA KARNS, 1928: The morphology and physiology of the salamander thyroid gland; III, The relation of the number of follicles to development and growth of the thyroid in Ambystoma maculatum, *Biol. Bull.*, LIV, 128–164.

———, and S. SCHWARTZBACH, 1927: The morphology and physiology of the salamander thyroid gland; II, The anterior lobe of the hypophysis as a control mechanism of the function of the thyroid gland, *Brit. Jour. Exp. Biol.*, V, 1–5.

VIALLI, M., 1929: L'apparato epifisario negli anfibi, *Arch. Zool. Ital.*, XIII, 423–452, 1 pl.

VINCENT, S., 1898: The comparative histology of the suprarenal capsules, *Int. Jour. Anat.*, XV, 282–303, 3 pls.

WAGGENER, ROY A., 1929: The biological significance of amphibian parathyroids, *Anat. Rec.*, XLI, 24–25.

WELTI, E., 1925: Masculinisation et féminisation de crapauds par greffe de glandes génitales hétérologues, *Compt. rend. Soc. Biol.*, XCIII, 1490–1492.

WILDER, I. W., 1925: "The Morphology of Amphibian Metamorphosis," Smith College, Northampton, Mass.

WILDER, MAGELE, 1929: The significance of the ultimobranchial body (postbranchial body, suprapericardial body): A comparative study of its occurrence in urodeles, *Jour. Morph. Phys.*, XLVII, 283–332.

WOLF, O. M., 1929: Effect of daily transplants of anterior lobe of pituitary on reproduction of frog (Rana pipiens Shreber), *Proc. Soc. Exp. Biol. Med.*, XXVI, 692–693.

———, 1929a: Effect of daily transplants of anterior lobe of the pituitary on reproduction of the frog (Rana pipiens Shreber), *Anat. Rec.*, XLIV, 206.

ZONDEK, H., and T. REITER, 1923: Hormonwirkung und Kationen, *Klin. Wochenschr.*, II, 1344–1346.

CHAPTER XIV

THE SENSE ORGANS AND THEIR FUNCTIONS

The sense organs are the receptors, either cells or more usually groups of cells, which respond to environmental changes. The resulting excitation is transmitted by means of nerves to effector organs which may bring the animal closer to some particular need or away from danger. Sense organs are usually formed of epidermal cells. They are especially sensitive to only one particular kind of stimulus, and are far more sensitive to this than are other cells of the body. A tactile papilla in the skin of a frog, for example, is more sensitive to a slight touch than is the nerve leading away from this spot. The kind of sensation produced by a sense organ is not dependent on the type of receptor but on the connections of the nerve in the brain or spinal cord. It is known in man that the same sensation is produced by stimulating either the sense organ or its nerve alone and hence that the receptor is not responsible for the quality of a sensation. The central connections are so different in frog and man that it would be difficult to postulate the qualities of the sensations of the former. Further, Amphibia are equipped with some sense organs not found in man. The skin, for example, is sensitive to light but there is little evidence as to the nature of the sensation which comes from light-exposed skin. Many reactions in Amphibia are reflex, presumably without representation in consciousness, and all may be discussed without reference to the probable sensations.

Sense organs may, therefore, be more properly called "receptors." They may be grouped according to the type of stimulation to which they are especially sensitive. The mechanoreceptors respond to certain degrees of mechanical pressure or certain frequencies of vibration. These include the pressure receptors of the skin and internal organs, the lateral-line organs of the skin, the gravity receptors of the inner ear, the sound receptors of the same, as well as the hunger receptors of the stomach. The chemoreceptors include the organs of taste, smell, and common

chemical sense. The photoreceptors are the light receptors of
eye and skin. The thermoreceptors are those especially sensitive
to slight changes of temperature and embrace the temperature
organs of the skin. In addition, there are pain receptors in both
the skin and some internal organs which cannot be classified
under any of these heads. For convenience of description the
sense organs may be grouped ac-
cording to their topographic
positions.

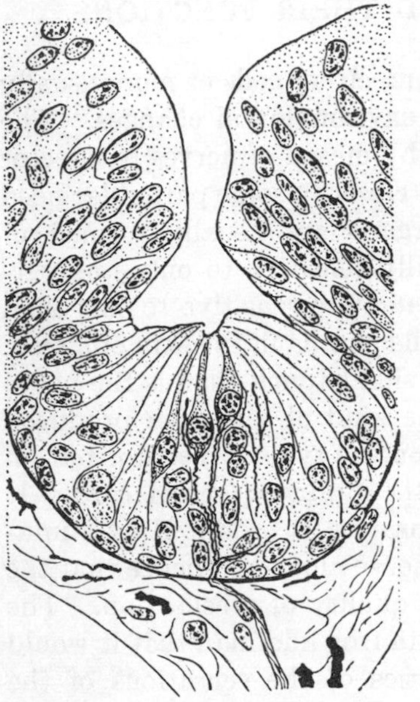

FIG. 113.—Vertical section of a
lateral line organ of *Siren lacertina*
showing nerve terminations about
the sense cells. (*After Chezar.*)

Lateral-line Organs.—The most
conspicuous sense organs of the
skin are the lateral-line organs.
These are little clusters of sense
cells usually forming shallow depressions in the surface and arranged generally in definite rows
on head and body. The lateral-
line organs represent an inheritance from the fishes in which the
same rows may be readily identified. As in fishes these sense cells
function in responding to vibrations of low frequency (Dye, 1921)
in an aquatic medium. Lateral-
line organs are present in all
thoroughly aquatic urodeles and
their larvae. They are present in
some mountain-brook species such
as the larger forms of Desmogna-
thus, but are inconspicuous or lacking in the more terrestrial
forms of the same genus. They are lacking in terrestrial
plethodontids. Although present in larvae of all Ambystoma, they show various stages of degeneration in the adults.
Among the Salientia lateral-line organs are present in the aquatic
larvae but usually are absent in the adults. They are found in
the adults of the Pipidae (Escher, 1925) and of such very aquatic
types as Bombina and *Ceratophrys laevis*.

The lateral-line organs of Amphibia are less specialized than
those of most fish in that they usually lie entirely within the epidermis. In Stereochilus they have sunk partly into the corium and

are found at the bottom of conspicuous "pores" on the head and body.

The lateral-line organs are pear-shaped with a shallow, usually ovate depression at the smaller, outer end. The organ consists of sense cells having a central position and of spindle-shaped, sustentacular cells surrounding them (Fig. 113). Charipper (1928) also distinguishes mantle or protective cells on the sides of the organ and basal cells next to the corium. The sense cells are club-shaped and have a refractive point or bristle which is proportionately longer in the larva than in the adult (Kingsbury, 1895) but in both cases reaches the surface of the depression where it projects into the medium of the environment.

In some tadpoles and urodeles the lateral-line organs are arranged singly in rows. In many others the organs divide to form many short series of from two to seven organs with the axis of each group either parallel or vertical to the main rows (Fig. 114). Kingsbury and Escher recognize four main rows on the head and three on either side of the body. One of the head rows, namely that on the cheek, may be conveniently divided into five differently directed parts. The Pipidae differ from urodeles in having an accessory row of lateral-line organs extending to near the midline of the back and in having the supraorbital row recurving and extending back into the frontal region. Salientia, also, differ from urodeles, except Ambystoma, in having the axes of the sense-organ groups of the upper body row extending in the same direction as this row, those of the two lower rows running vertical to it. The opposite arrangement of organ groups and body rows is maintained generally in urodeles. In some Amphibia the sense-organ groups on the head may be very numerous and somewhat irregular but nevertheless are referable to the same row patterns found in other recent species and in fossil Amphibia and fishes.

These rows are determined by the lateral-line nerves of which there is a preauditory component from the seventh cranial nerve and a postauditory component from the ninth and tenth. The three rows of lateral-line organs on each side of the body are supplied by three branches from the latter. The central connection of both lateral-line nerves is in the dorsal portion of the medulla. This suggests a close functional relationship of the lateral-line organs with the mechanisms of equilibrium and posture.

Lateral-line organs are readily lost when Amphibia become terrestrial. The common newt possesses a full equipment of these sense organs as a larva but during the terrestrial red eft stage they partially atrophy and are covered by adjacent epidermis to reappear again on the surface as fully functional structures when the newt takes up an aquatic mode of

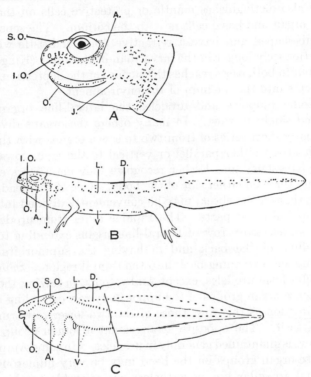

FIG. 114.—Lateral-line organs. The distribution of the lateral-line organs is indicated by small depressions in the skin. *A. Pleurodeles waltl (after Escher)*. *B. Triturus viridescens (after Kingsbury)*. *C. Rana heckscheri* tadpole.

Branches: *A.*, angular; *D.*, dorsal; *I.O.*, infra-orbital; *J.*, jugular; *L.*, lateral; *O.*, oral; *V.*, ventral; *S.O.*, supra-orbital.

living in adult life. Nevertheless, lateral-line organs are not present in all aquatic Amphibia, and here the immediate history of any one form may be of great significance. Thus they are not present in the aquatic toads Pseudis or Calyptocephalus nor in the caecilian Typhlonectes (Escher, 1925). The latter, although thoroughly aquatic, probably had fossorial ancestors. They are found in the larvae of *Salamandra atra* which live their whole larval life within the maternal oviducts (Escher, 1925). This seems to be an inheritance from the ancestral *Salamandra salamandra* which has aquatic larvae.

Tactile Organs.—The skin of Amphibia is sensitive to mechanical stimulations. Free nerve endings are abundant between the cells of the epidermis. Other nerve endings are associated with connective tissue capsules or with groups of specialized cells between which the nerves extend. When such groups occur in the corium they may raise the overlying epidermis into a papilla. Sense papillae have been described from the feet of frogs and from the back of the breeding female frog. Papillae having a similar form are found on the heads of some Salientia (Fig. 34B) and along the lips of some species of Desmognathus. The tentacle of the Gymnophiona is a tactile organ, and the tentacles of Xenopus larvae, as well as the cirri of certain plethodontids, may have similar functions. The tentacles of the adult Xenopus are not homologous with those of the larvae. They develop by a growth of the caudal ends of the lacrimal ducts and their function has not been determined.

Organs of Chemical Sense.—The outer surface of most fishes is open to chemical stimulations of a mildly irritating kind (Parker, 1922). With the development of land life in tetrapods and the consequent drying of the skin this capacity was restricted to the mucous membranes. The Amphibia still retain the common chemical sense in a marked degree over all the surfaces of their body. Free nerve endings of the spinal and cranial nerves in the epidermis are the type of nerve terminals concerned with the reception of chemical irritants. These receptors resemble those concerned with pain, but Crozier (1916) has shown that in the frog the same terminals do not function for both mechanical and chemical stimulations. Further, Sayle (1916) finds that fatigue resulting from chemical stimulation is different from that produced by mechanical stimulation. The presence of a delicate chemical sense in Amphibia would doubtless play a part in affecting their movements in nature. Stimulation of these sense organs would tend to induce avoiding or escape reactions. In this they would be distinguished from olfactory sensations which frequently induce approach reactions. The olfactory organs are the chief receptors for chemical stimulations in higher vertebrates and even in Amphibia they are more sensitive than the chemical sense organs of the skin.

Heat and Cold Receptors.—Amphibia are sensitive to changes in temperature. This has been well shown by Wright (1914) and others who have recorded the temperatures at which different species of frogs appear from their winter quarters. It has been assumed that free nerve endings in the epidermis are the cold receptors (Plate, 1924). Morgan (1922) noted that the reaction time of frogs was longer to heat than to cold stimulation and concluded that the heat receptors lay deeper in the skin. By treatment with cocaine Morgan eliminated the response to cold earlier than that to pain stimulation. The result suggests that the heat and cold receptors are different from pain receptors.

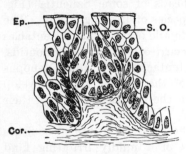

Fig. 115.—Taste bud from the tongue of *Necturus maculosus. Cor.*, corium of close connective tissue; *Ep.*, epithelium; *S.O.*, sensory organ situated on a papilla of connective tissue. (*After Kingsbury.*)

After cocainizing the skin a response to acid and to pain persisted beyond the response to heat, and the response to heat and cold beyond that to touch. Therefore the receptors for acid, heat, cold, pain, and touch in the skin of the frog are probably different.

Organs of Taste.—Although many fishes, such as the catfish, have taste buds over the entire outer surface of the body, these structures, and with them the sense of taste, became limited in the Amphibia to the mouth. The senses of smell and taste are closely allied physiologically but the organs are very different structurally. Taste buds are isolated groups of elongated cells widely distributed over the palate, jaws, and tongue (Fig. 115). The groups on the palate of urodele larvae are smaller than those of the tongue of adult frogs, and it has been suggested that these groups of sense organs in the frog may be tactile instead of gustatory organs. They consist of cylindrical as well as elongate cells (Niemack, 1893), both of which lack cilia, in contrast to most of the lining cells of the mouth. On the tongue of the frog the taste buds occupy the summits of fungiform papillae which are scattered among the filiform papillae and with them form the plushlike surface of the organ. There are no separate gustatory nerves as there are olfactory nerves, but gustatory fibers are included in several cranial nerves, apparently in the fifth, seventh, ninth, and tenth. The taste buds are sometimes encircled by dense spirals of nerve fibers which may possibly reenforce the sensory excitation of these organs (Herrick, 1925). In man different taste buds may be responsible for different taste qualities. The Giersbergs (1926) have shown that the same is probably true for Amphibia.

Olfactory Organs.—The organ of smell, which in most fishes lies with both inlet and outlet on the surface of the snout, became associated with the upper lip in the fish ancestors of tetrapods and had its outlet enclosed within the mouth in these forms. Caecilians and some other Amphibia (Kurepina, 1926, 1927) show in their development how this was apparently accomplished in phylogeny, for the choanae or internal nares arise from the caudal end of a furrow, the oro-nasal groove (Fig. 11), which sinks within the developing upper lip.

Some aquatic Amphibia, especially the perennibranchs, agree with the fishes in that the nasal chamber is lined with a series of folds. The depressions between the folds are clothed with sense cells, and the ridges are covered with ciliated respiratory epithelium. Larval urodeles in general have a discontinuous sensory area, while tadpoles and most metamorphosed Amphibia have an undivided one. In Salientia this is raised caudally into an *eminentia olfactoria*.

The olfactory epithelium consists of sense cells bearing several olfactory hairs on their free ends. It also includes ciliated supporting cells and basal cells. In tadpoles and larval urodeles the ciliated cells beat rapidly and help to drive a current through the nasal chamber. Wilder (1925) showed that in a plethodontid larva these cilia, together with those on the gills, maintained a steady current entering the nasal chamber. The sense cells vary greatly in length (Fig. 116), and in Rana some of the hairs may be longer than the thickness of the epithelium (Hopkins, 1926). The proximal end of each sense cell is drawn out into a fine process.

Two glandular masses develop in association with the nasal passage in metamorphosed Amphibia: an outer, guarding the external nares, and a more extensive inner series, which keeps the olfactory epithelium moist (Fig. 117). The secretion of the latter forms a mucous layer over the olfactory surfaces in those urodeles and Salientia which take air into the nasal chamber. Many olfactory hairs penetrate this layer and lie with their distal portions exposed to the air (Hopkins, 1926). In thoroughly aquatic forms the mucus does not form a layer and the hairs stand out in the water in the nasal passage. Thus, in neither case does the mucus form a medium in which odorous substances are dissolved before they stimulate the hairs.

The olfactory hairs of Amphibia are functional both in an air and in a water medium, as has been well shown in the case of the newt (Matthes, 1926). The olfactory organ, however, reaches its highest state of development in terrestrial forms. In the larvae of frogs and salamanders the olfactory stream passes

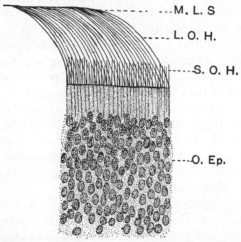

Fig. 116.—Diagram of the olfactory epithelium of a frog. The long hairs reach the surface of the mucus and are non-moving. The shorter ones fail to reach this surface and exhibit ciliary activity. *O.Ep.*, olfactory epithelium; *L.O.H.*, long, non-moving, olfactory hairs; *M.L.S.*, surface of mucous layer; *S.O.H.*, short, moving, olfactory hairs. (*After Hopkins.*)

freely inward from the nasal cavity to the mouth. Its return to the nasal passage is prevented in urodele larvae by a simple flap of mucosa acting as a valve, while in tadpoles a double fold or fringe has a more complex form but similar function. During metamorphosis the choanal valves are lost and a new mechanism for closing the nasal passage appears at its other end. As shown by Bruner (1901, 1914), a constrictor and two dilators of the external nares develop at this time or shortly before the choanal valves are lost. In metamorphosed Amphibia the olfactory stream under muscular control passes freely in and out through the nasal cavity. The inspired stream tends to move through the mesial part of the nasal chamber; the expired, through the lateral. The latter region becomes more or less devoid of olfactory epithelium, except at one point, where a special sense area develops. This is Jacobson's organ (Fig. 117), and it serves to test the food substances in the mouth. In frogs Jacobson's organ lies in a sac at the anterior mesial corner of the nasal chamber. In urodeles it has usually a lateral position which, in spite of the studies of Wilder (1892), Seydel (1895), and Anton (1908), has caused various investigators to doubt its homology

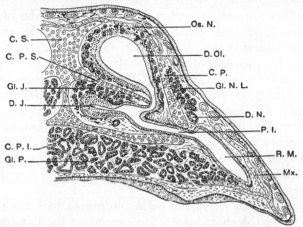

FIG. 117.—Cross-section of nasal cavity of a tree frog showing Jacobson's organ and the glands associated with the nasal cavity. *C.P.*, cartilago paranasalis; *C.P.I.*, cartilago paraseptalis inferior; *C.P.S.*, cartilago paraseptalis superior; *C.S.*, cartilago septi; *D.J.*, recessus medialis nasi (ductus Jacobsoni); *D.N.*, ductus nasolacrimalis; *D.Ol.*, ductus olfactorius; *Gl.J.*, glandula Jacobsoni; *Gl.N.L.*, glandula nasalis lateralis; *Gl.P.*, glandula palatinus; *Mx.*, maxilla; *Os.N.*, os nasale; *P.I.*, pars intermedia; *R.M.*, recessus maxillaris. (*After Mihalkovics.*)

with the mouth tester of frogs. The perennibranchs present certain deviations from the larval condition. Siren and Amphiuma have both developed a modification of the choanal valve which permits its being opened at will (Bruner, 1914*a*), and both forms which are terrestrial at times, have a well-developed Jacobson's organ. Cryptobranchus, which represents a partly metamorphosed type, has lost the choanal valves and developed a Jacobson's organ. This structure arises in the larvae in anticipation of its use after metamorphosis, and hence it is not surprising to find that Siren and Amphiuma with their special valves have elaborated this structure while Necturus and Proteus which retain the larval valves have failed to develop it. It is interesting that Megalobatrachus should have its Jacobson's organ proportionately larger in early life than later (Fleissig, 1909). This would confirm the conclusion that the structure first developed in connection with terrestrialism and that its elaboration in Siren and Amphiuma is correlated with their occasional excursions on land. The olfactory nerve fibers extending to Jacobson's organ frequently form a bundle distinct from those connecting with the remainder of the nasal chamber.

Caecilians apparently sprang from a different order of extinct Amphibia from that which gave rise to the frogs and salamanders, and they are unique in possessing a short retractile tentacle on either side of the face. Its base becomes associated with the nasal passage and especially with a secondary olfactory area usually described as Jacobson's organ. By movements of the tentacle, odorous substances are apparently brought in contact with this sensory region, and hence Laubmann (1927) describes the region as a tactile nose able to detect food independently of the respiratory stream. The great development of the olfactory region in caecilians is correlated with their burrowing habits and rudimentary eyes.

Eyes.—The first tetrapods were confronted with the problem of modifying the shortsighted fish eye into a mechanism better adapted for vision in the air. Amphibia have a smaller lens than fish, and it lies behind the iris. It is not round except in certain larval forms but flattened on its outer surface, even in the primitive hynobiid salamanders (Okajima, 1910). In frogs and toads this flattening is carried farther than in urodeles. The retreat of the lens away from the cornea, as well as its flattening, would tend to make the amphibian eye farsighted, an advantageous condition not realizable in water because of the opacity of this medium. The eye in its new environment required at the outset protective lids and glands to keep it clean and moist. Special muscles of accommodation developed to increase the efficiency of focus, and as the first tetrapods were devoid of necks, other muscles were modified to periscope the eyeball above the surface of the head and to pull it down when it was in danger of injury. The eyes of Amphibia are of interest in that they show stages in the transition from the eyes of fish to those of higher vertebrates

The eyes of modern Amphibia vary enormously in size. Arboreal and terrestrial forms tend to have larger ones than fossorial or aquatic types. The eyes are directed laterally in most forms, but in Centrolenella, Zachaenus, and a few other Salientia they are directed partly forward and possibly effect a binocular vision. Verrier (1927) estimated that even in the European tree frog 40 per cent of the field of vision was binocular.

The eyeball is covered distally by a transparent cellular membrane, the cornea, the remainder, or concealed portions, being protected by a dense fibrous coat, the sclera. The latter is strengthened in the adults of some primitive urodeles, as well as in the larvae of most forms, by a ring or cup of cartilage (Stadt-

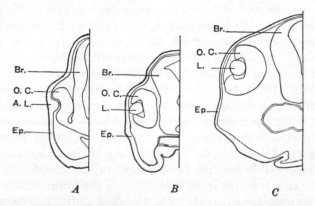

FIG. 118.—Sections representing three stages in the development of the eye of the frog, *Rana esculenta*. *A.L.*, anlage of lens; *Br.*, brain; *Ep.*, epidermis; *L.*, lens; *O.C.*, optic cup. (*After Giesbrecht.*)

müller, 1914; Okajima and Tsusaki, 1921). This cartilage, which is also found in frogs, was partly ossified at least, in some of the first tetrapods. It becomes enormously thick in Cryptobranchus, where Plate (1924) considers it a case of disharmonic growth conditioned by the degeneration of the eyes of this form. The cornea is arched in metamorphosed Amphibia and due to the inward migration of the lens (Fig. 118) is part of the refractive system. The cornea of larval Amphibia is frequently double, as in the case of certain bottom-living fish. The inner cornea arises from subcutaneous tissues and later fuses with the outer on metamorphosis (Giesbrecht, 1925).

The eyelids first develop at metamorphosis. They are reduced in some aquatic Salientia and entirely absent in two genera of pipid toads. The upper eyelid of Amphibia is merely a thick fold of integument incapable of independent movement. The lower eyelid undergoes various modifications within the group. In some urodeles, such as *Hydromantes italicus*, the lower eyelid lacks muscles, but in others, as Triturus, strands from the *M. periorbita* penetrate the temporal and nasal sections of its upper edge (Franz, 1924). The upper portion of the lower lid is thinned and slightly folded on itself in our common newt. The folding is carried further in the primitive Salientia until finally, in Rana and many other frogs, it is a thin, translucent membrane which folds inside the thicker lower part, the whole structure being N-shaped in cross-section. The upper part is called the "nictitating membrane," although it seems to have arisen wholly within the Amphibia. It is possibly homologous with the nictitating membrane of other vertebrates, however. It arises during ontogeny from a small mass of undifferentiated tissue embedded within the integument at the anterior border of the tadpole eye. Lindeman (1929) has shown that the extirpation of this mass prevents the nictitating membrane from forming during metamorphosis, while the removal of the ventral border of the eye results in its partial regeneration and a perfect nictitating membrane being formed. Hence the anterior mass of tissue appears to be alone responsible for the development of the nictitating membrane. In a few tree frogs both parts of the lower lid are translucent or even transparent. The so-called nictitating membrane has attached to either end of its thicker upper margin a tendon which encircles the greater part of the eyeball. When the eyeball is retracted within the orbit, the nictitating membrane by the pull of the tendon is automatically drawn up over the cornea. It is folded again partly by the protrusion of the eyeball but chiefly by the contraction of a special muscle which arises from the *levator bulbi*.

Correlated with the development of lids, eye glands made their appearance for the first time in the Amphibia. Primitively in the group a single gland is found extending the length of the lower eyelid and opening by numerous ducts on the conjunctiva. This condition is found in most Caudata. In Salamandra the gland is partly divided into two heads: an anterior Harderian and a posterior lacrimal mass characteristic of the higher vertebrates. In the Salientia only the anterior of these two glands is retained. In the Gymnophiona a single enormously hypertrophied gland is present occupying the whole eye socket and functioning to lubricate the tentacle. Developmental studies have shown this gland to arise from the same region as the eye gland of urodeles and to be homologous with it.

The secretion of the eye glands is conducted to the nasal chamber by the lacrimal duct. In urodeles it opens on the conjunctiva near the inner corner of the eye, while in the Salientia it usually opens in the middle of the lower lid. Recently metamorphosed Salientia (Piersol, 1887) and certain primitive Caudata (Okajima, 1910) may have the duct opening on the surface of the skin near the inner corner of the eye. This seems to be the original position of the mouth of the lacrimal duct in Gymnophiona. Lids, eye glands, and lacrimal duct are formed during or just before metamorphosis. Their complete absence in the perennibranchs is due to the failure of these forms to metamorphose rather than to any secondary degeneration, as many writers assume.

The eyes of many Amphibia, particularly the tree frogs, are very beautiful, for the iris, often vividly marked with gold or red, is clearly visible through the transparent cornea. Some of this pigment is found not in pigment cells but in the smooth muscles which bring about a rapid contraction or expansion of the iris under the direct action of light. The sphincters lie near the aperture in the iris, while the dilators extend radially and lie more laterally. The aperture, the pupil, varies greatly in form throughout the Amphibia and has been used by systematists in defining natural groups of Salientia. It is horizontal in most frogs and toads, vertical in the Spadefoot Toads, while in certain genera of discoglossids and Hylidae it may be three- or four-cornered.

Accommodation.—The eyes of Amphibia are of considerable phylogenetic interest in that the mechanism of accommodation is intermediate between that of fish and Amniota. The lens lies behind the iris and is held in place by a series of delicate radiating fibers which extend from the outer margin of the lens to the ciliary body, a vasculated fold of the inner coat of the eye capsule. The eye at rest is moderately farsighted. Accommodation is accomplished not by a change in the form of the lens as in Amniota but by a change of its position as in fishes. In frogs a dorsal and ventral *protractor lentis* (Fig. 119) is present in the ciliary fold. Its contraction moves the lens outward, not inward as does the lens muscle of fishes. In urodeles there is only a single ventral muscle lying in a papilla. This functions the same as the ventral *protractor* of frogs and is considered by Tretjakoff (1906) to be homologous with it. The urodele *protractor* is believed by Plate (1924) to be homologous with the fish *retractor*, and hence the Amphibia may owe this system to their piscine ancestors. In

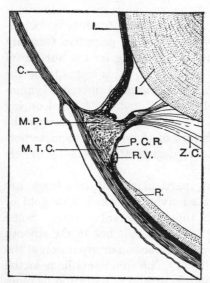

FIG. 119.—Vertical meridian section of a frog's eye, showing muscles of accommodation. *C.*, cornea; *I.*, iris; *L.*, lens; *M.P.L.*, M. protractor lentis; *M.T.C.*, M. tensor chorioideae; *P.C.R.*, pars ciliaris retinae; *R.*, retina; *R.V.*, ring vessel; *Z.C.*, zonula ciliaris. (*After Tretjakoff.*)

all Amphibia there is a second muscular system which is not found in fish. This is the *tensor chorioideae*, a series of meridionally arranged fibers in the periphery of the ciliary region. Streuli (1925) believes this functions antagonistically to the *protractor*, but Beer (1899) and Plate (1924) present evidence to show that it functions in moving the lens in the same direction. The *tensor chorioideae* becomes the ciliary muscle of the eye in amniotes (Plate, 1924).

The extent of accommodation varies with the species but shows some correlation with the species habits. It is apparently greatest in the terrestrial Bufo and least in such aquatic forms as Bombina. Newts have been reported to be nearsighted on land but not in the water.

Retina.—The eye is fundamentally unlike other sense organs in that the retina is not directly evolved from the external ectoderm but from part of the central nervous system. It arose in phylogeny from an aggregation of direction eyes (Parker, 1908) which were inverted on the development of a tubelike central nervous system. Thus the rods and cones, the only photosensitive cells in the eye, are directed away from the lens and light passes through several layers of nerve fibers and their nuclei as well as much supporting tissue before reaching the sensitive cells.

Between lens and the innermost of the retinal layers is a solid mass of transparent connective tissue, the *vitreous humor*. This is penetrated by a network of fibers and blood vessels and covered by a thin membrane in the frogs. In the urodeles the fibrous material is less developed. The outer chamber of the eye, that between cornea and lens, is filled by a watery fluid, the *aqueous humor*.

The retina consists of an outer pigmented epithelium against which the rods and cones abut. The nuclei of the rods and cones form a layer immediately central to them. Their axons do not connect directly with the optic nerve, but two successive layers of neurons are intercalated. The eye is the only sense organ which contains such connecting neurons within its limits. The rods are of two kinds in Rana: red with a long, and green with a short outer segment. The latter type of rod is lacking in Necturus, Salamandra, and various other urodeles. Rods of the former type owe their color to the visual purple which quickly bleaches in light, the products of this decomposition inducing an excitation in the rods. The visual green is allied to visual purple and has the same function. Cones are smaller than the rods and less numerous. They are believed to function in color vision, different cones being stimulated by light of different wave lengths. Form perception is accomplished by the stimulation of both rods and cones in the different parts of the retina.

Rods and cones consist chemically and physically of two parts, the outer and inner segments (Fig. 120). The outer segment, which is strongly refractive, is in the form of a cylinder in the rods and of a peaked cap in the cones. The inner segment is characterized in frogs and toads by a planoparabolic lenslike structure. In urodeles there are present two lenslike bodies, a proximal biconvex body, fitting into a distal planoconcave body, the ellipsoid. Further differentiations have been recorded in the rods and cones of Amphibia (for review see Arey, 1928). The cones contract on exposure to light, even when not fully differentiated (Detwiler, 1923). Double cones are regularly present in the eyes of various urodeles, and as the members of each pair differ in size, they probably have different functions. The eyes of salamanders function not only during development but apparently also during degeneracy. Those of cave salamanders having a very degenerate retina may be sensitive to light. Dubois (1890) found that while the skin of Proteus is very sensitive to light, the latent period of reaction was more than doubled by covering the vestigial eyes with lamp black. On the other hand, Obreshkove (1921) concluded that the well-developed eyes in the tadpoles of *Rana clamitans* played no part in the responses of the tadpoles to light. Probably under other conditions of illumination the eyes would have important functions.

Rods and cones are evenly distributed over the retina of Necturus (Palmer, 1912), but in Rana a thickened portion of the retina seems to mark a region of acute vision since cones are especially abundant here. Chievitz (1889) reports two species of Bufo as having a shallow depression in this region, an incipient

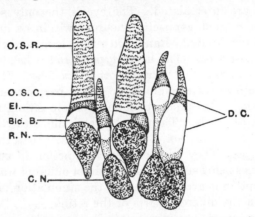

Fig. 120.—Visual cells of a salamander. The rods and cones from the retina of a larval Ambystoma. *Bic.B.*, paraboloid; *C.N.*, cone nucleus; *D.C.*, double cone; *El.*, ellipsoid; *O.S.C.*, outer segment of cone; *O.S.R.*, outer segment of rod; *R.N.*, rod nucleus. (*After Detwiler and Laurens.*)

fovea developed in species known to have a better vision than Rana.

Keenness of vision is dependent not only on a focusing of the lens in such a way that a clear image is thrown on the retina but also on proper illumination of the retina. In strong light the iris rapidly contracts and the pigment cells in the retina send out processes which cut down the amount of light reaching the rods and cones. The dark-adapted eye of the frog exhibits not only a contraction of the pigment cells but a rod contraction and a cone elongation. The pigment contraction is, however, influenced by temperature. Less contraction is found to accompany exposures at high temperatures than at low temperatures in the dark (Detwiler and Lewis, 1926).

Some species of Amphibia are diurnal, but their retinas have not been investigated to determine whether they differ from those of nocturnal relatives. It may be noted, however, that some forms, such as Necturus and Gyrinophilus, which are primarily if not entirely nocturnal, possess both rods and cones. A few frogs have an appendage from both the upper and lower margins of the pupil. Its chief function would seem to be secretory and not the masking of light from the retina.

Degeneration of the Eye.—In addition to the usual six eye muscles of vertebrates, the Amphibia possess a special *retractor bulbi*, which pulls the eyeball within the orbit, and a *levator bulbi*, which raises the eyeball again. In blind vertebrates the eye muscles frequently degenerate. In caecilians the typical eye musculature has been modified by the degeneration of some muscles and nerves and by the transfer of others to adjacent regions where they have different functions. The *retractor bulbi*, is transformed into a *retractor tentaculi;* the *rectus internus*, into a retractor of the tentacular sheath; and the *levator bulbi*, into compressor and dilator muscles of the orbital glands (Norris, 1917).

In addition to most burrowing Gymnophiona, which exhibit various stages in the degeneration of the eyes, there are three other Amphibia, species of salamanders, all inhabitants of caves, which are blind in the adult stage. The European Proteus has been most extensively studied. Its eye is essentially a case of arrested development (Schlampp, 1892; Kohl, 1895), although certain degenerative changes have occurred. The American Typhlomolge exhibits further degenerative changes. The eye muscles and lens have vanished; retina and vitreal cavity are greatly modified. Probably in Typhlomolge, as in Typhlotriton and Proteus, the eye develops normally until a certain stage when growth is checked, differentiation ceases, and degenerative changes arise.

Ears.—The most primitive embolomerous Amphibia swam in the aquatic medium of their fish ancestors and were equipped with an ear apparatus only slightly different from that of fish. With the development of land life the gill pocket between mandible and hyoid no longer broke through to the outside as a spiracle, but its end abutted against the integument in the spiracular region. The integument of this spiracular region became, then, thinned. The resulting drum head, or tympanum, characterizes most

Salientia, although a few have the integument unmodified and separable from the underlying drum, and many burrowing or aquatic types as well as all the urodeles lack both drum and middle ear. This might be considered evidence that the urodeles sprang from aquatic or burrowing ancestors. Amphibia were primitively equipped with a tympanum which was fully exposed on the side of the head. It is curious that in one frog (*Rana cavitympanum* of Siam), the tympanum has sunk below the surface and lies at the end of an external ear opening as in mammals.

In the first land vertebrates as well as in their immediate ancestors, the support of the lower jaw was shifted from the

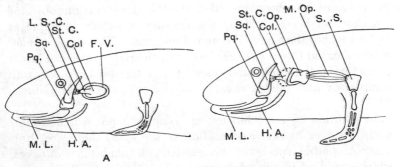

Fig. 121.—Diagram of the sound transmitting apparatus of an aquatic larval (*A*) and a terrestrial adult salamander (*B*). *Col.*, columella; *F.V.*, fenestra vestibuli; *H.A.*, hyoid arch; *L.S-C.*, ligamentum squamoso-columellare; *M.L.*, skeleton of the lower jaw; *M.Op.*, musculus opercularis; *Op.*, operculum; *Pq.*, palatoquadratum; *Sq.*, os squamosum; *S.S.*, suprascapula; *St.C.*, stilus columellae. (*After Kingsbury and Reed.*)

hyomandibular to the quadrate. The freed element sank into the spiracular cavity and assumed a new function of transmitting sound vibrations from the tympanum to the ear capsule. In Eogirinus, this hyomandibular, now called a "columella," merely abutted against the ear capsule, but very early in labyrinthodont phylogeny a fenestra was formed which increased the efficiency of transmitting vibrations to the perilymph, the fluid surrounding the membranous labyrinth or inner ear.

Modern Amphibia show in their ear apparatus some evidence of terrestrial ancestry. In addition to the columella which has its platelike proximal end fitting into the *fenestra vestibuli*, there is present primitively in both frogs and urodeles a second bony or cartilaginous plate in the same fenestra. This element, the operculum, is primitively not attached to the columella but is equipped with a muscle which attaches to the shoulder girdle and serves to transmit vibrations from the ground via the forelegs to the perilymph (Fig. 121). The operculum usually develops first at metamorphosis and is, therefore, absent not only in larvae but also in most of the perennibranchs. In Amphiuma and Necturus (Reed, 1920) it is present but fused to the columella. In aquatic Amphibia the operculum and its muscle would be practically functionless. Hence, it is not surprising to find operculum and columella fused in Pipa. In metamorphosed urodeles of the more advanced families, the columella undergoes various modes of degeneration, any one mode being usually found throughout a natural group of genera (Reed, 1920; Dunn, 1922).

The loss of the outer and middle ear in burrowing toads such as Pelobates does not seem to inconvenience them during the breeding season, for the loud calls of the males would be readily transmitted through the water in which the sexes congregate during the breeding season. The degeneration of the Eustachian tube in Bombina and Pelobates has not gone so far as it has in the urodeles. Both possess a tube (Litzelmann, 1923), but it never widens out to form a middle ear. The rudimentary ear ossicles and the absence of Eustachian tubes in Ascaphus would seem to be correlated with a mountain-brook life where acoustic conditions are obviously bad. Ascaphus, however, apparently lacks a voice entirely.

Inner Ear.—The inner ear in all vertebrates is primarily an organ of equilibrium. In fishes this organ is also able to detect certain vibrations. With the development of land life in the Amphibia, a special organ of hearing is evolved out of part of it. The inner ear, being fundamentally a part of the lateral-line system, arises as a placode on either side of the hind brain. It forms a vesicle and, propelled by not clearly understood factors (Streeter, 1921), leaves the skin and migrates to its final position. There it eventually becomes surrounded by cartilage, which is incorporated into the skull as the otic capsule. The vesicle thins to form the membranous labyrinth and remains separated from the otic capsule by a lymphlike fluid, the perilymph. The labyrinth itself is not hollow but filled with a similar fluid. In forming the labyrinth the vesicle becomes constricted into a dorsal *utriculus* and a ventral *sacculus*. In some frogs the *sacculus* may be constricted into a smaller upper and a larger lower vesicle.

The *utriculus* gives rise to the semicircular canals which are arranged in the three planes characteristic of all gnathostomes (Fig. 122). The anterior and posterior canals are arranged vertically and at an angle of 90 degrees to one another and 45 degrees to the median plane of the animal's body. The third is at right angles to the other two and lies horizontally on their outer side. The *sacculus* develops a small evagination, the *lagena*, which is destined to form the cochlea of higher vertebrates.

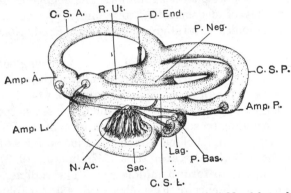

Fig. 122.—Membranous labyrinth of the inner ear of *Megalobatrachus japonicus*. The left labyrinth viewed from the outside. *Amp.A.*, ampulla anterior; *Amp.L.*, ampulla lateralis; *Amp.P.*, ampulla posterior; *C.S.A.*, canalis semicircularis anterior; *C.S.L.*, canalis semicircularis lateralis; *C.S.P.*, canalis semicircularis posterior; *D.End.*, ductus endolymphaticus; *Lag.*, lagena; *N.Ac.*, nervus acusticus; *P.Bas.*, pars basilaris; *P.Neg.*, pars neglecta; *R.Ut.*, recessus utriculi; *Sac.*, sacculus. (*After Okajima.*)

The sense organs arise from a common anlage which divides into seven or eight areas. A patch of sense cells comes to lie at one end of each of the semicircular canals. Each is covered by a gelatinous cap, the *cupula*, and the canal at this point is swollen into an *ampulla*. The *utriculus* becomes equipped with a *macula utriculi* and a smaller *m. neglecta* (which is doubled in the caecilians), the *sacculus* retains a *macula sacculi* and a *papilla lagenae*. These four sense areas of the *utriculus* and the *sacculus* have the sense cells extended into long processes over which lie a gelatinous cover and in addition a layer of "hearing sand," crystals of calcium carbonate. Amphibia differ remarkably from fish in possessing an additional sense area, the *papilla basilaris*, which splits off from the *papilla lagenae*. It is covered by a movable tectorial membrane (Fig. 123) and would seem to serve as the chief organ of hearing. This organ is lacking in many perennibranchs and is best developed in Salientia where it lies in a small evagination of the lagena. A second hearing organ of Salientia and of certain primitive urodeles including Ambystoma (Norris, 1892) is the *macula neglecta* which in these forms is also covered with a tectorial membrane.

The *papilla basilaris* alone of the sense areas was destined for elaborate specialization in phylogeny, for it alone has developed into the organ of sharp hearing found in mammals and birds. Plate (1924) suggests that this may have been due to its more favorable position near the perilymphatic duct and near a thin place in the *sacculus* wall which would readily permit the transference of vibrations from the perilymph to the endolymph.

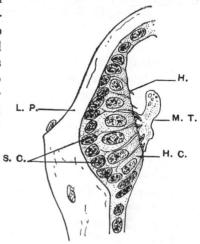

FIG. 123.—Cross-section through papilla basilaris of the newt, *Triturus cristatus*. *H.*, sensory hair; *H.C.*, hair cell; *L.P.*, lamina propria; *M.T.*, membrana tectori; *S.C.*, supporting cells. (*After Proebsting.*)

An advance of obscure functional significance over the conditions in the fish ear is found in the perilymphatic duct. This grows out from the mesial wall of the *sacculus* and into the brain cavity. In the Salientia it forms with its mate a ring around the hind brain, and continues posteriorly as an unpaired sac along the spinal cord as far as the seventh vertebra. Its wall, which may become partitioned by many septa, secretes a calcareous fluid which distends the sac to form a series of white diverticula overlying the spinal ganglia. It has been said that this enormous supply of calcium carbonate was utilized by growing bone, but Herter (1922) showed that tadpoles deprived of these sacs grew as well as the controls. Possibly the vertebral sacs transmit vibrations impinging on the back. They are lacking in Bombina and Discoglossus, although present in most higher Salientia, (Whiteside, 1922). The endolymphatic sacs of each side may or may not fuse in the urodeles and the type of modification agrees closely with the phylogenetic scheme (Dempster, 1930). The sacs never extend into the neural canal of the vertebrae in urodeles, and this restriction is correlated with poorly developed auditory powers in this group.

The several parts of the inner ear are supplied by branches of the eighth cranial nerve. The sense areas are formed of two kinds of cells: a flask-shaped sense cell, ending in a hairlike point, and a narrower supporting cell. Sound vibrations are transmitted through the ear ossicles to the perilymph which in turn transmits the vibration to the membranous labyrinth including the tectorial membranes overlying the two sense areas believed to be especially sensitive to sound waves.

Functions of the Ear.—The inner ear was originally an organ of equilibrium, and in all vertebrates it has a very important function to perform in this capacity. Tree frogs on swaying limbs or salamanders in the swirl of mountain streams make reflexly the proper movements to maintain their equilibrium. The sense cells are stimulated when the animal is thrown to one side or even when it is rotated slightly from a proper balance. Compensatory movements of limbs, body muscles, and eyes are automatically called forth by the nervous impulses initiated from the stimulated sense cells.

There is still some uncertainty as to the specific functions of each of the sense areas. McNally and Tait (1925) have presented evidence to show that in frogs the semicircular canals detect quick or slow movements of direction in either a straight or an angular course. Each vertical canal is associated with the limb of that quarter of the body toward which it faces, the anterior pair controlling the forelimbs and the posterior pair the hind limbs. Stimulation of a vertical canal brings forth an extension of the particular limb of that quarter. Stimulation of a horizontal canal leads to a movement of at least two and usually four limbs. Thus, the semicircular canals and their associated nerves are mechanisms which prevent stumbling or toppling over in any direction away from the normal position, and they react with great speed in bringing about a compensatory movement of the animal's limbs and body. The utricular *macula*, on the other hand, is an organ of static equilibrium which notes deviations from the normal direction of the pull of gravity. The saccular *macula* is not in any way concerned with equilibrium and hence would seem to play some part in recording sound vibrations.

There have been many experiments on removing parts of the inner ear and noting the effect on an animal's movements. From these it is not clear that the utricular *macula* is the only organ of static equilibrium (Pike, 1923; Fischer, 1926). The different results may be due in part to injury to adjacent areas. Removal of the whole ear brings about forced movements and attitudes. The head and body are bent toward the operated side (Greene and Laurens, 1922), and the legs of the opposite side assume an extended and braced position. The ear is closely associated with the tonus reflexes of the musculature, and some of the movements it conditions are due to changes in these reflexes. In the course of time, irregularities of locomotion caused by the removal of one of the ears of tadpoles may be in part corrected (Streeter, 1906). This would seem to be due to learning to use the eyes as an aid to equilibrium. Herter (1921), however, is of the opinion that the sense of touch may be utilized by some tadpoles in learning to correct the locomotor disturbances resulting from a loss of one labyrinth. Streeter found that if both ear vesicles of the wood frog were removed at an early stage of development, the tadpoles were never able to swim effectively.

When frogs are rotated on a revolving table they make compensatory movements with their heads. This may be due not entirely to a stimulation of the labyrinth but also to visual stimuli. Gruenberg (1907) arranged frogs in a stationary position and revolved a cylinder of various figures and colors about them. The frogs made compensatory movements similar to those made when the table was rotated and the environment was stationary. The response to the visual stimulus, however, was relatively weaker and slower than that to the dynamic stimulus of rotation. Thus, the labyrinth mechanism is the chief organ of equilibrium whether or not it receives support from the eyes.

Other Internal Mechanoreceptors.—The receptors which induce a state of hunger in ourselves and which produce impulses calling forth food-seeking reactions in frogs and other Amphibia are located in the walls of the stomach and are stimulated by hunger contractions of the empty stomach. No distinctive types of receptors have been described from this region. Many nerves send branched arborizations among the muscles, however, and these apparently also serve as pressure receptors. Some afferent nerves in various parts of the body end in bulbous end organs in tendons and joints. Stimulations from these organs, produced by pressure or pull of adjacent tissues during locomotion, play an essential rôle in the coordination of bodily movements.

Dominant Senses.—A well-developed sense organ would be considered good evidence that the sense in question played an important part in the life of its owner. An examination of the structure of the sense organs in Amphibia gives no clear evidence as to which are the dominant senses. Experiments on common forms, however, have shed some light on this question. Amphibia may respond to stimulations in the laboratory which they never receive in nature. If a weak electric current is passed through an aquarium, tadpoles will swim or at least turn toward the anode (Scheminsky, 1924) in the same automatic way moths seek a flame. Most responses of Amphibia have a decided utility, however, which may be considered together with the response.

Smell, Taste, and Common Chemical Sense.—Food is detected by most Amphibia chiefly by sight. It has been demonstrated that some Amphibia are able to detect and to locate food by smell alone (Copeland, 1913; Burr, 1916; Nicholas, 1922). Newts which live both in and out of water are capable of smelling in both media (Matthes, 1924). Newts approach and nose quiescent edible objects, and feeding reactions are elicited only if the olfactory stimulations are adequate. Common toad tadpoles react to olfactory stimulation, but adults make no response (Risser, 1914). Although all toads are more or less crepuscular and some are apparently nocturnal, Risser found that *B. americanus* would not eat food in the dark. Locher (1927) noted that feeding reactions could be induced in *Bufo calamita* by motionless odorous objects, and hence within the genus Bufo, species may vary in their olfactory abilities. No doubt burrowing toads with well-developed olfactory organs must depend to a large extent on odors in detecting their prey. The absence of olfactory powers in some toads is surprising in view of the well-developed "nose-brain" of these and other Amphibia. The larvae, however, of toads and other Amphibia, have acute olfactory powers. Apparently the sense of smell in most amphibian larvae is of the same order if not so keen as that of fish.

This alone might account for the generous endowment of nose brain.

The sense of taste is very closely allied to that of smell. The amount of stimulating substance is, of course, usually greater in the case of taste, and the central connections in the brain are totally different. The response to the stimulation of a taste bud in Amphibia is a snapping or swallowing reaction, while that to an olfactory stimulation is a movement of head or body. These different responses are due to the different connections of sense organs with motor tracts in the two cases. The Giersbergs (1926) have shown that the European newts can distinguish various taste qualities. By cocainizing part of the nerve endings in the tongue, they demonstrated that the tongue could be made insensitive to quinine while remaining sensitive to salt and acid. This suggests a certain specificity in the different taste buds. Some tadpoles, such as those of the Wood Frog and Spade-foot Toad, prefer meat to a vegetable diet. Obnoxious substances are often rejected by adult frogs. Still, adult Amphibia are such indiscriminate feeders that they would seem to have little need of a well-defined sense of taste.

The chief chemical sense which controls the general movements of Amphibia is probably neither smell nor taste but a common cutaneous sensitivity which occurs in our own bodies only on exposed mucous surfaces. Such a common chemical sense has been demonstrated in the frog and in Necturus (Sayle, 1916). It is difficult to conceive the sensation which must come from the entire surface of an amphibian's body as the animal moves into waters of a different acidity.

Whatever may be the nature of the sensations received from the skin of Amphibia, there is a considerable evidence to indicate that the tonus of the muscles is maintained by excitations received from this body cover. Wertheimer (1924) showed that removing a section of the skin from the thigh of a frog lessens the tonus of the adjacent muscles. Brief immersions of the frog's leg in a solution of novocaine had the same effect, while a return to water brought the tonus back to normal.

Hearing.—One of the most impressive sounds of nature is the great choruses of frogs in the spring. These arise from the voices of males and serve to attract females and other males to the breeding grounds. There is no doubt that some sounds have considerable significance in the life of frogs. Many male frogs kept in aquaria will call at the sound of splashing water even long after their breeding season.   But at the sound of the human voice most Amphibia show no response other than a slowing down of the respiratory rate in some forms.   What significance, therefore, has sound in the ordinary course of their lives?

Yerkes (1905) showed that sounds had a pronounced indirect effect on the common frogs, Rana, for if a tactile stimulation accompanied or soon followed the sound, the response was greater than it would have been without the sound.   The frog responded to sounds of from 50 to 10,000 vibrations a second. Yerkes found that the reinforcing influence of sound was greatest during the breeding season.   In one case the influence of the sound of a wooden gong was much increased by the operation of cutting away columella and tympanum.   This is of interest, for some frogs, such as Pelobates, lose the columella in the adult and nevertheless are apparently fully able to hear sounds of their breeding companions calling in the water.   That frogs without a columella can really hear and not merely feel the sound vibrations was shown by the fact that Yerkes obtained no further reinforcing influence when the eighth nerve was cut.

Bruyn and Van Nifterik (1920) have extended these observations to the European toad.   In the case of *Rana clamitans*, Yerkes found that if the sound was produced more than one second before the tactile stimulation no reinforcing influence was induced.   In the toad, Bruyn and Van Nifterik found that there was a great influence even at an interval of 10 seconds.   This difference of the influence of sound in Rana and Bufo is correlated with their mode of life.   The toad is a roaming terrestrial animal, and sound is of much greater significance to it than to the aquatic frog.   Once an insect has given away its location by a sound, the toad is on the *qui vive* and holds this tuning of its muscles longer than the frog.   In higher vertebrates the retention of the sound stimulus is of long duration, and hence the toad may be said to be mentally "higher" than the frog.   What the significance of sounds may mean to tree frogs which locate their prey at long distances, or to fossorial toads which make little use of their eyes, has not been demonstrated.   Patterson (1920) found that a whistle caused only slight inhibition of the normal gastric movements of the bullfrog.   It would be interesting to know if sounds do not influence the stomach contractions of terrestrial frogs to a greater extent.

A sense of hearing has been claimed for some salamanders (Cochran, 1911), but Kuroda (1926) failed to demonstrate it by laboratory methods. The structure of the auditory apparatus suggests that salamanders receive vibrations transmitted through the lower jaw from the substratum when, as larvae, they rest on the bottoms of ponds. In adult life, vibrations are largely transmitted through the forelimbs of salamanders. It is probable that sense organs other than the auditory are especially significant as a warning mechanism in these forms. Unfortunately, the hearing of purely terrestrial salamanders has not been tested by laboratory methods. Kuroda experimented with Triturus and Hynobius. He failed to obtain in them the changes in respiratory movements induced in Rana and Bufo by a ringing of a bell suspended from the ceiling. Although this can hardly be considered final proof of deafness, it must be concluded that a sense of hearing has not been adequately demonstrated in the Caudata. Vibrations of low frequency in the water stimulate the lateral-line organs. These can be considered neither tactile nor auditory organs.

Vision and Sensitivity to Light.—Most Amphibia avoid a strong light, and many species are nocturnal. The skin of both frogs and urodeles is sensitive to light rays, even to those which have been passed through water and freed of all heat waves. Such light apparently does not produce a painful irritation, for frogs and salamanders after seeking a retreat in a dark cranny will frequently turn and face the light. Further, frogs which had their eyes and cerebral hemispheres removed were found to turn and jump toward the source of light (Parker, 1903). In salamanders the skin of the appendages seems more sensitive to light than that of the body.

The movement of Amphibia toward or away from light has been assumed to be a tropistic response. Photosensitive material is apparently present in the skin and is connected by nerves with the muscles of limbs and body. The tension of homologous muscles on the two sides of the animal is influenced in the same mechanical manner as gravity affects them through the intermediary of the internal ear. The animal will turn until the tension on the two sets of muscles is the same and will then continue in as straight a line as the imperfections of its locomotor apparatus permit. It seems probable that the skin rather than the eyes serves as the control station receiving the light waves and directing the tension in the appropriate muscles, for Cole (1907) showed that a frog possessing only one eye will orientate itself toward light in the same manner as normal frogs. The tropistic response is influenced considerably by external factors. In Necturus the reaction time varies inversely with the temperature (Cole, 1922). Torelle (1903) found that *Rana pipiens* and *Rana clamitans* are positive to light at ordinary temperature, while below 10°C. they are negative. This is doubtless one of the factors inducing frogs to hibernate in the fall.

There are marked differences in the reactions of different species to light and these are largely responsible for their distribution during the day. The larvae of *Ambystoma maculatum*, which frequent sunny pools, are positively heliotropic, while the nocturnal larvae of *Eurycea lucifuga* and *Necturus maculosus* are negative. The marked preference of certain frogs for green or blue light (Pearse, 1910) might account in part for their hunting for insects among green grass instead of along exposed shores of the pond. Frogs, toads, and the newt have a color vision similar to that of man (Hess, 1910, 1912). They are able to see food placed in the blue, green, and the red region of the spectrum with the same acuity as the human eye in a similar state of adaptation. Further, they have the power of adaptation of the retina to darkness which resembles but does not equal that of man.

The phototropism of the Amphibia is overriden by responses to the field of vision. Regardless of the tropistic action of the light, frogs and toads are usually attracted by a small object moving in the field and will attempt to seize and swallow such an object. But the reaction to these details of the field of vision are again influenced by other factors. Periods of hunger, sexual activity, fatigue, and low temperature may greatly alter the results. Cole (1907) found that at temperatures of 6 to 10°C. *Rana clamitans* moved toward the smaller of two illuminated areas but that at higher temperatures it went toward the larger. Further, there are less definable causes which alter the results. Franz (1913) found that certain frog tadpoles were not markedly phototropic when swimming in a large tank. When placed in the confined space of a watch glass they orientated themselves in the direction of the light. I have found that young tadpoles of *Hyla versicolor* in a large vessel swim toward the light when the water is disturbed, and this may account for Franz's results. The phototropic response may be reversed in Amphibia by feeding. Starved newts are negatively phototropic, while well-fed ones are either positively phototropic or indifferent to light (Stier, 1926). Young toads are negatively heliotropic to strong light (10,000ca.m.) and positively to weak light and to diffuse daylight and sunlight (Riley, 1913). A similar differential effect of strong and weak light may account for the well-known fact that many Amphibia after seeking a dark retreat turn and face the light. Riley found that if a toad was stimulated by contact with another toad, the former usually turned and jumped away but frequently followed up the avoiding reaction by a definite response to light. Thus, mechanical stimulation may furnish the impulse to locomotion but light is effective in determining the direction of movement. Young toads are notably diurnal, while old individuals tend to be crepuscular or nocturnal in their activities. Laboratory and field observations have not always been in so close agreement. Laurens (1914) was unable to recognize any phototropic response in *Rana pipiens* and *Rana sylvatica* tadpoles, and yet the former frequently bask in shallow water. This may, however, be a temperature response. Cole and Dean (1917) showed that in *Rana clamitans* there was a change in phototropism with age. The young tadpoles were indifferent, the older larvae positively phototropic. No doubt species differ enormously in the phototropic responses of their larvae.

Amphibia depend, to a large extent, on their vision as the chief means of obtaining food and avoiding danger. Choruses of frogs usually cease on the appearance of an intruder, while they are less affected by the noises he might make. The details of the visual field may have considerable significance for a frog which has learned the shape of an object on which his food may be expected (Biederman, 1927). The size as well as shape of an object also has significance. Frogs catch insects on the wing. Salamanders and toads cautiously stalk a fly until within reach of the tongue. They pause before the snap probably for the purpose of better fixation (Whitman, 1898). Vision with its enriched sensory relations gives the Amphibia a great range of possible responses to their surroundings and this range increases the opportunities for learning certain tricks in preference to others.

Rheotropism.—Many salamanders and some frogs live more or less in streams. When in the water such animals will usually head upstream and make some effort to stem the current. It has usually been assumed that stream animals tend to keep their visual fields the same and that their locomotory efforts against the current are made for this purpose. But Steinmann (1914) has reinvestigated the problem in tadpoles and newts and would attribute the rheotropic response to compensatory reflexes initiated by the labyrinth. Amphibia, being bilaterally symmetrical, tend to move in a straight line. Each deviation stimulates the labyrinth to make compensatory reflex movements of the muscles to bring it back to the original position. The lateral-line organs, eye, ear, nose, and other sense organs, exert a supplementary influence on muscle tone. If the homologous sense organs of either side of the body are equally stimulated, the muscle tone of the two sides remains the same. Hence, in a stream, Amphibia would head into the current automatically, if in contact with the bottom, in order that the stimulation on both sides of the body might be the same. Steinmann did not work with typical stream Amphibia and it is possible that these might respond more to the visual field than the pond forms investigated in regard to their responses to current.

Thigmotaxis.—Most Amphibia, being nocturnal, are found during the daylight hours only under logs, stones, and other débris. Small Appalachian streams in which not a single salamander may be seen during the day are frequently alive during the night with Desmognathus of several species. Toads and other terrestrial Salientia usually hide away during the daylight hours in some crevice or burrow. This tendency of Amphibia to hide is not merely the manifestation of a negative phototropism. Some species appear to be more or less positively thigmotactic, that is, possess a tendency to move into situations which will bring a considerable surface of their bodies in contact with solid objects. *Desmognathus fuscus*, for example, will take refuge in glass bottles left lying on the surface of the soil exposed to the light, usually orientating the body with head toward the mouth of the bottle (Wilder, 1913). The larvae of the Blind Salamander, Typhlotriton, has been said to exhibit a greater positive thigmotaxis than negative phototropism, but observations by Mrs. Pope and myself have failed to confirm this conclusion. The larvae will frequently lie quietly in grooves for considerable periods, however, even when exposed to illuminations avoided by the species. There is thus a certain thigmotactic response in Typhlotriton larvae even though their reaction to light plays a more important rôle in sending them to cover. The same is probably true of most nocturnal Amphibia.

Responses to Internal Stimulation.—The daily movements of Amphibia are frequently initiated by stimulations from the internal organs. If the frog or salamander has not fed for some days there is an increase in the amplitude of the hunger contractions of the stomach. Patterson (1917) has shown that in the frog this increase is directly proportional to the length of the fast. The gastric hunger movements of the turtle show a periodicity, a feature common to higher vertebrates, but both Necturus and the Bullfrog exhibit continuous contractions of the stomach (Patterson, 1921) and this may be considered a more primitive mechanism. The hunger contractions of the frog stomach are completely inhibited at temperatures below 13 and above 35°C. Since between these limits gastric hunger movements increase with the temperature, it is apparent that environmental temperatures have a direct effect on the food-seeking activity of Amphibia. The bodily changes induced by anterior pituitary hormone during the breeding season, however, may prevent these food-seeking reactions of a hungry frog. At least at the height of the breeding season salamanders and frogs do not feed.

Szymanski (1918) found there was a daily rhythm in the activity of *Hyla arborea*. During July and August there were two periods daily of activity, with one peak between 12:00 m. and 1:00 p. m. and the other between 8:00 and 9:00 p. m. The periods of greatest quiet lay between 5:00 and 6:00 p. m. and 5:00 and 6:00 a. m. It would be interesting to know if the peaks of activity were controlled by hunger contractions and whether they could be changed by altering the time of feeding.

Aquatic Amphibia rise frequently to the surface for air. No doubt the exhaustion of the oxygen supply in the lungs induces reflexes which lead to the replenishing of the lungs with fresh air. Amphibia react not only to stimulations impinging upon them from without, but they also respond to a continuous stream of impulses coming from their muscles and internal organs. There are sense organs in the muscles, tendons, and deeper tissues of the animal which keep it informed as to its posture. Probably many, if not all, of the impulses from these organs carry no sensation with them but induce motor effects automatically. Kinesthetic stimulation may play a part in directing the movements of some Amphibia. Toads which learned their way about a glass plate continued for several trials to follow this path even after the glass was removed. The toads may have been directed by associations involving other sensory mechanisms, however, as will be indicated in another chapter.

Amphibia, with their moist skins, are in continual danger of desiccation. Terrestrial forms seek moist situations and absorb water through their skins. Probably increased osmotic pressure in the body fluids induced by desiccation releases moisture-seeking movements. Special sensory receptors concerned with the sense of thirst have not been described in any vertebrate, nor have any cutaneous sense organs been reported to be especially differentiated for detecting differences in humidity.

References

ANTON, WILHELM, 1908: Beitrag zur Morphologie des Jacobsonschen Organs und der Nasenhöhle der Cryptobranchiaten, *Morph. Jahrb.*, XXXVIII, 448–470.

AREY, L. B., 1928: Visual cells and retinal pigment, "Special Cytology," II, 889–926, New York.

BEER, THOMAS, 1899: Die Accommodation des Auges bei den Amphibien, *Arch. Ges. Physiol.* LXXIII, 501–534.

BIEDERMAN, S., 1927: Les sens et la memoire des formes d'un objet chez les anoures; l'inversion de l'habitudes après ou sans amortissement, (L'expérience optique des batraciens II-e mémoire), *Prace Inst. Nenck.*, No. 56, 1–5.

BRUNER, H. L., 1901: The smooth facial muscles of Anura and Salamandrina, a contribution to the anatomy and physiology of the respiratory mechanism of the amphibians, *Morph. Jahrb.*, XXIX, 317–364, pl. 17, 18.

―――, 1914: Jacobson's organ and the respiratory mechanism of amphibians, *Morph. Jahrb.*, XLVIII, 157–165.

―――, 1914a: The mechanism of pulmonary respiration in amphibians with gill clefts, *Morph. Jahrb.*, XLVIII, 63–82.

BRUYN, E. M. M., and C. H. M. VAN NIFTERIK, 1920: Influence du son sur la réaction d'une excitation tactile chez les grenouilles et les crapauds, *Arch. Néer. Physiol. Hom. Anim.*, Sér. III c, V, 363–379.

BURR, H. S., 1916: The effects of the removal of the nasal pits in Amblystoma embryos, *Jour. Exp. Zool.*, XX, 27–57.

CHARIPPER, H. A., 1928: Studies on the lateral line system of Amphibia; I. Cytology and innervation of the lateral line organs of Necturus maculosus, *Jour. Comp. Neurol.*, XLIV, 425–448, 3 pl.

CHIEVITZ, J. H., 1889: Untersuchungen über die Area Centralis Retinae, *Arch. Anat. Physiol. (Anat. Abt.)*, 1889, Suppl. 139–196.

COCHRAN, M. ETHEL, 1911: The biology of the red-backed salamander (Plethodon cinereus erythronotus Green), *Biol. Bull.*, XX, 332–349.

COLE, L. J., 1907: An experimental study of the image-forming powers of various types of eyes, *Proc. Amer. Acad. Arts Sci.*, XLII, 335–417.

———, 1922: The effect of temperature on the phototropic response of Necturus, *Jour. Gen. Physiol.*, IV, 569–572.

COLE, W. H., and C. F. DEAN, 1917: The photokinetic reactions of frog tadpoles, *Jour. Exp. Zool.*, XXIII, 361–370.

COPELAND, MANTON, 1913: The olfactory reactions of the spotted newt, Diemyctylus viridescens (Rafinesque), *Jour. Anim. Behav.*, III, 260–273.

CROZIER, W. J., 1916: Regarding the existence of the common chemical sense in vertebrates, *Jour. Comp. Neurol.*, XXVI, 1–8.

———, 1916a: The taste of acids, *Jour. Comp. Neurol.*, XXVI, 453–462.

DEMPSTER, W. T., 1930: The morphology of the amphibian endolymphatic organ, *Jour. Morph. Physiol. L.*, 71–126, pls. 1–4.

DETWILER, S. R., 1923: Studies on the retina; The identity of the developing visual cells in Amblystoma larvae as revealed by their responses to light, *Jour. Comp. Neurol.*, XXXVI, 113–122.

———, and R. W. LEWIS, 1926: Temperature and retinal-pigment migration in the eyes of the frog, *Jour. Comp. Neurol.*, XLI, 153–169.

DUBOIS, RAPHAEL, 1890: Sur la perception des radiations lumineuses par la peau, chez les Protées aveugles des grottes de la Carniole, *Compt. rend. Acad. Sci.*, Paris, CX, 358–360.

DUNN, E. R., 1922: The sound-transmitting apparatus of salamanders and the phylogeny of the Caudata, *Amer. Naturalist*, LVI, 418–427.

DYE, W. J. PAUL, 1921: The relation of the lateral line organs of Necturus to hearing, *Jour. Comp. Psych.*, I, 469–471.

ESCHER, KONRAD, 1925: Das Verhalten der Seitenorgane der Wirbeltiere und ihrer Nerven beim Übergang zum Landleben, *Acta Zool.*, VI, 1925, 307–414.

FISCHER, M. H., 1926: Die Funktion des Vestibularapparates (der Bogengänge Otolithen) bei Fischen, Amphibien, Reptilien und Vögeln, Bethe's "Handb. Norm. Path. Physiol.," Berlin, XI, 797–867.

FLEISSIG, JULIUS, 1909: Zur Anatomie der Nasenhöhle von Cryptobranchus japonicus, *Anat. Anz.*, XXXV, 48–54.

FRANZ, V., 1913: Die phototaktischen Erscheinungen im Tierreiche und ihre Rolle im Freileben der Tiere, *Zool. Jahrb.*, XXXIII, *Abt. allg. Zool. Physiol.*, 259–286.

———, 1924: Mikroskopische Anatomie der Hilfsteile des Sehorgans der Wirbeltiere, *Erg. Anat. Entwick.*, XXV, 241–390.

GIERSBERG, H., and K. GIERSBERG, 1926: Untersuchungen über den Geschmackssinn der Molche, *Zeitschr. vergl. Physiol.*, III, 337–388.

GIESBRECHT, ERICH, 1925: Beiträge zur Entwicklung der Cornea und zur Gestaltung der Orbitalhöhle bei den einheimischen Amphibien, *Zeitschr. Wiss. Zool.*, CXXIV, 305–359, 2 pl.

GREENE, W. F., and HENRY LAURENS, 1922: The effect of extirpation of the embryonic ear and eye on equilibration in Amblystoma punctatum, *Amer. Jour. Physiol.*, LXIV, 120–143, 3 pl.

GRUENBERG, BENJAMIN C., 1907: Compensatory motions and the semi-circular canals, *Jour. Exp. Zool.*, IV, 447–467.

GRYNFELTT, E., 1910: Sur l'anatomie comparée de l'appareil de l'accommodation dans l'oeil des vertébrés, *Compt. rend. Ass. Anat. Réun.*, XII, 76–88.

HERRICK, C. J., 1925: The innervation of palatal taste buds and teeth of Amblystoma, *Jour. Comp. Neurol.*, XXXVIII, 389–397.

HERTER, KONRAD, 1921: Untersuchungen über die nicht-akustischen Labyrinthfunktionen bei Anurenlarven, *Zeitschr. allg. Physiol.*, XIX, 335–414.

———, 1922: Ein Beitrag zum Kalksackproblem der Frösche, *Anat. Anz.*, LV, 530–536.

HESS, C., 1910: Untersuchungen über den Lichtsinn bei Reptilien und Amphibien, *Arch. ges. Physiol.*, CXXXII, 255–295.

———, 1912: Über Lichtsinn und Farbensinn in der Tierreihe, *Arch. Psych. Nervenkrankh.*, L, 597–598, *Med. Klin. Jahr.*, VIII, 1511–1513.

HOPKINS, A. E., 1926: The olfactory receptors in vertebrates, *Jour. Comp. Neurol.*, XLI, 253–289.

KINGSBURY, B. F., 1895: The lateral-line system of sense organs in some American Amphibia, and comparison with the dipnoans, *Trans. Amer. Micr. Soc.*, XVII, 115–146, pl. 1–5.

KOHL, C., 1895: Rudimentäre Wirbelthieraugen, III Teil, Zusammenfassung, *Bibl. Zool.*, V, 181–274.

KUREPINA, M., 1926: Entwicklung der primären Choanen bei Amphibien, 1 Teil, Anura., *Rev. Zool. Russe.*, VI, 72–74.

———, 1927: Entwicklung der primären Choanen bei Amphibien, II Teil, Urodela, *Rev. Zool. Russe.*, VII, 28–30.

KURODA, RYO, 1926: Experimental researches upon the sense of hearing in lower vertebrates, including reptiles, amphibians and fishes, *Comp. Psych. Monog.*, III, 1–50.

LAUBMANN, W., 1927: Über die Morphogenese vom Gehirn und Geruchsorgan der Gymnophionen, *Zeitschr. Anat. Entwick.*, LXXXIV, 597–637.

LAURENS, H., 1914: The reactions of normal and eyeless amphibian larvae to light, *Jour. Exp. Zool.*, XVI, 195–211.

LINDEMAN, V. F., 1929: An experimental study on the nictitating membrane of the frog Rana pipiens, *Proc. Soc. Exp. Biol. Med.* XXVII, 177.

LITZELMANN, E., 1923: Entwicklungsgeschichtliche und vergleichend-anatomische Untersuchungen über den Visceralapparat der Amphibien, *Zeitschr. Anat. Entwick.*, LXVII, 457–493.

LOCHER, CHARLOTTE J. S., 1927: Der Nahrungserwerb von Bufo calamita Laurenti, *Zeitschr. vergl. Physiol.*, VI, 378–384.

MATTHES, E., 1924: Weitere Untersuchungen über das Geruchsvermögen der Amphibien, *Verh. D. Zool. Ges.*, XXIX, 46–48.

———, 1926: Die physiologische Doppelnatur des Geruchsorganes der Urodelen im Hinblick auf seine morphologische Zusammensetzung aus Haupthöhle und "Jacobsonschem Organ," *Zeitschr. vergl. Physiol.*, IV, 81–102.

McNALLY, W. S., and J. TAIT, 1925: Ablation experiments on the labyrinth of the frog, *Amer. Jour. Physiol.*, LXXV, 155–179.

MORGAN, ANN H., 1922: The temperature senses in the frog's skin, *Jour. Exper. Zool.*, XXXV, 83–110.

NICHOLAS, J. S., 1922: The reactions of Amblystoma tigrinum to olfactory stimuli, *Jour. Exp. Zool.*, XXXV, 257–281.

NIEMACK, J., 1893: Der nervöse Apparat in den Endscheiben der Frosch-zunge, *Anat. Hefte*, II, 238–246, pl. 12–13.

NORRIS, H. W., 1892: Studies on the development of the ear of Amblystoma. I. Development of the auditory vesicle, *Jour. Morph.*, VII, 23–34, 4 pls.

———, 1917: The eyeball and associated structures in the blindworms, *Proc. Iowa Acad.*, XXIV, 299–300.

OBRESHKOVE, VASIL, 1921: The photic reactions of tadpoles in relation to the Bunsen-Roscoe law, *Jour. Exp. Zool.*, XXXIV, 235–279.

OKAJIMA, K., 1910: Untersuchungen über die Sinnesorgane von Onycho-dactylus, *Zeitschr. Wiss. Zool.*, XCIV, 171–239.

———, and T. TSUSAKI, 1921: Beiträge zur Morphologie des Skleral-knorpels bei den Urodelen, *Zeitschr. Anat. Entw.*, LX, 631–651.

PALMER, SAMUEL C., 1912: The numerical relations of the histological elements in the retina of Necturus maculosus (Raf.), *Jour. Comp. Neurol.*, XXII, 405–446, 3 pls.

PARKER, G. H., 1903: The skin and the eyes as receptive organs in the reactions of frogs to light, *Amer. Jour. Physiol.*, X, 28–36.

———, 1908: The origin of the lateral of vertebrate eyes, *Amer. Naturalist*, XLII, 601–609.

———, 1922: "Smell, Taste, and Allied Senses in the Vertebrates," Philadelphia.

PATTERSON, T. L., 1917: Contributions to the physiology of the stomach, XXXVI. The physiology of the gastric hunger contractions in the Amphibia and the Reptilia, comparative studies I., *Amer. Jour. Physiol.*, XLII, 50–87.

———, 1920: Vagus and splanchnic influence on the gastric hunger move-ments of the frog, comparative studies III., *Amer. Jour. Physiol.*, LIII, 293–306.

———, 1921: Movements of the empty stomach of Necturus, *Amer. Jour. Physiol.*, LV, 283.

PEARSE, A. S., 1910: The reactions of amphibians to light, *Proc. Amer. Acad. Arts. Sci.*, XLV, 161–208.

PIERSOL, G. A., 1887: Beiträge zur Histologie der Harder'schen Drüsen der Amphibien, *Arch. Mikr. Anat.*, XXIX, 594–608, 2 pls.

PIKE, F. H., 1923: The function of the vestibular apparatus, *Physiol. Rev.*, III, 209–240.

PLATE, LUDWIG, 1924: "Allgemeine Zoologie und Abstammungslehre. II, Die Sinnesorgane der Tiere." Jena.

REED, H. D., 1920: The morphology of the sound-transmitting apparatus in caudate Amphibia and its phylogenetic significance, *Jour. Morph.*, XXXIII, 325–387, pls. 1–6.

RILEY, C. F. CURTIS, 1913: Responses of young toads to light and contact, *Jour. Anim. Behav.*, III, 179–214.

RISSER, J., 1914: Olfactory reactions in amphibians, *Jour. Exp. Zool.*, XVI, 617–652.

SAYLE, MARY H., 1916: The reactions of Necturus to stimuli received through the skin, *Jour. Anim. Behav.*, VI, 81–101.

SCHEMINSKY, FERDINAND, 1924: Versuche über Elektrotaxis und Elektronarkose, *Arch. ges. Physiol.*, CCII, 200–216.

SCHLAMPP, K. W., 1892: Das Auge des Grottenolmes (Proteus anguineus), *Zeitschr. Wiss. Zool.*, LIII, 537–557, pl. 21.

SEYDEL, O., 1895: Über die Nasenhöhle und das Jacobson'sche Organ der Amphibien, *Morph. Jahrb.*, XXIII, 453–543.

STADTMÜLLER, FRANZ, 1914: Ein Beitrag zur Kenntnis des Vorkommens und der Bedeutung Hyalinknorpeliger Elemente in der Sclera der Urodelen, *Anat. Hefte*, LI, 427–465.

STEINMAN, PAUL, 1914: Über die Bedeutung des Labyrinthes und der Seitenorgane für die Rheotaxis und die Beibehaltung der Bewegungsrichtung bei Fischen und Amphibien, *Verh. Naturf. Ges. Basel*, XXV, 212–243.

STIER, T. J. B., 1926: Reversal of phototropism in Diemyctylus viridescens, *Jour. Gen. Physiol.*, IX, 521–523.

STREETER, G. L., 1906: Some experiments on the developing ear vesicle of the tadpole with relation to equilibrium, *Jour. Exp. Zool.*, III, 543–558.

――――, 1921: Migration of the ear vesicle in the tadpole during normal development, *Anat. Rec.*, XXI, 115–126.

STREULI, HEINRICH, 1925: Die Akkommodation des Wirbeltierauges, *Die Naturw.*, XIII, 477–485.

SZYMANSKI, J. S., 1918: Abhandlungen zum Aufbau der Lehre von den Handlungen der Tiere, *Arch. ges. Physiol.*, CLXX, 1–244.

TORELLE, E., 1903: The response of the frog to light, *Amer. Jour. Physiol.*, IX, 466–488.

TRETJAKOFF, D., 1906: Der Musculus protractor lentis im Urodelenauge, *Anat. Anz.*, XXVIII, 25–32.

VERRIER, M. L., 1927: Sur la détermination du champ visuel anatomique chez les poissons et les batraciens, *Compt. rend. Acad. Sci.*, CLXXXIV, 1482–1484.

WERTHEIMER, ERNST, 1924: Über die Rolle der Haut für den Muskeltonus beim Frosch, *Arch. ges. Physiol.*, CCV, 634–636.

WHITESIDE, B., 1922: The development of the saccus endolymphaticus in Rana temporaria L., *Amer. Jour. Anat.*, XXX, 231–266.

WHITMAN, C. O., 1898: Animal behavior, *Woods Hole Biol. Lec.*, 1898, 285–338.

WILDER, HARRIS H., 1892: Die Nasengegend von Menopoma alleghaniense und Amphiuma tridactylum, *Zool. Jahrb. Abt. Anat.*, V, 155–173, pls. 12–13.

WILDER, I. W., 1913: The life history of Desmognathus fusca, *Biol. Bull. Woods Hole*, XXIV, 251–292, 293–342, 6 pls.

――――, 1925: "The Morphology of Amphibian Metamorphosis," Smith College, Northampton, Mass.

WRIGHT, A. H., 1914: North American Anura: life-histories of the Anura of Ithaca, N. Y., Washington *Carnegie Inst. Pub.* 197, pls. 1–21.

YERKES, R. M., 1905: The sense of hearing in frogs, *Jour. Comp. Neurol. Psych.*, XV, 279–304.

CHAPTER XV

THE NERVOUS SYSTEM

Amphibia respond to external stimulations in a variety of ways. Living cells from any part of the body have the property of transmitting excitations, but certain cells, the neurons, are specialized for this purpose and their fibers are usually grouped together to form nerves. Cilia on the ectoderm of the embryo may beat, and heart tissue may pulsate, before any nervous connection has been established with these tissues, but most effector organs, such as muscles or glands, do not react until they receive stimulations from the nerves. The latter receive their impulses, or states of excitation, from the sense organs. The complex series of nerves which form the nervous system is thus a mechanism for conducting and correlating impulses received from the sense organs and transmitting them to organs of response.

A stimulus received at any one point of a nerve cell tends to be transmitted in all directions throughout its length. In some invertebrates the nerve cells are possibly joined to form a net, but in higher types each neuron retains its own identity, a cell membrane separating the terminal branches of two adjacent cells. The neurons possess a polarity, certain processes, the dendrites, conducting the nerve impulses toward the cell body and a usually longer, less-branching process, the axon, transmitting the impulse away in the direction of the effector organ. The basis of this polarity seems to be in the synapse or point of contact between the axon of one neuron and the dendrites of another. The state of excitation can be transmitted across the synapse in only one direction, from the axon of one cell to the dendrites of the other. Hence, the nerve impulse always travels from the sensory to the motor neurons. This "law of forward direction," first formulated over a hundred years ago, finds its logical explanation in the theory of the synapse as developed by Sherrington and others. A similar one-way conductivity is found in the myoneural junction between axon and muscle.

The nerves surrounding the digestive tract of vertebrates frequently form a plexus, and it has been assumed that this might represent a true nerve net inherited from invertebrate ancestors. In the frog, however, Cole (1925) has shown that there is a differentiation within this plexus of axons and dendrites, the neurons anastomosing only by their dendrites. Further, only a few nerve cells enter into these fusions, which seem to be a secondary modification rather than a primitive inheritance.

Reflex Arc.—Neurons are arranged in functional units, the reflex arcs, each with a neuron receiving the impulse from the

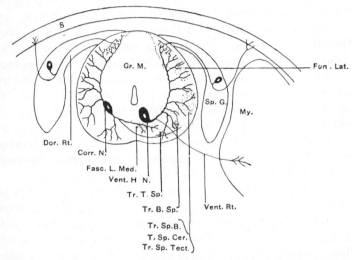

Fig. 124.—Diagrammatic cross-section of the spinal cord of a larval salamander showing the relation of the sensory to the motor neurons. *Corr.N.*, correlation neuron; *Dor.Rt.*, dorsal root; *Fasc.L.Med.*, fasciculus longitudinalis medialis; *Fun.Lat.*, funiculus lateralis; *Gr.M.*, gray matter; *My.*, myotome; *S.*, skin; *Sp.G.*, spinal ganglion; *Tr.B.Sp.*, tractus bulbo-spinalis; *Tr.T.Sp.*, tractus tecto-spinalis; *Tr.Sp.B.*, tractus spino-bulbaris; *T.Sp.Cer.*, tractus spino-cerebellaris; *Tr.Sp.Tect.*, tractus spino-tectalis; *Vent.H.N.*, ventral horn neuron; *Vent.Rt.*, ventral root. (*After Herrick and Coghill.*)

sense organ, another neuron transmitting it to an effector organ, and, generally, a third intercalated between the two (Fig. 124). Reflex arcs are usually complicated by the addition of several cells of this third category; twigs from their axons, called "collaterals," making possible the transmission of impulses to several adjustors or effectors. The passage of an impulse through a reflex arc requires more time than is consumed by the impulse traveling the same length of nerve and stimulating the same end organ alone. Hence, the synapse and the myoneural junction apparently present some functional modification in the passage of an impulse. The delay increases with the number of synapses involved in the arc. Nervous impulses are transmitted at different rates in different fibers, the rates being much greater in medullated than in non-medullated nerves, and greater in fibers of large than in those of small diameter. Possibly some of the delay in the passage of an impulse through a reflex arc is due to the small fibers of the central nervous system. Drugs may be employed to increase or lower the conductivity of impulses, presumably at the synapses, and no doubt the physiological condition of the animal, as, for example, the amount of oxygen in the blood, has a marked effect on conduction over the synapses. In brief, the character of a reflex is dependent not only on the structure of the arc but also on the functional conditions which exist at any one time throughout the system.

Repeated use of particular paths of conduction increases their conductivity for succeeding impulses. This is apparently due to a change in the synapse which makes it less resistant to excitations. The synaptic change apparently forms the basis of learning, although it is possible that other phenomena, such as combined activity of great numbers of neurons or, during an early stage of development, the growth of the axons or dendrites, may play some rôle. The process of synaptic change is reversible—a possible explanation of the loss of learned responses or of forgetting.

The repetition of a stimulus may produce other effects. If a single stimulation is not adequate to produce a response, the repetition of this stimulus at frequent intervals may have the desired effect, apparently because the resistance at the synapse is lowered by the repetition. Continued stimulation, however, will eventually lead to failure of response, apparently as a result of the fatigue products acting at the synapse. Frequently the result of a stimulation is the inhibition of an activity. This has been interpreted as due to increase of resistance at the synapse, the refractory period of the synapse having been prolonged by too great frequency of the impulses arriving there. According to this explanation, each successive excitation of the nerve would fall within the refractory phase, and no response would result.

The axons of many of the neurons are covered by a white fatty substance, the myelin sheath, which apparently serves to insulate them, preventing impulses in adjacent axons from influencing one another. Some fibers are covered merely by a nucleated membrane as in many of the axons of both the central and sympathetic nervous systems.   In many parts of the central nervous system several nerve cells of one functional type occur together, forming a center or nucleus.   A grouping of nerve cell bodies outside of the central nervous system is called a "ganglion."   The larger groupings of nerves into systems may be conveniently considered under the divisions: brain, spinal cord, and autonomic system.

Brain.—Amphibia inherited their brains as well as the remainder of their organization from piscine ancestors.   The primitive crossopterygian fishes left in their fossilized skulls little evidence of the type of brain they possessed, but the dipnoans, which sprang from a closely related stock, possess a brain which is essentially like that of the Amphibia both in its method of development and in the arrangement of nuclei and commissures. We may assume that the crossopterygian ancestors of Amphibia had a similar brain.   The most distinctive feature of this brain was the evagination of the hemispheres, the latter constructed on the same plan as the hemispheres of higher vertebrates and contrasted with the everted forebrain of teleosts, with its membranous non-nervous roof.   Herrick (1921, 1924) has suggested that this type of forebrain was originally an adaptation to life in poorly oxygenated water.   The nervous tissues secure their supply of oxygen not only from the blood but also from the cerebrospinal fluid, and the latter would be excluded from the interior of thickenings of nervous tissue such as is found in the forebrain of teleosts.   Solid masses of nuclei such as are found surrounding the ventricles of some fish and birds are well adapted for the performance of complex types of instinctive habits, but thin-walled, widely evaginated cerebral hemispheres, capable of indefinite expansion without a great thickening of the wall, were more suitable as a foundation for the elaboration of the mammalian brain with its capacity for rapid learning.

In spite of the great potentiality for future development found in the forebrain of Amphibia, no great progress in this direction was made by modern Amphibia.   This is because they have still retained for the most part the primitive arrangement of the nerve-cell bodies around the ventricles, while the nerve fibers lie external to them as an unbroken aggregation of white matter.   The road to advancement lay through the development of a more diffuse distribution of the cell bodies and their fibers, also in the aggregation of special clusters of cells to discharge in fiber paths having specific functions.

The brain arises during development by a differentiation of the anterior part of the neural plate, the edges of which roll over during gastrulation to form a tube. Very early three enlargements common to the brains of all vertebrates develop. These are the forebrain, midbrain and hindbrain. The forebrain again becomes differentiated into a telencephalon and a thalamencephalon, while the hindbrain develops a cerebellum poorly marked off from the remainder of the hindbrain, the medulla oblongata. Thickenings or other differentiations appear in all five regions. The original cavity of the tube remains to form the ventricles of the brain.

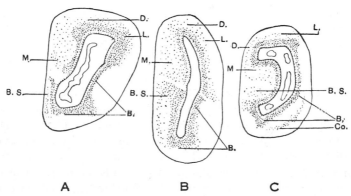

A   B   C

Fig. 125.—Diagrammatic cross-section of the forebrains of (*A*) salamander, (*B*) frog, and (*C*) caecilian, to show the principal nuclei. *B.*, nucleus basalis; *B.S.*, nucleus basimedialis superior; *Co.*, cortex olfactoria; *D.*, area dorsalis pallii; *L.*, area lateralis pallii; *M.*, area medialis pallii. (*After Kuhlenbeck.*)

Forebrain.—The forebrain of Salientia is shorter and more compressed than that of most urodeles. Nevertheless, the evagination of the hemispheres is carried farther, since the unpaired ventricle at the posterior end is smaller in frogs than in urodeles. Two enlargements at the anterior end of the hemispheres are the olfactory lobes from which the olfactory nerves arise. They are ventral in Hynobius as in frogs, but in the latter they are fused in the midline. The ventral position of the lobes is probably primitive, although in most urodeles they have a more lateral position, markedly so in the newt and in Siren. In the specialized Eurycea the lobes are also ventral (Röthig

1912). In the Gymnophiona they are very large and ring shaped but separate, as in the salamanders (Kuhlenbeck, 1922).

Each cerebral hemisphere may be divided into a dorsal pallium and a ventral subpallium. In the Salientia a groove on the surface separates one region from the other and limiting sulci occur on the inner surface of the ventricles in most Amphibia. A further division into an internal hippocampus and external pyriform primordium of the pallium, and an internal septum and an external striatum of the subpallium, is indicated by the distribution of the nerve bundles and cell groups within each hemishhere (Fig. 125).

In urodeles the septum or ventral median nucleus is not large, although in various species, such as Cryptobranchus and Siren, it is sufficiently developed to form an *eminentia septalis* which projects into the ventricle (Röthig, 1912). In the Salientia there is a hypertrophy of the septal regions which are proportionately further developed than in any vertebrate (Kiesewalter, 1928).

Fibers from the olfactory bulbs extend to nearly all parts of the cerebral hemisphere. The anterior olfactory nucleus and parts of the pyriform area are largely made up of incoming fibers. The septum and striatum are chiefly synaptic stations where olfactory fibers join with ascending and descending fibers from the thalamus and midbrain. The striatum of urodeles is relatively undifferentiated, the cell bodies maintaining for the most part their primitive periventricular position. The elaboration of the striatum is correlated in part with the development of Jacobson's organ (Herrick, 1921a) and in part with the increase in exteroceptive tracts. Thus, Necturus and Proteus, being larval types without a Jacobson's organ, have a very poorly developed striatum, while the Salientia and Gymnophiona, with their large Jacobson's organs, approach the reptiles in the enlargement of this region. Jacobson's organ is a mechanism for testing the contents of the mouth and it arose as an important aid to terrestrialism. Correlated with the development of this organ, there appeared an accessory olfactory lobe on each side, a well-defined ventral lateral nerve tract within the hemisphere, and an amygdaloid nucleus in the striatum. Plethodontids, although advanced types, have small Jacobson's organs and relatively undifferentiated forebrains (Herrick, 1921). In the Salientia there is an outward migration of striatal cells, well marked even in the tadpoles (Söderberg, 1922). In the Gymnophiona a true cortex or correlation center of laminated cells is formed in the outer portion of the striatum separate from the periventricular series (Kuhlenbeck, 1922). In higher vertebrates the striatum becomes one of the chief reflex centers governing motor reactions by reason of its tract connections with lower and higher centers (projection tracts), but in the Amphibia it is still dominated by the olfactory components (Herrick, 1927).

The hippocampus and pyriform areas show a wandering of cells toward the periphery, which is carried farther in Salientia than

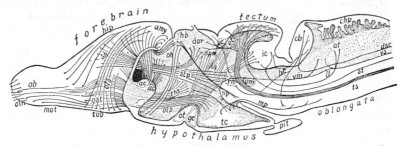

Fig. 126.—Plan of the chief fibre tracts in the brain of the frog. *a.c.*, anterior commissure; *amy.*, amygdala; *a.t.*, acoustic tubercle; *b.c.*, brachium conjunctivum; *c.b.*, cerebellum; *ch.p.*, chorioid plexus; *dor.*, dorsal nucleus of the thalamus; *d.s.c.*, dorsal spino-cerebellar tract; *g.c.*, geniculate or postoptic commissure; *hb.*, habenula; *hip.*, hippocampus; *hp.*, habenulo-peduncular tract; *i.c.*, inferior colliculus; *l.g.*, lateral geniculate body; *l.l.*, lateral lemniscus; *m.o.t.*, medial olfactory tract; *m.p.*, mamillary peduncle; *n.p.c.*, nucleus of the posterior commissure; *o.b.*, olfactory bulb; *o.h.*, olfacto-habenular tract; *ol.n.*, olfactory nerve; *ol.p.*, olfacto-peduncular tract or medial forebrain bundle; *ol.s.*, olfacto-septal fibres; *om.*, oculomotor nerve; *ost.*, striatal nucleus; *o.t.*, optic tract; *p.c.*, posterior commissure; *pit.*, pituitary body (hypophysis); *r.n.*, red nucleus; *s.h.*, septo-hippocampal fibres; *s.t.*, spino-tectal tract; *s.t.p.*, lateral forebrain bundle; *t.c.*, tuber cinereum of hypothalamus; *th.s.*, septo-thalamic tract or medial forebrain bundle; *t.s.*, tecto-bulbar and tecto-spinal tract; *tub.*, olfactory tubercle; *v.m.*, vestibulo-mesencephalic tract; *v.s.*, vestibulo-spinal tract. (*After Papez.*)

in urodeles (Kiesewalter, 1928; Kuhlenbeck, 1929). This corticogenesis does not reach in the adult frog the extreme found in the striatum of tadpoles or of Gymnophiona. Such wandering of cells leads in reptiles and in mammals to the development of cell laminae in the pallium well separated from the periventricular cells (Kiesewalter, 1928). They become correlation centers, while the latter remain pathways for relatively simple reflexes. With the development of a cortex there is an increase in the number of non-olfactory fibers which make their way from the thalamus into the forebrain (Fig. 126). Some of these ascending fibers are already present in the forebrain of Amphibia. Bindewald (1914) and Herrick (1927) consider the striatum to represent an olfactotactile and olfactovisceral center. This integration of olfactory with other senses is still largely of a reflex character. The development of a cortex adds more sensory data, and more possible routes for impulses to travel. It introduces hesitancy into behavior and opportunity for training to influence the final efferent path selected. Although fishes and Amphibia have some associational tissue and are able to learn, the Gymnophiona have developed a distinct basal cortex. The pallial cortex first appears in reptiles. Further, in Amphibia there are no tracts leading directly from the forebrain to any centers below the level of the midbrain as in higher forms (Von Monakow, 1910). Thus, while in mammals injury to the pallial cortex greatly affects the reactions of the animal, frogs deprived of their entire forebrain swim, feed, and breed very much as do normal frogs (Schrader, 1887). Decerebrate frogs lack a certain spontaneity of reaction (Loeser, 1905). Variety of response is erased, for distracting or confusing sensory impulses are ruled out by the operation. Since the result is the same even when olfactory impulses are not involved, it is clear that the forebrain functions in correlating various sensory data, if only into reflex patterns. Electric stimulation of the forebrain of Amphibia leads to no motor response (Bickel, 1898; Chauchard, 1927), hence the contribution of nerve impulses from this region is primarily sensory.

Thalamus.—Immediately caudal to the unpaired forebrain is the thalamus. From this region of the brain the optic vesicles arise as evaginations. The retinas agree with the cerebral hemispheres in being outpockets of the brain. The optic nerve (Fig. 127) consists of tertiary fibers, two synapses having occurred in the sense organ itself, namely, within the eyeball. The optic nerve enters the anterior, ventral border of the thalamus, all the fibers crossing to the side opposite the retina of their origin before curving up around the thalamus to penetrate the midbrain behind.

Two other afferent nerves enter the thalamus on each side. The *nervus terminalis* enters the forebrain at the ventral border of the olfactory lobe in Necturus (McKibben, 1911), continues back to the superficial border of the hemispheres, and penetrates the thalamus ventrolaterally to extend as far as the posterior tubercle (Herrick, 1927). The exact function of this nerve is unknown, but it probably receives stimuli from sense organs of the snout. The second afferent nerve is the parietal, which extends from the pineal organ to the region of the posterior tubercle. The pineal organ arises as a dorsal evagination of the thalamus and seems to have important endocrine functions. Whether or not it is really sensory at any stage of development is a disputed point. Since a pineal foramen is present in the skulls of some fossil Amphibia, it was probably originally a sensory organ,

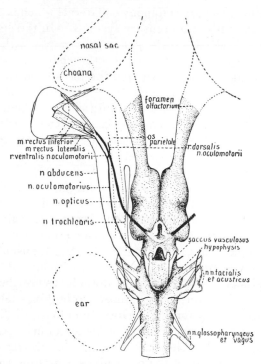

Fig. 127.—Ventral aspect of the brain of Necturus showing relation of cranial nerves to nasal sac, eye, and ear. (*After McKibben.*)

a third eye, as in some modern reptiles. The pineal organ is best developed among many modern Amphibia in the larvae.

The peripheral connections of the midbrain may be considered with those of the thalamus. The mesencephalic root of the trigeminus nerve enters the posterior part of the midbrain and makes important connections with the optic fibers. The two eye-muscle nerves, oculomotor and trochlear, enter the midbrain as in all vertebrates. The first supplies the superior and inferior rectus muscles and the inferior oblique. The latter supplies the superior

oblique alone.   The lateral rectus muscles of the eye are innervated through the abducens, which enters ventrally in the anterior
part of the medulla.   The *retractor bulbi*, well developed in the
Salientia, is innervated in part through the abducens and in
part through fibers (of sympathetic origin) coming from the
ciliary ganglion (Gaupp, 1899).

In passing through the thalamus on the way to the midbrain
roof, the optic nerves give off many collaterals which make synaptic connections with other sensory systems.   In the epithalamus
or habenula, optic fibers are joined in synapse with olfactory
fibers.   The hypothalamus, on the other hand, is a center of
visceral correlation where taste and impulses from the digestive
tract are integrated with smell (Herrick, 1917; Röthig, 1926).
The thalamus of Necturus has a diffuse field of synaptic connections, while in Ambystoma there is a tendency for localization
of groups of synapses.   Nevertheless, the general arrangement of
nuclei in the thalamus is essentially the same not only in all
Amphibia but in all Anamnia (Kuhlenbeck, 1929a).

Midbrain Roof.—The roof of the midbrain receives the bulk
of the optic fibers.   In most Amphibia it forms a prominent
swelling on the dorsal surface of the brain.   In Salientia with
well-developed eyes, it is a bilobed structure, the two parts
forming the optic lobes.   In urodeles the eyes are usually smaller
and the midbrain roof is less swollen and without a division into
well-marked lobes.   As in fish, the optic lobes are the center of
vision.   In higher vertebrates most optic fibers end in the
thalamus, where they form a synaptic junction with fibers of the
optic radiation to the visual cortex of the forebrain.   Amphibians
are of interest, for they show the first stage in this transference of
the optic center; many of the optic fibers in passing through the
thalamus send off collaterals there.   Herrick (1925) describes
three important aggregations of synaptic connections in the
thalamus related to the optic system and these are especially
well defined in Salientia.   Further, in some forms, especially in
adult frogs, there is an extension of the optic fibers into the
cerebral hemispheres.   They form the thalamofrontal tract which
in mammals is destined to become the optic radiation.   The
enlarged eyes of the frog may be responsible in part for the
bilobed roof of the midbrain and the radiation of optic tracts
into the forebrain.   In the small-eyed Pipa (Fig. 128A) the
optic lobes are large but confluent, as in most urodeles (Grönberg,

1894). In mammals somesthetic tracts penetrate the region to form an inferior colliculus on each side. As a result, the midbrain roof becomes quadripartite to form the *corpora quadrigemina*. In Amphibia a root from the trigeminus and the sensory lemniscus fibers bring in a variety of sensory data, including impulses from tactile organs, lateral-line components, and proprioceptive centers for integration with the optic impulses. A rudiment of the inferior colliculus is present in all Amphibia but is more pronounced in Salientia than urodeles. In Pipa it is most emphasized, an interesting parallelism to the condition in mammals. The cells which effect these synapses in the midbrain roof tend to align themselves in layers of functionally different nerves. In Necturus these are large neurons covering more or less of the entire roof, in Ambystoma they are small and show some lamination, while in Salientia the stratification is well established.

The base of the midbrain or cerebral peduncles transmits the motor impulses to lower levels. These peduncles include the nucleus of the motor tegmentum and embrace the final common motor paths for which the sensory impulses of forebrain, thalamus, and midbrain compete.

An experimental investigation of the midbrain and thalamus has confirmed and further extended the conclusion reached as to the function of these parts of the brain. Chauchard (1927) showed that an electric stimulation of the anterior part of the optic lobes induced a movement of the hind limbs, a similar stimulation of the posterior part effected a forelimb movement, while the middle-region stimulation brought movements in the eye muscles. Baglioni (1911) had previously shown that the grasping reflex could be produced in the male frog by electrical stimulation of the optic lobes. In view of the importance of body size of the female in sex recognition in frogs, it is interesting that Schrader (1887) should have found that removal of the optic lobes caused a loss in the sense of touch. The ablation of these lobes also induced a permanent darkening of the coloration. Color change is known to be affected in many Amphibia by both sight and touch; and in view of these experiments it would seem that the correlation was effected in the midbrain. Stimulation of the midbrain had the further effect of profoundly altering the respiratory rate (Martin, 1878). In higher vertebrates the thoracic muscles of respiration find their centers of control in this region, and possibly the midbrain controls pharyngeal respiration in Amphibia (Babák 1913).

Cerebellum.—The two posterior parts of the brain, cerebellum and medulla, are intimately related, the former being a dorsal growth from the latter.   The cerebellum consists of a medial pair of corpora cerebelli and a more lateral pair of auricular lobes which form a direct continuation of the acousticolateral area of the medulla from which they arise during their development (Herrick, 1914).   The corpora cerebelli do not form a middorsal connection in Necturus and Amphiuma as in most Amphibia. The cerebellum of fish is more highly developed than in any Amphibia and there is a great elaboration of the auricular lobes in correlation with the extensive lateral-line system.   The reduction of the corpora cerebelli in Amphibia is correlated with their simple locomotory movements.   The cerebellum is generally considered to be the station controlling postural activity, integrating impulses from the organs of equilibrium with those of muscle tone, but injuries to the medulla of the frog evoke disturbances of locomotion and posture usually attributed to defects in the cerebellum (Loeser, 1905).   It would seem that some of the components usually found in the cerebellum occur in the anterior portion of the medulla, particularly in the acousticolateral area.

The chief peripheral connection of the cerebellum is with the auditory nerve.   The mesencephalic root of the trigeminus passes through the cerebellum but has no terminals there in urodeles as it has in Salientia.   The cerebellum is proportionately larger in the larval Ambystoma than in the adult.   At metamorphosis there is a reduction of the auricular lobe in aquatic Amphibia due to the disappearance of the lateral-line system and only vestibular components are left in the auricular lobes (Larsell, 1925).   In Salientia, at least, there is a loss of the lateral-line connection from cerebellum to hypothalamus.   Tadpoles would seem to have an important lateral-line and possible gustatory control over their movements, while in the adult frog a vestibular-optic control replaces it.   As in the case of forebrain and thalamus, this control of the cerebellum is by the integration of sensory rather than motor components.   The character of the Purkinje cells of the cerebellum together with their lamination is adapted to the summation, reinforcement and diffusion of excitations.   The histological structure of the cerebellum of Salientia is more complex than that of urodeles. The first indication of a true cerebellar nucleus appears, as well as the beginnings of the dentate nucleus of higher forms with its important descending tracts to the peduncles of the midbrain. Further, the Purkinje cells in Salientia have a far more definitive structure than in urodeles, and there is a true lamination of the cells and fibers.

Medulla.—The medulla, the most posterior part of the brain, has the appearance of a slightly widened and flattened portion of the spinal cord. Its dorsal surface is, however, largely membranous and a cluster of blood vessels forms as the choroid plexus, a vascular diverticulum of this membrane, extending into its ventricle. Like the spinal cord, the medulla is divided into a basal medial motor region and a dorsal sensory area which, because of the membranous roof, is largely lateral. The fifth to tenth cranial nerves enter the medulla and bifurcate to send ascending and descending fibers of specific functions the length of the medulla (Kuhlenbeck, 1927; Kappers and Fortuyn, 1921). The dorsal zone is the acousticolateral area. This forms the rhomboidal lip which merges directly into the auricular lobe of the cerebellum. The medial longitudinal zone is formed by the visceral sensory fibers of the seventh, ninth, and tenth cranial nerves. The ventral sensory zone of the medulla is formed by cutaneous sensory fibers of the fifth and tenth nerves.

The Amphibia are noteworthy in showing the first rudiment of the cochlea of higher vertebrates. In correlation with division of function in the inner ear, there are two centers for the eighth nerve in the medulla of frogs, the vestibular nucleus being the more ventral. With the appearance of a separate dorsal nucleus in Salientia there is also found an acoustic center homologous to the superior olive of mammals which is concerned in the transmission of acoustic impulses from the eighth cranial nerve to the midbrain. It may also have a more direct connection with the motor portion of the cord.

Between the dorsal and ventral portions of the medulla lies the reticular formation or region of synaptic junction between sensory and motor fibers. In the anterior part of this region in urodeles occur the giant cells of Mauthner which send their axons throughout the length of the spinal cord to the tail musculature and function in the regulation of swimming movements (Detwiler, 1927a). Vestibular and lateral-line fibers make synaptic connections with these cells.

In the ventral motor portion of the medulla the nuclei of the third to twelfth cranial nerves are arranged in their numerical order. In primitive Amphibia more of the medulla was contained within the skull than in modern Amphibia, for all 12 cranial nerves made exit from the skull as in mammals. In recent Amphibia the twelfth nerve and the eleventh, when present, lie beyond the skull and form spinal nerves. The frogs show a greater separation of the motor nuclei from one another than do the urodeles. This is particularly true of the nuclei of the seventh, ninth, and tenth nerves. Also, the sensory nuclei of the fifth and seventh nerves show anastomosis in urodeles, not present in the Salientia.

The reaction of frogs after removal of various parts of the medulla confirms the conclusions reached from an examination of the structure of this part of the brain. Few motor responses are controlled by any one level alone. The croaking reflex which is influenced by the optic lobes persists if the medulla is retained (Steiner, 1885; Schrader, 1887). The swallowing reflex is initiated primarily by impulses from the trigeminus. It is produced by efferent fibers in the facialis. The movements of the tongue depend on the function of the hypoglossus nerve, and they persist after the destruction of the swallowing reflex mechanism (Schrader, 1887). Locomotion is more dependent on caudal than on cephalic levels of the medulla according to Schrader (1887), but some motor coordination of the limbs can be maintained by the spinal cord alone (Goltz, 1869). As stated above, some of the locomotor postural functions controlled by the cerebellum of higher forms are assumed by the medulla of Amphibia. In urodeles Mauthner's cells seem to have an important rôle in swimming movements. Control over respiration is in part effected by the vagus fibers with their center in the medulla (Baglioni, 1900). Pharyngeal, nasal, and other muscles are actively concerned in buccal respiration, however. Hence, all levels of the medulla are probably concerned in the respiratory cycle, and impulses from the midbrain may modify the action. The vagus, with its center in the medulla, has further both a digestive and a vasomotor control (Bottazzi, 1899, 1904), the primitive character of the vagus being that of a digestive nerve and the other functions being only gradually acquired in the course of vertebrate evolution. Muchin (1895), by electric stimulation of the medulla, was able to induce movements of the eye, maxillary muscles, tongue, or head according to whether he stimulated the region of the abducens, facialis, hypoglossus, or vagus centers. It is seen from this discussion that the midbrain and medulla hold centers involving most of the important responses of the animal to both the internal and external environment. This is true of most cold-blooded forms, where the midbrain particularly performs functions largely relegated to anterior levels of the brain in higher vertebrates.

Phylogeny of the Brain.—The progressive modification of the brain as a whole does not follow closely the phylogenetic scheme. The simplicity of the brain of Necturus seems in all probability to be a retained larval character. But Siren, which is also chiefly larval in organization, exhibits a well-marked development of the septal region of the forebrain (Röthig, 1912). The Salientia, which stand nearer the branchiosaur ancestors in most of their skeletal organization than do the urodeles, have a greater development of the corpus striatum, a truly reptilian character. Söderberg (1922) and Kuhlenbeck (1927) considered the brain of the Salientia more primitive than that of the urodeles. The chief evidence Söderberg brought forward for this conclusion was the supposed retrogressive change at the time of metamorphosis in tadpoles. It might also be added that as the labyrinthodonts stood nearer the reptiles in their skeleton than do modern Amphibia, they probably did likewise in their brains. The urodele brain is more schematic than that of the frogs and hence has been more secondarily modified.

The Gymnophiona, which may have evolved from lepospondyls instead of branchiosaurs, have a brain modified by a regression of the optic centers and an elaboration of the olfactory ones. As Kuhlenbeck (1922) showed in Hypogeophis, the forebrain and especially its basal parts are greatly elaborated (Fig. 128C), while the thalamus, midbrain, and cerebellum are insignificant. The Gymnophiona approach the reptiles in the great development of the striatum and in the flexure of the medulla. Since the Gymnophiona lead such a specialized life, it is difficult to decide whether or not these features are primitive amphibian characters. Both Kuhlenbeck (1922) and Schmid (1929) find various similarities between the brains of Gymnophiona and urodeles not shared by the Salientia.

A retrogressive change in the brains of Amphibia might have been caused by a degeneration of sense organs. Destroying the eye of the growing tadpole brings about marked reduction in the midbrain (Dürken 1912). The converse experiment of building up the brain by increasing a sensory area has been performed on Ambystoma. Burr (1922) transplanted the large olfactory placode of *Ambystoma tigrinum* on the small *A. maculatum* and obtained an increase in the number of cells of the cerebral hemisphere of the host. This increase extended to the secondary and tertiary nuclear centers. Thus, axons growing into embryonic

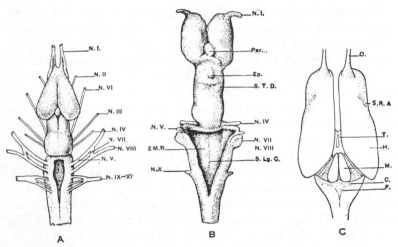

Fig. 128.—Amphibian brains, dorsal view. *A.* Adult *Pipa pipa.* (*After Grünberg.*) *B.* Larva of *Hynobius nebulosus.* (*After Sumi.*) *C.* Adult *Hypogeophis rostratus.* (*After Kuhlenbeck.*) *C.*, cerebellum; *E.M.R.*, eminentia medialis rhombencephali; *Ep.*, epiphysis; *F.*, fossa rhomboidea; *H.*, lobus hemisphaericus; *M.*, mesencephalon; *N.I.-N.XI.*, cranial nerves I-XI; *O.*, nervus olfactorius; *Par.*, paraphysis; *S.Lg.C.*, sulcus longitudinalis centralis; *S.R.A.*, sulcus rhinalis anterior; *S.T.D.*, sulcus transversus diencephalomesencephalicus; *T.*, thalamus.

brain tissue are potent factors in the further elaboration of the brain.

Such experiments are very suggestive of the way the brain was built up during phylogeny. An increased growth in one center might have a corresponding effect on another. An equally important change in phylogeny was the grouping of nerves of related functions in discrete areas. Such a progressive change has only well begun in the Amphibia. In the higher vertebrates there is an attraction of most of the somatic connections to the striatum and later their projection to separate centers on the pallium. Such a brain is far better adapted both for judging and for learning than the brain of Amphibia. The fore-brain and thalamus of Amphibia are still only accessories and not full-fledged essentials of all reactions, as in mammals. The brain evolution of higher vertebrates, however, is made along lines first clearly indicated by the amphibians. The further integration of sensory components and their intimate connections with motor activity gradually brought about an increasingly specific reaction to significant factors of the environment. With the specialization of hands, feet, and other structures as complex organs of response, there arose within each dominant system of final common paths many subsidiary systems, each requiring its own central adjustor, above which developed the higher centers of correlation. These correlation centers arose at the chief cross-roads of impulse traffic, namely, reticular formation, cerebellum, midbrain, thalamus, and corpus striatum (Herrick, 1929).

Spinal Cord and Nerves.—The spinal cord arises in the same way as the brain by the folding over and fusion of the margins of the neural plate. Like most of the brain it may be divided into a dorsal afferent and ventral efferent series of fiber tracts and related centers. In cross-section the spinal cord of Amphibia resembles that of other vertebrates in having a typical butterfly-like arrangement of gray matter surrounding the central canal or lumen resulting from the inturned neural plate. The most dorsal portion of the wings is formed by nuclei where somatic afferent fibers terminate; more ventral are the visceral afferent centers. The lower portion of the wings is formed by the visceral efferent cell bodies above and the somatic efferent ones below. The axons extending from these centers form the surrounding white matter of the cord. Some fibers are confined to one segment but the great majority extend forward or backward along the cord. Further, axons from the medulla may extend for varying distances into the cord. In the frog, fibers extend from the ninth and tenth cranial nerves to the second and third spinal segments, from the eighth nerve as far as the sixth segment, from the fifth nerve to the lumbar enlargements, while fibers from Mauthner's cells extend the length of the cord (Kuhlenbeck, 1929).

The cord is supplied with a series of spinal nerves which may be as few as 10 or 11 pairs in frogs. Each spinal nerve arises from the cord by two roots: a dorsal one containing sensory fibers running to the cord and a ventral one with motor fibers leading away from it. The sensory fibers of the nerve have their cell bodies in the ganglion of the dorsal root, while those of the motor components are contained within the spinal cord. The former position is very probably secondary, since the spinal ganglia arise from a neural crest or laterally extended margin of the neural plate. It is interesting that some urodele larvae during early development contain sensory cell bodies still within the spinal cord. These are the Rohon-Beard cells which receive sensory impulses from the muscles with some of their dendrites, from the skin with others, and send axons conducting these impulses forward. Such an arrangement is probably a primitive vertebrate condition.

The dorsal and ventral roots unite close to the vertebral column to form a mixed nerve, which divides again into a dorsal branch supplying the skin and muscles of the upper surface of the body and a ventral branch innervating the ventral and limb muscles. Several of these ventral rami unite in the brachial and pelvic regions to form plexuses. Such plexuses, although considered homologous in frog and salamander, may be formed of different spinal nerves. The growing limb bud has been shown by experiment (Detwiler, 1927) to attract the spinal nerves. Forelimb buds transplanted over six segments posterior to their original position induce new spinal nerves to innervate them.

The visceral fibers of the nerve roots extend into the ventral ramus of the mixed nerve for a short distance and then leave as a ramus communicans to end in the sympathetic ganglia. In this way visceral efferent fibers never extend all the way from spinal cord to smooth muscle or gland without a synapse in the periphery.

The chief function of the spinal cord is that of a motor effector. The hind and midbrain have an important control over locomotion, but the limbs alone, if properly stimulated, can perform normal locomotor movements provided their centers in the spinal cord are left intact (Loeser, 1905). Van Rynberk (1909) placed the center controlling forelimb movements in the second spinal segment. A severe injury to the spinal column in mammals will usually prevent all movement in the hind limbs, but the spinal column of salamanders may be sectioned between fore- and hind limb without preventing the synchronous movements of the limbs in walking (Snyder, 1904; Ten Cate, 1928). In this case the afferent stimulus for releasing walking movements of the hind limbs would seem to be the slight tactile stimulation to the soles of the hind feet on being dragged forward by the forelimbs. Coordinated movements of the limbs cease after sectioning of the dorsal root (Hering, 1897). Nicholas (1928) found that in Ambystoma larvae, after removing a large section of the spinal cord, there was still coordination between fore- and hind limbs. This he attributed to the pull of the body muscles transferring stimulations between the two segments. The relations of these stimulations to normal locomotion will be considered in the discussion of habits.

The coordination of movement between the members of any one pair of limbs is controlled by nervous connections within the spinal cord. In the case of the forelimbs of *Ambystoma maculatum*, this coordination is accomplished by the fifth spinal nerve and its spinal connections. Grafted limbs which receive only a very small branch of this nerve carry out well-defined coordinated movements in both forearm and hand (Detwiler and Carpenter, 1929). Further, severing the sixth and seventh spinal nerves does not prevent coordinated function in the graft. There can be no extensor or flexor nerve in this case, but a very extensive branching of the fifth nerve within the muscles must occur to bring about the various limb movements. Limbs grafted to the ear region of Ambystoma move synchronously or alternately with the swallowing or gill movements (Detwiler, 1930), because their motor nerves are derived from the nerves of this region and hence have the same central connections.

Autonomic System.—The name autonomic system is given to that part of the peripheral nervous system which innervates smooth muscles and glands. It is autonomic in the sense of having its own series of ganglia isolated from the central nervous system but connected with it by the rami communicantes (Fig. 129). The cell bodies of most somatic sensory neurons also lie outside the central nervous system in the dorsal root of the spinal nerves or near the base of cranial nerves. These form sensory and not motor ganglia, as in the present case, however. The autonomic system consists of a cranio-sacral or parasympathetic outflow and a thoracico-lumbar or sympathetic outflow. Although afferent visceral neurons accompany the efferent neurons, they have their ganglia in the dorsal roots and extend all the way from the sense organs to the central nervous system and hence conform to the ordinary type of somatic afferent fibers. The parasympathetic outflow consists essentially of visceral fibers

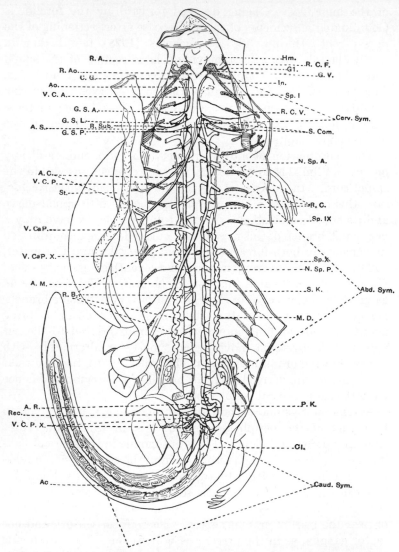

Fig. 129.—The autonomic nervous system of Necturus. *Abd. Sym.*, abdominal sympathetic; *A.C.*, coeliac artery; *Ac.*, aorta caudalis; *A.M.*, mesenteric artery; *Ao.*, aorta; *A.R.*, renal artery; *A.S.*, subclavian artery; *Caud. Sym.*, caudal sympathetic; *Cerv.Sym.*, cervical portion of sympathetic system; *C.G.*, first cervical ganglion; *Cl.*, cloaca; *Gl.*, ramus glossopharyngeus of the vagus; *G.S.A.*, anterior subclavian ganglion; *G.S.L.*, lateral subclavian ganglion; *G.S.P*; posterior subclavian ganglion; *G.V.*, vagus ganglion; *Hm.*, hyomandibular branch of the facial nerve; *In.*, ramus intestinalis of N. vagi; *M.D.*, Müllerian duct; *N.Sp.A,*. anterior splanchnic nerve; *N.Sp.P.*, posterior splanchnic nerve; *P.K.*, pelvic kidney; *R.A.*, anterior ramus of the vagus; *R.Ao.*, radix aortae (root of aorta);

of the vagus system, innervating respiratory, digestive, and circulatory structures. Associated with these are fibers from the third, seventh, and ninth cranial nerves. Kuntz (1911) has traced the peripheral wandering of parasympathetic ganglion cells from the hind brain of the frog along the paths of the vagi and has established their morphological identity with other cells in the central nervous system. Kuntz has also shown that the cells of the sympathetic ganglia migrate to the periphery largely from the dorsal root ganglia. They eventually form the series of ganglia underlying the vertebral column. Two longitudinal strands, the sympathetic trunks, connect the ganglia with one another. Other sympathetic ganglia are found among the viscera and in the head region, closely associated with the cranial nerves. Sympathetic fibers, after making a synapse in these ganglia, proceed peripherally, where they innervate for the most part the same structures supplied by the parasympathetic fibers. The sympathetic and parasympathetic fibers are antagonistic in their effects. The action of the first is to halt the peristaltic movements of the gut, to tighten the sphincters of the same, and to increase the heart beat. The parasympathetic impulses have an exactly opposite effect, and their normal functioning insures proper digestion, respiration, and heart beat according to the extent of vagus control. The responses of smooth muscles and glands innervated by the autonomic system are far more diffused, less localized than those of the skeletal muscles. This is dependent on the number and arrangement of the neurons, which permit the impulse from one preganglionic fiber to be transmitted to several motor neurons in the autonomic system.

In mammals, when under extreme stress, such as is produced by asphyxia physiologically, or danger psychologically, there is a great increase of heart beat, very large rise of blood pressure, and an increase in respiration. Much blood is sent from the intestines and viscera to the muscles in general, so that skeletal response is secured by well-nourished muscles. Further to fortify this response, more sugar is released into the blood stream, and

---

R.B., renal branches of the sympathetic to the Müllerian duct; *R.C.*, rami communicantes; *R.C.F.*, ramus communicans of the N. facialis with the pharyngeal nerve, *R.C.V.*, ramus communicans of vagus nerve; *Rec.*, rectum; *R.Sub.*, subclavian ramus; *S.Com.*, Stannius commissure connecting right and left chain; *S.K.*, sexual kidney; *Sp.I.*, first spinal nerve; *Sp.IX.*, ninth spinal nerve; *Sp.X.*, tenth spinal nerve; *St.*, stomach; *V.C.A.*, vena cardinalis anterior; *V.CaP.*, vena cava posterior; *V.CaP.X.*, vena cava posterior dissected; *V.C.P.*, posterior cardinal vein; *V.C.P.X.*, posterior cut end of vena cava posterior. (*After Andersson.*)

intestinal movements are stopped or much decreased so that the blood can be sent to the surface. Such a condition is evoked in man by an emotional stress such as anger, rage, or fear (Cannon, 1915). The extent to which this complex of sympathetic defense responses are organized in amphibians is not very clear, but as bodily changes apparently occur under stress we may assume that Amphibia experience emotions if only in a rudimentary form and that the mechanisms evolved are probably basically the same.

References

BABÁK, E., 1913: Zur Atemcentrentätigkeit der Amphibien, *Fol. Neurobiol.*, VII, *Ergheft*, 175–185.

BAGLIONI, S., 1900: Der Atmungsmechanismus des Frosches, *Arch. Anat. Physiol.*, Suppl. Bd., 33–59.

————, 1900a: Chemische Reizung des Grosshirns beim Frosche, *Zentralbl. Physiol.*, XIV, 97–99.

————, 1911: Zur Kenntnis der Zentrentätigkeit bei der sexuellen Umklammerung der Amphibien, *Zentralbl. Physiol.*, XXV, 233–238.

BICKEL, A., 1898: Zur vergleichenden Physiologie des Grosshirns, *Arch. ges. Physiol.*, LXXII, 190–215.

BINDEWALD, C. A. E., 1914: Das Vorderhirn von Amblystoma mexicanum, *Arch. mikr. Anat.*, LXXXIV, Abt. 1, 1–74, 1 pl.

BOTTAZZI, PHILLIP, 1899: The action of the vagus and the sympathetic on the oesophagus of the toad, *Jour. Physiol.*, XXV, 157–164.

BURR, H. S., 1922: The early development of the cerebral hemispheres in Amblystoma, *Jour. Comp. Neurol.*, XXXIV, 277–301.

CANNON, W. B., 1915: "Bodily Changes in Pain, Hunger, Fear and Rage," New York.

CHAUCHARD, A., 1927: Les localisations cérébrales motrices chez les vertébrés inférieurs, *Compt. rend. Acad. Sci. Paris*, CLXXXV, 667–669.

COGHILL, G. E., 1928: Correlated anatomical and physiological studies on the growth of the nervous system of Amphibia, VIII. The development of the pattern of differentiation in the cerebrum of Amblystoma punctatum, *Jour. Comp. Neurol.*, XLV, 227–247.

COLE, ELBERT C., 1925: Anastomosing cells in the myenteric plexus of the frog, *Jour. Comp. Neurol.*, XXXVIII, 375–387.

DETWILER, S. R., 1927: Die Morphogenese des peripheren und zentralen Nervensystems der Amphibien im Licht experimenteller Forschungen, *Die Naturw.*, XV, 873–879.

————, 1927a: Experimental studies on Mauthner's cell in Amblystoma, *Jour. Exp. Zool.*, XLVIII, 15–30, 2 pls.

————, 1930: Observations upon the growth, function, and nerve supply of limbs when grafted to the head of salamander embryos, *Jour. Exp. Zool.*, LV, 319–379.

———— and R. L. CARPENTER, 1929: An experimental study of the mechanism of coordinated movements in heterotopic limbs, *Jour. Comp. Neurol.*, XLVII, 427–447.

Dürken, B., 1912: Über frühzeitige Exstirpation von Extremitätenanlagen beim Frosch; Ein experimenteller Beitrag zur Entwicklungsphysiologie und Morphologie der Wirbeltiere unter besonderer Berücksichtigung des Nervensystems, *Zeitschr. Wiss. Zool.*, XCIX, 189–355, 7 pls.

Gaupp, Ernst, 1899: "Ecker's und Wiedersheim's Anatomie des Frosches," 2 *abt.*, Braunschweig.

Goltz, F., 1869: "Beiträge zur Lehre von den Funktionen der Nervenzentren des Frosches," Berlin.

Grönberg, G., 1894: Zur Anatomie der Pipa americana; 2. Verdauungs-, Respirations- und Urogenitalorgane sammt Nervensystem, *Zool. Jahrb. Anat.*, VII, 629–646, 2 pls.

Hering, H. E., 1897: Über Bewegungstörungen nach zentripetaler Lähmung, *Arch. exp. Path. Pharm.*, XXXVIII, 266–283.

Herrick, C. Judson, 1914: The cerebellum of Necturus and other urodele Amphibia, *Jour. Comp. Neurol.*, XXIV, 1–29.

———, 1917: The internal structure of the mid-brain and thalamus of Necturus, *Jour. Comp. Neurol.*, XXVIII, 215–348.

———, 1921: A sketch of the origin of the cerebral hemispheres, *Jour. Comp. Neurol.*, XXXII, 429–454.

———, 1921a: The connections of the vomero-nasal nerve, accessory olfactory bulb and amygdala in Amphibia, *Jour. Comp. Neurol.*, XXXIII, 213–280.

———, 1924: The amphibian forebrain; I. Amblystoma, external form, *Jour. Comp. Neurol.*, XXXVII, 361–371.

———, 1924a: The amphibian forebrain; II. The olfactory bulb of Amblystoma, *Jour. Comp. Neurol.*, XXXVII, 373–396.

———, 1925: Amphibian forebrain; III. The optic tracts and centers of Amblystoma and the frog, *Jour. Comp. Neurol.*, XXXIX, 433–489.

———, 1927: The Amphibian forebrain; IV. The cerebral hemispheres of Amblystoma, *Jour. Comp. Neurol.*, XLIII, 231–325.

———, 1929: Anatomical patterns and behavior patterns, *Physiol. Zool.*, II, 439–448.

Kappers, C. U. A., and E. B. D. Fortuyn, 1921: "Vergleichende Anatomie des Nervensystems," Haarlem, 2 vols.

Kiesewalter, C., 1928: Zur allgemeinen und speziellen Morphogenie des Hemisphärenhirns der Tetrapoden, *Jena. Zeitschr.*, LXIII, 369–454, 2 pls.

Kuhlenbeck, H., 1922: "Zur Morphologie des Gymnophionengehirns," *Jena. Zeitschr.* LVIII, 453–484.

———, 1927: "Vorlesungen über das Zentralnervensystem der Wirbeltiere," Jena.

———, 1929: Die Grundbestandteile des Endhirns im Lichte der Bauplanlehre, *Anat. Anz.*, LXVII, 1–51.

———, 1929a: Über die Grundbestandteile des Zwischenhirnbauplans der Anamnier, *Morph. Jahrb.*, LXIII, 50–95.

Kuntz, Albert, 1911: The development of the sympathetic nervous system in the Amphibia, *Jour. Comp. Neurol.*, XXI, 397–416.

Larsell, O., 1925: The development of the cerebellum in the frog (Hyla regilla) in relation to the vestibular and lateral-line systems, *Jour. Comp. Neurol.*, XXXIX, 249–289.

LOESER, W., 1905: A study of the functions of the different parts of the frog's brain, *Jour. Comp. Neurol.*, XV, 355–373.

MARTIN, H. N., 1878: The normal respiratory movements of the frog, and the influence upon its respiratory centre of stimulation of the optic lobes, *Jour. Physiol.*, I, 131–170.

MCKIBBEN, PAUL S., 1911: The nervus terminalis in urodele Amphibia, *Jour. Comp. Neurol.*, XXI, 261–309.

MONAKOW, C. VON., 1910: "Aufbau und Lokalisation der Bewegungen beim Menschen," Leipzig.

MUCHIN, N., 1895: Die unipolare Reizung des verlängerten Markes des Frosches, *Zeitschr. Biol.*, XXXII, 29–48.

NICHOLAS, J. S., 1928: Effects of experimental block of the amphibian nervous system, *Proc. Soc. Exp. Biol. Med.*, XXV, 662.

RÖTHIG, PAUL, 1912: Beiträge zum Studium des Centralnervensystems der Wirbeltiere, 5. *Verh. Akad. Wet. Amsterdam, II Sekt.*, XVII, 1–23, 25 pls.

———, 1926: Beiträge zum Studium des Zentralnervensystems der Wirbeltiere; 10. Über die Faserzüge im Vorder-und Zwischenhirn der Anuren, *Zeitschr. mikr. Anat. Forsch.*, V, 23–58.

SCHMID, H., 1929: Anatomischer Bau und Entwicklung der Plexus chorioidei in der Wirbeltierreihe und beim Menschen, *Zeitschr. mikr. Anat. Forsch.*, XVI, 413–498, 1 pl.

SCHRADER, M. E. G., 1887: Zur Physiologie der Froschgehirns, *Arch. ges. Physiol.*, XLI, 75–90.

SNYDER, CHARLES D., 1904: Locomotion in Batrachoseps with severed nerve cord, *Biol. Bull.*, VII, 280–288.

SÖDERBERG, GERTIE, 1922: Contributions to the forebrain morphology in amphibians, *Acta Zool.*, III, 65–121.

STEINER, J., 1885: "Die Funktionen des Zentralnervensystems und ihre Phylogenese; 1 Abt. Untersuchen über die Physiologie des Froschhirns," Braunschweig.

TEN CATE, J., 1928: Contribution à la physiologie de la moelle épiniere chez Triton cristatus, *Arch. Neér. Physiol. Hom. Anim.*, Sér. IIIc, XII, 213–253.

VAN RYNBERK, G., 1909: Über unisegmentale (monomere) Rückenmarksreflexe; I. Versuche an Bufo vulgaris, *Fol. Neuro-biol.*, II, 718–729.

CHAPTER XVI

INSTINCT AND INTELLIGENCE

The evolution of the Amphibia is closely correlated with changes in their habits. These habits may be either learned or instinctive. As in the case of other animals, Amphibia develop with certain combinations of neurons connected with sense organs and muscles. It is the normal response of these inherited patterns of neurons to certain sensory stimuli which is called an "instinct." Not only the number and kind of reflex arcs involved determines the nature of the response but also the time and intensity relations of the nerve impulses arriving at the synapses as well as the conductivity of the synapses at a particular moment. As indicated in the preceding chapter, the internal state of an organism may have a profound effect on permitting impulses to pass from one neuron to another. Age, nutrition, hormones from the gonads, pituitary, and other glands of internal secretion, the osmotic condition of the body fluids, the amount of oxygen in the blood, these and many other factors may influence behavior in an amphibian by modifying the synaptic resistances. Internal states may also shift the dominance of certain reflexes. Thus in most animals the protective reflexes take precedence over other reflexes, but in frogs during the breeding season, the clasping reflex may take possession of the final common path and be prepotent over the avoiding reflexes stimulated by noxious stimuli.

Although instinct involves a series of reflex arcs, it differs from a reflex in more than its complexity. An important characteristic of the instinct is the delay in its completion. A persistent tendency toward some biological end is set up by a given stimulus and this releases a series of responses directed toward a future result which is finally attained. The mating instinct of the newt leads through a long series of reflex responses on the part of both sexes to the final deposition of the spermatophore by the male and its taking up by the female. The possible habits which an animal may possess are limited by its inherited nervous organization and by the range of its modifiability during life.

The central nervous system of the Amphibia is so much simpler than that of higher vertebrates, that it is surprising to find many of the instinctive habits of the higher forms already established in the group, if only in a rudimentary form. The question of the origin of these instincts and reflexes may be considered first from the ontogenetic side.

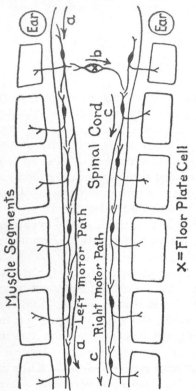

FIG. 130.—A diagram of the neuromotor mechanism of swimming in Ambystoma. The initial impulse, *a*, passes tailward and excites the muscle segments to a wave of contraction which progresses tailward. The neurons of the motor tract in the anterior region develop collaterals which form a synapse with the commissural cells of the floor plate. Hence the impulse also passes at *b* to the motor system of the other side where it passes tailward, *c*, inducing a second wave of contraction which follows the first after a brief interval. (*After Coghill.*)

Development of Reflexes in Ambystoma.—If the young Ambystoma embryo is removed from the egg capsule and tested in regard to its reaction to tactile stimulation, it will be found to pass during development through five stages which Coghill (1929) has called the "non-motile," "early-flexure," "coil," "S-reaction," and "swimming stages." A light touch on the skin brings no response at first. Later the head is moved away from the source of stimulation. A little later the bending involves more and more of the trunk until the embryo is thrown into a coil. Still later, the flexure, which begins in the head region and progresses tailward, is reversed in the head region before it has passed entirely through the trunk. Finally, this last reaction is repeated at sufficient intervals to effect locomotion. Coghill has shown that the anatomical basis of this orderly series of events lies in the growth of nerves in medulla and spinal cord. Afferent neurons grow across the motor tract of their own side of the cord at its anterior end, to form synapses with commissural cells which convey the excitation to the motor tract of the opposite side (Fig. 130). Impulses traveling these neurons induce a turning of the head away from the source of stimulation. Reversed flexure movements are caused by the excitation of sensory nerve endings in the muscles on the side of contraction and by the conduction of that excitation to the muscles of the opposite side. These reversed flexures may lead to some locomotion but not to typical swimming movements. It is apparently the growth of motor fibers on the original side of stimulation which permits, during the swimming stage, a contraction of the muscles of this side. Since more synapses are involved in shunting the excitation to the opposite side, the flexure away from the side of stimulation follows the first flexure after a brief interval. During both the S-reaction and the swimming stage the first flexure is the stimulus for the second, and the second for the third. Experience and exercise play no part in teaching Ambystoma how to swim. Nerves grow because of their own potentialities, and the series of different responses arise as new synapses are formed between the nerve processes.

The reflexes of walking in Ambystoma are derived, as Coghill (1929) has shown, from this swimming-reaction pattern. The first motor nerves reaching the muscles of the limb are branches of the same fibers that are stimulating the trunk muscles into contraction. The first movements of the limb are, therefore, correlated with body movements, and the limbs respond to postural stimulations earlier than to external influences. Walking has not arisen by the coordination of local reflexes in the appendages. The arm is moved as a whole before the forearm gains independent action, and the forearm develops its reflexes before the digits acquire theirs. The basis of this development of local reflexes within a larger pattern is the growing of collaterals from already functioning nerves into new territory. The tongue of Ambystoma receives branches from the motor neurons engaged in integrating trunk movements long before the tongue has muscle tissue in it (Coghill, 1929). Thus, adaptive movements of tongue or limbs have not arisen by a coordination of local reflexes which at the beginning had considerable independence. Rather, reflexes arise by the individuation of portions of a larger behavior pattern. During both ontogeny and phylogeny the swimming movements of the trunk are reduced, while the limbs of

Amphibia acquire a greater independence of action. In salamanders the primitive sinuous movements of the trunk have not
been wholly given up in even the most efficient walkers.

Walking, just like swimming, is, therefore, native and
unlearned. Matthews and Detwiler (1926) reared Ambystoma
larvae 8 days in chloretone and found that at the end of this time
they had developed the same reflexes as in controls which had
been active during this period. The work has been extended to
Wood-frog tadpoles by Carmichael (1926) with similar results.
Carmichael (1927) has also repeated the experiments on Ambystoma larvae. He has found that the first observable response in
an individual reared in chloretone was on release from anaesthetic
essentially the same as in one that had been free-moving during
the same period of growth. It is from such observations as these
that we must conclude that "Nerve cells, like seeds planted by a
gardener, spring up and grow according to a definite pattern,"
and it is the position and interrelationships of the twigs of the
growing plant which give at various stages of development the
different behavior patterns to the organism which happens to
bear this sprouting seed. Walking, as well as swimming, is the
end result of nerve growth and adjustment. Experience has
nothing to do with the form into which the behavior of the animal
is cast.

Multiple Uses of Single Reflexes and Instincts.—It sometimes
happens that the same reflex may gain a different significance in
different groups of animals. For example, one of the most striking reflexes among Salientia is the so-called "unken" reflex.
The European Fire-bellied Toad, *Bombina bombina*, if suddenly
disturbed will bend its head and legs sharply back over the body
and turn the ventral surfaces of its forearms upward in such a way
that more or less of its gaudily colored undersurfaces are exposed
(Fig. 131). This habit also appears in the same form in the brightly
colored but unrelated *Dendrophryniscus stelzneri* (Fernandez,
1927) and has often been assumed to be a warning attitude on the
part of the toad, for its skin is more poisonous than that of various
other European Salientia. It is assumed that the toad's possible
enemies, if sufficiently warned, would avoid an encounter. Löhner (1919) has found that the reflex may be evoked even in decapitated animals and hence must have its coordinating centers in the
cord. The typical unken reflex is characterized not only by a
distinctive posture and immobility but also by a closure of the

eyes, a slowing down of the respiratory movements, and an increase in the skin secretion. Though decapitated animals assume the characteristic pose, the reflex is not present at its maximum. Thus, the brain of the intact animal has some influence on this reflex. Whatever may be the significance of the reflex in Bombina, Hinsche (1926) has shown that the same reflex is present in the drab-colored Midwife Toad, Alytes, and, further, that various European species of Rana and Bufo exhibit more or less of the reaction. In these forms the reflex might be of assistance in avoiding obstacles to locomotion. The Bullfrog, *Rana catesbeiana*, if cornered, will sometimes thrust out its arms and flatten its body. The back is not curved upward as in Bombina, but otherwise the reaction has a considerable resemblance to the unken reflex. At low temperatures the reflex of Bombina is

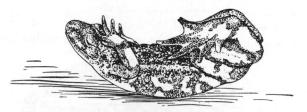

Fig. 131.—The "unken reflex" of *Bombina bombina*.

incomplete and resembles that of Rana, giving further evidence that both reflexes have the same neuromuscular basis in spite of the different functional significance in the two groups. The reflex has also been compared with the induced state of tonic immobility in animals and with hypnotism in man. Frogs stroked on the back or laid ventral side up frequently "play dead." The reaction is so different from the avoiding movements of the unken reflex that the two phenomena would seem to have a different nervous basis. Whether or not the unken reflex is a type of tonic immobility, both types of response need not involve the higher centers of the brain. If the back of a decerebrate frog is rubbed, it exhibits the usual hypnotic response. Further, the response is greater in the female than in the male (Verworn, 1897). This response may have some significance in the mating process, a vigorous grip of the male tending to throw the female into a state of tonic immobility and thus prevent her escape.

The unken reflex is an example of stereotyped behavior common to a natural group of forms and yet modified according to the species. Have all reflexes and instincts been gradually modified in this way during phylogeny? In the ontogeny of Ambystoma, Coghill showed that the growth of certain axons and dendrites a fraction of a millimeter changed a helpless individual into one capable of exploring its environment. Similarly, in phylogeny, we should expect totally new behavior patterns to arise fully formed as the result of small morphological changes of the nerve patterns. Nevertheless, some reflexes and instincts have remained relatively stable during evolution, while others, such as the unken reflex, have been gradually modified. Since the walking reflexes have arisen from the swimming reflex pattern by individuation of parts during ontogeny, the same phenomena of individuation might be expected to account for the origin of new reflex patterns from a more generalized behavior pattern during phylogeny.

Defense Reaction.—One of the most complete studies of the phylogenetic change in a behavior pattern in Amphibia has been

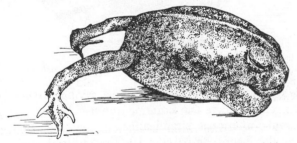

FIG. 132.—The defense-fight reaction of *Bufo calamita*. (*After Hinsche.*)

made by Hinsche (1928). Most Salientia when annoyed will inflate their lungs and bow their heads, assuming a defensive attitude. The inflation increases the size of the body and removes all wrinkles from the skin. Smooth, swollen frogs are both difficult to seize and difficult to swallow. Some toads add to this defense reaction several aggresive movements. The limbs are stretched, bringing the body clear from the ground, and then the whole body is brought forward in a butting reaction (Fig. 132). At the same time, the Spade-foot Toads may give a "fright cry," and frogs may scream with open mouths. Apparently, Ceratophrys and *Leptobrachium carinense* add effective biting movements to this chain of reactions. There is no doubt that both the defensive and offensive components of this series of events are effective in warding off the attacks of both snakes and birds. The inflation of the body and the straightening of the limbs are part of the defensive mechanism of lizards, and hence at least this part of the response may be considered an ancient inheritance from the early tetrapods.

The defense-fight reaction may be evoked in Salientia by either optical or tactile stimulations. Hinsche found that color had no modifying influence but that both the size and the speed of the approaching object were important considerations. Small objects elicited a feeding reaction in *Bufo vulgaris*, while objects larger than 75 sq. cm., unless possessing projecting parts, induced no response. Toads suddenly confronted by a mass of wriggling worms lowered their heads and charged, but when the worms began to disentangle themselves this defense-fight response was replaced by the feeding reaction. By using the legless lizard, Anguis, of different sizes, Hinsche was able to establish that *B. vulgaris* would react to a moving wormlike creature of less than 23 cm. in length, chiefly by the feeding response, while similar creatures above that size evoked principally the defense-fight reaction. Large snakes were not effective as a whole but only in so far as their head and tongue came within the requirements necessary to induce the response. The sight of harmless animals, such as rabbit and guinea pig, as well as of such objects as a rubber tube, could call forth the response, while many enemies either too large or too swift brought no reaction. The approaching animal, in brief, is not received as an enemy but only as a bearer of certain adequate stimuli. The defense-fight reactions of Bufo are specific not to hostile enemies but to a complex of stimuli. Nevertheless the reaction was found to be effective against the toad's greatest enemies, snakes, which were of sufficient size and approached slowly enough to call forth the response. The touch of a snake's tongue or head augmented the response evoked by the sight of the snake.

Many factors modified the response of toads to possible enemies. During states of maximal excitation all moving objects, whatever the nature of the movement, were effective. Toads in a corner responded more quickly with a defense-fight reaction than those with avenues of escape open to them. The flight response was in a certain sense antagonistic to the defense-fight response. It was, perhaps, for this reason that frogs capable of rapid flight failed to exhibit a complete defense-fight reaction under laboratory conditions. In their phylogeny the flight response had been developed to the detriment of the alternative response. In the same way, natural selection may have provided that the snapping reflexes of Ceratophrys, a cannibalistic form, were made part of the fight response rather than that they remained a wholly separate reaction induced by the sight of small moving objects as in the case of the toad.

The various components of the defense-fight reaction, although linked closely in this response, are apparently used separately under other circumstances. Thus the humping of the back with the lowering of the head is used in skin shedding. The same reflex helps the male to maintain his grip on the female, and Hinsche finds the defense kicks used by embracing males to ward off their competitors the same as the rearing reflexes in the defense-fight response. In burrowing, the crouching and rearing would also be effective. Similarly, the eye-closing reflex has important functions other than those concerned with protecting the eyes. In most Salientia and many urodeles the retraction of the eyeballs aids in the swallowing, for the eyeballs are forced partly into the mouth cavity and tend to carry the food toward the midline and posteriorly. Hinsche (1926 *b*) has shown that tactile stimulations of a limited part of the roof of the mouth induces the reflex in the toad, and no doubt the pressure of food on this area calls forth reflexly the retraction of the eyeballs. Thus, reflexes, whether or not part of an original pattern, may be used separately for totally different functions.

Even though the reflexes may be linked in certain patterns, interfering reflexes or states of excitation must be absent before any one complete chain of responses may be elicitated. Evolution has proceeded by the shunting in of new reflexes as well as by a modification of the old. Species, such as *Bufo calamita*, which are given short legs by heredity, are not able to exhibit the same manifestations of the defense-fight reaction as longer-legged species. The form of the animal, as well as its state of excitement may both modify the response.

Phylogenetic Change of Instincts.—Many behavior patterns of Amphibia exhibit phylogenetic changes. Such, for example, may be seen in the courtship of salamanders. Here reflexes are linked together as in the case of the defense-fight reaction, but a longer interval occurs between the several responses. Courtship behavior is, thus, a good example of an instinct, and the phylo-

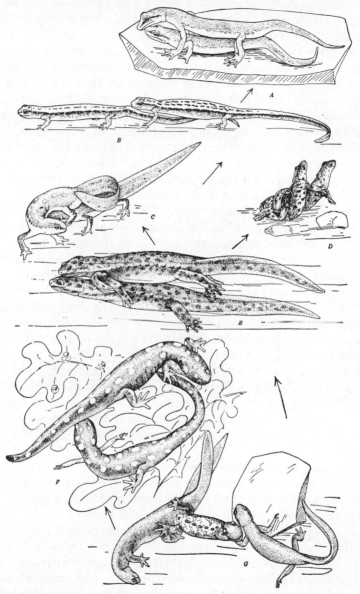

Fig. 133.—The evolution of the courtship of some salamanders. A. *Hydro-mantes genei*. B. *Eurycea bislineata*. C. *Triturus viridescens*. D. *Euproctus asper*. (*After Dahne*.) E. *Pleurodeles waltl*. F. *Ambystoma maculatum*. (*After Breder*.) G. *Hynobius lichenatus*. (*After Sasaki*.)

genetic change of this instinct within a single group of Amphibia may be considered in some detail (Fig. 133). The most primitive urodeles living are the Hynobiidae. The males come first from hibernation and resort to temporary pools, slow-moving streams, and in a few instances to lakes. They are followed a day or so later by the females, which soon begin to lay their paired sacs of eggs. Sasaki (1924) has made detailed observations on *Hynobius lichenatus*. The female selects a rock or other submerged object and an attempt is made to glue the egg sacs to it. This is followed by backward movements for the purpose of drawing the remainder of the egg sacs out of the oviducts. The males, which up to this point are indifferent to the females, now dart rapidly forward and clutch the egg sacs with their forelimbs, while they push the females away with the hind ones. The males rub the egg sacs with their cloacal lips while fertilizing them, and the movements of their hind limbs assist in the delivery of the eggs. The males still cling to the eggs for a period after the female has deposited the spawn and has sought concealment under some object.

The Cryptobranchidae may be considered permanent hynobiid larvae or partly metamorphosed forms of large size. Although living throughout the year in the water, they become gregarious during the breeding season, which occurs in the fall, as with some specimens of *H. lichenatus*. Fertilization is external as in the Hynobiidae, and the sight of the string of eggs seems to be the immediate stimulus for the emission of the sperm (Smith, 1907). The tendency for the male hynobiids to remain with the eggs is extended in the cryptobranchids, for here the males stay with them until hatching and may frequently devour part of their trust.

The ambystomids show a close relationship to the hynobiids, but they have developed a true courtship which can be evolved only with difficulty from the pattern of the hynobiids and cryptobranchids. The males precede the females to the pond and, in *Ambystoma maculatum* at least, engage in a *Liebesspiel* on the appearance of the females. The males twine back and forth over one another and rub their snouts against each other's tail or body, beginning usually at a posterior point and working forward, the most aggressive male frequently pushing his head under the body of another. In the axolotl, according to Gasco (1881), both sexes take part in these caressing movements. Wright and Allen (1909) found that the mere presence of the female in the jar with males excited them to sexual activity, but whether the males could sense the eggs in the body of the female or were stimulated by some other factor was not determined. The female axolotl noses the cloaca of the male, apparently attracted by the secretion of the abdominal gland. Males of this and other species of Ambystoma have been found to fan their tails in the direction of the female during courtship, apparently to waft the same secretion toward her. The male of one species of the genus, *A. jeffersonianum*, apparently seizes the female with his hind legs (Wright, 1908). In brief, there occur in Ambystoma elaborate rubbing movements directed toward the females, and apparently it is the secretions released by the male which hold her interest. The nature of the sensory stimulations which first arouse the interest of the male in the female is unknown. The courtship of Ambystoma is directed toward stimulating the female to the point where she will pick up the spermatophore which the male deposits. Gasco (1881) describes the female axolotl as pressing the spermatophore into her cloaca with her hind limbs, but in *A. maculatum* the cloacal lips take up the spermatophore unaided. Fertilization is internal, the males taking no interest in the eggs which are laid several days or more after impregnation.

The courtship of all the other families of salamanders, as far as known, seems to have been built out of the pattern of Ambystoma by the elaboration of one or more phases of it. The primitive salamandrids Tylototriton, Pleurodeles, and Salamandra have given up the random rubbing movements and elaborate further one reaction found in Ambystoma. The male creeps under the female and seizes her front legs from behind, with his front legs. The "piggy-back ride" which follows finally results in the emission of the spermatophore by the male and its being secured by the female. This peculiar courtship, which may occur either on land or in water according to the species, is probably found in other salamandrids such as Chioglossa (Boulenger, 1910), but it does not occur outside the family. In some species more or less of the nosing and cloacal display also occurs. A few primitive salamandrids have seized upon other phases of the courtship seen in Ambystoma and developed them along other channels. Klinge (1915) reports the male *Triturus pyrrhogaster*, a Japanese newt, as partly gripping the female from above with both pairs of limbs while lashing with his tail to drive secretions of the cloaca toward her. One forelimb is placed over her neck and one hind limb across her back to hold her while the cloacal secretion is wafted toward her. After the spermatophore is deposited and the female has brought her cloaca in contact with it, the male may bite the female in the inguinal region and this is said to aid in the taking up of the spermatophore (Klingel-höffer, 1930).

The western newt of America, *T. torosus*, is probably closely related to *T. pyrrhogaster*, and its courtship is essentially the same. The male grips the female with fore- (Schreitmuller, 1909) or both pairs of limbs (Storer, 1925). The eastern newt, *T. viridescens*, uses its hind limbs for the same purpose and brings its cheek against the snout of the female. The cheek is equipped with a battery of hedonic glands which serve to quiet the female (Rogoff, 1927) and finally to induce her to follow the male while he moves off a short distance and emits the spermatophore. It is probable that similar hedonic glands are found in the tail spine of *Salamandra caucasica*, but their functioning has never been observed. Schlosser's account (1925) of the courtship of *Salamandra atra* suggests that hedonic glands may function in this species as well. Apparently the male seizes the female about the neck with his forelimbs and rubs some of his secretion into her nostrils. Whether *S. atra* also carries the female in a preliminary "piggy-back ride" as in *S. salamandra* is not known, for a complete courtship of the species has not been witnessed.

The European newts of the genus Triturus represent anatomically a more advanced group of salamandrids than the species just mentioned. They have developed still another mode of interesting the female in the business of picking up the spermatophore. The males are for the most part conspicuously colored and they display themselves before the female. Sexual dimorphism of color is found also in *T. pyrrhogaster*, the female having a red stripe on the tail, the male a black one. This difference may help the clutching males to distinguish females from their own sex, but the dark tail is not used in display. The nosing and tail lashing movements of Ambystoma also occur in the European newts.

Strotgen (1927) saw the diminutive Salamandrina deposit spermatophores. Since the male was following the female, the courtship may resemble that of Ambystoma. The mountain newts of Europe, Euproctus, are not conspicuously colored, and since they live in mountain streams or near the bottom of lakes, they have little opportunity for display. They, on the other hand, seem to have elaborated the entwining phase of the courtship of Ambystoma. The males lie in wait for the female and seize her with either tail or teeth. The fore- or hind limbs are also used, according to the species, to maintain the grip. The spermatophore may be either deposited near the cloaca of the female or transmitted directly into it. In brief, various natural groups of genera or species of salamandrids are each characterized by its own distinctive type of courtship, the most essential features of which seem to be a further specialization of part of the courtship exhibited by Ambystoma. The Salamandridae probably did not evolve directly from ambystomids, but both may have evolved from the same stock. It would seem that this stock exhibited a generalized type of courtship which was retained by Ambystoma, but parts of it were modified in different ways by the various natural groups of salamandrids.

The Plethodontidae, which evolved directly from salamandrids, seem to have specialized in hedonic glands as the source of stimulation. While these glands are restricted to the cheek of the newt and apparently the tail of *Salamandra caucasica*, they are widely distributed over cheeks, body, and tail of most male plethodontids. Their courtship was first made known in *Eurycea bislineata*. The male noses the female and frequently bends his head across her cheek exactly as in the case of the newt in amplexus. The female finally shows an interest in him and steps across his tail to press her snout tightly against the glands in his tail base. The pair then engage in a grotesque walk, the male bending his tail sharply at the base. Other plethodontids, as shown by Noble and Brady (1930), may differ from Eurycea in certain details of the first phase of the courtship. It is interesting that the "tail walk" should proceed in exactly the same manner in both the aquatic Eurycea and the terrestrial Hemidactylium, although possibly lost in Hydromantes. The character of the medium, thus, fails to modify the courtship pattern in both salamandrids and plethodontids. The courtship pattern would seem to have evolved in phylogeny without a close habitat correlation.

It would appear that any behavior as complex as the courtship of Salamandra or Eurycea, and involving the two sexes for its successful conclusion, must have some psychical content. The development of specialized courtships out of a more general pattern tends to keep the derived groups from ever crossing. Even if the germ cells could be cross-fertilized, no interbreeding would occur in nature, for the groups would not be psychically, that is, instinctively compatible. Within any one group of related species there appear to be other mechanisms which prevent crossing. Thus, Noble and Brady found that Stereochilus and Eurycea would not court with one another. Since the males nosed the females before rejecting them, there was apparently some odor in the skin of the females which was distasteful to the males.

Mechanism of Instinct.—Although the courtship of many salamanders has a very stereotyped form, the centers in the central nervous system controlling this or any other instinct have never been determined. Each instinct probably embraces a great many centers. As suggested by the breeding of Eurycea, one center aroused by an initial stimulation makes possible the activation of a second center by a different type of sensory impulse from that which aroused the first center. Various instincts such as the hunting reaction may be induced by impulses from visceral centers. Instincts are, therefore, internal states of readiness which exist until the proper stimulus releases the culminating reflexes. In the hunting reaction the stimulus would be the sight of food, and the culminating reaction the snapping and swallowing reflexes. During the breeding season, the hormones from the gonads make possible the functioning of certain reflexes such as the clasping reaction, but the mating instinct is not satisfied until a series of reflexes have functioned, more or less in their proper order.

The unfolding of an instinct such as that of hunting discloses that one stimulus and response may predispose a second reflex to function. Further, Amphibia differ in the degree to which they "warm up" to a situation. For example, Yerkes (1905) found that if a sound was produced near a frog within two seconds of the time of a tactile stimulation, the response to the latter was greater than if there was no sound. If the sound came over 2 seconds before the tactile stimulus, it had no "significance" for the frog; that is, the response was not affected. Bruyn and Van Nifterik (1920) found in the toad that even with an interval of 10 seconds between noise and tactile stimulus there was still a great reinforcement of the reaction. Sound has thus a much greater significance for toad than for frog. Once an insect has given away its location by a sound, the toad is "tuned up" and holds this tuning much longer than the frog. The toad is thus better equipped to hunt than the frog. Although neither frogs nor toads respond to ordinary sounds by movement, toads have a greater power of retention than frogs, and this persisting nervous state makes them better fitted to survive competition on land.

Thus, a nerve center such as the acoustic nuclei in toads does not always discharge instantly into a motor tract. It remains pent up, predisposing a second center, over which it has no motor control, to function more effectively when the proper external stimulus arrives. Worms which were writhing too violently, due to the fact that they were fastened to a pin, did not induce the feeding reactions of *Bufo calamita*, according to the observations of Franz, so quickly as did normal worms. Many Amphibia make use of certain stimuli to put them on guard when hunting, and other excitations to release the snapping reflexes. Thus, salamander larvae turn their heads toward forceps thrust in their aquaria, for they feel the vibrations with their lateral-line organs. When these stimulations are reinforced by olfactory or optic impulses, the snapping reflex is finally evoked. Whitman (1899) has shown that a similar cautious approach toward possible food is employed by both young and old Necturus. The adults are very successful in capturing living prey, merely because they have inherited a nervous organization which demands deliberation or warming up before the final attack. Instincts may in some cases take as good care of an organism as intelligence in the same circumstance could do.

If the vibratory stimulations impinging on a Necturus should be excessive, they would evoke not approach, but flight movements in the animal. One cutaneous area can produce different reflexes according to the quality or nature of the applied excitation.. Detrimental stimulations evoke defense or preservation reflexes, while useful excitations call out other movements which are usually opposed. This is well shown by Ten Cate's experiments (1928) on locomotion in the newt. A gentle stimulation of the soles of the hind feet after the spinal cord has been cut brought forth walking movements; a stronger stimulation of the same area released defense reactions. The modifying influence of a reflex might come through the central nervous system from another center. Thus, unusual visual impressions in either

Necturus or the newt might evoke flight movements of the limbs instead of an approach. Such behavior need not possess any psychical content. If a frog with its brain entirely destroyed is slightly pinched on one foot, it will withdraw this appendage; a stronger pinch evokes kicking reflexes; a more violent pinch produces jumping movements. Obviously here the increased stimulation has brought additional efferent paths into the reflex. The higher centers of the brain may in the same way increase or decrease the number of arcs involved whether or not these impulses from higher up also have some psychical qualities. The higher nerve centers of the brain thus inhibit or facilitate the activities of the various reflex arcs of the spinal cord. Typical reflex responses to definite stimuli occur more uniformly after the brain has been destroyed than before.

Learned Behavior.—Although instinct is unlearned behavior, it may, like most other inherited features of an organism, be modified by environmental influences. The more loosely organized an instinct is the more chance there is for trial and error, and this in turn allows experience to modify the pattern in favor of one reaction instead of another. Learning is due to the increased conductivity of certain neural paths. As discussed in the preceding chapter, the change apparently occurs at the synapses of much used neurons. In all vertebrates the forebrain, especially the cerebral cortex, contains the neural pathways which are most subject to modification through use; in other words, these neurons form the center of associative memory. Burnett (1912) has experimented with decerebrate frogs. He found that in learning a maze, the normal frogs of the species he used (*R. pipiens* and *R. boylii*) would make their escape after about 20 trials with rarely an error. For the decerebrate frogs over 100 trials were made and the last trial was no more successful than the first. Further, the reflex excitability of the decerebrate frog is heightened, owing to the loss of inhibitory influences from the higher centers. Burnett concluded that the decerebrate frog is incapable of forming even the simplest associations. Hence, in Amphibia as in other vertebrates, the forebrain must be considered the primary seat of learning.

Although all animals are able to learn, that is, to modify their inherited reactions, it is not until the development of a cortex in the cerebral hemispheres of higher vertebrates that a type of brain is evolved which makes possible numerous juxtapositions of sensory data and also gives the possibility that training may influence to a considerable degree the effector path selected. Such a brain is less stereotyped but more adaptable than the brain of lower forms with their closely knit set of instincts. Hence, in a changing environment it would surely succeed, while the latter might fail to find an environment sufficiently stimulating to release its highly organized chains of reflexes.

Amphibia, in spite of their rudimentary or lacking cortex, are able to learn other things besides running mazes. As everyone knows who has kept salamanders or frogs for any length of time in aquaria, most regularly fed Amphibia soon learn the source of their food and expectingly turn their heads when anyone approaches their tank. Toads fed only once a week learned the feeding time after only 30 or 40 feedings and displayed distinctive reactions on these occasions even before the food was presented (Vandel, 1927). Schaeffer (1911) found that three common species of Rana learned to avoid disagreeable objects such as hairy caterpillars in from four to seven trials. This learned habit persisted for at least 10 days. When assisted by the punishment of an electric shock, a Pond Frog learned to avoid earthworms treated with chemicals in only two trials. Buytendijk (1918) found that two European species of toad would seize red ants, *Formica rufa*, but after a single experience would avoid not only an ant but even spiders and flies. The following day ants were avoided but spiders were taken. Rarely, a toad would seize an ant on the second day, but usually it was not until the third or fourth day after the capture of the first ant that others were taken. Thus, toads may learn as quickly as mammals, but they remember for only a limited period. Razwilowska (1927) taught a frog to associate a square of a certain size with food. When only the square was presented, the frog reacted as if food were present. This is the more surprising in that Franz (1927) showed that even after feeding *Rana temporaria* and *Bufo calamita* for months with meal worms, they would respond only to moving, never to the quiescent, objects. A meal worm had no "significance" for these Amphibia unless it moved. Buytendijk (1918) found that a toad may seize a moving piece of paper but after one experience will not make a second attempt for some minutes. If, however, the toad is fed an insect, it will return to the attack on the paper. Experience thus changes the significance of an object. A single successful capture of an insect

modifies the reaction of the toad toward another object.   It
changes the toad's "point of view."

Any object in a stable environment has a different significance
for Amphibia at different times.   This significance varies not
only with experience but also with the physiological state of the
animal.   Haecker (1912) found that axolotls could be taught to
distinguish between a piece of meat and one of wood of the same
size.   During the breeding season the number of errors in making

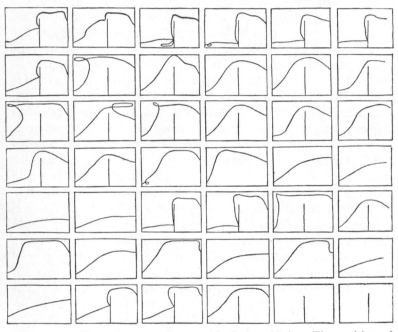

Fig. 134.—Glass plate experiment with *Bufo calamita*.   The position of
the glass plate and the path selected by the toad are indicated for successive
trials.   (*After Buytendijk*.)

this distinction increased.   Flower (1927) found that axolotls
during metamorphosis completely forgot earlier feeding experi-
ences and had to be taught all over again.   Sexual activity and
metamorphosis may thus affect the learned behavior.   No
doubt hunger, noise, and other stimulations would also have an
effect on learned behavior, whether or not acting directly on the
reflexes.

Amphibia show some aptitude in learning motor habits.
Terrestrial forms such as toads and newts learn to find their way

through a maze more quickly than aquatic species as the frog. Buytendijk (1918*a*) showed that toads in seeking for obscurity will learn after only nine trials how to avoid a glass plate placed directly in their way. Buytendijk found, as Cummings (1910) had observed in a British newt, that movements once made tended to be repeated in later trials (Fig. 134). Motor reactions which are not harmful or which do not conflict with some beneficial activity tend to persist. This "muscular memory" is doubtless of assistance in helping toads find their way back to their usual retreat after a night of hunting. Buytendijk found that useless motor habits not only persisted a long time in the toads he studied but could even reappear with more or less modification after they had once disappeared.

Homing is not accomplished entirely by muscular memory. As Franz (1927) showed with toads, vision plays an important rôle in controlling the orientation. Rana has not so good eyesight as Bufo, and Franz showed that it found its way back to an accustomed retreat with greater difficulty. The observations of Yerkes (1903) make it clear, however, that vision plays a part in the homing of *Rana clamitans* (Chap. XVII).

Intelligence.—In comparing toads with frogs, the former were found not only to learn more quickly but to react more promptly to many stimulations. Toads have, therefore, a greater intelligence than frogs, for intelligence is not measured merely by ability to learn. Responsiveness, curiosity, and persistence are factors entering into the intelligence of toads and other vertebrates. Franz (1927) concluded that *Bufo calamita* in its prompt handling of complex food situations was on the same psychological plane as reptiles. It is doubtful if Bufo, placed in the water, the home territory of Rana, would prove as much a master of the situation as the frog. Nevertheless, Hinsche (1926*a*) showed that if the toad was gradually conditioned to the water it would voluntarily return to it. Under these conditions, the toad developed Rana-like movements which it never ordinarily discloses. Apparently the aquatic environment permitted the functioning of reflexes which usually do not appear during the life of the toad. If Hinsche's interpretation is correct, other Amphibia also may well have instincts and reflexes which they never exhibit, merely because the conditions of their present life do not activate them. The voluntary return to the water induced by Hinsche may be compared with the normal migration

to the ponds in the spring.   Apparently an environmental factor
can release an instinct in the toad, usually activated only by
secretions from the gonads.

It is highly probable that other Salientia are as intelligent and
as versatile as the toad.   Biederman (1927) reports the European
Tree Toad as having a retentive memory, and Yerkes (1903)
found that the Pond Frog, *Rana clamitans,* could remember its
way out of a maze after the lapse of a month.   The various
European Salientia differ greatly in their speed of learning and
ability to remember.   Nevertheless, the Amphibia as a group are
not better endowed with ability to learn and to remember than
some fish (Hempelmann, 1926).   Learning seems to have played
only a minor part in the success of the various groups of Amphibia.
The instinct patterns are so much more in evidence than learned
behavior throughout all groups of Amphibia, that the latter type
of behavior may well be neglected in considering the evolution of
the groups.

References

BIEDERMAN, S., 1927: Le sens et la mémoire des formes d'un objet chez
    les anoures; L'inversion de l'habitudes après ou sans amortissement
    (L'expérience optique des Batraciens, IIe mémoire), *Prace. Inst.
    Nenck.,* No. 56, 1–5.

BOULENGER, G. A., 1910: "Les batraciens et principalement ceux d'Europe,"
    Paris.

BRUYN, E. M. M., and C. H. M. VAN NIFTERICK, 1920: Influence du son
    sur le réaction d'une excitation tactile chez les grenouilles et les crapauds,
    Arch. Neér. Physiol. Hom. Anim., Sér. IIIc, V, 363–379.

BURNETT, T. C., 1912: Some observations on decerebrate frogs with especial
    reference to the formation of associations, *Amer. Jour. Physiol.,* XXX,
    80–87.

BUYTENDIJK, F. J. J., 1918: L'instinct d'alimentation et l'expérience chez
    les crapauds, *Arch. Neér Physiol. Hom. Anim.,* Sér. IIIc, II, 217–228.

————, 1918a: Instinct de la recherche du nid et expérience chez les crapauds
    (Bufo vulgaris et Bufo calamita), *Arch. Neér. Physiol. Hom. Anim.,*
    Sér. IIIc, II, 1–50.

CARMICHAEL, L., 1926: The development of behavior in vertebrates experi-
    mentally removed from the influence of external stimulation, *Psych.
    Rev.,* XXXIII, 51–58.

————, 1927: A further study of the development of behavior in vertebrates
    experimentally removed from the influence of external stimulation,
    Psych. Rev., XXXIV, 34–47.

COGHILL, G. E., 1929: "Anatomy and the Problem of Behavior," New York.

CUMMINGS, B. F., 1910: The formation of useless habits in two British
    newts (Molge cristata, Laur, and M. palmata, Schneid.), with observa-
    tions on their general behavior, *Zoologist,* XIV, 161–175, 211–222, 272.

FERNANDEZ, KATI, 1927: Sobre la biologia y reproducción de batracios Argentinos (Segunda parte), *Bol. Acad. Nac. Cienc. Cordoba*, XXIX, 271–328.

FLOWER, S. S., 1927: Loss of memory accompanying metamorphosis in amphibians, *Proc. Zool. Soc.*, Part I, 155–156.

FRANZ, V., 1927: Zur tierpsychologischen Stellung von Rana temporaria und Bufo calamita, *Biol. Zentralbl.*, XLVII, 1–12.

GASCO, F., 1881: Les amours des axolotls, *Zool. Anz.*, IV, 313–316, 329–340.

HAECKER, V., 1912: Über Lernversuche bei Axolotln, *Arch. ges. Psychol.*, XXV, 1–35.

HEMPELMANN, FRIEDRICH, 1926: "Tierpsychologie vom Standpunkte des Biologen," Leipzig.

HINSCHE, G., 1926: Vergleichende Untersuchungen zum sogenannten Unkenreflex, *Biol. Zentralbl.*, XLVI, 296–305.

———, 1926a: Vergleichende Untersuchungen von Haltungs- und Bewegungsreaktionen bei Anuren, *Zeitschr. Indukt. Abstamm. Vererb.* XLIII, 252–260.

———, 1926b: Untersuchungen über den Augenschlussreflex bei Bufo vulgaris und einige seiner Beziehungen zu anderen Reaktionen, *Biol. Zentralbl.*, XLVI, 742–747.

———, 1928: Kampfreaktionen bei einheimischen Anuren, *Biol. Zentralbl.*, XLVIII, 577–616.

KLINGE, W., 1915: Triton pyrrhogaster, *Wochenschr. Aquar.-Terrar.-Kde.*, XII, 427–431.

LÖHNER, L., 1919: Über einen eigentümlichen Reflex der Feuerunken, *Arch. ges. Physiol.*, CLXXIV, 324–351.

MATTHEWS, S. A., and S. R. DETWILER, 1926: The reactions of Amblystoma embryos following prolonged treatment with chloretone, *Jour. Exp. Zool.*, XLV, 279–292.

NOBLE, G. K., and M. K. BRADY, 1930: The courtship of the plethodontid salamanders *Copeia*, 52–54.

RAZWILOWSKA, S., 1927: Le sens et la mémoire des dimensions d'un objet ches les anoures; Types du comportment individuels; Coexistence des plusieurs processus d'association independant l'un de l'autre (L'expérience optique des batraciens, IIIe mémoire), *Prace Inst. Nenck.*, No. 60, 1–24.

ROGOFF, J. L., 1927: The hedonic glands of Triturus viridescens; a structural and functional study, *Anat. Rec.*, XXXIV, 132–133.

SASAKI, M., 1924: On a Japanese salamander, in Lake Kuttarush, which propagates like the axolotl, *Jour. Coll. Agric. Hok. Imp. Univ.*, XV, Part I, 1–36.

SCHAEFFER, ASA A., 1911: Habit formation in frogs, *Jour. Anim. Behav.*, I, 309–335.

SCHLOSSER, E., 1925: Tierbeobachtungen im Allgau, *Blätt. Aquar.-Terrar-Kde.*, XXXVI, 222.

SCHREITMÜLLER, W., 1909: Einiges über Liebesspiele und Begattung von Triton torosus Eschscholz nebst einer Notiz über Triturus viridescens Rafinesque var. (Neu Orleans), *Wochenschr. Aquar.-Terrar.-Kde.*, VI, *Beilage Lacerta;* 102–104.

SMITH, B. G., 1907: The life history and habits of Cryptobranchus allegheniensis, *Biol. Bull*, XIII, 5–39.

STORER, T. I., 1925: A Synopsis of the Amphibia of California, *Univ. Calif. Pub. Zool.*, XXVII, 1–343, 18 pls.

STROTGEN, F., 1927: Liebesspiele und Begattung bei den Brillensalamandern, *Blatt. Aquar.-Terrar.-Kde.*, XXXVIII, 94–95.

TEN CATE, J., 1928: Contribution à la physiologie de la moelle épiniere chez Triton cristatus, *Arch. Neér. Physiol. Hom. Anim.*, Sér. IIIc, XII, 213–253.

VANDEL, A., 1927: Acquisition d'habitude chez le crapaud, *Bull. Soc. Zool. France*, LII, 50–51.

VERWORN, MAX, 1897: Tonische Reflexe, *Arch. ges. Physiol.*, LXV, 63–80.

WHITMAN, C. O., 1899: Animal behavior, *Woods Hole Biol. Lec.*, 1898, 285–338.

WRIGHT, A. H., 1908: Notes on the breeding habits of Amblystoma punctatum, *Biol. Bull.*, XIV, 284–289.

—— and ARTHUR A. ALLEN, 1909: The early breeding habits *of* Amblystoma punctatum, *Amer. Naturalist*, XLIII, 687–692.

YERKES, R. M., 1903: The instincts, habits and reactions of the frog, *Psych. Rev. Monog.*, IV, 579–638

——, 1905: The sense of hearing in frogs, *Jour. Comp. Neurol. Psych.*, XV, 279–304.

CHAPTER XVII

THE WAYS OF AMPHIBIA

The behavior of Amphibia has been briefly analyzed in the previous chapter, but little space has been given to the placing of these behavior patterns in their natural surroundings. Since Amphibia learn little during their life, it is chiefly their instincts which direct their movements. A few of the major activities of Amphibia may be discussed in relation to their natural setting.

Migration.—Frogs, toads, and salamanders undergo periodic migrations. There is such a close resemblance between these migrations and those of fishes and birds that the causes and controlling factors are apparently much the same. In the spring most northern Amphibia come to the ponds or streams to breed, the males usually preceding the females by one or more days. This order of arrival at the breeding grounds occurs also in the purely aquatic Megalobatrachus (Tago, 1929) and is characteristic of many other groups of vertebrates. As with birds, the male frogs and toads select calling stations and endeavor to attract females toward them by their cries (Fig. 135). With salamanders, voice plays no part in either migration or sex recognition, and hence the early appearance of the males has no obvious advantage. In correlation with the absence of voice the process of successful mating is much more complicated in salamanders than in frogs.

The problem of the causes of migration has two different aspects: first, the development of a sensitivity toward certain external stimuli, and, second, the nature of the directing mechanism of migration activated by this change. The first process is primarily controlled in Amphibia by the seasonal hypertrophy of the gonads, which in turn are under hormonal control, especially by the anterior pituitary gland. Sexually immature individuals do not take part in the chief migrations. The final releasing factor of the migratory impulse is a climatic change. Wright (1914) showed the close correlation between the migration of certain frogs of northeastern United States and the land or water temperatures of the region, while others have stressed the importance of a sudden increase of humidity in producing the spring movements (Cummins, 1920; Noble and Noble, 1923). Heavy spring showers usually initiate the migration of salamanders of both local and foreign species (Kunitomo, 1910). In the tropics, cooling thunderstorms of the wet season bring forth thousands of loudly calling frogs. Bles (1906) showed the importance of a slight cooling of the water in stimulating the breeding activities of African water frogs, Xenopus. Frogs are as sensitive to changes of temperature as are human beings (Babák, 1912), and laboratory experiments have shown that salamanders distinguish between regions of different humidities

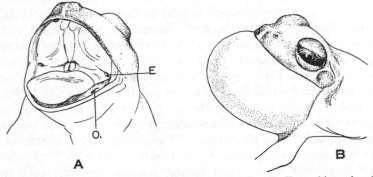

Fig. 135.—The vocal pouch of *Scaphiopus holbrookii*. *E.*, Eustachian tube; *O.*, left orifice to pouch.

(Shelford, 1914). In addition to temperature and rain, local conditions may affect the migrations of a species. Thus, Piersol (1929) has shown that *Ambystoma maculatum* of a certain region near Toronto deposited its eggs over an extended season with the maxima about 10 days apart. This was due to the fact that the adults hibernated in two banks which were unequally exposed to the sun.

Nevertheless, Amphibia do not always show a close correlation between migration and certain temperature and humidity levels. Storer (1925) found that various western toads and frogs had a protracted breeding season, and other species exhibited a certain correlation between egg laying and times of flood. Migration may in certain cases take place without any external stimulation, for salamanders which are bred in the laboratory frequently retain for a time a periodicity in their egg laying and probably, therefore, in their desire to migrate. Toads which were allowed to hibernate in the laboratory at room temperature have been known to appear in the spring at the right season and to call loudly for mates before making an effort to find food or water. It is highly probable that the migrations of many Amphibia are controlled by such rhythms which are in turn determined by climatic changes of previous seasons. These rhythms as suggested by recent endocrine studies are directly controlled by hormones released from the anterior lobe of the pituitary. Both frogs and salamanders may be induced to lay their eggs out of season by treating them with fresh anterior pituitary substance (Chap. XIII). The release of this hormone from the pituitary gland is probably under nervous control. This would account for the close correlation of breeding with certain favorable climatic conditions. Under laboratory conditions, certain species, such as *Pleurodeles waltl*, may be induced to lay their eggs merely by placing them in an ice box over night and transferring them the next morning to tanks suitable for breeding. The sudden rise in temperature releases the ovulation cycle, and both courtship and breeding will frequently follow.

Direction of Migration.—The second problem of migration is the nature of the directing mechanism. This is probably not a simple tropistic phenomenon, for Amphibia breed in a great variety of situations, each species usually in a distinctive habitat. Many land species migrate to ponds to breed, others to mountain streams (Salamandra, etc.); some species move from trees to the ground (some Eleutherodactylus) or from trees to bushes over the water (Phyllomedusa). Parker found that the migration of the young Loggerhead Turtle into the sea was not controlled by any stimulus received from the water. It was due in part to a positive geotropic response and in part to a peculiar phototropic response in that the animal responded to a detail of its retinal image and moved always in the direction of a clear and open horizon. Czeloth (1930) has attempted by laboratory and field study to determine the kind of sensory data which direct the annual migrations of European newts to and from the ponds. He finds that both aquatic and terrestrial individuals will follow the odors of garden earth or of decayed wood. Although newts are able to sense and move toward damp situations, their response to earthy odors is stronger. Individuals freshly removed from the water exhibit a marked positive geotropism but eventually orient themselves in the direction of the water and will move up and down inclines to reach it. In such cases the newts may be responding to either moisture gradients or odors of water vegetation. In the fall other kinds of sensory data may prove more attractive. At this time of year the tendency of newts to seek cover may extend to their directing themselves toward any object, such as a wood, which tends to darken portions of the horizon. The European Salamandra responds apparently much more specifically to environmental factors in the fall, because at this season great numbers of individuals seek the same retreat and form inpressive aggregations during hibernation.

It sometimes happens that in birds and fishes the breeding site may correspond to the probable home of the migrants' ancestors. In another chapter it is pointed out that the breeding habits of Amphibia frequently change more slowly than the adult characters of a form. If a species retains the same breeding habits of an ancestral form, it will tend to migrate to the same breeding grounds. Thus, in Amphibia the derived species may migrate to the ancestral home to lay its eggs. The mountain salamander, *Desmognathus fuscus carolinensis*, returns to the proximity of mountain streams and lays its eggs in the same manner as its close relative *D. f. fuscus* which never lives far away from the water. In cases, however, where the mode of life history has changed, the breeding habitat may give no clue as to the center of dispersal of a group. For example, Hemidactylium seems to have been derived from the terrestrial Plethodon, but its mode of life history is such that the species is forced to make annual migrations to the borders of ponds.

The phenomenon of migration, or at least of the spring migration, may be considered a secondary sexual character found in both sexes. The problem of migration is to determine, first, the sensory mechanisms directing the movements and, second, how the sex hormones elaborate or activate these mechanisms and especially their central connections. In the discussion of the secondary sexual characters it was pointed out that various structures may appear during the breeding season and owe their development to the presence of gonad hormones released at this time. There are probably no special sense organs developed in the breeding season to direct migration, but existing perceptual mechanisms are especially sensitized by the sex hormones and then suddenly called into action by an external stimulus, a climatic change.

A comparison may be made between the migration of the young and of adult Amphibia. During metamorphosis there is a great increase in metabolism and a need for oxygen. It would seem to be primarily this factor which drives the metamorphosing Amphibia to land. It is known that the metabolism of adult Amphibia changes during the breeding season, but no marked drying of the skin or other bodily change has been noticed which would account for the migration of the adults in the reverse direction. The animals react to certain stimuli which did not interest them at other seasons. If the olfactory sense plays such an important rôle in migration as Czeloth's work (1930) seems to indicate, some correlation between the direction of the wind and the direction of migration would be expected. Naturalists have often noted that the spring migrations of Amphibia frequently follow definite routes, but they have not correlated these routes with air currents. The reverse migration away from the grounds after the breeding reflexes have been released is, as would be expected, a far more haphazard affair. In the case of the western Spade-foot Toad, *Scaphiopus hammondi,* Goldsmith (1926) showed that while at first the adults tended to move away from the pools, making 60 to 150 meters a night along the drainage lines, the migrants after one or two nights of rapid centrifugal movement spread out and moved more or less at random. Czeloth (1930) found, however, that immature newts captured in the act of migration from the ponds regained their original orientation when released. In general, nevertheless, when the breeding instinct is aroused, species react to certain sensory data in a more or less reflex manner; while after the final reflexes have been completed, the species return to their usual manner of living. Since the sensory and neuromotor mechanisms of the various species are unlike, different breeding sites are selected and competition is avoided.

The "homing instinct" is frequently brought forward in discussions of migration in other vertebrates. This ability to find one's way home is not well marked in some salamanders (Cummings, 1912; Storer, 1925), but the species which perform the longest migrations have not been investigated in this regard. Amphibia when they become sexually mature return to the type of breeding site characteristic of the species and hence learning could play no part during the first breeding season.   It seems that homing has little to do with the phenomenon of migration.

Although several kinds of sensory data are used by Amphibia during their migrations, one of the most important in frogs and toads would seem to be the voices of other males of the same species.   The first males which happen to reach suitable breeding grounds begin to call.   Other males and later females are attracted by the sounds to the same vicinity.   In this way three or four species may be found breeding in colonies along the same lake without any overlapping of breeding territory (Noble and Noble, 1923).   In frogs as in birds, the breeding territory is usually marked out by the males, and voice in both seems to alter or direct the migration route, or at least the path of the individual, on nearing the breeding site.

Homing.—Laboratory experiments have demonstrated that frogs, toads, and salamanders are able to learn how to find their way through a labyrinth to an accustomed spot.   In the case of frogs and toads, it would seem that the animals are attuned to a certain number of visual impressions and that new scenes are avoided apparently because of discordant feelings which they arouse.   Since useless movements frequently reappear in successive trials, it would seem that Amphibia have also a "muscle memory," at least for short distances.   This obligates them to repeat the same kind and number of movements on each return home after one or more successful performances.

Field observations have demonstrated that Salientia make frequent use of their homing ability whatever may be the nature of their sensory impressions.   Toads regularly return to the same shelter at night.   The large South American frog *Leptodactylus pentadactylus* may have well-marked dens.   During the breeding season many tree frogs which hide during the day will return to precisely the same calling station every night.   This is especially noticeable when the calling station is on an exposed portion of an isolated limb.   Breder (1925) found that the males of *Hyla rosenbergi*, in Panama, returned on successive nights to the mud basins they had constructed along the stream bed for the care of their eggs and tadpoles.

Franz (1927) found that frogs could not home so well as toads, but I have frequently noted in the case of Bullfrogs that certain places along the lake shore are occupied on successive nights during the breeding season by single calling males, while no frogs are in the same place during the day. McAtee (1921) reports a Bullfrog, readily distinguishable by a missing front foot, being twice removed for considerable distances from its home territory to new quarters along the same pond and each time returning to the home site.

Although salamanders are able to learn a maze, they show little homing instinct as far as is known. Storer (1925) found that both Batrachoseps and Ensatina moved about considerably and were not to be found on successive nights in the same retreat.

The most interesting cases of homing have been recorded among frogs of a species that was comparatively slow in learning a laboratory maze. Breder, Breder, and Redmond (1927) found by carefully labeling individual Pond Frogs, *Rana clamitans*, that two out of three caught in a spring and released several hundred feet away on the other side of a stream returned to their home spring, even though they had to cross the water where other Pond Frogs resided. Moreover, an individual captured in the stream and released in the spring returned to its home stream. Another individual transferred from one pool near a stream to another pool on the same side of the stream returned to its home pool, even though other pools intervened and Pond Frogs were living in both pools and stream. Further, there were no obvious differences in the character of the selected habitats. Hence, Pond Frogs even out of the breeding season may have favorite territories to which they return. This is the more surprising in that the species was found to be capable of a considerable random wandering in the same locality.

Yerkes (1903) experimented with this same species of frog in a maze which was arranged with the walls of one alley red and the other white. After the maze had been learned, the color was reversed. This change confused the frogs and they selected the blind alley instead of the outlet, although their previous records had been perfect. This shows that sight as well as kinaesthetic stimulations entered into the learning process. Yerkes further showed that *Rana clamitans* could remember a maze very well. After a 30-day interval, there were 40 per cent of the mistakes at the exit and only 20 per cent at the entrance. This was probably explicable by the fact that the colors acted as aids at the entrance, whereas at the exit there were no such important associational clues. On the day after this series of trials, the record was perfect. These data when combined with the field observations reported above permit us to conclude that frogs are familiar with details in their local habitats and that if they stray from this home they may find their way back even after long periods of time by making use of land marks to a large extent.

Voice.—The Amphibia were apparently the first vertebrates to develop a voice. At least, some Carboniferous forms were provided with a well-developed otic notch across which a tympanum was probably stretched. It is possible that the Rachitomi used their ears only in detecting danger, but in the modern frogs and toads with large tympana the voice is already well established and used for a variety of purposes.

The chief function of the voice of frogs and toads is to attract mates. Only the males are usually provided with a loud voice, the females being either mute or only able to make cries lower than those of the male. From detailed observations on tree frogs it has been determined that the males select the breeding spot and attract the females until they actually come in contact with the body of the male singers. The males of other species, such as Bufo and Scaphiopus, usually do not wait until the females approach so closely but break off their singing abruptly and make an effort to grasp any approaching individuals of either sex. In the case of the American Toad it has been shown that the voice of the male has a strong influence of attraction on the female (Wellman, 1917). On the other hand, the South African *Bufo rosei* is reported to lack a voice. How the males of this species find their mates is not known.

Frogs and toads may be directed to ponds because of their special sensitivity toward marsh odors or gradients of humidity during the breeding season, but once they have arrived on the breeding grounds the voice of the male would seem to play an important rôle in restricting the range of the colony. Goldsmith (1926) placed a series of *Scaphiopus hammondii* in an open container and gradually approached a chorus of the same species. At a distance of a mile the toads remained quiet, but when within 600 yards of the pool they became markedly active. At this distance the chorus was very audible. There is no evidence that toads hear better than man, and yet, since many species travel long distances to the breeding pools, factors other than voice must be of significance in these migrations.

Species which breed in temporary pools, such a the Spring Peeper, *Hyla crucifer*, or the Spade-foot Toad, *Scaphiopus hol-*

brookii, often have louder voices than forms which spend their lives near permanent bodies of water. Small species usually have shriller voices than large species. Each species has its own characteristic voice, and one of the surest ways of distinguishing closely related species is to discriminate first between their voices at night and then run them down separately with the aid of a hand lamp. Often the voice of a grog or toad will give a clue as to the relationships of a species. The southern toad, *Bufo terrestris*, has nearly the same cry as the northern *Bufo americanus*, but the pitch is higher. Similarly, the southern *Rana sphenocephala* has a higher pitched and more rapid call than the northern *Rana pipiens*, although the syllables in the two cries are very much alike. The two Cricket Frogs have a marked similarity in voice. *Acris gryllus crepitans*, however, chirps slowly two, three, or four times, and never are the syllables given in the quick succession or the continuous rhythmic clicking which characterizes the more northern *Acris g. gryllus*. The Swamp Tree Frogs, Pseudacris, have recently been referred to Hyla, and the voice of the species confirms this arrangement. *Nigrita* has a voice almost exactly like *triseriata*, but the former barely begins the crescendo of notes so characteristic of the latter. In striking contrast, *ocularis*, which is structurally more Hyla-like than the other species and climbs bushes in Hyla fashion, cries in a shrill voice, "Pé-teet." *Ocularis* is apparently the smallest frog in the United States and the cry "Petit" seems highly appropriate. Of especial interest is the first syllable, which has very much the quality of the familiar peep of *Hyla crucifer*. Voice has also been used as evidence of relationship in some exotic frogs, perhaps most recently by Blanchard (1929), in discussing the relationships of certain species of Crinia in Tasmania. Where related species are about the same size, the voices may be nearly similar. Where size has changed frequently in evolution, it would be dangerous to use voice characters as a clue to relationships. In the chapter dealing with life histories, the hylas of Santo Domingo have been considered a closely related group of species, but they differ greatly in size and their voices have very little resemblance.

When a frog calls, the mouth and nostrils are kept tightly closed and the air is driven back and forth between lungs and mouth. Usually one or two slits are present on the floor of the mouth, and the air escaping through them is caught in a pocket of the sub-

hyoid or adjacent muscles which it dilates into one or more balloon-like resonating organs. The sacs are diverticula of the
mouth-cavity lining covered by more or less thinned sheets of
muscle and skin. When the skin is so modified that it balloons
out into a large translucent sac under the chin or into a pair of
such sacs one on either side of the throat, the sacs are said to be
"external." But if the skin of the throat is not thinned, the
whole throat merely assuming a swollen appearance when the
frog calls, the sacs are said to be "internal." Closely related
species of a single genus, such as Hyla, may have different types
of vocal sacs, or again one distinctive type may be found in many
species of a genus, for example in the African Hyperolius. It is
remarkable that precisely the same type of vocal sac has evolved
independently in some of the Ranidae, Hylidae, and Bufonidae.

Bullfrogs and other species having internal sacs frequently call
under water. The voice of those species which have the external
type is modified if the sacs upon inflating meet some obstruction.
The Gray Tree Toad, *Hyla versicolor*, has two different calls: one
a melodious trill given with fully inflated pouch and the other a
feeble bleat, not unlike the cry of a young turkey, made when the
pouch is only half inflated. The western *Hyla regilla* and
apparently a few other tree frogs have more than one sex call,
but the males of the vast majority of Salientia have only a single
cry in each species. These cries range from the melodious drone
of the American Toad to the metallic clang of the Marsupial
Frog, *Gastrotheca monticola;* and from the clattering hammer of
the Carpenter Frog, *Rana virgatipes*, to the birdlike notes of
Hyla phaeocrypta. A few West Indian tree frogs (Eleutherodactylus) may prove to have no voice at all, for they have never
been heard to sing, although extensively collected. Recent field
and laboratory observation indicates that Ascaphus is voiceless
even at the height of the breeding season. The frog lives in
rapidly flowing mountain streams, where the males would have
difficulty in making themselves heard.

Significance of Voice.—Besides the breeding call of the males,
most Salientia are able to produce a few guttural croaks or chirps.
As pointed out below, these sounds are of great importance to
frogs and toads in the recognition of sex. The females of several
European Salientia and one of our western toads, *Scaphiopus
hammondii*, have been credited with low voices (Storer, 1925).
Dähne (1914) described the voice of the female Midwife Toad,

Alytes obstetricans, as louder than that of the male. Lankes (1928) has recorded a voice in the female *Hyla caerulea,* feebler but of higher tone than the males. It would seem that a distinctive voice might aid in the recognition of sex, although no observations have confirmed this opinion.

Frogs and toads when escaping from their enemies will often croak or chirp. The croak which usually accompanies the splash of a frog into the water is, of course, well known. Many Salientia when pinched or startled give vent to a very different cry. It may be a scream, as in many ranas; a loud clatter, as in *Scaphiopus holbrookii;* or a shrill squeal, as in *Eleutherodactylus inoptatus.* In all cases the mouth is held widely open, and the lungs are only partly deflated at each note. Dickerson (1906) records that both sexes of *Hyla arenicolor* may give such cries, and Lankes (1928) reports the male *Hyla caerulea* giving it without provocation. The cry is often given when a frog is seized by a snake, and while it may fail to frighten off the serpent, it may at least warn other frogs in the neighborhood.

It is, perhaps, dangerous to speak of the emotions of so passive a creature as a frog. But it should be noted that the reactions of an individual toward the sex cry and the pain cry are totally different. Voice in the frogs and toads has advanced beyond its probable original use as a means of attracting mates together. Many Salientia, such as the proverbial tree toad, will call loudly when the humidity is suddenly raised. Some pond frogs call after the breeding season has passed. These cries, like the summer songs of birds, may not be an expression of sex desire, but with the limited repertoire at a frog's disposal they may be precisely like the sex call. In the fall, with the ripening of the gonads, some northern and many southern frogs begin to call persistently. There are several records of species, which normally breed in the spring, having laid in the fall. Hence the summer cries of frogs may be in their final analysis merely a premature awakening of the sex instincts. There must be, nevertheless, various grades of desire. Krefft (1911) reports a female *Nectophrynoides tornieri* quietly listening to the song of a male, and on several occasions I have found female Cricket Frogs, *Acris gryllus,* sitting in a circle with heads directed toward a calling male.

In urodeles the voice plays no part in the breeding process, and most species seem to be silent throughout life. The newts sometimes give a faint squeak when coming up to the surface for air or when roughly handled in the water. The lungless *Aneides lugubris* is known to be able to make a squeaking noise. Geyer (1927) has recorded several instances of salamanders, both lunged and lungless species, giving sounds. The larger salamanders, Siren and Amphiuma, have been credited with whistling sounds, and the giant Megalobatrachus with a shrill cry. In all these cases the sound is probably accidental and associated with the sudden emptying of the lungs or buccal cavity. At least it is not known to have any significant effect on the behavior of the creature's associates.

Recognition of Sex.—It is frequently difficult for the collector to distinguish the sexes of Amphibia in the field. How do the breeding males distinguish the females from their own sex? Females come to the breeding grounds attracted in part by the call of the male. In the case of tree toads stated above, the female may even follow the voice until she strikes the male's body. Most male frogs and toads seize any object of about their own size moving near them; a tree toad, when touched by the female, turns and embraces her. Nevertheless, no male frog recognizes the female as a sexual object. If the object embraced possesses certain qualities it is retained until the time of egg laying. The first requirement in the Wood Frog, *Rana sylvatica*, is a wide girth and resistance to compression. Male Wood Frogs injected with water until they had the same firmness as a female with eggs were seized and retained as long as females (Noble and Farris, 1929). A second requirement in the Wood Frog, and especially in the common toad, is silence. The male frog, when embraced by another, croaks; the female remains silent. This differential action has been claimed to be the sole basis of sex recognition, since males were supposed to disdain an embraced partner which croaked. Male toads do not croak but chirp when seized. A colony of breeding toads make a continuous chirping sound, reminding one of a flock of young chicks in great distress. There can be little doubt but that the warning croak or chirp is one of the factors in sex recognition in some frogs and toads, although Hinsche (1926) failed to find evidence of it in the European toad, *Bufo vulgaris*. There are, however, other factors which are equally important. Certain European Salientia are said to interchange calls during the breeding season. The subject is in need of further investigation, especially as the females of all American species have been found to be silent on the breeding grounds, although some at least are capable of emitting loud croaks at other times (Koppanyi and Pearcy, 1924).

The factors permitting sex recognition in frogs and toads would seem to vary with the species, but in all cases there would seem to be more than one. In addition to body size and silence there is clearly an agitation factor in some forms. Hinsche obtained evidence that it was the vibration of the flanks of the female *Bufo vulgaris* and the jolting movements of her locomotion which were chiefly responsible for the male retaining his grip. The skin of the female *B. vulgaris* is rougher than that of the male, and Hinsche found that smooth, hard objects induce failure of the clasping reflex. Males would also not be held by the males, because during the breeding season they change their gait to a hop which makes that sex difficult to catch. There are thus various factors both before and after the embrace which insure that females will be seized instead of males and that they will be held until the time of fertilization. In *Rana esculenta*, Lullies (1926) found that the normal breathing movements of the female during respiration stimulated the clasping reflex. At the height of the season the reflex may be easily evoked in most Salientia but the grip is retained only when other adequate stimuli are present. In species which breed in colonies, the sex calls of the males induce other males to call and the general chorus and activity of the colony stimulates all participants. This in turn seems to increase the speed and strength of the clasping reflex but in the Wood Frog, at least, it does not produce a continuance of the embrace unless the size and resistance requirements are met. Male Wood Frogs release females after egg laying for the same reason that they reject males at the beginning of the period, namely, the body seized does not have sufficient girth or firmness.

The clasping reflex is, therefore, a means to sex recognition in frogs. The spontaneity of this reflex rises and falls with the season. During the breeding period a slight touch on the chest of the male frog induces a vigorous clutching movement but out of the season, no response. Busquet (1910) has shown that the reflex may be evoked at other times of the year by cutting below the medulla. The higher centers and, according to Busquet, the cerebellum in particular exert an inhibitory influence on the clasping reflex which prevents its functioning. During the breeding season the testicular hormone counteracts this inhibitory influence of the higher centers, permitting the clasping reflex to come again into evidence. Hinsche has found evidence that in some cases during the feeding activity of toads the embrace reaction may be released, even though the toads were not at the height of the breeding season. The mechanism by which the higher centers were shunted off in this case is not known. It was shown long ago that frogs raised in the dark have a greater reflex excitability than those raised in the light (Langendorff, 1877) and apparently because, as in the case of the clasping reflex, a dominating higher center, vision, was prevented from functioning.

In urodeles the method of sex recognition seems to approach that of mammals, for in the newt and all plethodontids secretions are released from distinctive skin glands which play an important rôle in courtship. In brightly colored European newts it would seem that the difference of color between the sexes might have some significance. In birds sight and sound alone apparently suffice in discriminating male from female, but here the actions of the two sexes are often very unlike. Various salamanders engage in courtship antics, and their differential behavior finally leads to breeding. In some fishes and Crustacea it is the different behavior of the sexes when two breeding individuals chance to meet which results in reactions leading to a fertilization of the eggs (Holmes, 1916). In Amphibia the matter of meeting is not left so much to chance. Frogs, with a few possible exceptions, are endowed with voices with which they make their whereabouts known, while salamanders frequently exhibit courtship displays which tend to hold the sexes together. The salamanders, as discussed in the previous chapter, have devised several ways of making sure that the female will be present and in the proper position for picking up the spermatophore when it is produced. The olfactory sense seems to play the most important part in sex discrimination in salamanders (Chap. XVI). Jordan (1893) found that newts, however, would emit spermatophores when only males were present. There are several factors involved in the courtship display of newts and other salamanders.

Parental Instinct.—Few other instincts have contributed as much to the success of higher vertebrates as that of parental care. This first manifested itself among vertebrates in a brooding instinct or tendency for one or more parents to remain with the eggs. The instinct appears in a very complex form among various invertebrates and fish; among Amphibia it seems to have independently developed several times.

In the hynobiid salamanders the males remain with the eggs for varying periods to fertilize them. They exhibit an active interest in the eggs and drive the females away in their struggle to gain possession of the eggs. As stated above, the crypto-branchids which have evolved from hynobiids extend this guard-ing until the eggs hatch. Both sexes devour the eggs, but as the guarding male can eat only a small proportion of them, this habit has not interfered with the success of the species. Most Amphibia which lay their eggs in the water abandon them after fertilization, but among those which deposit large-yolked eggs, the female frequently remains with them. Whitman (1899) conceived that the chief utility of this brooding instinct was originally the rest it gave to the parent following oviposition. The protection afforded would be quite sufficient to insure the development of the instinct, natural selection favoring those individuals which keep their position long enough for the eggs to hatch.

The brooding habit is well established in the primitive pletho-dontids. Since many of these forms, such as *Gyrinophilus danielsi*, lay their eggs under stones in streams, the protective value of the instinct is not very great. The habit, however, was carried over to the specialized terrestrial plethodontids where this aspect becomes of the greatest importance. The damp body of the parent assures the eggs sufficient moisture, and her dermal secretions apparently prevent mold from growing over them; at least eggs of some species removed from the parent are usually destroyed by mold. The habit has permitted some forms such as *Aneides lugubris* to lay their eggs in comparatively dry situations.

The bond between parent and eggs is so strong that some terres-trial plethodontids will move their eggs with them when dis-turbed, and most return to the egg mass after being frightened away (Fig. 136). This return of the mother to her charge has been witnessed also in the large Amphiuma which, although primarily an aquatic form, lays its eggs under logs on land. The nature of the sensory impressions directing the parent, whether olfactory, optic, or something more subtle, is entirely unknown. Wilder found that a female *Desmognathus fuscus* will brood the eggs of another female if these are suitably arranged. Hence a female salamander apparently does not recognize its own eggs. The bond between parent and eggs may be considered an instinct and as such to have arisen in the same way as other instincts (Chap. XVI).

The brooding instinct seems to have arisen fully formed in many groups. Thus, most species of Ambystoma abandon their eggs in the water, but *A. opacum* deposits its eggs on land in the fall and curls around them. Although the terrestrial eggs of Desmognathus and other salamanders are sometimes found without parents, it seems probable that the parents may have been destroyed, rather than have failed to exhibit the brooding instinct. It has been shown that *A. opacum*, however, does not return to its eggs when disturbed. Hence, the bond between parents and eggs is not great in this species, and the brooding habit may have

Fig. 136.—Female *Desmognathus fuscus* brooding her eggs.

resulted merely from exhaustion of the female after egg laying. The brooding of Necturus may have even less biological significance. Bishop (1927) found that females occupy the "nest" after the young have departed. Since some adults use these nests as retreats throughout the year, the brooding of Necturus may be merely the result of the disinclination of the adult to leave a favorite retreat.

In higher vertebrates an extension of the brooding instinct leads to care of the young. Among salamanders only some terrestrial plethodontids, Aneides (Storer, 1925), Hemidactylium (Blanchard, 1923), and possibly Plethodon remain with the young after they hatch. In these cases probably little or no protection is given to the young, unless it be that the moist body of the parent prevents their desiccation. Among frogs the habit of brooding the eggs has led to various modifications of the female's body. Protopipa and Pipa carry the eggs in individual sacs on the back until the young hatch fully formed. The Marsupial Frogs, Gastrotheca, employ a single sac, and the young may escape as tadpoles or as metamorphosed frogs. In the case of Gastrotheca, the origin of the sac may be traced to shallow folds bordering the egg mass carried on the back of the female Cryptobatrachus. Once the brooding habit was established in this group of South American tree frogs, it led to marked structural changes in the parent. Less marked changes of the integument have been noted in other brooding frogs, but in no case have emotional bonds been established which make possible the protection of the young after hatching.

The males of various species of frogs have been found guarding the eggs. This habit may not be a true brooding instinct but merely the tendency of the males to remain near their calling stations. In some forms, however, such as the Australian foam nest builder, *Adelotus brevis*, there seems to be a real attraction of the male parent (Deckert, 1929) toward the eggs. This habit seems to have led in the neotropical Phyllobates and Dendrobates to the male's transporting the tadpoles apparently from the place of egg laying to the pools (Noble, 1927). It also may have led to the remarkable habit of the male Rhinoderma of carrying its eggs in the vocal pouch until the young are fully formed.

Feeding Habits.—Frogs and toads eat animal food when adult and either animal food or plant food when larvae. The bulk of the food consists of insects, spiders, millipeds, snails, worms, and similar small fry. It was found in the laboratory that toads could learn after a single experience to avoid an obnoxious insect, and Haber (1926) has observed a toad attempting to disgorge a stinkbug (pentatomid), which it had seized. Insects giving off acrid or irritating substances were found by Haber to form but a small portion of the diet of *Hyla cinerea*. Nevertheless, it has frequently been noted that neither frogs nor toads have marked food preferences. Goldsmith (1925) found that the Spade-foot Toad, *Scaphiopus hammondii*, devoured all types of surface insects, ants of the genus Atta being the predominant form. The diet varies more or less with the habitat of the species; frogs naturally capture more aquatic forms than toads do. Detailed studies have been made of the diet of frogs (Surface, 1913; Drake, 1914; Munz, 1920), tree frogs (Storer, 1925; Haber, 1926), and particularly the common toads (Kirkland, 1897, 1904; Hodge, 1898; Garman, 1901; Kellogg, 1922), while some observations are available on species of other genera and families (Noble, 1924). Ants and termites, which are eaten by most Salientia, rise to a high percentage in certain slow-moving, burrowing types, while they almost disappear from the diet of aquatic forms. Many large and a few medium-sized frogs have been found to be cannibalistic. This is particularly true of the larger species of Ceratophrys of South America and the brilliant *Rana ornatissima* of Africa, but observations are not sufficiently numerous to determine what percentage of their yearly diet consists of their fellow frogs.

It is interesting that the tadpole of *Ceratophrys ornata* should be largely cannibalistic, feeding on the larvae of other frogs. Tadpoles in general show greater food preferences than adult frogs, for some are exclusively vegetarian, others carnivorous, while the majority take a mixed diet. The common water silk, Spirogyra, forms one of the best foods for most tadpoles reared in the laboratory. This diet may be varied with strips of water-soaked beef which foul the water less quickly than pieces of earthworm.

Terrestrial Salientia, and especially toads, although indiscriminate feeders, are of economic value, for they devour the dominant insects or other invertebrates of any one locality; and around greenhouses, gardens, or farms such dominant forms are usually pests. Kirkland (1897) found that enough food was taken by the common toad to fill the stomach completely four times in 24 hours. Pack (1922) records a case where the toad was of real value in fighting an outbreak of sugar-beet webworms. If toads could be transported in great numbers across the country, they might be of service in counteracting plagues.

Urodeles apparently restrict themselves to an animal diet during both larval and adult life. They show a greater tendency to take quiescent food than most frogs. Thus Necturus has been reported to devour great numbers of fish eggs and Cryptobranchus, Pleurodeles, Salamandrina, Ensatina, and Aneides have on occasions eaten their own eggs. Storer (1925) is inclined to believe that fungus found in the stomach of the latter form was eaten intentionally. Similarly, algae taken from the stomach of Siren has been described as present in too great a quantity to have been devoured accidentally with the animal food known to form a large part of their diet (Dunn, 1924). Size may have an important influence on diet. The small Salamandrina does not feed well on Enchytraei, apparently because the small tongue is fitted only for the capture of dry food such as insects (Klingelhöffer, 1930). As in the case of frogs, the larger species are frequently cannibalistic. Dicamptodon, Ambystoma, Gyrinophilus, and Aneides have been reported to eat smaller species of salamanders. In the laboratory the large *Desmognathus quadramaculatus* may be kept in good health on a diet consisting of smaller species of Desmognathus exclusively. No species of urodele is known to restrict its diet to a particular kind of animal food.

The different manner of capturing prey would account for such differences as exist between the diet of adult frogs and urodeles. Hargitt (1912) found that tree frogs usually leap to take their prey, rarely stalking it. They usually wait for the prey to come within leaping distance, which may be a matter of several feet, and when they spring they rarely miss. If the prey should come within close range, it is apparently not seen. In striking contrast the response of newts to a moving object is a stealthy approach. The object is then nosed and if found satisfactory the snapping reflexes are evoked (Copeland 1913). Newts will snap at movable inedible objects and also at invisible edible substances such as fine suspensions of beef juice. Some newts will feed after their optic and olfactory nerves are cut and when the lateral-line organs alone are apparently functioning as distance perceptors (Matthes, 1924). Hence, while the normal order of events in the feeding process is optic stimulations inducing the approach reaction, followed by olfactory stimulations evoking the nosing and finally the snapping reactions, the last reaction may be called forth by sight, smell, or lateral-line stimulation alone.

Smell has also been found to function without vision in the case of Ambystoma larvae (Nicholas, 1922). Smell would seem to be of great importance to Amphiuma, for Hargitt (1892) found that clams form a large part of its diet. Whether aquatic Salientia depend more on smell than terrestrial ones do is not known, but the evidence suggests that vision may be used to the exclusion of smell in some land forms. Such species would not be able to devour eggs or other immobile food, for it is a moving object in the field of vision which excites motor reactions in most Amphibia.

The evolution of the higher groups of vertebrates seems closely correlated with changes in food habits. There is little evidence of such correlation in Amphibia. Gyrinophilus, perhaps the most cannibalistic plethodontid, does not have proportionately longer teeth than many small species of the same family. The marked changes of dentition within such genera as Desmognathus is not known to have any correlated changes in diet. Morphological change may have induced a few restrictions of diet. The large toads of Africa feed rarely if ever on mammals, whether or not this is due to their toothless jaws (Noble, 1924). The narrowing of the mouth in the Pipidae may have brought certain adaptive changes especially in the fingers which became important aids in feeding. No other Amphibia stuff their food into the mouth with their fingers nor even habitually hold the food with their forelimbs while devouring it. But the tongueless Xenopus is very adept in seizing its prey with its long fingers and forcing it into its comparatively small mouth. In Pipa a rosette of papillae tip the ends of each finger and are provided with tactile organs which apparently aid in locating living food.

Long teeth when they occur in the Amphibia are frequently used to good effect. Powerful jaws have no doubt been of assistance to the tadpole of *Ceratophrys ornata* in devouring other tadpoles. The adult of this species has enlarged dagger teeth in the upper jaw which are said to serve as effective weapons. Dr. W. M. Mann found that the Solomon Island Ceratobatrachus, which unlike most frogs has teeth in both jaws, exhibited bulldog tenacity in holding to a seized object.

Responses to Temperature Change.—A lowering of temperature below 8°C. was found to induce laboratory frogs to seek a retreat under objects in the bottom of the tank (Torelle, 1903). As pointed out by Holmes (1927), this may not be so much a reversal of the phototropism as a release of instincts to dive down and crawl under objects. The normal stereotropic response of toads is more pronounced at low than at high temperatures (Riley, 1913). Toads burrow into the ground on the approach of cold weather and while digging with their hind feet presumably keep their original orientation as regards light. Toads may burrow to a depth of 18 inches in sandy soil and 8 inches in clay ground (Butler, 1885). Frogs hibernate in mud in the bottom of ponds, in springs, or in damp spots in the woods. Some merely dig under decaying vegetation or other débris in their normal habitats. A single species may hibernate in different situations in different parts of its range. McAtee found that

Eurycea bislineata in Indiana will come out of the water in November and pass the winter under logs and stones near streams. In the New York region the same species is never found on land in midwinter but may be collected in numbers by turning over the stones in the deeper portions of flowing streams.

Brooks (1918) found that between the temperatures of 5 and 20°C. the warmer the water the greater the time *Rana pipiens* spent at the surface. No doubt other frogs would be affected the same way, although each species would have its own range of response. Cole (1922) found that the higher the temperature the shorter the reaction time to light. Lutz (1918) showed that warming lowers the thresholds for both reflex and nerve-muscle responses in the frog. Between 4 and 30°C. the reflex threshold is lowered to a much greater degree than the nerve-muscle threshold. Hence temperature would seem to act directly on the synapse between the neurons in the reflex arcs. At low temperature the normal reflexes to environmental stimulations are unable to appear. It may be noted also that the integumental sense organs of the frog require a higher temperature to induce a response if the temperature increase is gradual than they do if it is sudden (Morgan, 1922), and, hence, sudden changes in temperature would have a more marked effect on frogs in nature than gradual ones.

Wright (1914) finds that most species hibernating on land are responsive to climatic changes earlier than those hibernating in the water. The rule does not always hold, however, for hibernating *H. crucifer*, an early breeder, has been found in springs in midwinter, while *H. versicolor*, a late breeder, digs down in the débris in the bottom of the holes in the trees where it spends the late summer. Brook salamanders such as *Desmognathus fuscus* hibernate under rocks in running water, and here it cannot be merely a negative phototropism which brings them there. Pond species, such as the newt, usually remain in the ponds during the winter, although from the observations of Wolterstorff (1922) cold must slow down their activity greatly. Szymanski (1914) recorded on a kymograph the movements of Salamandra during hibernation. From November to January there was no movement of the body, although a slight change occurred in the position of the limbs. Tiger salamanders have been described as passing the winter in the bottom of the pools (Shelford, 1913). Other species of Ambystoma, such as *A. maculatum*, undoubtedly hibernate on land.   In spite of the different temperatures of these situations the two forms breed almost simultaneously in the East, the water-hibernating species a little before the land-wintering form.

Since egg laying is controlled by the secretions of the anterior pituitary gland, the functioning of the latter is apparently influenced by temperature. Barthélémy (1926) records *Rana fusca*, however, exhibiting an increase in weight, *i.e.*, evidence of sexual activity, in the spring even when low temperatures were maintained.   Hence, hormone control is partly free from temperature control.

The utility of hibernation is obvious.   Levy (1900) found that frogs could live under water at temperatures of from 0 to 9°C. without injury for long periods, while they would surely die if they attempted to winter in their usual habitats.   Some European frogs have been credited with surviving temperatures of −4 to −6°C. (Muller-Erzbach, 1891).   *Rana pipiens* dies at temperatures a little lower than a degree below freezing.   Cameron (1914) found that death was due to a specific temperature effect on the coordinating centers of the central nervous system. The heart tissue survives at temperatures nearly 3° below freezing and the body-muscle tissue at practically the same (Cameron and Brownlee, 1913).   Frogs and salamanders frozen in blocks of ice frequently survive for short periods.   In the case of Amphibia hibernating on land, the dryness of the winter air would have a detrimental influence perhaps equal to that of the cold (Hecht, 1928).

Frogs frequently mate in the spring directly after coming from hibernation.   Barthélémy (1926) found that hibernation was necessary for the maturation of the eggs of *Rana fusca*.   Hibernation was found not to be essential, however, for the health of various Californian toads, frogs, and tree frogs.   *Rana aurora draytonii*, for example, hibernates in some California localities but not in others.   Frogs in the laboratory do not hibernate unless the temperature is lowered.

Temperature Preferences.—Amphibia frequently change their habitat at the time of hibernating.   Abbott (1882) describes the Cricket Frog, *Acris gryllus*, as leaving the ponds and migrating to rocky ravines in the fall where it hibernates under stones and logs out of water.   Terrestrial salamanders, such as *Desmognathus fuscus carolinensis*, hibernate under rocks in mountain streams.

Where many salamanders have been found together in hibernating dens, as, for example, in the case of *Salamandra salamandra*, there must have been some movement in the fall if only to look for suitable hibernating quarters. Such movements never take on the appearance of the spring migration, but they have various parallels in the fall migration of some birds and mammals.

The various species of Amphibia have certain temperature optima at which they live best. This may be only a few degrees above freezing in the case of Ascaphus, which lives at high altitudes in northwestern United States. Frog tadpoles frequently seek the warmer margins of pools whether they be attracted there by the greater light or by the higher temperature. Brues (1927) found the tadpoles of various frogs in the hot spring waters, ranging from 104 to 106°F. Most Amphibia cannot stand high temperatures for any period, the optimum for both *Rana pipiens* and Necturus lying near 18°C. (Sayle, 1916; Cameron, 1921). The greater temperature tolerance of *Eurycea multiplicata* over that of Typhlotriton is apparently the chief factor permitting the former to wander in and out of caves. Reese (1906) found that Necturus was affected more than Cryptobranchus by extremely high temperatures, however, and yet the former lives in a greater variety of habitats. Hence, in one species, temperature may have an important control over distribution and in another, other factors may be more important. It may be said that attempts to determine the ability of Amphibia to discriminate between temperatures have not been successful. Pearse (1909) found that toads in the dark were indifferent to a steam pipe and salamanders in the laboratory usually react poorly to gradients of temperature.

Responses to Humidity Change.—Amphibia with their thin, moist skins are very sensitive to changes in humidity, and their habitat selection as well as their daily movements may be controlled to a large extent by their reaction to this change. Goldsmith (1926) found that digging reactions were induced in the Spade-foot Toad, *Scaphiopus hammondii,* by evaporation, and this species was sensitive to a humidity change of 10 per cent at a temperature of 27°C. Shelford (1914) studied the effects of evaporation on both frogs and salamanders. Responses occurred whether the evaporation was due to the dryness, warmth, or movements of the air. *Plethodon glutinosus* was clearly more sensitive than the much smaller *Plethodon cinereus*. This is surprising, for the surface per unit of weight is greater in small objects. The observation is of especial interest, for it gives an explanation as to why the former species lives in damper situations than the latter. Both salamanders and frogs were stimulated at once by dry air and endeavored to avoid it. Toads survived the treatment longer than frogs, a fact which would be expected because of their thicker skins. Shelford suggests that the responses of Amphibia to humidity change may be due to a disturbance in the neutrality of the body fluids due to the changing rates of evaporation. Probably the drying of the skin would also have a direct effect on the integumental sense organs. Rapid drying is far more serious to the health of Amphibia than slow drying. Frogs die after a loss of less than 15 per cent of their weight if the evaporation is rapid, while they may survive nearly twice this loss if it is slow (Kunde, 1857). Toads may even stand a loss of 50 per cent of their weight (Langlois and Pellegrin, 1902), a great increase in the density of their blood occurring during the experiment.

Most Amphibia wander at night when the humidity is greater than during the day. The migrations and breeding of many frogs and salamanders are initiated by the rains, although the temperature factor may also be important as well. Many small tree frogs have the same climbing mechanisms of large species but they rarely ascend tall trees, apparently because of the high evaporation rate of such an exposed position. At times of draught the amphibian inhabitants of certain ponds or trees may come together in the damper or more favorable shelters. Various species of desert frogs have been described as undergoing a true aestivation. The Sardinian cave salamander, *Hydromantes genei*, has been reported to aestivate during the summer months even in the laboratory where moist conditions were presumably maintained (Mertens, 1923). Whether or not any of these Amphibia really aestivate, there is no doubt that the different humidity requirements of the various species are one of the most important factors limiting their ranges and activities.

Defense.—Amphibia have few methods of defending themselves from their enemies. As a group they are relatively immobile. Their habit of maintaining a fixed posture between movements results in their frequently being overlooked by possible enemies. Their first reaction to distant disturbances is an inhibition of all movement, even the respiratory movements of the throat. When danger approaches, they usually seek safety in flight, most seeking crevices and other natural shelters, a few, burrows which they had previously dug. Some of the larger species apparently defend themselves by biting. This is true of Gyrinophilus, Cryptobranchus, Aneides, as well as the usually good-natured *Plethodon glutinosus* and *Desmognathus fuscus*. Diller (1907) found an 8-inch Ambystoma with a grip on a 2-foot garter snake, and it was apparent that the salamander was having the better of the struggle. The large South American frog, *Ceratophrys dorsata*, can inflict a serious bite and does not hesitate to use its teeth when annoyed. In this species, as in various forms of Rana, the mento-Meckelian bones originally used for closing the nostrils are hypertrophied into a formidable spike. Brook salamanders, such as Desmognathus and Eurycea, are able to twist strenuously in the hand when seized, and Amphiuma is notorious for its ability both to bite and to twist at the same time.

Frogs in the act of leaping often release the contents of their urinary bladders, thus lightening their bodies and screening their path of retreat. Amphibia receive their chief protection from their skin glands, the mucus making them slippery and difficult to hold, while the poison or granular glands have frequently a serious effect on such tissues as the lining of a dog's mouth. Some burrowing Salientia, especially certain Spade-foot Toads, develop secondary deposits of bone in the skin of the head. In a few genera (Ceratophrys, Melgalophrys, and Brachycephalus) of unrelated families, this deposition of bone may extend to the skin of the back. A number of tree frogs, Hyla, Gastrotheca, etc., develop a similar armature, and the correlation of secondary bone deposits and special habitats is not close.

Certain movements of Amphibia may increase the flow of the skin secretions. The "warning attitude" of Bombina is accompanied by such a flow. The salamander, *Ensatina eschscholtzii* (Fig. 137), stands high on its legs when annoyed and waves its tail, which actively secretes (Hubbard, 1903). Frogs and toads have a limited repertoire of defense reactions. Most species will blow up their lungs, close the eyes, and bend the head in a crouching attitude. Hinsche (1923) finds that this reaction is called forth in toads by either tactile or visual stimulations but not by sounds. It is better developed in old than young individuals.

Many frogs and toads when pinched will open their mouths and give a shrill cry. It would seem to be an important frightening device, although critical field observations concerning its effectiveness are lacking. Hinsche (1923) finds that this frightening reaction may be induced in Bufo, but the toad opens its mouth and straightens its legs without producing a sound. Hinsche (1928) has shown that the head-bending and leg-straightening reaction is part of a complex series of defense reactions common to many Salientia. In the course of phylogeny, some parts of this series of reflexes, such as the warning cry, are lost, while other phases, such as the pushing with bowed head, are modified. It is interesting that the more terrestrial Salientia should exhibit the series of reflexes in their most developed form. As discussed in another chapter (page 381), many reflexes, such as the "unken reflex" and the scream reaction, exhibit a gradual

Fig. 137.—*Ensatina eschscholtzii* defending itself against a Ring-necked Snake. (*After Hubbard.*)

modification in phylogeny but the change is not always closely correlated with an obvious utility.

Tonic Immobility.—Salamanders, frogs, and toads may be readily thrown into a state of tonic immobility which, under certain circumstances, may prove a protective measure. Young toads when picked up will frequently partially contract their limbs and become immobile (Mangold, 1925). This behavior has been compared with the hypnotic state produced in man by suggestion. It is commonly seen in such salamanders as Plethodon and Ambystoma, which when handled gently often exhibit a "death feint." It may be most readily induced in both frogs and salamanders by placing the individual on its back and holding it there a moment. The death feint usually lasts only a few minutes, but it may be prolonged over an hour if disturbing sensory impressions are avoided. A sudden tactile or visual stimulation will arouse the frog or salamander from this state.

Mangold and Eckstein (1919) have studied the reflex excitability in certain European frogs which had been hypnotized, that is, thrown into this state of tonic immobility. This was tested by counting the number of electric shocks necessary to induce the springing reflex when these stimulations were of the same intensity and given at the rate of 21 to 24 per minute. They found a decided lowering of the reflex excitability in hypnotized frogs. The degree of lowering was dependent on the depth of the hypnotic state. Frogs hypnotized by being placed on their back were much less sensitive to stimulations than those hypnotized belly down. This is correlated with the more easy inducement of hypnosis and slower awakening of frogs placed on their back.

The protective value of tonic immobility in Amphibia is not great. In certain birds brooding their eggs in exposed situations and in certain insects which resemble twigs, the ability quickly to assume and hold a stiff posture on the approach of danger has great survival value. In these forms the stimulus which frightens the creature sets up the hypnotic state. In Amphibia hypnosis is produced only by sudden tactile stimulations, although a more extended development of this type of response might have great advantages.

Leaping of Salamanders and Frogs.—One of the most surprising escape reactions of salamanders is the leaping movements of terrestrial plethodontids. The tail is struck sharply against the ground at the same moment that a spring is made with the short legs. The combined effect is a leap frequently greater than the length of the animal's body. In such a defenseless creature as *Plethodon cinereus* this leap may well be an important method of escape, but it may also be a means of aggression, especially useful in capturing food.

The tails of many terrestrial salamanders when seized may be readily thrown off by their owners. The mechanism of this autotomy is different from that in lizards, the break occurring in the myoseptum and extending between the vertebrae. In lizards a special breakage plane is developed across each vertebra. Autotomy in salamanders resembles that in lizards in that the musculature is broken off nearer the tail base than the skin is. The raw flesh on the freed tail induces writhing movements in the discarded appendage, while the extra skin on the tail base curls over the wound and facilitates healing. In a few terrestrial plethodontids such as Hemidactylium and Ensatina a double or single groove occurs around the tail base and the split occurs here instead of anywhere along the tail as in Plethodon.

One mechanism of escape which has a strong appeal to the imagination is found in the much discussed "Flying Frog" of Borneo and adjacent regions. Wallace, in his "Malay Archipelago," tells of the tree frog, *Polypedates nigropalmatus*, which has large webs between all its digits, being brought to him by a Chinese workman who claimed he had seen it engaged in a slanting flight from a high tree. Recently Ayyanger (1915) has recorded a slanting flight of 30 or 40 feet in the related *Polypedates malabaricus*. Cott (1926) watched tree frogs of a different family in Brazil and saw *Hyla venulosa* voluntarily leap off into space at a height of 40 feet from the ground. In a series of experiments Cott concluded that this species could fall 140 feet or more without injury. No doubt smaller frogs could fall even greater distances without injury because of their relatively greater surface as compared with their weight. Little frogs as a rule do not climb tall trees, however.

References

ABBOTT, C. C., 1882: Notes on the habits of the Savannah Cricket Frog (Acris crepitans), *Amer. Naturalist*, XVI, 701–711.

AYYANGER, M. P., 1915: A South Indian flying frog, Rhacophorus malabaricus (Jerdon), *Rec. Ind. Mus. Calcutta*, XI, 140–142.

BABÁK, E., 1912: Über die Temperaturempfindlichkeit der Amphibien. Zugleich ein Beitrag zur Energetik des Nervengeschehens, *Zeitschr. Psych. Leipzig.*, *Abt.* 2, XLVII, 34–45.

BARTHÉLÉMY, H., 1926: Recherches biométriques et expérimentales sur l'hibernation, la maturation et la surmaturation de la grenouille rousse ♀ (Rana fusca), *Compt. rend. Acad. Sci.*, CLXXXII, 1653–1654.

BISHOP, S. C., 1927: The amphibians and reptiles of Allegany State Park, *N. Y. State Mus.*, *Albany*, *Handb.*, III, 1–141.

BLANCHARD, F. N., 1923: The life history of the four-toed salamander, *Amer. Naturalist*, LVII, 262–268.

———, 1929: Re-discovery of Crinia tasmaniensis, *Australian Zoologist*, V, 324–328.

BLES, E. J., 1906: The life history of Xenopus laevis Daud., *Trans. Roy. Soc. Edinburgh*, XLI, 789–821, 4 pls.

BREDER, C. M., 1925: In Darien Jungles, *Nat. Hist.*, XXV, 325–337.

———, R. B. BREDER, and A. C. REDMOND, 1927: Frog tagging: A method of studying anuran life habits, *Zoologica*, IX, 201–229.

BROOKS, E. S., 1918: Reactions of frogs to heat and cold, *Amer. Jour. Physiol.*, XLVI, 493–501.

BRUES, C. T., 1927: Studies on the fauna of hot springs in the western United States and the biology of thermophilous animals, *Proc. Amer. Acad. Arts. Sci.*, VI, No. 4, 140–228, 6 pls.

BUSQUET, H., 1910: Existence chez la grenouille mâle d'un centre médullaire permanent présidant à la copulation. Action inhibitrice du cervelet sur le centre de la copulation chez la grenouille. Independence fonctionelle de ce centre vis-à-vis du testicule, *Compt. rend. Soc. Biol.*, LXVIII, 880–881, 911–913.

BUTLER, A. W., 1885: Hibernation of the lower vertebrates, *Amer. Naturalist*, XIX, 37–40.

CAMERON, A. T., 1914: Further experiments on the effect of low temperatures on the frog, *Proc. Trans. Roy. Soc. Canada*, VIII, Sec. IV, 261–266.

———, 1921: Further experiments on conditions influencing the life history of the frog, *Proc. Trans. Roy. Soc. Canada*, XV, Sec. V, 13–21.

———, and J. I. BROWNLEE, 1913: The effect of low temperatures on the frog, *Proc. Trans. Roy. Soc. Canada*, VII, Sec. IV, 107–124.

COLE, L. J., 1922: The effect of temperature on the phototropic response of Necturus, *Jour. Gen. Physiol.*, IV, 569–572.

COPELAND, MANTON, 1913: The olfactory reactions of the spotted newt, Diemyctylus viridescens (Rafinesque), *Jour. Anim. Behav.*, III, 260–273.

COTT, H. B., 1926: Observations on the life-habits of some batrachians and reptiles from the Lower Amazon, *Proc. Zool. Soc. London*, 1926, II, 1159–1178, 6 pls.

CUMMINGS, B. F., 1912: Distant orientation in Amphibia, *Proc. Zool. Soc. London*, 1912, I, 8–19.

CUMMINS, HAROLD, 1920: The rôle of voice and coloration in spring migration and sex recognition in frogs, *Jour. Exp. Zool.*, XXX, 325–343.

CZELOTH, H., 1930: Untersuchungen über die Raumorientierung von Triton, *Zeitschr. vergl. Physiol.*, XIII, 74–163.

DÄHNE, CURT, 1914: Alytes obstetricans und seine Brutpflege, *Blätt. Aquar.-Terrar.-Kde.*, XXV, 227–229.

DAVENPORT, C. B., and W. E. CASTLE, 1895: Studies in Morphogenesis; III. On the acclimatization of organisms to high temperatures, *Arch. Entw. Mech.*, II, 227–249.

DECKERT, KURT, 1929: Import und Nachzucht von Adelotus brevis Günther (Ein neuer australischer Wasserfrosch), *Lacerta.*, 1929, No. 5, 17–18 (*Beilage zur Wochenschr. Aquar.-Terrar.-Kde.*, XXVI, No. 18).

DICKERSON, MARY C., 1906: "The Frog Book," New York.

DILLER, J. S., 1907: A salamander-snake fight, *Science, n. s.*, XXVI, 907–908.

DRAKE, CARL J., 1914: The food of Rana pipiens Shreber, *Ohio Naturalist*, XIV, 257–269.

DUNN, E. R., 1924: Siren, a herbivorous salamander, *Science, n. s.* LIX, 145.

FRANZ, V., 1927: Zur tierpsychologischen Stellung von Rana temporaria und Bufo calamita, *Biol. Zentralbl.*, XLVII, 1–12.

GARMAN, H., 1901: The food of the toad, *Kentucky Agr. Exp. Sta. Bull.*, No. 91.

GEYER, H., 1927: Über Lautäusserungen der Molche, *Blätt Aquar.-Terrar.-Kde.*, XXXIX, 27–28.

GOLDSMITH, G. W., 1924–25: Habits and reactions of Scaphiopus hammondi, *Yr. Bk. Carnegie Inst. Wash.*, XXIV, 340–341.

———, 1925–26: Habits and reactions of Scaphiopus hammondi, *Yr. Bk. Carnegie Inst. Wash.*, XXV, 369–370.

HABER, V. R., 1926: The food of the Carolina tree frog, Hyla cinerea Schneider, *Jour. Comp. Psych.*, VI, 189–220.

HARGITT, C. W., 1892: On some habits of Amphiuma means, *Science*, XX, 159.

———, 1912: Behavior and color changes of tree frogs, *Jour. Anim. Behav.*, II, 51–78.

HECHT, G., 1928: Probleme der Überwinterung, *Blätt. Aquar.-Terrar.-Kde.* XXXIX, 52–55.

HINSCHE, G., 1923: Über Bewegungs und Haltungsreaktionen bei Kröten, *Biol. Zentralbl.*, XLIII, 16–26.

———, 1926: Über Brunst und Kopulationsreaktionen des Bufo vulgaris, *Zeitschr. vergl. Physiol.*, IV, 564–606.

———, 1928: Kampfreaktionen bei einheimschen Anuren, *Biol. Zentralbl.*, XLVIII, 577–617.

HODGE, C. F., 1898: "The Common Toad," Worcester, Mass.

HOLMES, S. J., 1916: "Studies in Animal Behavior," Boston.

———, 1927: "The Biology of the Frog," New York.

HUBBARD, MARIAN E., 1903: Correlated protective devices in some California salamanders, *Univ. Cal. Pub. Zool.*, I, 157–170.

JORDAN, E. O., 1893: The habits and development of the newt, *Jour. Morph.*, VIII, 269–366, 15 pls.

KELLOGG, REMINGTON, 1922: The Toad, *U. S. Dept. Agr. Bur. Biol. Survey. MS.*

KIRKLAND, A. H., 1897: The habits, food and economic value of the American toad, *Hatch Exp. Sta., Mass. Agr. Coll., Amherst, Bull.* 46, 1–29.

———, 1904: Usefulness of the American toad, *U. S. Dept. Agr. Farmer's Bull.* 196.

KOPPÁNYI, T., and J. F. PEARCY, 1924: Studies on the clasping reflex in Amphibia, *Amer. Jour. Physiol.*, LXXI, 34–39.

KREFFT, PAUL, 1911: Über einen lebendiggebärenden Froschlurch Deutsch-Ostafrikas (Nectophryne tornieri Roux), *Zool. Anz.*, XXXVII, 457–462.

KUNDE, F., 1857: Über Wasserentziehung und Bildung vorübergehender Katarakte, *Zeitschr. Wiss. Zool.*, VIII, 466–486.

KUNITOMO, K., 1910: Über die Entwickelungsgeschichte des Hynobius nebulosus, *Anat. Hefte*, XL, 193–284, 4 pls.

LANGENDORFF, O., 1877: Die Beziehungen des Sehorgans zu den reflexhemmenden Mechanismen des Froschgehirns, *Zeitschr. Anat. Entw.*, 1877, 435–442.

LANGLOIS, J. P., and J. PELLEGRIN, 1902: De la déshydratation chez le crapaud et des variations corrélatives de la densité du sang, *Compt. rend. Soc. Biol.*, LIV, 1377–1379.

LANKES, K., 1928: Zur Biologie des Korallensingers, Hyla caerulea, *Blätt. Aquar.-Terrar.-Kde.*, XXXIX, 6–7.

LEVY, M., 1899–1900: Das Leben der Frösche unter dem Wasser, *Zool. Garten*, XL, 147–148, XLI, 178–180.

LULLIES, H., 1926: Der Mechanismus des Umklammerungsreflexes, *Arch. ges. Physiol.*, CCXIV, 416–420.

LUTZ, B. R., 1918: Threshold values in the spinal frog; I. Comparison of the flexion reflex and the nerve-muscle response; II. Variations with change of temperature, *Amer. Jour. Physiol.*, XLV, 507–527.

MANGOLD, E., 1925: Methodik der Versuche über tierische Hypnose, *Abderhaldens Handb. biol. Arbeitsmeth.*, Abt. VI, Teil C-I, Heft 5 (Lief. 159), 320–368.

MANGOLD, E., and A. ECKSTEIN, 1919: Die Reflexerregbarkeit in der tierischen Hypnose, *Arch. ges. Physiol.*, CLXXVII, 1–37.

MATTHES, ERNST, 1924: Die Rolle des Gesichts-, Geruchs- und Erschütterungssinnes für den Nahrungserwerb von Triton, *Biol. Zentralbl.*, XLIV, 72–87.

MCATEE, W. L., 1921: Homing and other habits of the bullfrog, *Copeia*, No. 96, 39–40.

MERTENS, R., 1923: Zur Biologie des Höhlenmolches, Spelerpes fuscus Bonaparte, *Blätt. Aquar.-Terrar.-Kde.*, XXXIV, 171–174.

MORGAN, ANN H., 1922: The temperature senses in the frog's skin, *Jour. Exp. Zool.*, XXXV, 83–110.

MÜLLER-ERZBACH, W., 1891: Die Widerstandsfähigkeit des Frosches gegen das Einfrieren, *Zool. Anz.*, XIV, 383–4.

MUNZ, PHILIP A., 1920: A study of the food habits of the Ithacan species of Anura during transformation, *Pomona Coll. Jour. Ent. and Zool.*, XII, 33–56.

NICHOLAS, J. S., 1922: The reactions of Amblystoma tigrinum to olfactory stimuli, *Jour. Exp. Zool.*, XXXV, 257–281.

NOBLE, G. K., 1924: Contributions to the herpetology of the Belgian Congo based on the collection of the American Museum Congo Expedition; Part III, Amphibia, *Bull. Amer. Mus. Nat. Hist.*, XLIX, 147–347.

————, 1927: The value of life history data in the study of the evolution of the Amphibia, *Ann. N. Y. Acad. Sci.*, XXX, 31–128, 1 pl.

————, and E. J. FARRIS, 1929: The method of sex recognition in the wood-frog, Rana sylvatica Le Conte, *Amer. Mus. Novit.*, No. 363, 1–17.

————, and R. C. NOBLE, 1923: The Anderson Tree Frog, (Hyla andersonii Baird); Observations on its habits and life history, *Zoologica*, II, No. 18, 416–455.

PACK, H. J., 1922: Toads in regulating insect outbreaks, *Copeia*, No. 107, 46–47.

PATCH, E. M., 1927: Biometric studies upon development and growth in Amblystoma punctatum and tigrinum, *Proc. Soc. Exp. Biol. Med.*, XXV, 218–219.

PEARSE, A. S., 1909: The reactions of amphibians to light, *Proc. Amer. Acad. Arts Sci.*, XLV, 161–208.

PIERSOL, W. H., 1929: Pathological polyspermy in eggs of Ambystoma jeffersonianum (Green), *Trans. Roy. Canadian Inst.*, XVII, 57–74.

REESE, A. M., 1906: Observations on the reactions of Cryptobranchus and Necturus to light and heat, *Biol. Bull.*, XI, 93–99.

RILEY, C. F. CURTIS, 1913: Responses of young toads to light and contact, *Jour. Anim. Behav.*, III, 179–214.

SAYLE, MARY H., 1916: The reactions of Necturus to stimuli received through the skin, *Jour. Anim. Behav.*, VI, 81–101.

SHELFORD, V. E., 1913: "Animal Communities in Temperate America," Univ. Chicago Press.

———, 1914: Modification of the behavior of land animals by contact with air of high evaporation power, *Jour. Anim. Behav.*, IV, 31–49.

STORER, T. I., 1925: A synopsis of the Amphibia of California, *Univ. Cal. Pub. Zool.*, XXVII, 1–343, 18 pls.

SURFACE, H. A., 1913: First report on the economic features of the amphibians of Pennsylvania, *Zool. Bull., Pa. Dept. Agr.*, III, Nos. 3–4, 66–152, 11 pls.

SZYMANSKI, J. S., 1914: Eine Methode zur Untersuchung der Ruhe- und Aktivitätsperioden bei Tieren, *Arch. ges. Physiol.*, CLVIII, 343–385.

TAGO, K., 1929: Notes on the habits and life history of Megalobatrachus japonicus, 10*th Congres. Internat. Zool. Budapest*, 1927, 828–838.

TORELLE, E., 1903: The response of the frog to light, *Amer. Jour. Physiol.*, IX, 466–488.

WELLMAN, G. B., 1917: Notes on the breeding habits of the American toad, *Copeia*, No. 51, 107–108.

WHITMAN, C. O., 1899: Animal behavior, *Woods Hole Biol. Lect.*, 1898, 285–335.

WOLTERSTORFF, W., 1922: Verhalten der Molche bei Kälte, *Blätt. Aquar.-Terrar.-Kde.*, XXXIII, 69–72.

WRIGHT, A. H., 1914: North American Anura; Life-histories of the Anura of Ithaca, New York, *Carnegie Inst. Wash. Pub.*, No. 197, 21 pls.

YERKES, R. M., 1903: The instincts, habits, and reactions of the frog, *Psych. Rev. Monog.*, IV, 579–638.

CHAPTER XVIII

THE RELATION OF AMPHIBIA TO THEIR ENVIRONMENT

Frequent reference has been made above to the close relation between Amphibia and their environment. Certain aspects of this subject require further consideration.

Metabolism of Amphibia.—Amphibia are cold-blooded; they lack the mechanisms which give the higher types both freedom from environmental change and constancy of chemical activity at the optimum conditions for the expenditure of their energies. Low body temperature means slow chemical changes, such as those of digestion, also lower velocity of nerve conduction and a throttling down of many other body activities which in the homoiotherms produce a more active and efficient organism. Thus the digestive enzymes of both salamanders and frogs exhibit their greatest degree of activity at about 37°C., which is the optimum temperature for mammals (Kenyon, 1925). Such a body temperature is practically never realized in Amphibia. In fact, most Amphibia are so adjusted they would die at that temperature. Hence their energy sources, the food and oxygen, are made available at a much slower rate in these forms. The range of metabolic rate in Amphibia is from eighteen to one hundred eighty times slower than that of small mammals and birds. Amphibia are not able to make use, to the fullest extent, of either their nervous or their motor systems. They remain slaves of their surroundings.

Although in a general way Van't Hoff's law that the velocity of chemical process is approximately doubled for every rise of 10°C. applies to metabolic processes in amphibians and has been shown by Laurens (1914) to hold for the rate of the heart beat in Ambystoma, its applicability is not absolute. Krogh (1916) has reviewed the works of investigators showing that the "law" applies better in the intermediate ranges than at high and low temperature extremes. Oxygen consumption has been found greater at low temperature and lower at high temperature than the amount expected by this law. Furthermore, the seasonal maximum of metabolism does not necessarily come at the height of summer heat but rather appears during the mating season, in early spring.   This is undoubtedly due to the influence of internal secretions set up by the sexual cycle and indicates the profound regulatory and modifying effect of hormonic influences on chemical processes, which otherwise would appear to conform strictly to inorganic laws.

Many factors influence the body temperature and hence affect the metabolism of Amphibia.   Water is such a good conductor that immersed Amphibia follow closely the temperature of their aquatic environment.   Water affords a very stable medium which does not undergo the sudden fluctuations of temperature peculiar to the land environment.   The skin of Amphibia is moist and the loss of heat on land through evaporation may be greater than the actual heat production of the animal.   Rubner (1924) found that in *Rana esculenta* at 3°C. the cooling by evaporation would lower the body temperature to only half a degree above freezing; while at 30°C. the body temperature dropped to 25.4°C.   In dry air, frogs are always colder than their environment, while in high humidities they are warmer than their surroundings (Isserlin, 1902).   Tree frogs have on various occasions been reported resting on leaves exposed to the direct rays of a scorching tropical sun.   In these cases the temperature of the frogs was probably considerably below that of the surrounding atmosphere.   The moist skin affords the Amphibia a protection against overheating, but as the skin itself is subject to rapid desiccation, few Amphibia, other than the rough-skinned toads and salamanders, will remain long in a dry atmosphere.   These rough-skinned species depend largely on their lungs to prevent overheating.   The pulmonary evaporation mechanism is extensively employed in higher vertebrates for the lowering of body temperature.   The loss of heat through the skin or lungs of amphibians, is a temperature-regulating mechanism in its primitive form.   Since the mechanism of keeping the skin moist is dependent on the environment, it further restricts the habitat of these animals.

The pigmentation of an amphibian may affect its body temperature considerably.   Most species when cold expand their melanophores.   Arboreal species or forms living in exposed situations and subject to the cooling effect of winds on their moist skin are often able to change their coloration quickly. This is usually considered a concealing device, but it may equally function as a regulator of body temperature.

Temperature and Behavior.—Amphibia usually respond adaptively to thermal change. Frogs retreat to hibernation on the approach of cold weather and reappear on the advent of spring warmth. Each species, however, has its own temperature level to which it responds. Some salamanders, such as *Gyrinophilus porphyriticus*, select colder waters in which to live, and others, such as Necturus, undergo an annual migration to waters of warmer temperature. Species differ considerably in their range of tolerance and this range may determine their distribution or their time of appearance. Tropical frogs do not live well at temperatures northern frogs enjoy. In the case of the Indian *Rana hexadactyla*, Garten and Sulze (1913) showed that a cessation of reflex excitability occurred at 5°C., which is several degrees above the critical temperature for northern frogs of the same genus. Many forms, however, are able to acclimate themselves to a marked change of temperature if given a sufficient time. Davenport and Castle (1895) found that the upper limit in toad tadpoles could be increased several degrees, and these tadpoles are occasionally found in nature in water which is uncomfortably warm to touch. At the other extreme, Bufo lives in the Himalayas at an altitude of over 14,000 ft. and Scutiger has been collected 2,000 ft. higher in Tibet.

The relative humidity is well known to influence the movements of Amphibia. Since the skin is moist, it acts very much like the wick of a wet-bulb thermometer and depresses their body temperature below that of the environment. Hall and Root (1930) found that in an atmosphere of 7 per cent relative humidity at 20°C. *Plethodon glutinosus* suffered a depression of 9.21°, *Rana pipiens* 8.60°, and *Bufo fowleri* 7.33°. Thus the toad with its relatively drier skin was influenced least by the dry air. By way of contrast, certain rough-skinned lizards showed very little lowering of body temperature at the same humidity. Lowering of the body temperature is known to bring into function various reflexes not exhibited at higher temperatures (Chap. XVI). Hence humidity may have a far greater influence on the behavior of moist-skin Amphibia than it does on reptiles with their dry skin. Frogs may be warmer and better able to use their digestive and nervous mechanism on a rainy day than on a dry, sunny day. The development of a dry skin in the early reptiles was an important step in the direction of homoiothermism which the Amphibia failed to follow.

Metabolism and Behavior.—Specific differences of behavior may be due in part to specific differences of metabolism. Helff (1927) showed that marked differences in oxygen consumption existed between several species of Ambystoma. It was interesting to note that *A. tigrinum*, the most aquatic species, had the lowest rate. This is in keeping with the observations of Cronheim (1927): that the terrestrial *Rana temporaria* absorbed more oxygen than certain aquatic European frogs. Amphibia during metamorphosis undergo a rapid increase in oxygen consumption. The immediate cause for the adoption of land life might be in these cases a greater need for oxygen, but the oxygen need in turn would be conditioned by the specific metabolic rate which fluctuates around a certain mean.

Fuel of Metabolism.—Food is the fuel of metabolism. Starvation of frogs may result in a 40 per cent decrease in metabolism within a week (Hill, 1911). In these forms a low metabolic level was reached during inanition in 15 days and no marked drop occurred after this time. Hill suggests that the glycogen stores may have been exhausted after a week, and a shift from carbohydrate to fat metabolism may have occurred. Fat oxidation gives a lower energy supply than glycogen, hence is the chief source of energy for Amphibia during hibernation. Amphibia, like many mammals, tend to store fat during the summer and to utilize this food source during winter hibernation (Athanasiu, 1899; Dolk and Postma, 1927).

Small mammals are required to eat proportionately to their weight a greater amount of food than large mammals in order to keep warm, for their surface, which radiates heat, when compared with their bulk, is proportionately greater. Rubner (1924) has presented data which suggest that the "surface law" of decreasing energy consumption in relation to decreasing surface is applicable to amphibians when only a single species is considered.

Hormones and Metabolism.—The metabolism of Amphibia is greatly affected by the secretions from the glands of internal secretion, especially by the thyroid hormone. In this, Amphibia agree with mammals. During the breeding season there is a distinct rise of the metabolic rate which is most marked in the male (Cronheim, 1927). Metabolism decreases with age. It is noteworthy that animals which differentiate early and reproduce at a small size probably never reach the age of the slow-growing, less differentiated types. At least the large perennibranchs and derotremes have longer life records than any of the smaller Amphibia and the same relation between slow growth and age seems to maintain for higher vertebrates.

Although the metabolism of Amphibia differs from that of higher vertebrates in quantity rather than in kind, there is also the important distinction that warm-bloodedness has made possible a complex series of interlocking physiological systems which usually prohibit any marked slackening of the pace of living without bringing disaster. Thus, while both frogs and salamanders are known to have lived over a year without food, and frogs, at least, to have recovered after ice had formed in their blood and lymph spaces, no warm-blooded type could resist such adversities. Although Amphibia are deficient in nervous and other mechanisms which give the mammals the optimum conditions of energy transformation and body activity, they can subject themselves to far greater changes of their metabolic rate and survive. Few, however, can live at the high body temperatures found in mammals and birds. There is thus not only a difference in average level but in optimum temperature levels between Amphibia and higher forms.

Effect of the Environment.—Amphibia possess numerous structural and physiological adaptations which help them to live in particular environments. As discussed in a previous chapter (page 86), these have arisen for the most part by the gradual selection of favorable mutations by particular environments. All Amphibia are able to undergo certain adjustments during development and in some cases this influence of environment during ontogeny may be considerable. It is frequently possible to predict the habitat of a species merely by examining a specimen superficially. Thus, a frog with large adhesive discs on its toes is usually arboreal; a salamander with a broad tail fin, aquatic; or a toad with enlarged "spades" on its feet, fossorial. Numerous instances of such correlations have been given in the preceding chapters. On the other hand, two closely related species may have very different habits without showing correlated differences in structure. The common *Ambystoma tigrinum* may remain in the ponds during the summer months (Hay, 1892), while the related *A. maculatum* which does not seem externally less fitted for aquatic life is terrestrial throughout the greater part of the year. The tadpoles of *Rana clamitans* are vegetarian, those of *R. sylvatica* carnivorous (Hay, 1892), but the two species exhibit only slight differences in their dentition. *Hyla arenicolor* has a strong predilection for the vicinity of streams and yet does not appear better adapted for this habitat than *H. versicolor* or many other arboreal species. One would hardly guess from an external examination that Pseudobranchus burrows in the mud at the bottom of ponds while the closely related Siren never exhibits these proclivities. In brief, many habitat preferences of Amphibia are not reflected in any external characters.

In the chapters dealing with the various organs of Amphibia, frequent reference has been made to the ontogenetic effects of environmental factors. The form of the gill, for example, may be greatly influenced by the amount of oxygen available; not only are the gills of Salamandra and newts longer in water poor in oxygen but their epithelium is much thinner than that on the gills of larvae retained in the water rich in oxygen (Drastich, 1925). Similarly, Doms (1915) showed that the size and arborization of the external gills of *Rana esculenta* tadpoles increased with the temperature. It would appear probable that the environment during each ontogeny would have an influence on controlling the length of the gills in all Amphibia, although to what extent it is responsible for the many extraordinary types of gill form discussed in Chap. III is at present uncertain. The effect of the environment may not only be specific for certain tissues, but it may also be general on many parts of the body. It is this latter type of effect which may be dealt with in further detail here.

A decrease of available oxygen lowers the respiratory quotient in spite of the increase in respiratory surface. This is apparently due to the accumulation of the products of incomplete oxidation (Drastich, 1925). It also leads to a decrease in thyroid size and a slowing up of both development and differentiation. An increase in the temperature leads to a hypertrophy of the gills and a thinning of their epithelium apparently in correlation with the increased gas exchange. At the same time an increase in temperature leads to a decrease in the size of the body cells and their nuclei (Hartmann, 1922). A rise in the temperature increases the metabolic rate of Amphibia, and this in turn has many effects. The nitrogen excretion of frogs increases with a rise from 21 to 31°C. At the higher temperature a yellow pigment appears in the urine (Van der Heyde, 1921). The quantity of food the newt will take increases with the temperature and this influences directly the rate of growth (Springer, 1909). If the maximum quantity of food a newt will take at a low temperature be taken as a feeding basis, the rate of growth diminishes with an increase in temperature because the individuals at the higher temperatures are underfed. It has frequently been noted that tadpoles, when crowded, do not grow so rapidly as others less confined. Adolph (1929) has shown that this is not due to the lack of oxygen but merely because the physical disturbances of crowding prevent the tadpoles from eating as much as those in larger ranges. Similarly, axolotls and pond tadpoles accustomed to feed in quiet water grow more slowly in running water (Goetsch, 1928). This may be due to the fact that such larvae do not secure enough food or possibly to the fact that they are forced to use their food reserves more quickly. Among frogs in general, pond life has produced more giant tadpoles than stream life. The correlation is not, however, so close among the urodeles.

One of the most remarkable modifications attributed to differences in feeding is reported by Powers (1907) in *Ambystoma tigrinum*. He found that cannibal individuals differed remarkably in their elongate teeth, flat heads, and body proportions from non-cannibals of the same species. Special diets may lead to malformations of the tail or body in other salamanders (Klatt, 1927). Overfeeding with liver frequently leads to distended bodies and bent tail in both larvae and adult salamanders. A lack of minerals in the diet may produce a curvature of the spine and a reduction of pigmentation in larval Ambystoma, also peculiar twists in the tail of the adult (Patch, in press). Feeding European newts on a shellfish diet (Sphaerium) causes them to develop with a much shorter head than plankton-fed controls. Krohn (1930) attributes this change of head form primarily to an increase in the fluids of the brain ventricles. A one-sided diet is therefore to be avoided under laboratory conditions where healthy animals are required. The best initial food for Ambystoma larvae is an assortment of small aquatic crustacea, while earthworms containing considerable mineral matter should be added to a diet of beef or liver at a later stage. Whether or not peculiar diets have produced distinctive types in nature is unknown. The experiments of Powers have not been repeated by later investigators and his conclusions are in need of further confirmation. The question of the inheritance of these and other environmental effects has been considered in previous chapters.

Microscopic Parasites.—Amphibia suffer the depredations of many kinds of parasites (Jacob, 1909) some of which are highly pathogenic, producing diseases which resemble those of man. The newt picks up more parasites during its aquatic than during its terrestrial stage (Holl, 1928a). Further, the Cricket Frog, Acris, is more parasitized during the breeding season when it is largely aquatic than later in the season. Still, there is no definite evidence that disease has played a large part in controlling the distribution of any species of amphibian.

Several species of fungus are known to attack the skin and intestines of Amphibia. Saprolegnia forms pale, feltlike blotches over the skin of both frogs and salamanders, especially under laboratory conditions. Scott (1926) describes a Monilia which also forms felty growths on the skin of frogs, toads, and salamanders. The disease is highly contagious and usually fatal.

One of the commonest bacterial diseases of frogs in captivity is known as "red leg." This is caused by *Bacillus hydrophillus fuscus*, which produces a congestion of the blood vessels on the ventral surface of the body resulting in more or less hemorrhage beneath the skin. The frog becomes oedematous and if kept in water gains in weight due to the absorption of water through the skin without a compensatory release of water by the kidneys (McClure, 1925). The disease is usually fatal unless the frogs are kept at low temperatures for a period.

Other bacteria have been described from frogs (Stutzer, 1926), including the tubercle bacilli (Lichtenstein, 1920), but it is chiefly the Protozoa which infest Amphibia in great numbers. The intestines of frogs and salamanders are inhabited by many species of flagellates, infusorians, rhizopods, and sporozoans (Collin, 1913).

Hegner (1923) found that living flagellates of the Euglena type were the normal inhabitants of the intestines of tadpoles living in ponds rich in algae. Other flagellates, such as Trypanosoma, are frequently found in the blood of frogs and salamanders. Although it is a Trypanosoma which produces the African sleeping sickness and some species such as *T. inspinatum* are pathogenic in frogs, other species of the same parasite are not known to have serious effects upon their host. Some Trypanosomes are transmitted by leeches, the organisms gaining access to the wound made by the proboscis of the leech (Wenyon, 1926). The common newt, *Triturus viridescens*, is so frequently infected by *Trypanosoma diemyctyli* (Fig. 138) that it may be used as a ready source of supply for class-room demonstration of this parasite (Hegner, 1920).

The integument of aquatic Amphibia frequently supports a rich protozoan fauna. Wenrich (1924) reports one flagellate and seven ciliates from the skin of tadpoles, and Sassuchin (1928) has added a list of species which he has found in the slime of the tadpole skin. Under laboratory conditions Cryptobranchus

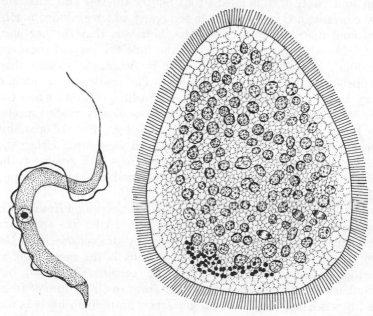

Fig. 138.—*Trypanosoma diemyctyli.* (*After Nigrelli.*)

Fig. 139.—*Opalina runarum,* a ciliate parasite of frogs. (*After Metcalf.*)

frequently develops a rich growth of Vorticella, and various free-swimming ciliates may be found in the mucous secretion of the integument. These in themselves do not appear to be pathogenic but they are often accompanied by a growth of mold which causes great injury.

Among the ciliates in the intestines of tadpoles and frogs the opalinids are perhaps the most common. These have a ciliated body, several nuclei, but no mouth. Although they may reach a diameter of nearly a millimeter, they apparently do little damage to the body of their host. Opalinids (Fig. 139) are found in many parts of the world and have been recorded from fish and salamanders as well as from frogs. Many species are common to several families of frogs, but Metcalf (1929), who has recently monographed the group, believes the distribution of the various genera lends support to his views of the migration routes of the frogs and toads which they parasitize. Thus, Zelleriella, which infests various genera of not closely related frogs, is found nowhere except in Australia and South and Central America. To Harrison and Metcalf this means that South America and Australia have been joined in past time in some way which excluded northern land masses. It may well be, however, that the northern opalinids were not in existence at the time the present southern opalinids were being carried south by whatever species they happened to parasitize at that time. The host-parasite method may be used in elucidating the relationships of hosts when the parasites are specific and when the same or closely related species are found in two animals of doubtful affinities. But the opalinids are not specific and they do not help in suggesting either the relationships of the various genera of frogs and toads or the migration routes which these genera followed in the past (Noble, 1925).

The Rhizopoda include many of the most common fresh-water Protozoa. They possess neither flagella nor cilia like the forms previously considered but move about by projections from the body called "pseudopodia." The amoeba is the most familiar example. Dysentery is produced by certain rhizopods, but whether the several genera described from the intestines of frogs and newts cause similar diseases in their amphibian hosts is not known.

The most characteristic parasitic Protozoa of Amphibia are the Sporozoa. They have neither cilia, flagella, nor pseudopodia and reproduce mainly by the formation of spores in great numbers at one time from their one-celled body. Sporozoa have been recorded from the kidneys, digestive tract, and various other organs of Amphibia. Guyenot and Ponse (1926) have described a species from the cells of Bidder's organ in the toad. The Hemosporidia live in the blood, certain species causing malaria and tick fever in mammals. Other species occur in the blood of Amphibia (Sanders, 1928) and certain of these are transmitted by the bite of a leech (Cleland and Johnston, 1910). Hemosporidia while found in the blood of all vertebrates are especially abundant in the cold-blooded groups including fishes and reptiles, as well as Amphibia.   Lankesterella is found in the red blood cells of frogs and is only about half the length of these corpuscles.

Larger Parasites.—Turning to the parasites which one may more readily see, the roundworms and flatworms are by far the most abundant.   Nematodes, which include the notorious hookworm of the Southern states, are found in both digestive tract and body cavity of frogs and salamanders.   Acanthocephali, which are closely allied to Nematoda but have hooks on the proboscis, have been recorded from the intestine of frogs.   The Trematoda, or flukes, are parasitic flatworms still possessing an alimentary tract but having suckers or adhesive organs.   The most frequently seen is Polystomum, which has a circle of distinct suckers at the posterior end of the body.   It is a common inhabitant of the urinary bladder of frogs.   Trematodes are also found in the intestines of both frogs and salamanders and new species have recently been described from American forms (Cort, 1919; Holl, 1928a).   Cestodes, which include the tapeworms, represent the most extreme specialization for parasitic life among the flatworms.   They are white and segmented.   Tapeworms have been found in the intestines of both European and American frogs. In addition to round- and flatworms, other wormlike parasites have been recorded from frogs, including a true oligochaete parasitic in the urogenital system of a South American tree frog (Michaelsen, 1926).

Under laboratory conditions salamanders are sometimes infested by a red mite which may cause annoyance both to the salamander and to the observer who wishes to keep the salamanders in good health.   Flies of several genera parasitize frogs and toads.   Some species lay their eggs in the nostrils of toads and the larvae which emerge make their way into the nasal chamber and other parts of the body.   Batrachomyia was described as a genus of flies, the larvae of which lie between skin and muscle of Australian frogs and, while producing enormous lumps in the skin, eventually escape without destroying their host (Skuse, 1889).

In the laboratory the infections of Amphibia frequently cause considerable inconvenience to the student.   Weak solutions of potassium permanganate, mercuro-chrome, copper sulphate, and iodine have been used with varying success to remove molds and external parasites.   Pennies kept in the aquaria usually release enough copper salts into the water to discourage the growth of molds. Amphibia weakened by disease will sometimes recover when placed for short periods in the ice box. The use of running water and the isolation of infected animals will frequently check the spread of the more common diseases.

Other Enemies.—Frogs and salamanders are harassed throughout life by legions of enemies and only a very small proportion of any one brood lives to reach maturity. Although the eggs are surrounded by a protective jelly, they are frequently eaten or destroyed, even some salamanders such as the newt, being responsible for some of the losses. Giant water bugs, dragonfly nymphs, larvae of water beetles, and many other aquatic insects destroy tadpoles in great numbers. Many microscopic crustacea attack salamander larvae, devouring first their gills. Fish, especially pike, bass, and catfish, prey upon tadpoles and young frogs. These formidable enemies frequent the larger ponds, which are usually avoided by Ambystoma during the breeding season but may form the regular breeding grounds of toads and several species of Rana. Large frogs will seize smaller individuals of their own or other species. This cannibalistic habit has been one of the factors which has led some frog culturists to abandon the rearing of bullfrogs for market (Wright, 1920). Salamander larvae frequently devour smaller individuals of the same or different species. This struggle for existence, larva against larva, has been recorded also among the tadpoles of frogs. De Villiers (1929) found that tadpoles of the South African *Rana grayi* frequented the same pools as the tadpoles of a brevicipitid Cacosternum. As the pools began to dwindle, only the Rana tadpoles survived. Direct observation in the laboratory showed that the Rana tadpoles would swallow the Cacosternum tadpole at a single gulp and this voracious habit was the apparent reason for the non-survival of Cacosternum under conditions of crowding. This case is by no means unique. Larvae of some species of Ceratophrys and Rana are also cannibalistic.

The greatest enemies of frogs are, probably, the snakes. Water snakes and garter snakes devour many of the smaller species. The spreading adder, Heterodon, feeds largely on toads and there are exotic snakes which are known to include a very high percentage of toads in their diet. Black snakes, copperheads, and various other local species have been shown to feed on terrestrial Salientia. Salamanders, because of their secretive habits, probably suffer less than frogs from the depredations of serpents. Other reptilian enemies of Amphibia include the aquatic turtles. In the United States the musk and snapping turtles are especially destructive of tadpoles and may seize frogs. Alligators are also reported to be foes of frogs. None of these species compares with snakes in their continuous persecution of the frog tribe.

Birds and mammals take a very high toll of amphibian life. Ponds abounding with newts and tadpoles have been picked clean of amphibian life by domestic ducks within a short time after their release in the area. Herons are well known to stalk the shallows in search of frogs or their tadpoles. Such a nocturnal and secretive salamander as *Plethodon cinereus* was found by Allen to be captured in some numbers by screech owls. The common crow was shown by Barrows to take frogs and toads more regularly than any other kinds of food. The mammalian enemies are less numerous than birds but include many familiar forms, such as weasels, skunks, and even rats and cats. Man, by draining the marshes and by collecting great numbers of frogs at all seasons, is rapidly exterminating frogs and toads from many parts of the country. The automobile has been considered the greatest enemy of the toad, and certainly the pollution of streams in the Alleghanies has done much to destroy the breeding grounds of Cryptobranchus. In many indirect ways man makes living precarious for Amphibia.

Length of Life.—The span of life attained by Amphibia is not known with certainty. A few species, however, have been in captivity for long periods. Wolterstorff (1928) records a Japanese newt, *Triturus pyrrhogaster*, which had been living in his possession for 25 years, and Debreuil (1925) a Spanish newt, *Pleurodeles waltl*, which had lived 20 years without leaving an aquarium. Common European toads have been credited with 36 years of life, and tree toads with 10 (Szabó, 1927) to 22 years. Of course the story that a toad can live for centuries entombed in stone or in old wells is sheer fable. The question was settled as long ago as 1777 by direct experiment, but the belief is still prevalent among many people.

In general, larger animals live longer than smaller ones (Mayenne, 1924). A specimen *Megalobatrachus maximus*, the largest salamander, has been kept 52 years in the Amsterdam aquarium. At this time it had reached the length of 114 cm., while a ten-year-old Siren was only 50 cm. long. Siren has been reported to live

25 years in captivity and Amphiuma 26. In general, the larger frogs and toads reach sexual maturity later than the smaller species. Larval life may last less than a month, as in the case of some Spade-foot Toads, Scaphiopus, to over 2 years, as in some Bullfrogs. Thoroughly aquatic Salienta, such as the Bullfrog, *Rana catesbeiana*, or the South American species, *Batrachophrynus microphthalmus* and *Pseudis paradoxa*, have a longer larval period (or at least reach a larger larval size) than more terrestrial forms. Large size is definitely correlated with an abundant secretion of the hormone from the anterior lobe of the pituitary gland. Further, the onset of metamorphosis is induced by the release of the colloid in the thyroid gland. Possibly the endocrine organs control the span of life by hastening or slowing up the rate at which both larval and adult differentiations take place.

Although some newts, *Triturus viridescens*, and Tiger Salamanders, *Ambystoma tigrinum*, may become sexually mature as larvae, most salamanders and frogs do not breed until a year or more after metamorphosis. Gadow (1901) records axolotls as becoming sexually mature at about six months of age, and certain European newts have been reported to reach sexual maturity in less than a year. Both *Plethodon cinereus* (Blanchard, 1928) and *Batrachoseps attenuatus* (Storer, 1925) reach sexual maturity 2 years after hatching, although they may not breed until nearly a year later. The tree frog, *Hyla arenicolor*, breeds when two years old. Storer (1925) found that of the western toads, *Bufo boreas halophilus* required 2 years, *Bufo canorus* 3 years, and *Bufo cognatus* 4 years to reach sexual maturity. This represents the range found in most frogs, although some species of Rana have been credited with even greater time to attain sexual maturity.

Age is determined by measuring all the individuals found in a single locality and plotting the sizes. If enough individuals are considered, the frequency modes may give the number of years required to reach sexual maturity, but they will not show the total age, for most species grow slowly, if at all, after reaching sexual maturity. Many species, particularly some tropical forms, seem to have an absolute size which the males soon attain, but this does not hold for many salamanders nor for some northern frogs.

References

ADOLPH, EDWARD F., 1929: The quantitative effect of crowding on the rate of growth of tadpoles, *Anat. Rec.*, XLIV, 227.

ATHANASIU, J., 1899: Über den Gehalt des Froschkörpers an Glykogen in den verschiedenen Jahreszeiten, *Arch. ges. Physiol.*, LXXIV, 561–569.

BLANCHARD, F. N., 1928: Topics from the life history and habits of the red-backed salamander in southern Michigan, *Amer. Naturalist*, LXII, 156–164.

CLELAND, J. BURTON, and J. JOHNSTON, 1910: The haematozoa of Australian batrachians, No. 1, *Sydney, N. S. W., Jour. Roy. Soc.*, XLIV, 252–260.

COLLIN, BERNARD, 1913: Sur un ensemble de Protistes parasites des batraciens, (Note Préliminaire), *Arch. Zool. Exp.*, LI, 59–76.

CORT, W. W., 1919: A new distome from Rana aurora, *Univ. Cal. Pub. Zool.*, XIX, 283–298, 5 pls.

CRONHEIM, WALTER, 1927: Gesamtstoffwechsel der Tiere; III. Kaltblütige Wirbeltiere (Poikilotherme); B. Amphibien und Reptilien, *Carl Oppenheimer's Handb. Biochem. Mensch. Tiere*, VII, 329–340.

DAVENPORT, C. B., and W. E. CASTLE, 1895: Studies in morphogenesis; III. On the acclimatization of organisms to high temperatures, *Arch. Entw. mech.*, II, 227–249.

DEBREUIL, C., 1925: [Note], *Bull. Soc. Nat. Acclim. France,* LXXII, 155–156.

DOLK, H. E., and N. POSTMA, 1927: Über die Haut—und die Lungenatmung von Rana temporaria, *Zeitschr. vergl. Physiol.*, V, 417–444.

DOMS, H., 1915: Über den Einfluss der Temperatur auf Wachstum und Differenzierung der Organe während der Entwickelung von Rana esculenta, *Arch. mikr. Anat.*, LXXXVII, 60.

DRASTICH, L., 1925: Über das Leben der Salamandra Larven bei hohem und niedrigem Sauerstoffpartialdruck, *Zeitschr. vergl. Physiol.*, II, 632–657.

GADOW, H., 1901: "Amphibia and Reptiles," *Cambridge Nat. Hist.*, VIII.

GARTEN, S., and W. SULZE, 1913: Über den Einfluss niederer Temperatur auf die Nerven eines tropischen Kaltblüters (Rana hexadactyla), *Zeitschr. Biol.*, LX, 163–185.

GOETSCH, W., 1928: Untersuchungen über wachstumhemmende Factoren, *Zool. Jahrb., Alg. Zool. Phys.*, XLV, 799–840.

GUYÈNOT, EMIL, et K. PONSE, 1926: Une Microsporidie, Plistophora bufonis, parasite de l'organe de Bidder du crapaud, *Rev. Suisse Zool.*, XXX, 213–250.

HALL, F. G., and R. W. ROOT, 1930: The influence of humidity on body temperature of certain poikilotherms, *Biol. Bull.*, LVIII, 52–58.

HARTMANN, OTTO, 1922: Über den Einfluss der Temperatur auf Grösse und Beschaffenheit von Zelle und Kern im Zusammenhang mit der Beeinflussung von Funktion, Wachstum, und Differenzierung der Zellen und Organe (Experimente an Amphibien), *Arch. Entw. Mech.*, XLIV, 114–196.

HAY, O. P., 1892: The batrachians and reptiles of the state of Indiana, *Ind. Dept. Geol. Nat. Resources Ann. Rept.*, 1891.

HEGNER, R. W., 1920: Blood inhabiting protozoa for class use (Trypanosoma diemyctyli), *Science*, LI, 187–188.

———, 1923: Observations and experiments on Euglenoidea in the digestive tract of frog and toad tadpoles, *Biol. Bull.*, XLV, 162–180.

HELFF, O. M., 1927: The rate of oxygen consumption in five species of Amblystoma larvae, *Jour. Exp. Zool.*, XLIX, 353–361.

HILL, A. V., 1911: The total energy exchanges of intact cold blooded animals at rest, *Jour. Physiol.*, XLIII, 379–394.

HOLL, F. J., 1928: Parasites of North Carolina amphibians, *Jour. Elisha Mitchell Sci. Soc.*, XLIV, 20.

———, 1928a: A new Trematode from the newt Triturus viridescens, *Jour. Elisha Mitchell Sci. Soc.*, XLIII, 181–183, 1 pl.

ISSERLIN, M., 1902: Über Temperatur und Wärmeproduction poikilothermer Tiere, *Arch. ges. Physiol.*, XC, 472–490.

JACOB, E., 1909: Zur Pathologie der Urodelen und Anuren, *Zool. Anz.*, XXXIV, 628–638.

KENYON, W. A., 1925: Digestive enzymes in poikilothermal vertebrates; An investigation of enzymes in fishes, with comparative studies on those of amphibians, reptiles and mammals, *Bull. Bur. Fish. Wash.*, XLI, 181–200.

KLATT, B., 1927: Fütterungsversuche an Tritonen; II. Die Bedeutung der Ausgangsgrösse, *Arch. Entw. Mech.*, CIX, 176–187.

KROGH, A., 1916: "The Respiratory Exchange of Animals and Man," London and New York.

KROHN, E., 1930: Fütterungsversuche an Tritonen; III. Die Veränderung der Kopfform des Teichmolches (M. vulgaris [taeniata]) infolge Muschelfleischfütterung, *Arch. Entw. Mech.*, CXXI, 545–597.

LAURENS, H., 1914: The influence of temperature on the rate of the heart beat in Amblystoma embryos, *Amer. Jour. Physiol.*, XXXV, 199–210.

LICHTENSTEIN, S., 1920: Ein Fall von spontaner Froschtuberkulose, *Zentralbl. Bakt. Parasit Infektionskr.*, Abt. I, LXXXV, 249–252.

MAYENNE, V. A., 1924: Zur Frage über die Dauer des Lebens der Fische, *Zool. Anz.*, LXI, 235–237.

MCCLURE, C. F. W., 1925: An experimental analysis of oedema in the frog with special reference to the oedema in red-leg disease, *Amer. Anat. Mem.*, No. 12, 39.

METCALF, M. M., 1929: Parasites and the aid they give in problems of taxonomy, geographical distribution and palaeontology, *Smithson. Misc. Coll.*, 81, No. 8.

MICHAELSEN, W., 1926: Schmardaella lutzi Mich., oligochaeto endoparasitico de hylidas sul-americanas; Über Schmardaella lutzi Mich., ein endoparasitisches Ologochät aus südamerikanischen Laubfröschen, *Mem. Inst. Oswaldo Cruz*, XIX, 231–243.

NOBLE, G. K., 1925: The evolution and dispersal of the frogs, *Amer. Naturalist*, LIX, 265–271.

POWERS, J. H., 1907: Morphological variation and its causes in Amblystoma tigrinum, *Stud. Univ. Nebraska*, VII, 197–274.

RUBNER, MAX, 1924: Aus dem Leben des Kaltblüters; II. Teil, Amphibien und Reptilien, *Biochem. Zeitschr.*, CXLVIII, 268–307.

SANDERS, ELIZABETH P., 1928: Observations and experiments on the haemogregarines of certain Amphibia, *Jour. Parasitol*, XIV, 188–192.

SASSUCHIN, D. N., 1928: Zur Frage über die ecto—und entoparasitischen Protozoen der Froschkaulquappen, *Archiv. Protistenkde*, LXIV, 71–92, 4 pls.

SCOTT, H. H., 1926: A mycotic disease of batrachians, *Proc. Zool. Soc. London*, Part II, 683–692, 5 pls.

SKUSE, F. A. A., 1889: Description of a new genus (Batrachomyia, W. S. Macleay M. S.), and two species of dipterous insects, parasitic upon Australian frogs, *Proc. Linn. Soc. N.S.W.* (2), IV, 171–177.

SPRINGER, ADA, 1909: A study of growth in the salamander Diemyctylus viridescens, *Jour. Exp. Zool.*, VI, 1–68.

STORER, T. I., 1925: A synopsis of the Amphibia of California, *Univ. Cal. Pub. Zool.*, XXVII, 1–343, 18 pls.

STUTZER, M. I., 1926: Darmbakterien der Kaltblüter, *Zentralbl. Bakt.*, Abt. II, LXVI, 344–354.

SZABÓ, I., 1927: Körpergrösse und Lebensdauer der Tiere, *Zool. Anz.*, LXXIV, 39–53.

VAN DER HEYDE, H. C., 1921: On the influence of temperature on the excretion of the hibernating frog, Rana virescens Kalm, *Biol. Bull.*, XLI, 249–255.

VILLIERS, C. G. S. DE, 1929: Some observations on the breeding habits of the Anura of the Stellenbosch flats, in particular of Cacosternum capense and Bufo angusticeps, *Ann. Transvaal. Mus.*, XIII, 123–141.

WENRICH, D. H., 1924: Protozoa on the skin and gills of tadpoles, *Trans. Amer. Micr. Soc.*, XLIII, 200–202.

WENYON, C. M., 1926: "Protozöology," London.

WOLTERSTORFF, W., 1928: Triton (Cynops) pyrrhogaster 25 Jahre, *Blätt. Aquar.-Terrar.-Kde.*, XXXIX, 183.

WRIGHT, A. H., 1920: Frogs: their natural history and utilization, *Bur. Fish. Doc.* 888, App. VI, *Rep. U. S. Comm. Fish.*, 1919.

CHAPTER XIX

GEOGRAPHIC DISTRIBUTION AND ECONOMIC VALUE

The distributions of the various groups of Amphibia are considered in some detail in the second part of this volume. It is, however, of some interest to compare distributions and to attempt to determine the probable routes of dispersal of each family. Such conclusions, if sound, should be in harmony with the conclusions of zoogeographers studying other groups of land animals of the same apparent age.

Geographical Distribution.—It is a well-known fact that the various groups of Amphibia show different geographical distributions. Urodeles are found primarily in the northern hemisphere, caecilians are circumtropical, while frogs and toads occur over the entire world except in regions of extreme cold or aridity. The various families have also different limits of distribution. Hynobiid salamanders are found only in Asia and adjacent islands; ambystomids, amphiumids, and sirenids only in North America. The small family of Cryptobranchidae have representatives living today only in Japan, China, and eastern North America; the Proteidae, only in Southern Europe and eastern United States. The salamandrids, with their center of maximum abundance of species in Europe, are widely spread in the northern hemisphere, while the Plethodontidae, the dominant group of North American salamanders, have two species in southern Europe and a few in the Andean region of South America. The Salientia have equally distinctive ranges: the Liopelmidae live today only in New Zealand and northwestern United States; the Discoglossidae, in Europe and Asia including the Philippines. The Pipidae are found in the tropics of Africa and South America; the Pelobatidae are holarctic but have invaded the tropics in the Philippines, the East Indies, and the Seychelle Islands. The small family of brachycephalid toads is confined to the neotropics. The large families of bufonids, hylids, ranids, and brevicipitids are distributed over most of the continents but do not have identical ranges. The Hylidae exhibit a broad hiatus in the

448

Indo-Malayan region, while the Ranidae are absent from South America except for Rana which has reached only the northern part of the continent.

The ranges occupied today by the urodeles do not coincide with those of the frogs; the geographic limits of each family of Amphibia have their own peculiarities. These differences are due to the different times at which the groups arose in the past, the different modes of living, and the different barriers which affected the dispersal of the groups. If a natural group of Amphibia today occupy two distinct territories, species of this group must at some previous period have lived in the intervening area. Unfortunately, Amphibia do not make good fossils and there is very little record of the ancient wanderings which must be postulated to account for present distributions.

Some reference may, nevertheless, be made to this meager record, for it is a fair index of the kinds of migration which occurred. Although the Cryptobranchidae are thoroughly aquatic urodeles, living today only in streams, they had during the latter part of the Tertiary a very wide distribution (Fig. 140). Fossil cryptobranchids are known from the Miocene of Europe and the Lower Pliocene of Nebraska, and hence the group formerly flourished in regions where today no living individuals occur. Similarly, the primitive salamandrid Tylototriton is confined today to the eastern Himalayas, Yunnan, Burma, and the Riu-Kiu Islands, but it also is known as a fossil from the Miocene beds of southern Europe. There are other definite cases, such as that of Spadefoot Toads from the Oligocene of Mongolia and the extinct family of toads, Palaeobatrachidae, from the Oligocene and Miocene of Europe, which show conclusively that amphibian faunas have existed in regions now devoid of these forms. They also show that groups which have passed through a region need not have left relic types behind as proof of these migrations.

The present distribution of the various groups of Amphibia demand that land connections existed in previous times between regions now separated by water. Europe and America were apparently connected, it would seem by way of Greenland, at a time when this northern region enjoyed a warmer climate. The European Proteus and the American Necturus are closely related and the only members of the distinct family Proteidae. The plethodontid genus Hydromantes has one species in the Sierra

Nevada of California, another in southeastern France and north-western Italy, while a third is in Sardinia.

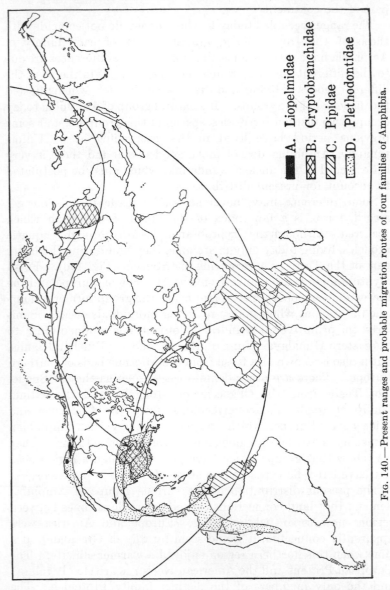

Fig. 140.—Present ranges and probable migration routes of four families of Amphibia.

A. Liopelmidae
B. Cryptobranchidae
C. Pipidae
D. Plethodontidae

A second land bridge, frequently postulated to explain the distribution of higher groups such as the mammals, connected

Alaska and Asia. It was apparently across this bridge that Cryptobranchus, Ascaphus, and the brevicipitids came from Asia. The narrow-mouthed toads included at least Microhylinae and Kalophryninae in their original migratory stock, for representatives of both subfamilies are now in China and the United States. The north-Pacific land bridge probably admitted pelobatids and some of the hylids to America; but here the evidence is not so conclusive.

Land Bridges.—The distribution, both present and past, of the Amphibia does not demand any other land bridges across the Atlantic or Pacific than those just indicated. Geologists have shown the extensive changes in elevation which have taken place on the continental masses. North and South America have been at various times connected and disconnected; further, there was, during parts of the Tertiary, less water between Asia and Australia than now exists. Apparently, the Amphibia made extensive migrations along these land masses. During the Mesozoic, Dinosaurs existed on all the continents; while during the Tertiary, various groups of mammals migrated over the greater part of the world. Salientia were in existence since Jurassic times at least, and it is not improbable that hylids and bufonids were established in the southern hemisphere before the beginning of the Tertiary. The frog faunas of South America and Australia have considerable resemblance. In both, bufonids and hylids are dominant types. This does not necessitate our assuming that these two continents must have been connected. It has recently been shown that toothed bufonids closely allied to Crinia of Australia existed in the Eocene of India (Noble, 1930). The bufonids of Australia are as closely related to the African forms as they are to the South American species. Hyla is found in Australia and South America, but this genus has been described as a fossil from the Miocene of Europe. When the world-wide distribution of the hylids and bufonids is considered, it becomes clear that both of these families in all probability arose in the north and spread southward along existing continental masses to their present ranges (Noble 1925). This retreat to the South is no more remarkable than that which our knowledge of fossils shows us to have taken place in many other groups, as, for example, in the pleurodire turtles.

There are many peculiarities of distribution for which we have at present no adequate explanation. Thus, pelobatids are now known from the Seychelle Islands but none from Africa. Were the Seychelle Islands formerly connected with India where pelobatids live today, or did pelobatids in former times abound in Africa? Toothed brevicipitids occur in Madagascar and southern Asia. The tree frog, Polypedates, is common to both regions. Is this evidence that Madagascar and Asia were connected? Madagascar lacks the pipids, bufonids, and caecilians of Africa, a fact which suggests a long isolation from the African mainland, but this region includes the modern and characteristically African Hyperolius and Megalixalus, which seems to indicate that frogs have been able to reach that island in recent times. From such data as these it seems probable that Madagascar may have been always separated from Africa but that long ago it received by flotsam-jetsam methods a few brevicipitids and ranids which underwent a remarkable radiation on that island. Similarly, the connection between Australia and Asia may never have been entirely complete in order to have admitted the few types of Salientia which underwent a specialization there.

Age and Area.—In determining the migration routes of animals it is important to know the relative age of the group and the methods of dispersal available to it. If the group is a comparatively modern one in which few extinctions have occurred, the center of dispersal will tend to lie near the center of the group range, at the intersection of the possible routes of migration. The oldest groups will tend to have the widest distribution and, because of the frequency of extinction, will also exhibit the most discontinuous ranges. This rule seems to hold for liopelmids and pipids but not for some other presumably ancient groups such as the hynobiid salamanders.

Most animals, including the Amphibia, gradually extend their ranges in the course of their normal wanderings. Nevertheless, the various species are usually restricted in their travels to distinctive habitats. This is not always the case, since various aquatic species have been known to make long overland journeys after rains. The dispersal of animals is augmented by the climatic cycles which bring profound changes in the environments of any one locality. When such changes occur, any animal with restricted habitat requirements must move out in order to survive. It was the recognition of this fact which led Matthew (1915) to conclude that the primitive forms of any group will in general be found on the periphery of the range, for most groups have survived one or more of these climatic cycles and have left the original home territory to more advanced types adapted to meet the new conditions. The rule does not apply to all groups of Amphibia. Some, such as the Plethodontidae, may have arisen in a region which has not undergone a marked change (Dunn, 1926) and the specialized derivatives of the original stock may be found anywhere throughout the range where habitat conditions permit.

Barriers to Dispersal.—The requirements of Amphibia, so important in limiting their migrations, vary with the species. Ascaphus thrives at temperatures a few degrees above freezing and dies in captivity unless kept cool. The smooth-skinned *Bufo alvarius* can live successfully only near streams, while its rough-skinned relative *B. cognatus* is at home in the desert. All Amphibia demand some moisture, but as this requirement varies with the species, due to the inherited morphological and physiological peculiarities of the form, the moisture content of any one locality may determine the species living there.

As in the case of fishes and birds, the distribution of Amphibia is often limited by their breeding-site preferences. Frogs or salamanders which lay their eggs near mountain streams usually do not wander far from these locations. Necturus is found more commonly in streams affording nesting sites than in those lacking a bed of suitable stones. On high mountains, such as the Andes, a large part of the frog fauna consists of species which skip over an aquatic larval stage and the only salamanders in the Andes, at least, are ovoviviparous species. Similarly, in rain forests such as those in Jamaica the frogs are species which avoid an aquatic stage or are forms with larvae adapted to living in the small amounts of water caught between the leaves. No doubt the direct development of Eleutherodactylus has been one of the principal factors in making this group of frogs one of the commonest in the neotropics. Again, in the deserts a premium is placed not only on species which can dig down to moisture but on digging forms which are able to undergo a very rapid development in the temporary pools left by showers. In brief, both the restrictions of the habitat for breeding as well as the breeding preferences of the species have greatly influenced the present distribution of Amphibia.

Aquarists have noted many times that various alpine species of salamander can be shipped or kept in captivity only with difficulty.   In the case of *Euproctus asper*, shallow running water at ordinary temperatures may be used as a substitute for the alpine-lake habitat of the species. *E. asper* has greatly reduced lungs, and apparently the oxygen requirements hold the species in waters rich in oxygen. On the other hand, some species of salamanders may be restricted to particular ranges because of a special sensitivity to high temperatures. Salamandrina, for example, in spite of its rough skin will frequently be killed by the heat of the hand (Klingelhöffer, 1930) and its temperature requirements may be the principal reason why it does not extend its range into the plains of Italy. Many Amphibia may have requirements difficult to define in physicochemical terms. The distribution of *Aneides lugubris* seems restricted to the live oaks in California (Storer, 1925). *Rana clamitans* and *R. catesbeiana* of the East live and breed in ponds; *Rana boylii* and *Hyla arenicolor* of the West lay their eggs in the stream habitats which they frequent throughout the year. Whether it is temperature, moisture, or current which holds the latter forms in these localities is difficult to say. It may be noted that the higher plethodontids, such as Plethodon, Hydromantes, and Oedipus, which have given up an early life in the water, have extensive ranges.

Many factors combine to make an amphibian a successful migrant. Bufo has a world-wide distribution except for Madagascar, Australia, and most of Polynesia. Toads of this genus are modern and hence presumably recent travelers. What makes Bufo a successful type while many far older forms seem on the verge of extinction? Some toads, such as *Bufo boreas halophilus* and *B. punctatus*, can withstand brackish and highly alkaline waters (Storer, 1925); others can live in deserts by digging for short depths underground. Some, such as *B. superciliaris* of Africa, are purely forest creatures; while others of the same region, notably *B. regularis*, have adapted themselves to a wide variety of conditions. Hardiness, adaptability, and aggressiveness may carry an amphibian a long distance in a short time. The common frog, *R. pipiens*, is a modern aquatic species but it has the widest range of any American Rana. It would seem that agressiveness was an important factor in the distribution of this species.

Many frogs and toads are found today on islands, especially in the East and West Indies. It has been assumed that their presence there indicates that the islands were at one time connected with the mainland, but there are other possibilities to consider. Hurricanes are known to strip trees completely of their leaves and to transport the contents of ponds for varying distances (Visher, 1925). Eggs could be readily carried in the débris, and as adult frogs are known to leap successfully from great heights (Cott, 1926), it is not improbable that they could make an aerial trip successfully. Storms frequently move against prevailing winds and hence would transport Malayan forms into

Fig. 141.—Speciation in Plethodon: (*A*) *Plethodon shermani*. (*B*) *P. metcalfi*. (*D*) *P. jordani*. (*E*) *P. yonahlossee*. They inhabit different mountain ranges in the Southern Appalachians and represent local modifications of the *Plethodon glutinosus* stock (*C*) which covers a wide range in eastern United States.

some of the East Indies and Central American forms to some of the West Indies. At times of storms, great masses of vegetation are carried by freshets out to sea. Tree frogs regularly make the trip in banana shipments from Central America to the United States and it is highly probable that they could survive a short sea voyage in a natural raft. Primitive man may have inadvertently carried some of the species. There are many possibilities and little certainty as to how most of these island Amphibia reached their present homes.

Frogs and toads are most abundant in the tropics, salamanders in temperate regions. Still, only two salamanders, an Ambystoma and a newt, reach Alaska although a Rana, a Bufo, and a Hyla occur there. Amphibia are unable to live in regions having a permanently frozen subsoil, but two species of Rana live north of the Arctic Circle in Norway and Russia and one salamander inhabits artic Asia.

Few genera of Amphibia are spread today over more than one continent, and here their distribution may be confined to certain environmental niches. Evolution is speeded up by diversity of environment. With the greater number of ecological niches that become available, the more chances there are for the isolation of new types. Hence, mountainous regions with their variety of habitat types tend to have more genera and species than lowlands with their uniform vegetation areas. Conversely, the number of species in a region is usually an index of the degree of environmental diversity (Fig. 141).

Where species are abundant, as in many recent genera of salamanders and frogs, it is frequently possible to trace out the relationships of the different species and plot these groupings on their map of distribution. The point where two or more such plotted groups intersect may be taken as the center of dispersal from which these related groups of species evolved. Such a center may not represent the original home of the genus but it will represent the point from which the species under consideration probably radiated. Applied to the fauna of the United States, the method has revealed considerable northern migration. This very probably followed closely after the retreat of the Pleistocene glaciers.

Economic Value.—Toads being indiscriminate feeders on insect life are valuable aids to the farmer in keeping down insect pests. Frogs swarm in the paddy fields of Japan and China and are undoubtedly useful in destroying obnoxious insects (Okada, 1927). Frogs and toads are active in the evening and hence supplement the efforts of birds in retaining the balance of nature.

Frogs' legs form a staple article of food in various parts of the world. Nearly a million frogs are killed each year in the United States for their legs (Chamberlain, 1900). Although various attempts have been made to farm frogs, "no definite successful mode of procedure has been evolved" (Wright, 1920) and practically the entire American crop is secured in the wild state. The principal species hunted for their legs are *Rana pipiens, R. catesbeiana*, and *R. palustris.* In New York State the first-mentioned species is taken most abundantly. As much as 500 pounds of frogs' legs have been netted in a single night by placing a half mile of cheesecloth screen, supported by sticks and leading to receptacles, near the shore where it would intercept frogs migrating to hibernate. *Rana pipiens* is frequently hunted in the uplands where this species goes to feed after the breeding season. Adams and Hankinson (1916) suggest that a frog farm, to be successful, should provide not only swamps but also upland feeding grounds where the frogs would be less crowded. No doubt the natural food in a swamp is not enough to provide for the large colony which gathers there during the breeding season. If captive frogs are closely crowded they must be given additional food. Still, it is doubtful if frogs can be raised in greater numbers than they are still captured in the wild state. As many as 150,000 frogs were held by one New York State dealer during the fall of 1915.

Dried toads and frogs are sold in China as food or for medicinal purposes (Henderson, 1864). Toad skins have been used in Japan and elsewhere as a source of fine leather. In Japan dried salamanders are employed as a vermifuge (Dunn 1923). The axolotl is sought in Mexico as an article of food. Many superstitions have been attached to frogs and salamanders. In parts of South China the brilliant *Polypedates dennysi* is worshiped by a cult and carried about in a chair by faithful members of this group (Pope, 1931).

One of the most important aspects of frogs and salamanders is their martyrdom to science. Amphibian larvae afford excellent material for studying many problems of developmental mechanics and endocrinology. The frog, especially *Rana pipiens*, has long been employed in laboratories of general physiology. Frogs and salamanders, standing at the base of the tetrapod series, have for many years been employed as a type form in university instruction in vertebrate zoology.

References

ADAMS, C. C., and T. L. HANKINSON, 1916: Notes on Oneida Lake fish and fisheries, *Trans. Amer. Fish. Soc.*, XLV, 154–169.

CHAMBERLAIN, F. M., 1900: "A Manual of Fish-culture Based on the Methods of the U. S. Commission of Fish and Fisheries," *rev. ed., U. S. Comm. Fish and Fisheries, Wash.*, 252–253.

COTT, HUGH, B., 1926: Observations on the life-habits of some batrachians and reptiles from the Lower Amazon, *Proc. Zool. Soc. London*, 1926, II, 1159–1178.

DUNN, E. R., 1923: The salamanders of the family Hynobiidae, *Proc. Amer. Acad. Arts Sci.*, LVIII, 445–523.

————, 1926: "The Salamanders of the Family Plethodontidae," Smith College, Northampton, Mass.

HENDERSON, JAMES, 1864: The medicine and medical practice of the Chinese, *Jour. Roy. Asiatic Soc. N. China Branch*, 1, n. s., 21–69.

KLINGELHÖFFER, W., 1930: *Terrarienkunde*, Lief 15–16, Stuttgart.

MATTHEW, W. D., 1915: Climate and evolution, *Ann. N. Y. Acad. Sci.*, XXIV, 171–318.

NOBLE, G. K., 1925: The evolution and dispersal of the frogs, *Amer. Naturalist*, LIX, 265–271.

————, 1930: The fossil frogs of the intertrappean beds of Bombay, India, *Amer. Mus. Novit.*, No. 401.

OKADA, Y., 1927: Frogs in Japan, *Copeia*, No. 158, 161–166.

POPE, C. H., 1931: Notes on Amphibia from Fukien, Hainan and other parts of China, *Bull. Amer. Mus. Nat. Hist.*, in press.

STORER, T. I., 1925: A synopsis of the Amphibia of California, *Univ. Cal. Pub. Zool.*, XXVII, 1–343, 18 pls.

VISHER, S. S., 1925: Tropical cyclones and the dispersal of life from island to island in the Pacific, *Ann. Rep. Smithson. Inst.*, 1925, 313–319.

WRIGHT, A. H., 1920: Frogs: their natural history and utilization, *Bur. Fish. Doc.* 888, App. VI, *Rept. U. S. Comm. Fish.*, 1919.

PART II

RELATIONSHIPS AND CLASSIFICATION

The frogs, toads, and salamanders include only some 1,900 species and 234 living genera. It is possible to discuss the mutual relations of these genera without giving a full description of each group. On the other hand, the fossil Amphibia are based so frequently upon incomplete skeletal material that only the broader relations will be considered here. The caecilians rarely find their way into biological laboratories and a synopsis of the genera has been omitted from the following account. Those who have the occasion to study caecilians will find Nieden's recent review (1913) of their classification useful. The bibliography at the close of the chapter includes the principal literature dealing with systematics of Amphibia.

ORDER 1. LABYRINTHODONTIA.—The labyrinthodonts or stegocephalians are crocodile- or salamander-like Amphibia which lived from the Lower Carboniferous to the Triassic period. As shown by the fossils, they had a skull completely roofed over with bone. Many more bony elements were present in their skulls than occur today in modern Amphibia; especially significant were an extra row of four bones lying behind the parietals, several extra bones in the orbit, and a lower jaw consisting of at least eight pieces on each side. The group receives its name from the enlarged teeth with greatly folded dentine found in both jaws. Many species were aquatic, as shown by the well-marked lateral-line canals on the skulls, but others, such as Cacops, may have been terrestrial. The suborders or grades of labyrinthodonts are distinguished primarily by differences in the vertebrae. In all, the vertebrae consist of neural arches and intercentra; and in all except the Stereospondyli, a free, ossified pleurocentrum is present. The various genera in the order have recently been revised by Watson (1919, 1926) and Romer (1930). The classification employed for this order is that adopted by Watson.

SUBORDER 1. EMBOLOMERI.—The most primitive Amphibia were the Embolomeri which lived from the Lower Carbon-

459

iferous through the Permian. The centra were double, that is, the intercentrum and pleurocentrum formed complete rings and the neural arch attached to one or both of them. The occipital condyle was single or triple, and a well-ossified basioccipital and basisphenoid were present. The palate was well ossified, broad pterygoid bones leaving very small vacuities between them and the parasphenoid. The various genera in the suborder have been grouped into the families Anthracosauridae, Loxommidae, Pholidogasteridae, and Cricotidae.

SUBORDER 2. RACHITOMI.—The rachitomous labyrinthodonts lived during the Permian and Triassic periods. They differ from their embolomerous ancestors in that each vertebra consists of a half-moon-shaped intercentrum and one or two pairs of pleurocentra in addition to the neural arch. The occipital

FIG. 142.—*Eryops megacephalus*, a rachitomous amphibian of the North American Permian. Restoration based on mounted skeleton.

condyle was triple or double and the interpterygoid vacuities wider than in the Embolomeri. The tabulars and dermosupraoccipitals in this group form occipital flanges, not present in the Embolomeri. Watson (1919) recognizes the following families: Eryopidae, Actinodontidae, Rhinesuchidae, Achelomidae, Dissorophidae, Trematopsidae, Zatrachydae, Archegosauridae, Trimerorachidae, Lydekkerinidae, Micropholidae, and Dwinasauridae. The last mentioned, to judge from its hyoid was apparently a neotenous group. The best-known rachitomous amphibian is Eryops (Fig. 142). It attained the length of 4 or 5 feet and resembled an alligator but had a shorter tail.

SUBORDER 3. STEREOSPONDYLI.—The most advanced suborder of labyrinthodonts lived during the Triassic period. They differed from the preceding in having the centrum formed almost entirely of the intercentrum, the pleurocentra being rudimentary or absent. Tendencies found in the Rachitomi are carried to an extreme in this group. The occipital condyle is double, the basioccipital and basisphenoid being reduced. The interpterygoid vacuities are increased in size and the occipital flanges are more extensive. Some genera such as Plagiosternum are very broad-headed and obviously aquatic; others resemble gavials and crocodiles in the form of their head. The genera are grouped into the families Capitosauridae, Trematosauridae, Metoposauridae, Mastodonsauridae, and Brachyopidae.

ORDER 2. PHYLLOSPONDYLI.—The branchiosaurs and their allies are small, salamander-like Amphibia, found in the Carboniferous and Permian deposits. They were derived from the primitive labyrinthodonts and resemble such forms as Eryops closely in the number and arrangement of elements forming the skull roof. They are believed to be the ancestors of both the Salientia and Caudata, although they seem highly specialized in certain features of their skull and girdles. The vertebrae of the typical Branchiosauridae are usually described as tubular with the spinal cord and notochord lying in one cavity. It seems, however, more probable that the vertebrae were formed epichordally as in Xenopus, the neural arch never growing down around the notochord. In this case the centrum would be represented by the thick floor of each vertebral ring. This conclusion derived from a study of original material received support in the recent work of Whittard (1930). Some branchiosaurs appear to have such vertebrae with opisthocoelous articulations like Xenopus. According to Bulman and Whittard (1926), the branchiosaurs were adapted to a life in muddy fresh waters and this is the normal habitat of Xenopus. The branchiosaurs resembled frogs in their well-marked transverse processes with short ribs, the cartilaginous pubis, the four fingers and five toes, and the general configuration of bones forming the palate. There were prevomers, palatines, and pterygoids, the latter narrow and separated by broad, interpterygoid vacuities from the narrow parasphenoid. A clavicle, cleithrum, and scapula were present but the coracoid remained cartilaginous as in some urodeles. Another urodele feature was the three pairs of external gills carried during a long larval life on broad gill arches well provided with "rakers" which may have been bony. The skull roof had a separate quadratojugal, as in frogs, and a lacrimal, as in some salamanders, for it had not undergone the loss of elements necessary to convert the skull into that of a modern amphibian. Although branchiosaurs lost their gills in adult life, no extensive reorganization of the skull occurred at the time of this metamorphosis.   The occiput was more cartilaginous than in frogs or salamanders.   Both exoccipitals and opisthotics were present (Whittard, 1930), however, but not so extensive as in modern species.

Frogs and salamanders may not have sprung from branchiosaurs but from Phyllospondyli closely related to the Branchiosauridae.   Other families which have been placed in this order are the Peliontidae, Colosteidae, Stegopidae, and Acanthostomatidae.   The first of these families is intermediate between labyrinthodonts and typical branchiosaurs.   Labyrinthodont teeth are present, also an ectopterygoid.   The pterygoid articulated with the anterior margin of the basisphenoid region as in primitive labyrinthodonts, whereas in later branchiosaurs it attached more posteriorly and dorsally, as in frogs.   Romer (1930) refers some vertebrae to the Colosteidae which were perichordal with a transverse process springing from the neural arch as in frogs. Possibly the epichordal and the perichordal types of vertebrae were already established in the phyllospondyl ancestors of the Salientia.   It is noteworthy that although the epichordal type of vertebrae characterizes many primitive Salientia, the most primitive group of Salientia, the Liopelmidae, apparently retains the perichordal type.

ORDER 3.   LEPOSPONDYLI.—The small Carboniferous and Permian Amphibia, which are neither labyrinthodonts nor Phyllospondyli, may be grouped together in a single order, although they include several very distinct evolutionary lines. Most lepospondyls have vertebrae composed of a single piece, the neural arch being continuous with the centrum which is well ossified, greatly constricting the chorda.   Most lepospondyls have the ribs articulating with the column intervertebrally, and this has been considered one of the principal characters separating lepospondyls from phyllospondyls and their apparent derivatives, the Salientia and Caudata.   In some lepospondyls there is a secondary shift of the rib to the side of the vertebra.   These lepospondyls are nevertheless readily distinguished from typical Branchiosauridae by their cylindrical centra.

SUBORDER 1.   ADELOSPONDYLI.—In this recently defined group (Watson, 1926a) the neural arch is joined by suture to a centrum which has a distinctive form, a pair of depressions penetrating the ventrolateral surface of each vertebra.   The most advanced member of the suborder is Lysorophus of the Lower Permian of North America, now known in some detail, thanks to the investigations of Sollas (1920). This genus is frequently referred to as a "Permian urodele," although it retains too many labyrinthodont characters to be considered a near relative of the Caudata.

SUBORDER 2. AISTOPODA.—Among the Carboniferous lepospondyls were several genera of legless, long-bodied Amphibia which are grouped here as a distinct suborder. They possessed elongate skulls, distinctive transverse processes, and peculiar ribs. They were the sirens and amphiumas of the Carboniferous swamps; and even at this early time leg reduction had been carried to completion in this one group.

SUBORDER 3. NECTRIDIA.—The skull structure of the more primitive genera of Nectridia was close to the embolomerous plan.

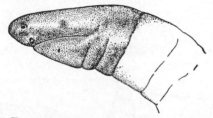

FIG. 143.—Head of *Caecilia tentaculata.*

Zygosphene-zygantrum articulations were present on the rather elongate neural arches. In the more advanced types as represented by Diplocaulus, the posterior angles of the head are pulled out to form a peculiar, triangular-shaped head. In spite of this specialization, Diplocaulus possessed many primitive features such as a separate coracoid (Douthitt, 1917) and possibly a fifth finger. All other Amphibia except certain Embolomeri have lost the outer finger, and hence the retention of this structure in one suborder of lepospondyls is of interest.

SUBORDER 4. GASTROCENTROPHORI.—The salamander or Amphiuma-like lepospondyls of the families Microbrachidae, Hylonomidae, Limnerpetontidae may be grouped together following the lead of Abel (1919), although their relation to each other and to the other suborders is not well defined.

ORDER 4. GYMNOPHIONA.—The Gymnophiona or caecilians are limbless, long-bodied Amphibia, living today and having no fossil representatives. They resemble large earthworms, for their bodies are usually provided with a series of transverse grooves. Within these folds are found in many genera a series of small scales. These are unquestionably an inheritance from the Carboniferous Amphibia. Other primitive features are a postfrontal (Ichthyophis), an ectopterygoid (Hypogeophis), and many features of the gill clefts, hyobranchial apparatus, and viscera recorded in the above chapters. Although the caecilians are highly modified for a burrowing life, they retain many very

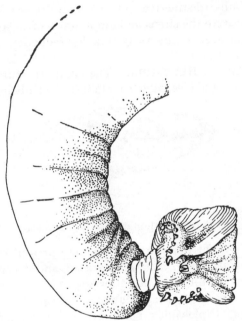

Fig. 144.—Everted intromittent organ of the male *Scolecomorphus uluguruensis.*

primitive features, and it seems certain that they originated from some other group of fossil Amphibia than did the frogs and salamanders; presumably they arose from lepospondyls. Among the distinctive features of the caecilians is the protrusible tentacle (Fig. 143) which is found on the side of the face between nostril and eye of all the species. Their lidless eyes are usually indistinct and frequently hidden under the bones of the skull. The males are provided with a protrusible copulatory organ (Fig. 144). One character they possess in common with the frogs is their short tail, the vent being nearly terminal.

Nieden (1913) recognizes 19 genera and 55 species of caecilians all belonging to a single family. The more primitive genera such as Ichthyophis and Rhinatrema possess scales and have the greatest number of skull elements, while the more specialized genera have lost the scales and exhibit various fusions of the skull elements. One genus, Typhlonectes, is aquatic and has developed a flattened tail. This genus gives birth to its young alive, while the more primitive genera, such as Ichthyophis and Rhinatrema, lay large-yolked eggs on land. There may or may not be an aquatic larval life according to the genus (see Chap. III). The Gymnophiona are found throughout the tropics but are absent from Madagascar. They are seldom seen owing to their burrowing habits.

ORDER 5. CAUDATA.—The salamanders and newts form a natural group of Amphibia derived from the Phyllospondyli. They retain many of the characters of their ancestors but have suffered numerous losses of both cranial and pectoral-girdle elements (see page 215). All urodeles possess tails, and their larvae, if aquatic, resemble their parents closely, having among other features teeth in both jaws. Thus, neither the adult nor larval urodeles can be confused with frogs, the Salientia, which apparently arose from the same stock. The adult Salientia early specialized for leaping and lost their tails. The larvae, if aquatic, are usually of the polliwog type, or at least never possess true teeth until metamorphosis.

The name "Caudata" is used today for the order by systematists. In the herpetological literature there are found other names for the same group: "Batrachia Gradientia," "Urodela," "Saurabatrachia," etc. The history of the early classifications and the origin of many of these names have been given by Gadow (1901) and Hoffman (1873 to 1878).

The Caudata are divided into five natural groups or suborders. The first three: Cryptobranchoidea, Ambystomoidea, and Salamandroidea, converge toward a common ancestor; but the ancestral stocks of the other two, Proteida and Meantes, are uncertain. The systematic position of Hylaeobatrachus from the Wealden formation of Belgium is unknown. It possessed branchial arches and was obviously of a larval type. Some authors place this oldest known urodele in a separate family.

SUBORDER 1. CRYPTOBRANCHOIDEA.—The most primitive Caudata retain a more generalized skeleton than the other urodeles. The angular is free, not fused with the prearticular, as in the other suborders. The second epibranchial is retained in the metamorphosed adult. The spine of the premaxillary is short, not separating the nasals. Certain features of the musculature are apparently distinctive. The *pubotibialis* and the *puboischiotibialis* of the thigh are fused. Fertilization in the Cryptobranchoidea is external, the cloacal gland complex which forms the spermatophores of most higher urodeles being reduced and including only one type of gland. The eggs are always laid in gelatinous sacs, whether these be short as in the Hynobiidae or pulled out into two long strings as in the Cryptobranchidae. The suborder includes only two families, the Hynobiidae, confined to the eastern Asiatic region, and the Cryptobranchidae, found in eastern Asia (including Japan) and the eastern United States.

Family 1. Hynobiidae.—The Asiatic land salamanders, often referred to the Ambystomidae, differ from the latter in retaining the primitive characters listed above. They represent a very uniform group both anatomically and in life history. The family includes five genera. Only one of these, Hynobius, has an extensive distribution. It ranges from the Urals to Kamchatka, Sakhalin, and Islands of Japan and from northern Siberia to Turkestan and Hupeh. The other four genera occupy very limited ranges in different parts of the range of Hynobius. They have apparently arisen directly from some species of Hynobius, which occur very near their respective ranges. The derived genera have undergone a number of parallel modifications. This is, perhaps, the usual mode of generic evolution in the Amphibia. A widespread stock gives rise to a number of local variants which differ from the original stock in features which the systematist considers of generic value. Similar generic characters have sometimes appeared independently in the divergent branches of the original stock. In the Salientia, the numerous cases of parallel evolution are particularly conspicuous (see page 88).

Pachypalaminus is known from only one species taken from a single locality—Odaigahara Mountain, Yamato, Hondo, Japan. It agrees closely with *Hynobius vandenburghi* of the same general region but differs in having a horny covering to the palms, soles, and tips of digits. Further, its premaxillary fontanelle is larger. Batrachuperus, known from two species, is restricted to Szechuan and to the Thibetan province of Kham. It has redeveloped the horny pads on the feet found in Pachypalaminus and in addition has weakened its prevomers in such a way that the vomerine teeth are restricted to two small widely separated patches, instead of forming the V-shaped series found in Hynobius and Pachypalaminus. Ranodon, which includes only one species, *sibiricus*, is known only from eastern Semiryechensk and western Chinese Turkestan but possibly has a greater range. It retains the unmodified feet of Hynobius but has two vomerine teeth patches separated as in Batrachuperus. It is a mountain-brook species and has its lungs partly reduced. In an adult 210 mm. long these were only 22 mm. in length. The last genus, Onychodactylus, is the most specialized. It ranges from Khabarovka, Maritime Government, and Wonsan, Korea, to Hondo and Shikoku. It includes two closely related species, *japonicus* and *fischeri*. These are lungless, like some brook species of other families. *Japonicus* is known to frequent mountain streams, secreting itself under rocks near the water very much as in the case of the American Dusky Salamander, *Desmognathus fuscus*. The vomerine teeth are in a nearly transverse and continuous series across the palate. The premaxillary fontanelle is large and the tail, long and nearly cylindrical. The larvae of Onychodactylus are distinctive, especially in the broad fins on their limbs (Fig. 53). The digit tips are provided with sharp recurved claws which are sometimes retained in the adults. Similar but much smaller claws are found in the larvae of some species of Hynobius, as, for example, in *peropus*. The gills of the larvae have very short rami in correlation with the current in which they live.

The functional significance of the few characters which distinguish the genera of Hynobiidae is not clear. Dunn sees in them adaptations toward a more aquatic life. The habits of only two genera, Onychodactylus and Ranodon, are known. These genera frequent mountain brooks but nevertheless lack the horny pads of the other two genera. The reduction of the prevomers occurs in terrestrial as well as in aquatic species of other families. Thus the only characters which can be labeled as closely correlated with a specific environment are the reduction of the lungs and certain features of the larvae (short gills, etc.).

It is not only difficult to pick out any highly adaptive characters in the Hynobiidae, but certain genera exhibit marked differences which almost surely have no adaptive significance. Perhaps the most striking of these is the loss of the fifth toe. In Batrachuperus this digit is lacking and also in *Hynobius keyserlingii,* which is frequently placed in a distinct genus, Salamandrella. The digit is usually absent in *Hynobius kimurai* and may occasionally be missing or absent in other species of Hynobius. In other families of urodeles the same toe may be lost, and in these its presence or absence is considered a generic character. But in the Hynobiidae the toe is so variable in length and its occurrence so haphazard that the species of Hynobius lacking it cannot be considered a natural group. Nor is it possible at the present time to imagine any reasonable functional excuse for its absence in Batrachuperus.

Family 2. Cryptobranchidae.—The two genera of giant salamanders which form this family are both semilarval, that is, incompletely metamorphosed types (Fig. 145) directly evolved from the hynobiids and exhibiting all the primitive features of the suborder. Megalobatrachus, found in China and Japan, is less larval than Cryptobranchus, the Hellbender, of eastern United States. Gills are lacking in both, but in the adult Megalobatrachus the spiracle is closed and only two epibranchials are usually retained on the essentially larval hyoid. In Cryptobranchus (Fig. 146) the spiracle remains open, as an outlet for water taken into the mouth during aquatic buccal respiration, and four epibranchials are retained. The eyes of both genera are devoid of eyelids, as is the case in the larvae of all urodeles. Aside from their giant size and semilarval habitus, the cryptobranchids may be distinguished from their hynobiid ancestors by various larval characters of the skull and hyoid, such as the parallel arrangement of maxillary and prevomerine teeth. The skeleton has, however, undergone certain specializations of its own. The whole skeleton is greatly flattened, especially the skull. The lacrimal and septomaxillary bones have been lost. The cryptobranchids are completely aquatic animals, and, as they have no gills when adult, the skin (including the epidermis) has become greatly vascularized.

Megalobatrachus embraces only a single species, *japonicus,* known from China and Japan. Cryptobranchus also includes only one species. This is widely distributed over eastern United States from the Great Lakes to Georgia and Louisiana. It is abundant only in the rivers which flow from the Allegheny highland. Megalobatrachus is known as a fossil from the Miocene of Europe.   The closely allied, if not identical, Andrias has been found in the Miocene and Upper Oligocene of the same region. A fossil cryptobranchid, Plicognathus, has been described from

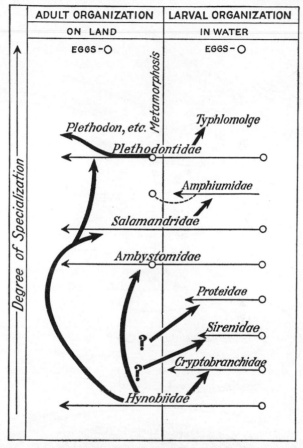

Fig. 145.—Diagram illustrating the phylogeny of the urodeles.   The heavy black arrows indicate the phylogenetic relations.   The narrow, horizontal arrows represent the ontogeny of the various families.   The degree of metamorphosis of the hyobranchial apparatus is employed as the chief criterion of metamorphosis in this diagram.   The "permanent larvae" are not closely related but have been derived from different groups.

the Lower Pliocene of Nebraska.   Hence the family at one time must have had much greater distribution than now.   The crypto-branchids are river salamanders, *japonicus* usually frequenting smaller streams than *alleganiensis*.

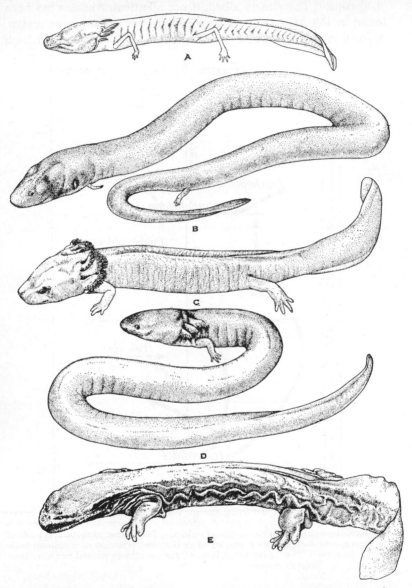

Fig. 146.—Permanent larvae: the perennibranch and derotreme salamanders.
A. Typhlomolge rathbuni.   B. Amphiuma means.   C. Necturus maculosus.   D. Siren lacertina.   E. Cryptobranchus alleganiensis.

SUBORDER 2.   AMBYSTOMOIDEA.—The salamanders of the family Ambystomidae are placed in a distinct suborder, although they have apparently arisen from hynobiids or from prohynobiids.

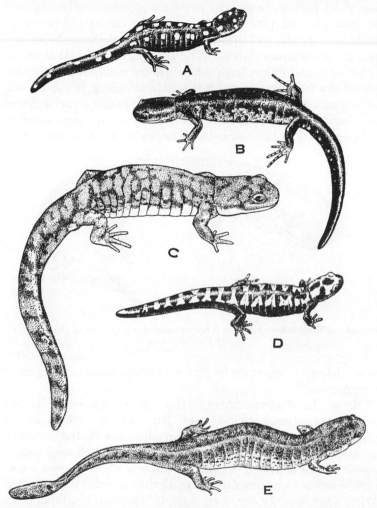

Fig. 147.—Some common species of Ambystoma: *A. Ambystoma maculatum. B. Ambystoma jeffersonianum.   C. Ambystoma tigrinum.   D. Ambystoma opacum.   E. Ambystoma texanum.*

They possess in common with the Salamandroidea certain advanced characters such as the fusion of angular to the prearticular, the loss of the second epibranchial, and the elongation and approach of the premaxillary spines. Fertilization is internal, and three sets of glands surround the cloaca of the male. The Ambystomoidea are distinguished from the Salamandroidea by their short prevomers without posterior processes extending over the parasphenoid region. The vertebrae are amphicoelous in the Ambystomidae and opisthocoelous in the Salamandridae and some other Salamandroidea. The skull agrees with that of the Hynobiidae and differs from that of the primitive salamandroids in lacking a frontosquamosal arch and in retaining, in two genera, the lacrimal. The hyoid is peculiar in possessing a cartilaginous cross-bar between the posterior cornua in a large percentage of the species. The body muscles as far as known are primitive, a

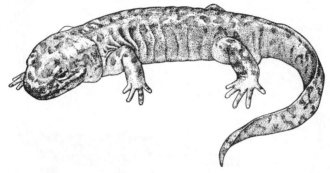

Fig. 148.—*Dicamptodon ensatus*, a large terrestrial salamander of the west coast of the United States.

rectus abdominis superficialis but no *rectus abdominis profundus* being present.

Family 1. Ambystomidae.—The three American genera Ambystoma, Dicamptodon, and Rhyacotriton comprise the family Ambystomidae, which is the only one in the suborder. Ambystoma includes 11 species widely scattered over North America from southern Alaska to Mexico. The species are all much alike in form but differ remarkably in color pattern (Fig. 147). They usually lay their eggs in the water, although the Marbled Salamander, *A. opacum*, deposits them on land in the fall. The larvae, however, are very similar (see page 51) and, being equipped with broad body and tail fins, are adapted to pond life.

Dicamptodon and Rhyacotriton are both western salamanders. The latter is apparently restricted to the Olympic Mountains, Washington, while the former ranges from southern British

Columbia to Southern California. The region they occupy is a humid coastal belt with moist atmosphere and soil. Both genera are represented by single species which can be distinguished from any species of Ambystoma on external characters. Dicamptodon is the largest land salamander in the world, attaining a length of 271 mm. It is heavily marked with blackish brown (Fig. 148). Rhyacotriton is apparently a dwarf derivative of Dicamptodon. It is uniform brown above except for a few white specks. Both genera differ from Ambystoma in possessing lacrimals. Rhyacotriton differs from Dicamptodon in lacking nasals. It is a mountain-stream form and has its lungs reduced to mere vestiges which, although only 5 or 7 mm. long, retain a circulation and are filled with air. The larvae of Rhyacotriton and Dicamptodon differ from the Ambystoma species in lacking a body fin, in having short bushy gills, and in being in other ways adapted to mountain-stream life (see page 49).

SUBORDER 3. SALAMANDROIDEA.—Any metamorphosed urodele having teeth on the roof of the palate well behind the internal nares is referable to the Salamandroidea. The prevomers of the three families in this suborder are either extended back as two dentigerous processes on each side of the parasphenoid or split off as one or two groups of teeth patches lying directly on the latter bone. The Salamandroidea is an extremely varied group including such aquatic forms as the newt and Amphiuma and such terrestrial types as the plethodons. It has the widest distribution of any suborder and seems to have arisen independently from prohynobiid ancestors not living today. Fertilization is internal, as in the Ambystomoidea, and three sets of glands surround the cloaca of the male; if one is absent it is the outermost, the abdominal gland.

Family 1. Salamandridae.—The European Salamandra and the holarctic newts are grouped together with some less known forms in the present family. The prevomerine teeth of the group are distinctive, being carried back as a long, sometimes S-shaped, row on each side of the parasphenoid. The vertebrae of the salamandrids are opisthocoelous, while with a few exceptions those of the genera in the other families of the suborder are amphicoelous. The primitive salamandrids are large, mostly rough-skinned newts, having a frontosquamosal arch (Fig. 149), four-pronged basihyals, high neural spines, and long ribs with uncinate processes. The more specialized newts have lost the arches and reduced the hyoid and ribs. The newts lack the stylus to the columella, while Salamandra and Chioglossa retain it fused to the periotic. The newts are frequently separated from the other salamandrids as a distinct family, the Pleurodelidae. Since these other genera were apparently derived from the primitive salamandrids, this arrangement has little in its favor. Newts retain a primitive body musculature (a *rectus abdominis superficialis*, but no *profundus*), while Salamandra is specialized in lacking the *obliquus internus* and in possessing both *rectus* muscles. Salamandra is more terrestrial than the newts.

The Salamandridae are Eurasian, except for the American newts, Triturus. The most primitive salamandrid is Tyloto-

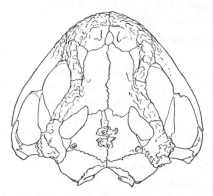

Fig. 149.—Dorsal aspect of the skull of *Tylototriton verrucosus* showing the fronto-squamosal arch which characterizes the primitive salamandrids.

triton, represented by two species: *verrucosus* in Yunnan and the eastern Himalayas and *andersoni* of Okinawa Island in the Loochoo Archipelago. These are rough-skinned newts, apparently rather terrestrial in habits. They retain a primitive skull pattern and the maxillaries extend posteriorly to the squamosals (to which is apparently fused the quadratojugals). The cartilaginous pterygoid of each side is fused to the maxillary, and the bony pterygoid nearly reaches the same element. A broad frontosquamosal arch is present and a secondary deposit of bone is found on various skull elements and on the neural spines. Pachytriton is apparently a smooth-skinned, aquatic derivative of Tylototriton. It is known from one species restricted to a small region in southeastern China. Its bony pterygoids are broadly attached to the maxillaries, while the latter are broadly

separated from the squamosals. The frontosquamosal arch
of each side is entire but very narrow. The typical newts, Triturus, Pleurodeles, and Euproctus, have apparently been
derived from the same stock as Pachytriton. Some forms (Fig.
150) such as *Pleurodeles waltl* are rough skinned and resemble
Tylototriton closely. They have specialized, however, in a
reduction of the maxillary and pterygoid elements, a reduction
which is carried farther in the Plethodontidae. In Triturus the
bony pterygoid is small and does not reach the maxillary, and the
latter is short, not reaching the squamosal. In all species of
the genus except *T. cristatus*, the frontosquamosal arch is either
present or represented by a tough ligament. Triturus, if assumed

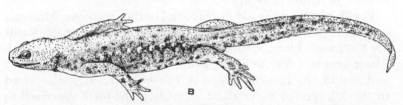

Fig. 150.—European salamandrids: *A. Euproctus asper. B. Pleurodeles waltl.*

to include Pleurodeles and Euproctus, embraces about 24 species
and numerous subspecies. These are scattered over eastern
Asia and Japan, North Africa, Europe, and North America. The
greater number and diversity of species are found in Europe.
Four species are found in North America. The western *T.
torosus* is a rough-skinned form and may have been derived from
Asiatic species. It is sometimes united with these species in a
separate genus, Notophthalmus. The eastern *T. viridescens* and
T. dorsalis and the southern *T. meridionalis* seem most closely
related to the European species.

The Italian Salamandrina is merely a European newt lacking
the fifth toe. As emphasized above, this loss has occurred
independently in many different groups of urodeles. Sala-

mandrina includes only a single species, *terdigitata*. It is a dark, rough-skinned form with a yellowish or pinkish mark between the eyes and a brightly marked under surface washed with salmon or carmine posteriorly.

The smooth-skinned Salamandra and Chioglossa are perhaps the most terrestrial salamandrids, although the latter genus often frequents the edges of streams and escapes into the water when disturbed. They agree with the typical newts in their reduced pterygoids and maxillaries. They differ from most newts in lacking the frontosquamosal arch and the pronounced neural spines. Both Salamandra and Chioglossa may be distinguished on external characters. Salamandra includes four species scattered over Europe as far east as the Caucasus. They all have squarish heads and some indication of the paratoid glands which are so characteristic of the common European *Salamandra salamandra*. Chioglossa includes a single slim-bodied species, *lusitanica*, inhabiting Spain and Portugal. Its most distinctive feature is a long protractile tongue free on all sides except for a median partition in front.

Fossil salamandrids have been found in the Oligocene, Miocene, and more recent formations of Europe. Most of these fossils are too fragmentary to establish definitely their relationship with living genera. Tylototriton, living today in southeastern Asia and one of the Loo-choo Islands, has been recently discovered in the Miocene of Switzerland. Possibly the fossil described as Heliarchon was the larva of some species of Tylototriton. Chelotriton, Heteroclitotriton, and Megalotriton may be related to the same genus, while Polysemia has more resemblance to Triturus. The latter genus has been reported from the Miocene and later formations of Europe. Although the mutual relationships of these genera are not known, it is certain that salamandrids were existing in Europe by at least the Oligocene. It is, therefore, not surprising that Europe is apparently the center of salamandrid specialization.

Family 2. Amphiumidae.—The large "Congo˙Eel" or "Conger," Amphiuma, of southeastern United States is a semilarval type (Fig. 146) derived from the salamandrids and agreeing with them in most important characters. It possesses lungs, a bony pterygoid, a posterior process from each prevomer. The premaxillary spines are elongated to separate the nasals, and a nasolabial groove is lacking. It parallels the plethodontids in the loss of the ypsiloid apparatus and the fusion of columella and operculum, the latter remaining attached by a narrow isthmus to the periotic. It has retained a number of larval characters such as the lidless eyes, the parallel arrangement of maxillary and vomerine teeth, the four branchial arches, and the amphicoelous vertebrae. These larval features have led to a misunderstanding of its true relationships, for in most texts Amphiuma is grouped in the same family with Cryptobranchus. Both genera are partly metamorphosed aquatic types, but they have arisen from very different stocks and have no close affinity. Amphiuma is readily distinguished from the latter by its elongated and rounded, not flattened, body, its salamandroid skull, and its distinctive hyoid. The first ceratobranchial and epibranchial are not separated and the second ceratobranchial is absent. Amphiuma includes two species, both inhabiting southeastern United States as far west as Louisiana and Missouri.

Family 3. Plethodontidae.—The majority of American urodeles are included in the family Plethodontidae. These may be brook dwelling or terrestrial. The family apparently arose in America from a salamandrid stock. One genus succeeded in extending southward to southern South America and another invaded Europe, where it is represented by two species in the Mediterranean region. The plethodontids are more specialized than the salamandrids in their vomerine teeth which are carried back by processes during ontogeny to lie over the parasphenoid, as either one or two dentigerous patches. The pterygoid either fails to ossify, remaining entirely cartilaginous throughout life, or is represented by a small bony nodule. The Plethodontidae embrace a very natural series of genera. They are all lungless and possess a nasolabial groove to assist in freeing the nostril from water. The latter character serves alone to distinguish any plethodontid, but without a hand lens the fine groove from nostril to lip is sometimes difficult to see. Correlated with a loss of lungs, the ypsiloid apparatus is reduced or absent. The otic apparatus seems at first distinctive, for the columella and operculum are fused into a single plate (with or without a style) which is attached by a narrow cartilaginous isthmus to the periotic. It is, however, probably derived from the type of otic apparatus found in the larval salamandrid. The body musculature of the plethodontids is specialized, resembling that of the terrestrial salamandrid, Salamandra.

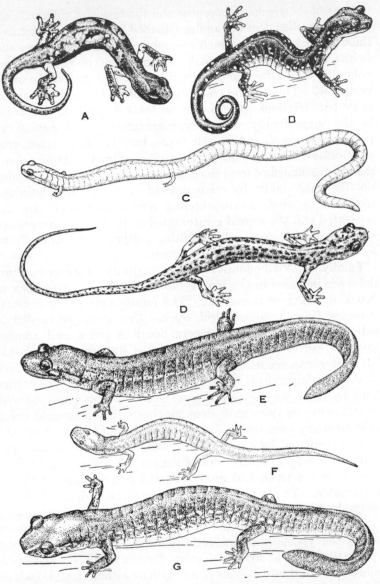

Fig. 151.—Plethodontid salamanders: *A. Hydromantes italicus. B. Aneides lugubris. C. Batrachoseps attenuatus. D. Eurycea lucifuga. E. Desmognathus quadra-maculatus. F. Typhlotriton spelaeus. G. Gyrinophilus porphyriticus.*

The evolution of the Plethodontidae has been studied most critically by Dunn (1926), who has no doubt sketched correctly the main outlines of the phylogeny of this dominant group of American salamanders. There are, however, a number of obscure points in the relationships of the various genera and the conclusions reached here are not always those accepted by Dunn.

The most primitive genera are Gyrinophilus (Fig. 151) and Pseudotriton. They are comparatively large mountain-brook or spring salamanders (4 to 7 inches long), reddish, pink, or salmon in color, suffused or spotted with a darker tone. They are confined to eastern United States and are the only reddish salamanders in this region save the land form of the water newt. The latter is small, terrestrial, bright vermillion or olive in color, and has a rough skin. Pseudotriton may be distinguished from Gyrinophilus by its usually redder skin, rounder face (the canthus rostralis lacking), and fused premaxillaries. *P. ruber* is the common, red stream salamander of the Appalachians from New York to the Carolinas.

Eurycea, which is represented by eight species in eastern United States, is very closely allied to Pseudotriton. It has the free mushroom tongue of that genus and the complete set of plethodontid skull elements. It is less specialized, however, than Gyrinophilus in a number of features. Its nasals do not overlap the premaxillary spines as in that genus, and its periotics and squamosals are not raised into sharp crests. If we are to assume that Eurycea was derived directly from Pseudotriton we must postulate a despecialization in phylogeny, a reversal of evolution. This is not difficult where the derived structure is a more juvenile condition, for a mere slowing up of the growth processes would give the desired result (see page 100). It is probable, however, that Eurycea was not directly derived from Pseudotriton but from some more thoroughly mountain-brook type, for it is less specialized in certain features not only of its skull but also of its anatomy, as, for example, its skin vascularization (Noble, 1925).

Manculus is a dwarf form of Eurycea ranging from the Carolinas to Texas. In color and body form it is almost identical with the juvenile *Eurycea bislineata cirrigera* of part of this region. It differs chiefly in the loss of the fifth (outer) toe. Manculus is apparently more terrestrial than most races of *Eurycea bislineata*.

Three highly specialized genera of plethodontids are of uncertain affinities, but they apparently diverged from the more generalized plethodontid stock represented today by the four genera just discussed. Stereochilus of the coastal plains of the Carolinas, Virginia, and Georgia is an aquatic form which retains the lateral-line organs on the head throughout life. These give the head a pitted appearance. Stereochilus is primitive (or juvenile) in retaining the parasphenoid teeth patches continuous with the vomerine series. It is specialized in having the premaxillary spines almost completely fused together (an aquatic adaptation correlated with the reduction of the premaxillary gland). Stereochilus is a small, drab-colored urodele easily recognized by its pitted head. Typhlotriton of the caves of Missouri and Arkansas has specialized in another direction. It is a blind salamander when adult and the only blind urodele which metamorphoses. The skin is only slightly pigmented, and the lids, which are visible in the adult, are drawn together (Fig. 151F). Typhlotriton agrees with Gyrinophilus and Stereochilus in its continuous vomero-parasphenoid series of teeth. Typhlomolge of the caves of Texas is a permanent larva which is completely blind (unlike the larvae of other blind salamanders). It is specialized in a nearly complete loss of skin pigment and in an elongation of its slim legs (Fig. 146). It was possibly derived from Typhlotriton, for it agrees closely with the larva of Eurycea and other primitive plethodontids. Stereochilus, Typhlotriton, and Typhlomolge are each known from only a single species which, because of its peculiar habits and habitat requirements, is very local.

A second group of genera, apparently derived from Eurycea or its allies but not showing in their anatomy a very close relationship to them, is formed by the dusky salamanders, Desmognathus and Leurognathus. The first of these two genera includes the commonest salamanders of eastern United States. They both have the tongue attached in front. Dunn considers this a primitive character, but as the late larva of Eurycea has an attached tongue it might equally well be considered a juvenile character. Desmognathus and Leurognathus are unquestionably specialized in the lost (or fused) prefrontals and in the modified occipital condyles, atlas, and temporal muscles which function in preventing the lower jaw from opening more than a third the usual gape (see above, page 264), the remainder of the opening being accomplished by raising the skull on the atlas. Leurognathus has been derived directly from Desmognathus quadramacula-

tus. It agrees very closely with this species in color pattern and form, but its head appears a trifle more depressed. An examination of its skull, however, reveals that a number of pronounced internal changes have occurred. The vomerine teeth are reduced or lost. The skull is flattened and the internal nares shifted laterally (Fig. 44). The premaxillary fontanelle is closed. The functional significance of the loss of teeth and flattening of the skull is not clear, but the reduction of the pre-maxillary fontanelle is probably correlated with a degeneration of the premaxillary gland, which could be of little use to aquatic forms, as they have no need of moistening their tongue with a sticky secretion. Leurognathus embraces two races confined to North Carolina, where *Desmognathus quadramaculatus* is most abundant. It is more aquatic than any species of Desmognathus. The latter genus includes seven forms extending from eastern Canada to Kansas. Most frequent the vicinity of mountain streams, but the small *D. fuscus carolinensis* and *D. f. ochrophaeus* have rounder tails and are more terrestrial than the others. The larvae (Fig. 152) may be distinguished from those of Eurycea in the same streams by their shorter, brushlike gills.

A third group of Plethodontidae includes Plethodon and its close allies. These are all terrestrial species, laying their eggs on land and, except for one genus, passing their entire life away from the water. Plethodon seems to be the central group of this series. It has free premaxillae

F I G. 1 5 2. — A larva of *Desmognathus phoca* showing the brush-like gills characteristic of the genus.

and a tongue attached in front but is otherwise essentially like Eurycea. Plethodon includes 11 species distributed over almost the entire United States and southern Canada. Hemidactylium, the four-toed salamander of the eastern United States, is a dwarf form of Plethodon which parallels to a certain extent Manculus, the dwarf form of Eurycea. Its outer toe has been lost. It also differs from Plethodon in the basal constriction of the tail, a provision for quick autotomy. *Hemidactylium scutatum*, the only species in the genus, may be readily distinguished from any species of Plethodon by its pale ventral surface spotted with large, black blotches. Hemidactylium ranges as far south as the Gulf states and as far west as Michigan and Arkansas.

Batrachoseps, the Worm Salamander, has been derived from Plethodon in the west and, like Hemidactylium, has lost the outer toe. It is much more specialized than that genus in its elongate body (Fig. 151, C). Its premaxillae are fused and it has lost the prefrontals. Ensatina is another western derivative of Plethodon and differs from this genus only in having a basal constriction of the tail and in possessing certain tubercles on the palm. Aneides, the last genus in this group, may have arisen from Plethodon in the east, for its least specialized species is found in West Virginia, Tennessee, and the Carolinas. Aneides is the most specialized of all these genera in its fused premaxillary spines, elongated maxillary and mandibular teeth, and bent maxillary bone free of teeth posteriorly. It also has Y-shaped terminal phalanges unlike any of the other genera in the group.

The last group of genera in the family is characterized, as far as known, by ovoviviparity. Dunn (1926, page 31) assumes that the genera arose from some terrestrial stock but makes no attempt to trace their ancestry among the known terrestrial plethodontids. Hydromantes seems closely related to Oedipus, as evinced by partly webbed digits (Fig. 151, A), the large nostrils in the young, the color pattern, and the weakening of the premaxillary spines. Some species of Oedipus have lost the prefrontals and septomaxillas, as in Hydromantes, and a few species have a non-constricted tail, as in that genus. Both Oedipus and Hydromantes have boletoid tongues and long epibranchials to support a long tongue. Lastly they are the only plethodontid genera with different species in two continents, which speaks well for their traveling ability. The only character which separates Hydromantes from all species of Oedipus is its unfused premaxillaries. In view of the known variability of this bone in a related genus (Eurycea), it does not seem necessary to hypothecate a separate ancestry for Hydromantes.

Oedipus includes 30 or more species spread over the neotropics. Except for three ambystomas in Mexico, the genus includes all the neotropical urodeles. Some species have broad, padlike feet with the digits hardly visible. Other species, usually referred to Oedipina, have very long bodies and short legs. This is a modification parallel to that of Batrachoseps and suggests common ancestry of the genera. Hydromantes is known from only three species: one the rare Yosemite Salamander, *H. platycephalus*, and the other two commonly combined under the name, *Spelerpes fuscus*. This name embraces two closely related forms: *H. genei* of Sardinia and *H. italicus* of the French Alps and part of Italy.

It has been assumed on the basis of life history that Oedipus and Hydromantes have arisen from Plethodon. The chief objection to this view is the occurrence of a free boletoid tongue in these genera and an attached tongue in Plethodon. It should also be considered that Plethodon has a broad distribution, while Eurycea, with which Oedipus agrees most closely in adult structure, has a restricted range in eastern United States. Thus, in reaching a conclusion in regard to the probable ancestry of Oedipus, we must weigh all its obvious terrestrial characters against its boletoid tongue. With the available data no final conclusion can be reached at this time.

SUBORDER 4. PROTEIDA.—The Mud Puppy, Necturus, and the European Blind Salamander, Proteus, form a natural group of permanently larval salamanders of unknown ancestry. They are placed in a distinct suborder, as their relationship to any of the other primary groups of urodeles is uncertain. They have no relationship to Spelerpes or to the Plethodontidae, as sometimes stated. Lungs are present but the ypsiloid apparatus is absent. They are, therefore, bottom walkers. The puboischium is distinctive. It is large and pointed anteriorly. Columella and operculum are fused together and are free from the periotic. The more obvious characters of the Proteida are all larval features found in the larvae of other families. The skull is largely cartilaginous, the maxillae are absent. Palatines and pterygoids form a continuous series. Eyelids are lacking, and long external gills are retained. The branchial apparatus is larval, but the fourth branchial arch is lost. The body muscles are larval in that the *rectus abdominis* is lacking. The Proteida may have originated from some salamandroid, for they possess the usual cloacal glands of that group and practice internal fertilization. Further the premaxillary spines are long in both genera, and the angular and prearticular are fused.

Family 1. Proteidae.—The European "Olm," Proteus, with its long, pigmentless body and its "very larval" appendages provided with only three fingers and two toes cannot be confused with other permanent larvae, nor can Necturus with its external gills and pigmented body. The internal characters which define the Proteidae are the same as those of the suborder. Necturus, the well-known Mud Puppy of zoological laboratories, is represented by only two species and one subspecies. *N. punctatus* is found chiefly in the lower courses of the rivers of North and South Carolina, but it manages to reach the Piedmont of North Carolina. It is a small, uniformly colored species and probably represents a dwarf derivative of *N. maculosus* confined to the Carolina coastal plain. The other Carolina Necturus resembles closely *maculosus*, the common Mud Puppy of eastern United States, but fails to reach the size of this species. It has, therefore, been considered a distinct subspecies, *N. maculosus lewisi*. The typical form, *N. m. maculosus*, ranges from the Great Lakes to Louisiana and east to the Atlantic.

SUBORDER 5. MEANTES.—The sirens are permanent larvae which have developed a few adult characters. They agree with the very young larvae of other families in possessing only the anterior appendages. Their relationships are uncertain. It is possible they were derived from some hynobiid, for the premaxillary spines are small and the nasals meet. No cloacal glands are present in either sex, and hence fertilization is very probably external. Both jaws are covered with horn, unlike those of all other urodeles save certain larval hynobiids and ambystomids which have a horny predentary sheath. They differ from larval hynobiids in the greatly elongated body, the fused angular and prearticular, and the distinctive skull form. It is frequently claimed that the Meantes are adults which have "reverted" to an aquatic habitat. The chief characters used to support this claim are the separate prevomers and pterygoids, the separate ossification of the coracoid, and the specialized Jacobson's organ. The latter two features are peculiar to the Meantes, while the first appears when the rest of the animal is a typical larva in structure (see page 102). The usual characters of a young larva are found in the adult sirens, namely lidless eyes, three pairs of external gills, and lacking maxillaries. The skin of Siren, unlike that of Pseudobranchus, is that of a typical land salamander. As stated before (page 103), the skin alone of all the structures of the juvenile Siren undergoes a typical metamorphosis.

Family 1.   Sirenidae.—The two genera included in the Sirenidae may be readily distinguished from all other permanent larvae by their possessing only the anterior appendages. Pseudobranchus is much smaller than Siren and is striped with brown and yellow on the body and is not uniform slate, like the half-grown Siren. It is a slimmer form than Siren and possesses only one branchial opening. Pseudobranchus, unlike Siren, is a burrowing salamander and when confined in aquaria readily burrows out of sight if the sandy floor is suitable. Siren, however, frequently works its way through the densely matted vegetation bordering its native ponds. Hence, the habits of the two genera are not sharply distinguished.

ORDER 6. SALIENTIA.—The frogs and toads form a natural group of Amphibia characterized by short, tailless bodies and long legs. The posterior limbs have four segments, not three as the salamanders, and these function as powerful levers, permitting most Salientia to make long leaps.

The frogs and toads are included in a single order, Salientia. Various names are in general use for the group: "Anura," "Batrachia Ecaudata," and "Batrachia," but the name used here has been adopted by most systematists.

Unfortunately the fossil record does not help in elucidating the evolution of the various suborders or families of Salientia. The oldest known fossils are Montsechobatrachus from the Upper Jurassic of Spain and Eobatrachus from the Upper Jurassic of Wyoming. The systematic position of neither genus has been definitely established, but since both exhibit the general proportions of the frogs and toads, it is obvious that the Salientia have possessed their characteristic body form since at least the Jurassic.

SUBORDER 1. AMPHICOELA.—The most primitive Salientia living today are included in the Amphicoela. They are distinguished from other frogs by their amphicoelous vertebrae, the interdorsal and interventral remaining cartilaginous as in the majority of urodeles. The suborder includes only a single family.

Family 1. Liopelmidae.—There are only two genera of Amphicoela and these are included in a single family, although one genus is found only in New Zealand and the other only in northwestern United States. Both genera are more primitive than other Salientia (Fig. 153) in possessing two tail-wagging muscles, the *pyriformis* and the *caudalipuboischiotibialis*, even though neither possesses a tail. Liopelma and Ascaphus are both small, grayish frogs sometimes suffused with pinks, browns, and yellows. Ascaphus is the only frog which possesses an extension of the cloaca in the male (Fig. 154).   This is used in copulation, fertilization being internal in this genus.

SUBORDER 2. OPISTHOCOELA.—The Discoglossidae and Pipidae are unquestionably closely related.   They are the only Salientia which exhibit typical opisthocoelous vertebrae, with well-fused centra (Fig. 155).   Their scapulae are shorter than in the other Salientia, even though some forms may be terrestrial and others aquatic.   The Opisthocoela are also primitive in possessing free ribs either in the larva or in the adult.   Their

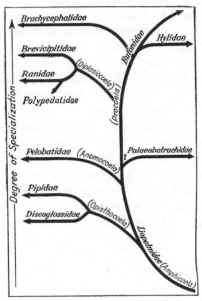

FIG. 153.—Diagram illustrating the phylogeny of the Salientia.

muscular system approaches closely that of the Liopelmidae.   On the other hand, some pipids have the most specialized skulls and sacra of all Salientia, and some discoglossids have the most advanced urogenital system.   The tongueless condition of the Pipidae is an extreme aquatic specialization almost paralleled by the tongue reduction in the thoroughly aquatic species of Batrachophrynus, a bufonid.

Family 1. Discoglossidae.—The Discoglossidae are far less specialized than the Pipidae, although some, such as Bombina, spend most of their time in the water.   They may be described as Opisthocoela with a fully arciferal pectoral girdle, ribs present in the adult, sacral vertebra free with biconvex centrum, presacral vertebrae not less than eight, tongue and eyelids present. The Discoglossidae include only two European, one Eurasian, and one Philippine genus. These may be readily distinguished by their external form, the European species being

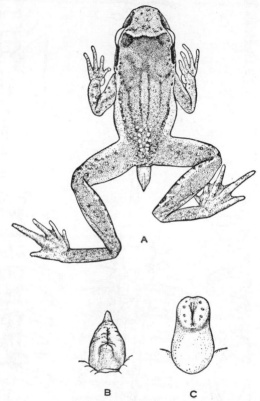

Fig. 154.—Male *Ascaphus truei: A.* Showing the cloacal appendage of this sex. *B.* The appendage viewed ventrally. *C.* The same fully distended, showing the spines which occur within the orifice of the cloaca.

well known. Bombina includes four species of depressed water toads, all variegated below, with black and some other tone, either white, red, or orange. Two of the species are European and two Chinese. Discoglossus includes only a single species, *pictus*, from southwestern Europe and northwestern Africa. It is a Rana-like frog, about the size of a Pond Frog, *R. clamitans*, and grayish in color, often with a pleasing pattern of

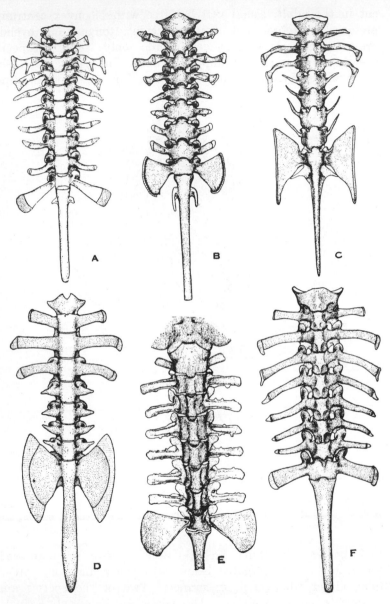

Fig. 155.—The principal types of vertebral columns of the Salientia: *A.* Amphicoelous—*Ascaphus truei. B.* Opisthocoelous—*Alytes obstetricans. C.* Opisthocoelous with fused coccyx—*Xenopus tropicalis. D.* Anomocoelous— *Scaphiopus couchii. E.* Procoelous—*Atelopus varius. F.* Diplasiocoelous— *Rana virgatipes.* The vertebral columns are viewed from the ventral aspect.

darker and lighter tones. Alytes is a smaller, more terrestrial, and rougher-skinned form. It is usually lighter in coloration. Alytes is represented by two species: one, *obstetricans*, is widely spread over western Europe, and the other, *cisternasii*, is restricted to Spain and Portugal. Barbourula, recently described from the Philippines, is a completely aquatic frog known from one Philippine species which resembles Ooeidozyga closely. Its most distinguishing feature is its webbed fingers.

Fossil discoglossids are known from the Upper Oligocene and Miocene of Europe. Latonia of the Upper Miocene of Switzerland shows some affinity to Discoglossus but differs in certain characters of its skull and in the larger size. The affinities of Pelophilus and Protopelobates are less certain. Alytes has been described from the Lower Miocene of Bonn. Although these few fossils give no picture of the origin or evolution of the Discoglossidae, it is obvious that the family was established in Europe by at least the Middle Tertiary.

Family 2. Pipidae.—The Aglossal Toads are purely aquatic Salientia. In correlation with this habitat they have lost a tongue and movable eyelids (except Pseudhymenochirus, which retains lower eyelids). Ribs are free in the larva but ankylose to the diapophyses on metamorphosis. Various fusions occur in the vertebral column, the presacral vertebrae numbering five to eight. The sacrum is fused to the coccyx (rarely free and with a single condyle). The pectoral girdle is partly or wholly firmisternal; the cartilages never broadly overlap as in the Discoglossidae. The African pipids differ strikingly from the South American genera (Fig. 156) in appearance and life history. They may be conveniently placed in different subfamilies. In each subfamily the most primitive genus possesses maxillary teeth and the more specialized ones lack these structures entirely. The Pipidae are found only in Africa and South America.

Sub-family 1. Xenopinae.—Pipids with simple pointed digits, the three inner toes tipped with black, horny claws; eggs, as far as known, small; the tadpole with two long tentacles and a right and left spiracular opening. The Xenopinae are African, and include three genera: Xenopus, Hymenochirus, and Pseudhymenochirus.

Xenopus has the widest distribution and is the most primitive. Its pectoral girdle is only partially firmisternal. The pterygoids of each side do not fuse together around the median opening of the Eustachian tubes, as in Hymenochirus.   The prevomers are present in *X. laevis* and *X. clivii*, although fused together.   The skull of even the most primitive species is, however, very specialized, especially in the fusion of the sphenethmoid and parasphenoid (which form a bony case for the brain), the reduced and forwardly extended squamosal, the reduced maxillae, and the peculiar Eustachian tube passage.   Xenopus is represented by five living species.

Hymenochirus is known from three or four species from the rain-forest and lower Congo.   It is the most specialized of all Pipidae in several features of the skeleton.   The pterygoids and

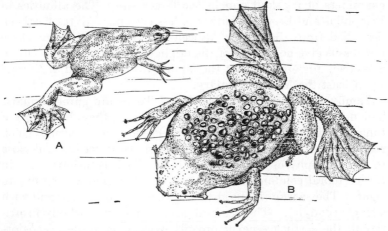

Fig. 156.—Pipid toads: *A. Xenopus mülleri.   B. Pipa pipa*, female with eggs.

exoccipitals are fused to form a complete cover to the Eustachian tubes, which open into the pharynx through a single median orifice.   The lateral wall of the brain case is completely ossified. The sacrum consists of the VII, VIII, and IX vertebrae fused together and to the coccyx.   All the vertebrae are irregularly sculptured, and in one skeleton examined, the IV vertebra was biconvex.   The I and II vertebrae are normally fused, which leaves only five presacral segments.   The most remarkable features are the bladelike flanges of bone which appear on the ilium, femur, tibia, fibula, tarsals, and metatarsals.   These are widest on the two outermost metatarsals (fourth and fifth). There are three flanges to each bone and they face in three directions.   No flanges appear on the forelimbs.   The pectoral girdle is completely firmisternal.

It is said that Hymenochirus shows affinity to Pipa. Aside from its lack of maxillary teeth there are a number of other resemblances. The most important seems to be the broad and laterally flanged frontoparietals, the large nasals, the greatly reduced squamosal, the overlapping, not laterally turned-up, zygapophyses, the flanging of the leg bones, and the synsacrum. It is, however, much more specialized than Pipa in its skull, sacrum, and leg bones. It would seem as easy to derive Hymenochirus from Xenopus as from Pipa. Further, the recently discovered Pseudhymenochirus seems an exact intermediate in external characters between Xenopus and Hymenochirus. Our knowledge of the skeleton of Pseudhymenochirus is so fragmentary that no detailed comparison can be made. It is known from only a single specimen found to the north of the African rain forest.

Subfamily 2. Pipinae.—Pipids with a starlike cluster of dermal appendages at the ends of their fingers, eggs carried in individual dermal pockets on the back of the female, the young escaping fully metamorphosed. The Pipinae include two closely allied genera from the Amazonian and northern parts of South America (including Trinidad). Protopipa is the less specialized in body form. It retains the maxillary teeth, while Pipa lacks them. Pipa includes three species differing in body size and egg size. *P. pipa* is the largest species and is also the flattest, with dermal flaps at the angles of the jaws and a filament at the premaxillary symphysis. The jaw flaps are reduced in *P. snethlageae*, the head is smaller, and the premaxillary filament is lacking. *P. snethlageae* does not reach the size of *P. pipa*. The smallest species is *P. parva*, which lacks the head ornaments entirely. *P. snethlageae* and Protopipa have the fewest number of eggs, but to judge from the embryos these are larger than in the other species and they are confined to only the median area of the parent's back.

SUBORDER 3. ANOMOCOELA.—The pelobatid toads in their skeleton and musculature form an intermediate group between the two preceding suborders and the bufonids. They do not merge into the latter, as is often stated, but form a rather uniform group of genera showing no close affinity to any living bufonids. The Pelobatidae are referred to a distinct suborder, the Anomocoela, which may be defined as follows: Salientia without free ossified ribs at any stage of development; sacral vertebrae procoelous, ankylosed to coccyx or, if free, with only a single artic ular condyle for the latter; presacral vertebrae eight, either uniformly procoelous or with free intervertebral discs.

Family 1. Pelobatidae.—Pelobatids may be either toad- or froglike in external appearance. They agree with bufoninae in their arciferal pectoral girdle and dilated sacral diapophyses. They differ from them in their single coccygeal condyle and primitive pectoral and thigh musculature (the latter specialized in the Sooglossinae). The *supracoracoideus* muscle is not differentiated into an *episterno-cleido-humeralis longus* and a *supracoracoideus profundus*. The *sartorius* and *semitendinosus* form a single muscle exposed on the ventral surface of the thigh. The Pelobatidae are distributed across the northern hemisphere from Mexico and the United States to southeastern Asia and the Philippines. They penetrate into the southern hemisphere in the East Indian region, where they occupy the western part of the Indo-Australian Archipelago but do not reach New Guinea or the Aru Islands. Further, one subfamily, the Sooglossinae, are restricted to the Seychelle Islands. The Pelobatidae are known from three natural groups of genera: the Megophryinae, Pelobatinae, and Sooglossinae.

Subfamily 1. Megophryinae.—Pelobatidae with free intervertebral discs (interdorsals) or at least these discs more or less exposed. Most species of the Megophryinae have their discs free. Their vertebrae thus approach the embolomerous type of the first tetrapods. This, however, is a purely secondary modification, but one found elsewhere among the Salientia only in the Criniinae. The vertebrae of the Megophryinae are more advanced than those of the Criniinae in that the notochord is replaced by calcification or ossification. In some species of Megophrys, better known as Megalophrys, the intervertebral discs may become more or less firmly attached to the vertebrae immediately anterior to them. The vertebral column in these specimens is procoelous, as in the Pelobatinae, and the vertebrae differ from those of the latter only in the extent to which the intervertebral discs are exposed. The Megophryinae embrace a group of Asiatic and East Indian pelobatids, some of large size and striking appearance (Fig. 157B).

The most primitive genus in the subfamily is the widespread Megophrys or Megalophrys (including Leptobrachium). It is represented by 25 species distributed across southern Asia and the western end of the Indo-Australian Archipelago. In Megalophrys the pupil is vertical; the maxillary teeth are well developed, but the vomerine may be more or less reduced or absent; the omosternum is cartilaginous or calcified; while the sternum has a long, bony style. Nesobia of the Natuna Islands is a Megalophrys with a horizontal pupil. Scutiger of the Himalayas is a rough-skinned, high-mountain Megalophrys with short maxillary teeth. Aelurophryne of the same region is a Scutiger which has carried the specialization farther and lost the maxillary teeth entirely. Ophryophryne, from the mountains of northern India, is a small-headed Megalophrys without teeth and with a horizontal pupil. The Bornean Leptobrachella is a diminutive Megalophrys with a cartilaginous sternum. Leptobrachella,

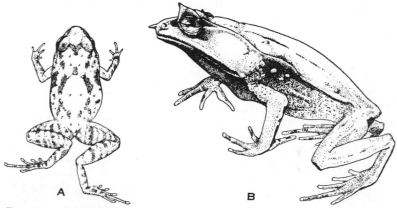

Fig. 157.—Pelobatid toads: *A. Sooglossus sechellensis. B. Megophrys nasuta.*

Ophryophryne, and Nesobia, are each known only from a single species. Scutiger is represented by two closely related species and the same may be said for Aelurophryne. Thus it is highly probable that all these genera are merely local specializations of the Megalophrys stock in comparatively recent times and not groups which have given rise to any of the higher Salientia, as some herpetologists have maintained.

Subfamily 2. *Pelobatinae.*—Pelobatids with the presacral vertebrae uniformly procoelus, sacrum fused to the coccyx, except in Pelodytes, which has a single condyle. The American Scaphiopus and the European Pelobates are popularly known as the "Spade-foot Toads," because of the broad, sharp-edged tubercle which they carry on the inner side of the foot. The bony core of this tubercle is formed by the prehallux greatly enlarged as an instrument for digging. Spade-foot Toads with their vertical pupil and smooth or slightly tubercular skins (Fig. 158) may be readily distinguished from the true toads, Bufo, which have a horizontal pupil and rough skin. Pelodytes, the third genus in the subfamily, lacks the "spade" of the other genera and is much slenderer and more froglike. It is known from two species, one in southwestern Europe and the other in the Caucasus.

The Pelobatinae are closely allied. Scaphiopus with its cartilaginous sternum seems more primitive than either Pelobates or Pelodytes, which have bony sternums. On the other hand, Pelodytes with its free coccyx and Rana-like habitus seems less specialized than either Pelobates or Scaphiopus. The three genera are obviously closely allied (Boulenger, 1899; Noble, 1924), although it is difficult to state which stands nearest the ancestral stock from which they sprang.

Fig. 158.—The eastern Spade-foot Toad, *Scaphiopus holbrookii*.

The history of the Pelobatinae dates back to at least the Oligocene. Macropelobates is known from the Oligocene of Mongolia. Pelobates and a closely allied genus have been described from the Lower Miocene of Europe. Other fossils, possibly identical with living species of Pelobates, have been reported from the Pleistocene of Germany. In brief, Spade-foot Toads were established in the Old World for the greater part of the Tertiary.

Subfamily 3. *Sooglossinae.*—Pelobatids with a free coccyx, a horizontal pupil, and a ranid type of thigh musculature (the *semitendinosus* is separate from the *sartorius* and lies deep within the thigh musculature; its distal tendon passes dorsal to that of the *gracilis major* and *minor*). The three Seychelle Island frogs, *Nesomantis thomasseti*, *Sooglossus sechellensis*, and *S. gardineri*, have recently been shown to be pelobatids (Noble, 1926), although the first two have the external appearance of the ranid Arthroleptis and the last of the bufonid Nectophrynoides. Sooglossus

(Fig. 157A) is merely a Nesomantis without vomerine teeth, but *gardineri* has succeeded in developing short webs between both fingers and toes while retaining the body form of *sechellensis*. Sooglossus lays its eggs on land and the larvae which are devoid of both internal gills and spiracle adhere to the back of the male.

SUBORDER 4. PROCOELA.—The true toads, tree toads, and brachycephalid toads form a very natural group of families characterized by a uniformly procoelous vertebral column and a double condyle to the coccyx. Very rarely, the latter is fused to the sacrum, but usually it is free and serves to distinguish the Procoela from the Anomocoela, or Pelobatidae. The presacral vertebrae are five to eight in number and lack ribs. The thigh musculature also is distinctive. The *semitendinosus* is separate from the *sartorius* (Fig. 96) and is more or less covered by the *gracilis* and *adductor* mass. Its tendon joins that of the *sartorius* and is ventral to (rarely pierces) the *gracilis major* and *minor*. The Procoela includes one extinct family, Palaeobatrachidae, and three recent ones, Bufonidae, Brachycephalidae, and Hylidae.

Family 1. Palaeobatrachidae.—The fossil toads of the genus Palaeobatrachus, and possibly Protopelobates, are grouped together in the family Palaeobatrachidae. They differ from the Pelobatidae in having a double condyle on the coccyx and in having the sacrum formed of two or three slightly dilated pre-coccygeal vertebrae. They are procoelous and cannot be confused with the Pipidae, which they seem to parallel in several respects, chiefly in the form of their appendages. In *Palaeobatrachus luedecki*, for example, the metacarpals are as long as the radius and only slightly shorter than the humerus. This suggests an aquatic life. The Palaeobatrachidae are sometimes described as Aglossa or at least as very primitive. Some species, possibly all, possessed maxillary and vomerine teeth. But aside from this they possessed few primitive characters. The first and second vertebrae were probably fused. The others were procoelous without a trace of the notochord (*luedecki*). Neither pectoral nor pelvic girdle approached closely to those of the obviously primitive Liopelmidae. The Palaeobatrachidae extend from the Jurassic (Vidal, 1902) to Miocene. They are known only from European formations.

It is not improbable that a number of different stocks are included under the name "Palaeobatrachus." Thus, in the Lower Miocene beds near Markersdorff, Czechoslovakia, there were found many skeletons of *Palaeobatrachus luedecki* and also some large tadpole skeletons attributed to the same species. These tadpoles have single frontoparietal plates similar to those of the adult skeletons. They also have long parasphenoids extending forward to a sharp point. In these features they resemble the tadpoles of Xenopus. In the Rott beds near Bonn, there is another type of tadpole attributed to *Palaeobatrachus diluvianus*. This has a much smaller head, separate frontoparietals, and a shorter parasphenoid. It seems hardly likely that these two tadpoles are referable to the same genus.

Family 2. Bufonidae.—The toads, including those with and those without maxillary teeth, form one of the dominant groups of Salientia. They resemble the Pelobatidae closely but, as indicated in the definition of the Procoela, have advanced beyond this group in both their skeletal anatomy and their musculature. The toothed bufonids are frequently designated as Cystignathidae or Leptodactylidae. They are more primitive than the toothless genera, but as they have given rise to toothless bufonids in different parts of the world, it makes a more natural system to group toothed and toothless genera together as a single family. The Bufonidae possess an arciferal pectoral girdle. The sacral diapophyses are cylindrical or dilated. The presacral vertebrae are usually eight, rarely seven. The terminal phalanges may be simple or T-shaped. The Bufonidae group themselves into seven subfamilies, some better defined than others.

Subfamily 1. *Criniinae: Australian Toads.*—Bufonidae usually with a persistent remnant of the notochord continuous throughout the vertebrae; sacral diapophyses more or less dilated; sternum broad, cartilaginous, rarely bony; maxillae usually very deep. The Australian Bufonidae, although represented by 16 genera, are particularly distinguished by their lack of specialization. They are all much alike, the characters which separate the genera being for the most part very trivial. The Criniinae are not sharply distinguished from the Pseudinae. They differ from most of the latter by their dilated sacral diapophyses, but unfortunately a few species of Paludicola, Eupemphix, and Calyptocephalus have also developed a slightly dilated sacrum. The deep maxillae serve to distinguish the skulls of most Criniinae. In these the maxillae are usually more than a fourth as wide as long, while in the Pseudinae they are much narrower. A few intermediates, however, exist, and in several species of both subfamilies a secondary deposit of bone over the skull elements extends their dimensions considerably. The most fundamental difference would seem to be the persistent notochord of the Criniinae, but this character has been checked for only a limited number of genera and was found to be lacking in one of these, namely Lechriodus. It must be admitted that until the anatomy of the Australian and South American bufonids has been more fully investigated no sharp distinction may be made between the Criniinae and Pseudinae. Among the peculiar osteological features found in some but not all Criniinae are the fusion of the first and second vertebrae, the broad extension of the premaxillaries, and the reduction in size of the squamosals.

Perhaps the most distinctive group of Criniinae are the large, smooth-skinned genera, with vertical pupils and normal fingers. Mixophyes is Rana-like with extensively webbed toes, the web extending between the metatarsals. Lechriodus (including Phanerotis, which apparently has the same shaped pupil) has the toes only slightly webbed. It is confined to New Guinea and the Aru Islands, not reaching Australia proper.

Ranaster and Limnodynastes are smaller Salientia with a transverse row of vomerine teeth behind the choanae. In Ranaster, a New Guinean genus, webs are lacking between the toes and the skin is very warty. Limnodynastes is widely spread over Australia. Its toes are either free or slightly webbed. It may be distinguished from Ranaster by its vertical pupil and less rugose skin.

Helioporus and Philocryphus are large Australian Criniinae with free fingers and webbed toes. The latter genus differs from the former only in its distinct tympanum.

One group of Australian genera is characterized by the disproportionate growth of the fingers. The first finger is much longer than the second and more or less opposed to it. This group embraces two genera, Chiroleptes and Mitrolysis. Chiroleptes (including Phractops) embraces species with the appearance of Pseudis and others resembling Ceratophrys. Thus it is probable that the species have very different habits while retaining the distinctive "opposable thumb" of the group. Mitrolysis is a Chiroleptes with a vertical pupil.

The greatest number of Criniinae are small Salientia, without webs between fingers or toes. The metatarsals in these are bound together. The omosternum and sternum are present and

cartilaginous, as in most Criniinae.   The central type is Crinia.
Pseudophryne is identical with it except in lacking maxillary
teeth.   Hyperolia may be described as a Crinia with a vertical
pupil.   Adelotus and Philoria have the horizontal pupil of Crinia.
They are said to differ from Crinia only in their larger sternum.
Cryptotis is apparently very similar to the same genus but is
said to have a rudimentary omosternum.   *Cryptotis brevis* is
remarkable for a long tusk-like process on the dentary.   An exact
analysis of the mutual relationships of these genera will have to
await a more complete knowledge of their anatomy.

The most aberrant Criniinae are the grotesque, fossorial
Myobatrachus and Notaden.   Both lack maxillary teeth and
have the sternum more or less calcified or bony.   Myobatrachus
has a smooth palate, while that of Notaden is covered with a
series of three soft folds.   The immediate ancestors of these
peculiar forms are not living in Australia today, but it is a fair
assumption that they were toothed forms and not so aberrant
as these genera.   Neither Myobatrachus nor Notaden shows in
their internal anatomy a close affinity to bufonids found today
outside Australia.   They are not Bufoninae, as often stated.

The Criniinae are structurally the most primitive bufonids.
They apparently left no fossil record except in India, when during
the Eocene a little frog closely allied to Crinia lived in considerable numbers.   This frog has recently been described under the
name of "Indobatrachus."   It previously masqueraded under
the name of "Rana" and "Oxyglossus," but even today its skeleton is not completely known.

Subfamily 2.   Heleophryninae.—Bufonidae with solid procoelous vertebrae, T-shaped terminal phalanges, and a distinctive
thigh musculature; the *semitendinosus* superficial as in the Pelobatidae but separated from the *sartorius* distally.   The only
genus of Bufonidae with maxillary teeth in Africa is sufficiently
distinct from the toothless forms on the same continent or from
the bufonids on other continents to warrant its separation as a
separate subfamily.   Heleophryne is now known from five species,
all from South Africa.   They have the appearance of slim-bodied
tree frogs or broad-disced species of Lechriodus.   The tadpoles
of three species are known.   These are all highly modified for life
in mountain streams.   The very recent discoveries of de Villiers
and his students indicate that two genera, one of them firmisternal, may have been confused under the name Heleophryne.

Subfamily 3. *Pseudinae: South American Frogs.*—Bufonidae with solid procoelous vertebrae, cylindrical or rarely slightly dilated sacral diapophyses, a cartilaginous omosternum and sternum (the latter sometimes calcified), and with maxillary teeth usually present. The Pseudinae represent the most primitive stock of neotropical bufonids. They are confined to South and Central America and the West Indies, except for a few stragglers which reach Texas and Florida. One genus, Eleutherodactylus, is represented by numerous species which form a large part of the Amphibian fauna of Central America and the West Indies. The Pseudinae, although not sharply distinguished from the Criniinae, cannot be confused with other neotropical bufonids because of their girdles. The sternum is broad and cartilaginous except in large specimens of Calyptocephalus, Ceratophrys, and Hylorina, where it may calcify. Bufo has a similar sternum but its sacral diapophyses are well dilated.

The Pseudinae are roughly divided into primarily water frogs, with webs between the toes, and terrestrial, or semiterrestrial, genera with shorter webs or none at all. The first group of genera have simple terminal phalanges and are more or less depressed in form. Considering Telmatobius the central type, Cycloramphus of eastern South America differs from it in that the vomerine teeth are in a line with the posterior edge of the choanae instead of being between them and, further, in that the males have a conspicuous gland on the groin of each side (Fig. 42, B). Grypiscus of Brazil seems to be a Cyloramphus with caducous odontoids on the lower jaw. Batrachophrynus of the Peruvian Andes is certainly a Telmatobius which has lost the maxillary and vomerine teeth. Calyptocephalus of Chili and Panama has specialized in the other direction. It may be described as a Telmatobius with a secondary deposit of bone on the skull, the skin being involved in the ossification. As in the case of most frogs which have undergone this type of specialization (*e.g.*, Hemiphractus), odontoids appear on the palatines. Pseudis parallels Chiroleptes of Australia in a disharmonic growth of the fingers, the first being longer and more or less opposed to the others. Pseudis has a broad distribution in eastern and southern South America.

The second group are all more or less terrestrial, except possibly Hylorina, which differs from all other bufonids in its exceedingly long hands and feet (Fig. 159). The central type here seems to be Borborocoetes, of wide distribution throughout South and Central America. It has maxillary and vomerine teeth, very short webs (sometimes lacking) between the toes, and non-dilated digit tips. The terminal phalanges are knobbed or bluntly T-shaped. Ceratophrys differs from this stock only in its larger head, more extensive webs between the toes, and simple terminal phalanges. Zachaenus may be described as a Borborocoetes with a rounded tongue having a flounced or crenulated edge. Possibly the tongue is highly extensible in life. Zachaenus is confined to eastern Brazil. Most species have a small, pointed head. Finally, Eleutherodactylus and Syrrhophus agree closely with Borborocoetes but have T-shaped terminal phalanges. A

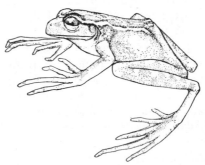

Fig. 159.—*Hylorina sylvatica*, a Chilean bufonid.

few species of Eleutherodactylus have extensive webs and others have none at all, some have broad digital discs and others apparently (but not actually, as shown by their histology) lack these adhesive discs. Syrrhophus is merely an Eleutherodactylus without vomerine teeth.

The history of the Pseudinae cannot be followed in the fossil record. Only Ceratophrys has been described as a fossil and this from the Pleistocene of Brazil.

Subfamily 4. Rhinophryninae.—The Mexican burrowing toad, Rhinophrynus, is so highly specialized that it may well be isolated in a subfamily distinct from the Pseudinae with which it seems to have the closest affinities. Its pectoral girdle alone is distinctive, the omosternum being rudimentary and the sternum entirely lacking. Teeth are lacking and the tongue is peculiar in that it is free anteriorly and apparently protrusible in mammal, rather than in frog, fashion. A close parallel occurs in the African bufonid Werneria. *Rhinophrynus dorsalis* is a round-bodied, smooth-skinned toad with a very small pointed head. Its coloration of pink and brown gives it a somewhat pathological appearance. Its toes are partly webbed, and an enormous cornified tubercle or "spade" covers the prehallux. The first toe is peculiar in that it possesses only one phalanx beyond the metatarsal and this is converted into a shovel-like segment. The sacral diapophyses are only moderately dilated. It is remarkable that the burrowing Salientia of the same body form as Rhinophrynus may have either cylindrical, slightly dilated or enormously dilated sacral diapophyses. Rhinophrynus, like many other specialized burrowers, feeds largely on termites.

Subfamily 5. Bufoninae: True Toads.—Bufonidae without maxillary teeth, sacral diapophyses dilated, sternum cartilaginous

Fig. 160.—*Nectophrynoides vivipara*, a viviparous toad of East Africa.

or calcified, omosternum absent or, if present, cartilaginous. The Bufoninae represent very probably an unnatural group of toads showing closest affinities to the Criniinae. Except for Bufo, they are confined to Africa and southern Asia. The most primitive genus is Nectophrynoides (Fig. 160) of East Africa, which differs from Pseudophryne of Australia in its larger head, wider sacrum, and larger omosternum. Further, its vertebral column is typically procoelous, the notochord is not retained, and the intervertebral discs are not loosely attached as in Pseudophryne. It differs remarkably from Pseudophryne in embracing the only ovoviviparous Salientia in the world (see page 74). Nectophryne of Africa, the Malay Peninsula, and the western part of the Indo-Australian Archipelago differs in the loss of the omosternum, and in the flattened, T-shaped terminal phalanges (spatulated). Some of the East Indian species seem to grade into Bufo (Fig.

161), but the majority are broad-webbed, arboreal forms. Two, perhaps all, of the African species have broad lamellae on the

Fig. 161.—*Bufo jerboa*, a long-legged toad of Sumatra, Borneo and the Malay Peninsula.

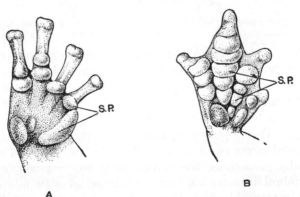

Fig. 162.—The enlargement of the articular tubercles to form pads. *A. Phrynella pulchra. B. Nectophryne afra.* S.P., sub-articular and palmar pads.

under surface of the hands and feet (Fig. 162). It is highly probable that the non-lamellated African species are referable to Nectophrynoides. The African Werneria is of uncertain affinities. It was described with a tongue free in front, as in Rhinophrynus. The genus is known only from the type. The Asiatic Pseudobufo is especially distinctive. It is a large, rough-skinned water toad (Fig. 163), known from the Malay Peninsula, Sumatra, and Borneo. It is distinguished by its extensively webbed toes and upwardly directed nostrils.

The last genus in the subfamily is the common toad Bufo. The distribution of this genus is world-wide except for New Guinea, Polynesia, Australia, and Madagascar. As in the case of Pseudobufo, its immediate relatives are unknown. It

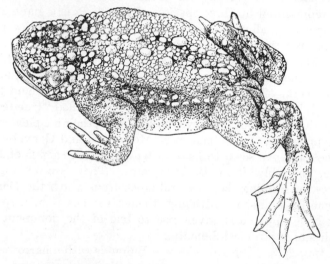

Fig. 163.—*Pseudobufo subasper*, an aquatic toad of India.

is not improbable, however, that Bufo descended from a toothed ancestor, for a tooth ridge develops in the tadpole, as shown by Oeder (1906). Bufo is distinguished from the other genera in the subfamily by a combination of characters: simple terminal phalanges, laterally directed nostrils, and partly webbed toes. Nevertheless, it seems to grade into both Nectophryne and Nectophrynoides. Some African species, such as *B. preussi*, have a smooth skin and possess an omosternum. Most species of Bufo lack the omosternum, are rough-skinned, and possess large paratoid glands. *Bufo micronotus* has the blunt, subspatulate terminal phalanges and the large eggs of Nectophrynoides, although it has the external appearance of a Bufo.

Fossil toads are not sufficiently numerous or complete to show how Bufo and related Bufoninae diverged in time. Most of the fossils come from the Miocene and later formations of Europe. Platosphus, Diplopelturus, Pliobatrachus, and Bufavus are of uncertain affinities.

Subfamily 6. *Elosiinae.*—Bufonidae with a pair of scute-like structures on the upper surface of each digit tip, the latter more or less dilated; omosternum and sternum cartilaginous; terminal phalanges T-shaped. The Elosiinae include three genera, Elosia, Megaelosia and Crossodactylus, all confined to eastern Brazil. Crossodactylus is merely an Elosia without vomerine teeth. It is represented by three species. Megaelosia is a giant Elosia having very small pseudoteeth (bony processes) on the lower jaw, a raised palatine ridge, and elongated maxillary teeth. Megaelosia, which is perhaps hardly generically distinct from Elosia, is interesting as illustrating the first stage in the development of pseudoteeth. These structures have appeared again and again in the Salientia and have until recently been called "true teeth." While their ontogeny has never been studied, their incipient stages are represented in such genera as Megaelosia and Genyophryne.

The Elosiinae seem to have arisen from some genus of Pseudinae, probably from Borborocoetes. They are of especial interest as forming the ancestral stock from which the Dendrobatinae have arisen. Although themselves not rich in species, they have apparently given rise to one of the dominant subfamilies of neotropical Salientia.

Subfamily 7. *Leptodactylinae.*—Bufonids with a narrow, bony sternum, either entire or divided at the posterior end. The Leptodactylinae are South American, a few species extending into Central America and the West Indies. The primitive member of the subfamily seems to be Physalaemus, which has the broadest sternum of all and seems to have arisen directly from Borborocoetes. The species of this genus were formerly referred to Paludicola, a genus which has recently been divided into three genera by Parker (1927). Physalaemus differs from Pleurodema in possessing a quadratojugal. Eupemphix is a Physalaemus which has lost the maxillary teeth. Limnomedusa is a large, slim Physalaemus with a vertical pupil. Leptodactylus (including Plectromantis) is a Physalaemus with the omosternum ossified. Edalorhina is a brightly colored Physalaemus with the tympanum very distinct. Thus, all the genera of Leptodactylinae are merely slightly modified members of the Physalaemus stock. Paludicola, in the broad sense, is such a widespread stock, of such varied body form and color, that it affords a possible ancestor for the other groups. Leptodactylus is the most dominant group of Leptodactylinae. It includes the so-called "South American Bull Frogs." Most of the species are Rana-like in appearance except for their prac-tically webless toes. Some species of Physalaemus resemble some forms of Leptodactylus closely.

Family 3. Brachycephalidae.—A large group of small neotropical toads has recently been shown to be closely allied to the Bufonidae and to have no relation-ship to the Ranidae or Brevicipitidae with which they were formerly confused. They may be described as Procoela with the two halves of the pectoral girdle partly or wholly fused in the midline. They differ from the Diplasiocoela not only in their uniformly procoelous vertebral column but also in their bufonid-like thigh muscles (the tendon of the *semitendinosus* passes ventral to that of the *gracilis major* and *minor*, not dorsal to it, as in the Diplasio-coela). The family is primarily terrestrial, and intercalary cartilages are lacking. The various genera frequently exhibit fusions in the vertebrae. In one genus from Mount Roraima (Oreophrynella), there are only five presacral segments (Fig. 164). The firmisternous condition

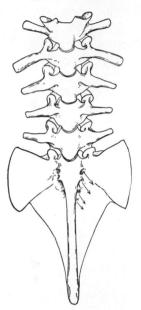

Fig. 164.—Vertebral column of *Oreophrynella quelchii* showing the ex-treme condition of verte-bral fusion found in the Salientia. The first and second vertebrae, also the seventh, eighth, and ninth, are fused.

of the pectoral girdle has been assumed at least three times within the family, once in each of the three subfamilies. The Brachycephalidae show more clearly than any other family of Salientia the details of their origin. Each subfamily has arisen from a different stock of bufonids, but as all the ancestral stocks were bufonids residing in the same general region, the Brachy-cephalidae may be considered a natural, even though a com-posite, family. It is interesting to note that the primitive genus of each subfamily is arciferal to a greater or lesser extent, and that the specialized ones are firmisternal.

The Brachycephalidae may be readily distinguished from both ranids and brevicipitids by external characters (Fig. 165).   No ranid other than Rana reached the neotropics, and the only brevicipitids are Microhylinae and Kalophryninae.   The latter

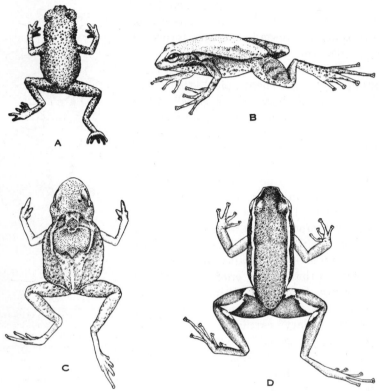

Fig. 165.—Brachycephalid frogs: *A. Oreophrynella quelchii.   B. Elosia nasus. C. Brachycephalus ephippium.   D. Dendrobates braccatus.*

are mostly small-headed forms resembling the American narrow-mouthed toads.   The Brachycephalidae, on the other hand, resemble their bufonid ancestors in head form.

Subfamily 1.   *Rhinodermatinae.*—Brachycephalids without digital dilations or scutes, omosternum and sternum cartilaginous. Sminthillus, found in Cuba and in both Peru and eastern Brazil, is only partly firmisternal.   It is obviously closely allied to Syrrhophus (Eleutherodactylus without vomerine teeth) and retains in all but one species the T-shaped terminal phalanges of that genus. Geobatrachus is known only from a single rare species inhabiting high altitudes of the Santa Marta Mountains in Colombia. It is characterized by its reduced digits, the outer being lost. Rhinoderma, the last genus, is a little Chilean frog well known for its breeding habits. The male carries the eggs and young in his vocal pouch (see page 71). Rhinoderma may be distinguished from the other genera by its toothless maxillaries and pointed snout.

Subfamily 2. *Dendrobatinae.*—Brachycephalids with a pair of dermal scutes on the upper surface of each digit tip, the latter more or less dilated into adhesive discs; omosternum present, frequently bony. The Dendrobatinae have clearly arisen from the bufonid Crossodactylus or a form closely allied to it. Crossodactylus shows a reduction in width of the coracoid cartilages, the first step in the development of the firmisternous girdle (Noble, 1926*a*). It also agrees closely with Hyloxalus in both external and internal characters. Phyllobates is merely a Hyloxalus without webs between the toes. Dendrobates is a Phyllobates without maxillary teeth. These three closely allied genera inhabit the northern half of South America and Central America. Phyllobates is represented by about 20 species (Barbour and Noble, 1920; Dunn, 1924), while Dendrobates has about half as many forms. They are chiefly forest frogs which frequent the vicinity of streams, at least when the males are releasing their charge of tadpoles which they carry on their backs (see p. 70). Phyllobates is represented by a number of species in the Andes which are ubiquitous along the edges of small streams.

Subfamily 3. *Brachycephalinae.*—Brachycephalids without an omosternum or digital scutes. In two of the four genera the pectoral girdle is partly fused (Fig. 87), and in the other two completely so. Dendrophryniscus of Paraguay, northern Argentina, and eastern Brazil includes a number of rough-skinned little toads, of which the best known is *D. stelzneri*. Oreophrynella, a broad-footed form, comes from the top of Mount Roraima in British Guiana. It agrees with Dendrophryniscus in its partly fused pectoral girdle. Its vertebral column, however, is much more specialized. Atelopus is a widely spread genus of often strangely colored toads. Most South American toads brightly variegated with black and yellow and having squarish heads and rather swollen feet, usually prove on dissection referable to

Atelopus.   Brachycephalus agrees with Atelopus in its firmisternous pectoral girdle, but its digits are more reduced (Fig.
165, *C*) and it carries a great calcareous plate on its back often
ankylosed to the neural spines.   Brachycephalus is a very small
toad known only from eastern Brazil.

Family 4.   Hylidae.—The true tree frogs, or Hylidae, may be
described as bufonids with intercalary cartilages and usually
with claw-shaped phalanges (Fig. 166).   They are procoelous,
usually with dilated sacral diapophyses.   Most, but not all, are
tree frogs.   Some, such as the Cricket Frog, Acris, are aquatic,
and others, such as Pternohyla, are terrestrial and more or less
fossorial.   There are 16 genera of hylids.   All of these save Hyla

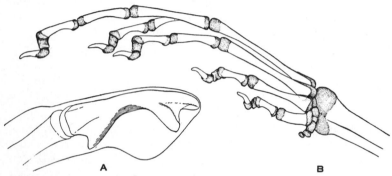

A   B

Fig. 166.—Arboreal adaptations in the phalanges.   Tree frogs have claw-
shaped terminal phalanges which rotate on intercalary cartilages or bones.
Arboreal salamanders may have recurved, spatulated terminal phalanges.   *A.
Aneides lugubris.   B. Hyla ocularis.*

are confined to the New World.   Two other genera, Hylella and
Nyctimystes, have been described from the East Indian region
(also Australia in the case of the former), but as these genera
are polyphyletic assemblages, scarcely distinct from Hyla, they
are not recognized here.   Hyla is spread almost entirely around
the world except for a hiatus in the Indo-Malayan (including Borneo), Polynesian, Ethiopian and Madagascan regions.
Hyla arborea meridionalis has been recorded from the Gulf of
Guinea but possibly through error (Noble, 1926).   Two hylas
have also been recently recorded from Java.   The Hylidae are
divided into two subfamilies.

Subfamily 1.   Hemiphractinae.—Hylidae in which the female
carries the eggs on the back, either exposed or enclosed in a
single sac; sacral diapophyses usually cylindrical or slightly

dilated; if well dilated, as in Gastrotheca and Amphignathodon, a dorsal pouch present in the female; terminal phalanges claw-shaped. The two subfamilies of Hylidae are sharply distinguished only in their modes of life history. The Hemiphractinae usually have a very slightly dilated sacrum and the skull more or less roofed over by dermal ossification, while most Hylinae have a dilated sacrum and little or no dermal ossification. A few large hylas, however, such as *H. taurina, maxima,* etc., have the sacrum scarcely more dilated than Hemiphractus, and several Hylinae, such as Diaglena and Pternohyla, are noted for their grotesque casques. The genera of Hemiphractinae are, nevertheless, well defined and apparently closely related.

Cryptobatrachus (Fig. 20, C) has the appearance of a Hyla, but its sacral diapophyses are nearly cylindrical. Hemiphractus (including Cerothyla) has the skull extended into a three-cornered casque (Fig. 168, A). It also possesses pseudoteeth on the lower jaw and palatines. Gastrotheca is not known to have any character save the dorsal pouch to distinguish it from all species of Hyla. In fact, the males of the various species of Gastrotheca, lacking the pouch, have been repeatedly described as "new species" of Hyla. Amphignathodon is a Gastrotheca which has redeveloped true teeth on the lower jaw. Amphignathodon is said to lack the omosternum, but it is actually present, the pectoral girdle resembling that of Gastrotheca closely. Cryptobatrachus and Gastrotheca are widely spread over northern South America; Hemiphractus occurs in Brazil, and northwestern South America including Panama; while Amphignathodon is known only from Ecuador.

The most remarkable osteological feature of the Hemiphractinae is the redevelopment of true teeth on the dentary of Amphignathodon. Such teeth do not occur in any other Salientia, the toothlike structures on the lower jaw of Ceratobatrachus, Dimorphognathus, etc., being mere bony processes from the jawbones without the characteristic features of teeth. May these teeth of Amphignathodon be considered atavistic structures—a reminiscence from Branchiosaur ancestors of the frogs? There does not seem to be any other satisfactory explanation for their sudden appearance in the specialized Amphignathodon.

The best known Hemiphractinae are the Marsupial Frogs. Because of the dictates of priority, this group long known by the appropriate name of "Nototrema" must be called "Gastro-

theca," although the theca, as stated above, is on the back not
on the belly. There are three main types of Marsupial Frogs.
In *G. pygmaea* the opening of the sac is represented by a long
slit extending the length of the back. In *G. ovifera* and its
allies the sac opens by a narrow mouth in the sacral region, the
eggs are large, and the young escape fully formed from the
pouch. In the last group, represented by *G. marsupiata* and
closely allied species, the pouch is the same as in *ovifera* but the
eggs are smaller and more numerous. The young hatch out as
tadpoles. Marsupial Frogs have the skull more or less covered
by a secondary deposit of bone. In a few forms such as *G.
weinlandii* the derm of the back is studded with numerous calcareous plates. In these species the young, during their sojourn
on their maternal parent's back, are safely enclosed within a
veritable coat of mail!

Subfamily 2. *Hylinae.*—Hylidae in which the eggs are laid
in or near the water; sacral diapophyses dilated; terminal phalanges claw- or T-shaped. There are 12 valid genera of Hylinae
and at least 3 others which are sometimes recognized. All of
these are closely allied to Hyla and differ in very few characters.
The most distinct are the neotropical Centrolene and Centrolenella, which have T-shaped terminal phalanges and frequently
truncated digital discs. The recently described Allophryne
is a toothless Centrolenella with peculiar scale-like patches of
roughened epidermis strewn over head and back. The American
Acris and particularly Pseudacris are not distinguished from
Hyla by any structural characters. Pseudacris (Fig. 167) is
merely a group of Hyla species with reduced webs. Microhyla,
Eleutherodactylus, and various other natural genera include
species with and others without webs on their toes. Acris
is a Rana-like Hyla, aquatic or terrestrial but never arboreal.
There are a number of neotropical hylas with small digital dilations similar to those of Acris, but none is so Rana-like. In the
Australian regions, however, there are a few hylas which resemble
Rana even more closely than Acris does. *H. nasuta* of Queensland, in form, color, dorsal folds, etc., is remarkably similar to
R. mascareniensis. Further, its intercalary cartilages are greatly
elongated as in Acris. It would seem that terrestrial life has
called forth a greater development of these primarily arboreal
structures (see page 95).

Amphodus (including Lophyohyla) may be described as a Hyla which has developed pseudoteeth on the lower jaw and parasphenoid. In Amphodus both dentary and prearticular are extended into a ragged sawtooth edge. Its palatines are similarly edged but the projections are not so elevated. The parasphenoid odontoids form a broad patch and many are fused together producing oblique ridges. Similar odontoids occasion-

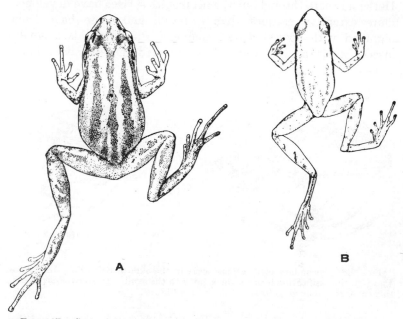

Fig. 167.—Several species of hylids lack webs between their toes and do not climb. The American species are frequently referred to the genus Pseudacris. *Hyla triseriata* (A) is a typical Pseudacris, while *H.ocularis* (B) climbs readily, especially up grass stems and bushes.

ally occur in other genera of Hylinae. In *Hyla* (*Nyctimantis*) *rugiceps* they occur on the prevomers together with the true vomerine teeth. The sacrum of Amphodus is moderately dilated and its ovarian eggs are small and densely pigmented. It has, therefore, probably no close affinity to Hemiphractus, which has developed similar bony extensions of the lower jawbones. Amphodus is known from Trinidad and Brazil.

A third group of Hylinae are characterized by the development of excessive bony growths on the skull. In these, strangely enough, the lower jawbones are not extended into pseudoteeth. A number of species of Hyla (*nigromaculatus, dominicensis*, etc.) develop complete caps of secondary dermal bone to the skull, and in *H. lichenata*, and to a lesser extent in *nigromaculatus*, the occipital region may be raised into a peculiar bony crown.   There is no doubt, from what has been said concerning the life histories of these forms (page 67), that they are very closely allied to species which lack any trace of a secondary bony cover to the skull. Here and there throughout the neotropics species have developed more extensive casques than *lichenata* and these have been dignified with special generic names.   Pternohyla is a small-disced Mexican Hyla which has extended the secondary bony

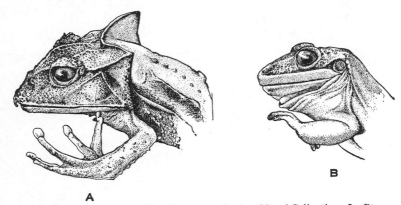

A   B

Fig. 168.—Secondary ossifications occur in the skin of Salientia. In *Pterno-hyla* (*B*), the ossification forms a thick cover to the skull. In *Hemiphractus* (*A*), this cover is extended to form a pair of broad horns.

growth until it forms in the adult a low ridge along the edge of the upper jaw (Fig. 168*B*).   Corythomantis is a Brazilian form with larger discs and more extensive casque.   The pupil is said to be rhombic, as in *H. vasta*.   In Triprion of Mexico the extension of the casque is carried slightly further, at least it is more sculptured, and odontoids appear on the parasphenoid and lateral portions of the palatines.   Specimens vary considerably in the number and extent of these odontoids, but the latter are never very numerous. Diaglena (including Tetraprion) is identical with Triprion, but the pupil is said to be horizontal, although, as in *H. vasta*, this may be a matter of pupil size at the moment of death.   These helmeted Hylinae are represented by very few species, and while it is customary to recognize them as distinct genera it is clear that they are all merely slightly aberrant hylas.   Perhaps the most distinctive is the small *Triprion petasatus* of Yucatan. The casque formation in this species has led to a widening of the ethmoid, a reduction in length of the palatines, and a broadening of the parasphenoid.

The last group of Hylinae is characterized by a vertical pupil. This is not a good character, for it has arisen independently in *H. vasta* and in *H. lichenata* of the West Indies (see page 89), also independently—to judge from the numerous differences which distinguish *granti* from *papua*—in the two Papuan species which have been linked together under the name of "Nyctimystes." In general, pupil form does not seem a reliable character in the Hylidae to distinguish related groups of species, for in this

Fig. 169.—*Phyllomedusa bicolor*, a South American tree frog possessing both opposable thumbs and inner toes.

family the pupil has changed its form too frequently. There is, however, one group of neotropical Hylinae which has added to the pupil character certain other features which seem to distinguish them as a natural group of species. These species are referred to Phyllomedusa (including Agalychnis). They are hylas which have developed a bright green color (sometimes brown in young), usually a red iris, a vertical pupil, and, most important of all, a disproportionate growth of the toes. The more primitive species, *moreleti*, *calcarifer*, and *spurrelli*, differ from Hyla in toe proportions, the disc of the first reaching the base of the disc of the second and not falling much short of this point, as in Hyla. They have broadly webbed toes and look like large specimens of *Hyla uranochroa* or *H. pulchella* except for their pupil form and toe proportions. The other species of Phyllomedusa show more or less reduction of the webs, an elongation of the first toe, a shortening of the second, together with a slight twisting of the first, until in the most specialized forms it opposes the other toes. The extreme species lose the digital dilations entirely, reduce the intercalary cartilages to thin wafers, and develop large parotoid glands (Fig. 169). There are no less than 18 species of Phyllomedusa distributed from Argentina to Mexico. They are very handsome and sometimes grotesque tree frogs. One of the most attractive is *P. perlata*, which has its paratoid glands extended along each side of the body as a row of pearl-like beads. The life history of the species of Phyllomedusa is distinctive and nearly uniform throughout the group (see page 69).

The genus Hyla is one of the largest and most stable groups of Salientia. It is remarkable that Hyla, as well as such different types as Rana and Bufo, are almost the only Salientia which have succeeded in spreading widely over both hemispheres. The history of these migrations is practically unknown. Only one fossil Hyla has been described. This is from the Miocene of Europe.

SUBORDER 5. DIPLASIOCOELA.—The true frogs, ranids; Old World tree frogs, polypedatids; and narrow-mouthed toads, brevicipitids, are closely allied. They have been grouped together in the suborder Diplasiocoela. The latter is defined as a primary group of Salientia having the centrum of its sacral vertebra convex anteriorly and with a double condyle posteriorly for the coccyx, the eighth vertebra biconcave and preceded by seven procoelous vertebrae (the first two rarely fused). The thigh musculature is always of the most specialized type (*semitendinosus* distinct from the *sartorius*, its distal tendon passing dorsal to the distal tendon of the *gracilis* mass). A few Diplasiocoela retain the uniformly procoelous vertebral column of the Procoela, but their thigh musculature remains specialized as evidence of their relationship. The Diplasiocoela include the most specialized of all Salientia. They are all firmisternal, without ribs, and therefore differ strikingly from most other Salientia except the Brachycephalidae. The latter are purely neotropical, and as the genera of Brachycephalidae are well defined, they should not be confused with the Diplasiocoela.

The suborder is cosmopolitan but each of the three families seems to have had its own center and time of dispersal. The Ranidae represents the most primitive stock. It gave rise on one hand to the Polypedatidae and on the other to the Brevicipitidae.

Family 1. Ranidae.—The true frogs are the most primitive Diplasiocoela. They are distinguished from the other two families in the suborder by their cylindrical or slightly dilated sacral diapophyses and digits without intercalary cartilages (Fig. 50). Ranids are primarily Old World frogs. Only one genus, Rana, reaches America. No ranid is found in Australia, except a representative of the same genus. Africa seems to have been a center of differentiation for ranids. Four of the six subfamilies are confined to this region. The other two are either peculiar to southern Asia, the East Indian and Polynesian islands, or are found in this region and in Africa. Rana is known as a fossil from the Miocene and later formations of Europe. Probably other described fossils, such as Ranavus and Aspherion, are not generically distinct from Rana. The fossil record throws very little light on the origin of the many genera of Ranidae. Emphasis must necessarily be laid on the anatomical characters in seeking relationships.

Subfamily 1. *Arthroleptinae.*—Small African ranids possessing horizontal pupils and lacking vomerine teeth. Arthroleptis and Phrynobatrachus are almost identical with Rana except for their small size and dentition. They are widely spread over Africa and are represented by many species. Cardioglossa of the rain forest and Schoutedenella of the Katanga, Africa, have apparently arisen independently from different stocks of Arthroleptis by a loss of their maxillary teeth. Dimorphognathus is closely related to *Arthroleptis batesii*, but the male possesses long pseudoteeth on the mandible (Fig. 40, B). Two of the six genera of Arthroleptinae are said to exhibit a cartilaginous instead of a bony sternum. This distinction may not prove to be a good one, for in most of the small species the sternum is more or less cartilaginous, while in the large species it tends to be bony. In most forms the sternum is short, but in the recently described Arthroleptellä it is long and bony. This genus seems to be hardly distinct from Arthroleptis.

The Arthroleptinae represent a natural group of genera in spite of the differences of dentition or ossification of the sternum. In some species of Arthroleptis, in Schoutedenella (Fig. 170) and in Cardioglossa the third finger of the male is greatly elongated. This secondary sexual character is not found elsewhere in the Amphibia. Just as in Rana, some species of Arthroleptis and Phrynobatrachus have their digit tips more or less dilated.

Correlated with this, the terminal phalanges may be more or less T-shaped. Every intergrade exists between the extremes. The pectoral girdle exhibits either a λ-shaped or an unforked omosternum. The vertebral column is sometimes entirely procoelous. The range of variation in Arthroleptis and Phrynobatrachus is closely paralleled by that in the genus Rana, except that the vertebral column is never normally procoelous in any species of Rana.

Arthroleptis and Phrynobatrachus form one of the dominant elements in the frog fauna of Africa. They are tiny frogs which

Fig. 170.—*Schoutedenella globosa*, male with the elongate fingers characteristic of his sex.

hop about on the forest floor or among brush in the more open country. The eggs of two species of Phrynobatrachus are known. They are laid in pools while one species of Arthroleptis (*stenodactylus*) lays its eggs in shallow burrows on land. When the life histories of more species are known it may be possible to distinguish Phrynobatrachus from Arthroleptis on the basis of life-history differences.

Subfamily 2. *Astylosterninae.*—West African ranids of average size, having a vertical pupil, a bony omosternum forked posteriorly, a broad cartilaginous or calcified sternum, and usually broad, calcified coracoid cartilages ("epicoracoid cartilages"). Three of the four genera have the terminal phalanges of two or more toes bent sharply downward and perforating the integument. The subfamily includes three monotypic genera from Spanish Guinea and the Cameroons: Scotobleps, Nyctibates, and Gampsosteonyx; also a fourth genus containing three species, all from the same region. The latter genus, Astylosternus, includes the famous "Hairy Frog," *A. robustus*, a species with a peculiar growth of villous processes in the male (see page 164).

There can be little doubt but that the Astylosterninae embrace a natural group of closely related species (Noble, 1924a). It is, therefore, interesting to note the evolutionary change which has taken place within this subfamily. The primitive Nyctibates and Scotobleps have the toes three-fourths webbed, the more specialized Astylosternus, slightly webbed, and Gampsosteonyx, free. In Nyctibates the terminal phalanges of both fingers and toes are simple and only slightly curved. In Scotobleps the fingers are as in Nyctibates, but the terminal phalanges of the second and third toes are long, sharply pointed, and bent downward at almost a right angle (Fig. 30). The points of these extraordinary "claws" may or may not perforate the integument of the toe tip. In *Astylosternus robustus* three toes are bent in the same peculiar way, only the first and fifth retaining terminal phalanges of the usual form. In *Astylosternus diadematus* the terminal phalanges of all five toes are slightly bent and perforate the derm; those of the fingers are slightly curved and swollen at the tips but not very different from the finger phalanges of Nyctibates. In Gampsosteonyx the toes are modified exactly as in *A. diadematus*. Just distal to the bent phalanges of Astylosternus, Gampsosteonyx, and apparently the others, there is embedded in the digit tip a nodule of bone which, to judge from its position, may have had its origin in the same blastema as the phalanges.

These extraordinary bent phalanges of the Astylosterninae are found elsewhere among Salientia only in certain African species of Rana (*R. mascareniensis*, *R. christyi*, etc.), where in all probability they had an independent origin. It is difficult to imagine any function for these structures. It is possible that they could give their owners a surer grip before leaping. But if so, why is the perforation of the derm such a haphazard matter? On further study the impression grows that these are abnormal structures carried along by the species, because they are not actually detrimental to the existence of their owners. Whatever is the functional significance of these structures, it is important to note their genesis. They did not evolve gradually in the phylogenesis of the group, but first two toes, then three, and then five were fully transformed.

Nothing is known of the detailed habits of the Astylosterninae. All the species are apparently forest frogs, and *A. robustus* at least must frequent mountain streams, for its tadpole is modified for life in swift streams. Scotobleps, however, has a tadpole of the polliwog type. The dermal papillae surround its mouth only below and on the sides, while the larval tooth formula is 1, 1-1, 1-1 // 1-1, 1-1, 1.

Subfamily 3. *Phrynopsinae.*—Small Rana-like African frogs with horizontal pupils and vomerine teeth but a cartilaginous unforked omosternum and sternum. Phrynopsis is readily recognized by its large head with elongated, spike-like teeth. Leptodactylodon has a small head and slightly dilated digital discs. The elongated teeth of Phrynopsis are single pointed, not bifid as those of Rana. Such teeth appear elsewhere in the Salientia; chiefly in the large-headed forms such as the larger species of Ceratophrys or in a few broad-headed forms, as *Leptopelis brevirostris* (see page 125).

Phrynopsis is known from two species: *boulengeri* of Mozambique and *ventrimaculata* of the Cameroons. Leptodactylodon is represented by three species, all confined to the Cameroons. None of the species is common in collections.

Subfamily 4. *Raninae.*—Ranids with a bony sternum, pointed or slightly dilated digit tips, no discs on either the upper or lower surfaces of the digital dilations when the latter are present. The Raninae include Rana and its close allies. Several of these have been described as possessing a cartilaginous sternum. It is nevertheless bony in adult specimens. The Raninae have the same extensive range of the family. This is because the subfamily includes the widespread Rana. The other six genera of Raninae have a very local distribution either in Africa or in southern Asia and the adjacent islands.

It is uncertain which genus of the subfamily approaches most closely to the stock from which the Raninae were derived. Nevertheless, all the genera may be defined by contrasting them with Rana. Nyctibatrachus is a small Rana with a vertical pupil. It has small discs and a slightly forked bony omosternum. Nyctibatrachus is known from four species, all Indian. Nannobatrachus includes a single species inhabiting Malabar. It may be described as a small Rana having a squarish pupil. Nannophrys embraces two small chunky species from Ceylon. These have a cartilaginous omosternum (bony sternum) and slightly dilated sacral diapophyses; otherwise they are identical with Rana. Oreobatrachus is merely a Bornean species of Rana which has lost the vomerine teeth. A parallel change has occurred in certain Asiatic and Central American species of Rana but these are not considered distinct genera. Oreobatrachus differs, however, from Rana in having a weak ridge between the Eustachian tube openings and a tongue less prominently notched posteriorly. It is a matter of opinion whether these can be considered valid generic differences. In fact, all of the small genera seem to be merely local specializations of a Rana stock.

The well-known water frog Oxyglossus, now known by the name of "Ooeidozyga," seems at first glance to be merely another case of a Rana without vomerine teeth. Its sternum in the adult is bony and the omosternum is bony and X-shaped. But its tongue is entire and pointed posteriorly except in the recently describéd *semipalmata* and sometimes in *laevis*. The notched tongue of these species represents a distinct approach to Oreobatrachus. Further, two species of Ooeidozyga have the same type of tadpole, readily distinguished from that of any species of Rana by its peculiar mouth (lips small, papillae and teeth absent, and dorsal fin folded to varying extent). Ooeidozyga has a wide range from southern China and the Philippines to Bengal and the western part of the Indo-Australian Archipelago, including Borneo and the Celebes.

Two large African frogs seem closely allied to one another and closely related to Rana. Gigantorana, which includes only the largest frog in the world, *goliath*, is perhaps not generically distinct from Rana. It differs, however, in that the coracoid cartilages ("epicoracoids") anterior to the coracoids are only weakly calcified. Its toes are extensively webbed and end in thick dilations. Conraua, also known from only a single large species restricted to the Cameroons, as in the case of *goliath*, has the same weakly calcified coracoid cartilages and extensively webbed toes tipped with thick dilations. Conraua differs from Gigantorana in its small tongue, unnotched posteriorly.

The enormous genus Rana has spread over the entire world except the southern part of South America, the southern and central parts of Australia, New Zealand, and eastern Polynesia. Numerous species of Rana occur in each continent except South America and Australia. The species agree well in general body form, although some are fossorial, others primarily aquatic, and still others terrestrial. The skeleton does not remain uniform throughout this series. This is especially true in Africa where some species assigned by Boulenger (1918) to a separate subgenus Ptychadena have the clavicles greatly bent and closely approaching the coracoids. Another group of species, many of which are burrowers, have the clavicles similarly bent and extremely narrowed. They are placed by Boulenger in another subgenus, Hildebrandtia. It is possible that these subgenera represent natural groups of species. In other genera, however, natural groups of species may also be picked out. The use of the subgeneric names has not yet become a practice in herpetology, and for the sake of uniformity they are not used here.

Three of Boulenger's subgenera of Rana from the East Indian and Asiatic regions have been raised to genera, for, although they are only slightly different from Rana, they represent the first divergence of a stock which eventually gave rise to the Polypedatidae. They are placed in a subfamily distinct from the Raninae in order better to represent this divergence. It is, therefore, not so much the degree of structural divergence as the mutual relationships which determine the final taxonomic assignment of a species.

The recently described Altirana is a Rana with broad, partly ossified sternum, a cartilaginous omosternum, a slightly notched tongue, and no vomerine teeth. It is known only from Tingri, Thibet.

Subfamily 5. Petropedetinae.—African ranids with a pair of dermal scutes on the upper surface of each digit tip. The two genera in the subfamily are readily distinguished by their size and palates. Arthroleptides is much larger than Petropedetes and lacks the vomerine teeth.

The skeleton of the Petropedetinae agrees closely with that of the Raninae. The omosternum is bony and either entire or slightly forked posteriorly. The terminal phalanges are T-shaped.

Dermal scutes apparently identical with those of the Petropedetinae have been redeveloped in one of the subfamilies of Brachycephalidae. This adds one more to the many cases of parallel evolution in the Salientia. Incipient scutes (grooves) are found in certain brevicipitids and bufonids. They have no known function.

Arthroleptides is known from a single species, *martiensseni*, from Tanganyika Territory. Petropedetes is believed to include five valid species from the Cameroons and Sierra Leone. The latter show considerable diversity in the extent of digital webbing. Very little is known of the habits of these frogs. The ovarian eggs of *P. palmipes* are under a millimeter in diameter and densely pigmented. This suggests that the eggs are laid in the water. The tadpole of one species has been described.

Subfamily 6. *Cornuferinae.*—Ranidae with digit tips more or less dilated and showing, either as a groove around the edge or as a complete disc on the ventral surface of each, some indication of the friction pad which characterizes the digital dilation of Polypedates. The 10 genera which comprise the Cornuferinae extend from Southern China, the Philippines, the Fijis and Solomons, westward across New Guinea and the Indo-Australian Archipelago to India; one genus, Hylarana, reaching Africa and northern Australia. The Cornuferinae have arisen from Rana in different parts of the range. They represent a very uniform group. Some of the genera apparently grade into others, making the limits of these groups almost impossible to define.

The widespread Hylarana is most closely allied to Rana and may not represent a natural group. It retains an unforked omosternum, as do most species of Rana. Its toes and usually the fingers have the upper surface of the digital dilations separated from the lower by a groove. Its tadpole and life history agree closely with those of Rana, although one species lays its eggs out of water, the beginning of an egg-laying habit which characterizes Polypedates (see page 66).

Micrixalus is merely a group of small species of Hylarana lacking vomerine teeth. Micrixalus is known from eight species distributed from Hainan and the Philippines to India. It grades into Staurois and differs from some species of that genus only in its Rana-like tadpole.

Staurois, as recently defined by Boulenger (1918*a*), would differ from Hylarana and Micrixalus only in that the friction pad on the ventral surface of each digital dilation is completely surrounded by a groove. An examination of these pads under a high magnification reveals that this distinction of incomplete vs. complete pads breaks down entirely. The cross-groove may be present or absent in different specimens of *Staurois hainanensis*. *S. natator* and *S. tuberlinguis* frequently lack the cross-groove, which is usually present in *S. nubilis*. On the other hand, on turning to the life history it is found that all species of Staurois recognized by Boulenger and some species of "Hylarana" have a highly specialized mountain-brook tadpole. In no other Salientia is there developed a large adhesive disc on the ventral surface of the tadpole's body just posterior to the mouth. It is shown above (page 62) that specialized larval structures may point as surely to species relationship as specialized adult structures. It is, therefore, advisable to redefine the genus Staurois in order that it may include all species having this same distinctive tadpole. Staurois may be considered to include a large series of species from Hainan, the Philippines, Borneo, and the Malay Peninsula, Sumatra, Java, Burma, and Siam. These have an unforked (or slightly notched) omosternum, nasals separated from each other and from the frontoparietal, and tadpole with a large, adhesive belly disc. The vomerine teeth may be present or absent; the friction discs on the ventral surface of the digital dilations may be completely or incompletely surrounded by a groove. In most features (pupil form, digital webbing, etc.) Staurois agrees with Hylarana. Under this definition many species formerly referred to Hylarana are placed in the genus Staurois. This applies to *whiteheadi, livida, cavitympanum, hosii, jerboa, afghana*, etc.

Although Staurois in its skeleton approaches most closely to Polypedates and may have given rise to that genus, another group of Cornuferinae parallel Staurois in the development of a partial or complete friction pad. These genera differ from Hylarana, Micrixalus, and Staurois in their omosternum, which is forked posteriorly. The least specialized of them seems to be Platymantis, which has only a lateral digital groove as in Micrixalus. It differs from the latter in its larger size, persistent vomerine teeth, and forked omosternum. Further, its toes are free or slightly webbed. The digital dilations of Platymantis may be very small. One species, *solomonis*, has the lateral groove only on the toes, the finger tips lacking it entirely. It is very likely that Platymantis arose directly from Rana and has no relationship to Micrixalus. It has a wide distribution in the Philippines, Halmahera, Kei Islands, New Guinea and neighboring islands, New Britain, the Solomons, and the Figis.

Discodeles of the Solomon Islands and the Fijis differs from Platymantis only in that the tongue bears an obtuse papilla in its center and that the toes are extensively webbed. In Cornufer the digital dilations are much larger than in either Platymantis or Discodeles and the friction pads are complete, that is, a cross-groove marks off a disc on the ventral surface of each dilation. Cornufer has, therefore, attained the same type of digital pad specialization found in Staurois and Polypedates. It is not closely related to these genera, for its toes are only slightly webbed, its omosternum is forked, and its nasals are large and in broad contact. Cornufer is found in Burma, the Philippines, Borneo, and the Solomon and Fiji Islands.

Ceratobatrachus was referred in earlier classifications to a distinct family of its own, for it was supposed to possess teeth on the lower jaw. These so-called "teeth" are merely excess bony growths of the lower jawbones. A similar modification has occurred in various families of Salientia. *Ceratobatrachus guentheri* is obviously related to *Platymantis solomonis*. They are both large-headed species with small discs and short webs between the toes. Their shoulder girdles are essentially alike. The skulls differ, however, for Ceratobatrachus has a secondary deposit of bone roofing the squamosal and ethmoid regions. Pseudoteeth appear on the lower jaw but no odontoids are present on the palatine, as in most frogs which have undergone a similar specialization. There is hardly any more difference between *Ceratobatrachus guentheri* and *Platymantis solomonis* than between the species of Chiroleptes or Ceratophrys having a complete secondary skull roof and those species of the same genera without this bony elaboration. Ceratobatrachus, however, has gone farther than these forms in the development of pseudoteeth along the lower jaw. Both *guentheri* and *solomonis* occur in the same locality. The former is confined to the Solomons.

The life history, as far as it is available, confirms the relationship as outlined above. *Guentheri* and *solomonis* have large eggs. Discodeles and Cornufer practice direct development (see page 64), and the encapsuled froglet before hatching is characterized by certain apparently distinctive structures.

There remain in the Cornuferinae three monotypic genera to discuss. All of these are very rare, disced species allied to Cornufer but lacking vomerine teeth and webs between the toes. Batrachylodes of the Solomons, like many other species which have lost the vomerine teeth, is a dwarf form. Simomantis of Borneo seems to be a Staurois with webbed fingers. Its omosternum is unforked, and vomerine teeth are absent. It has a typical Polypedates pad on the ventral surface of the digits and also a groove on the dorsal surface. Palmatorappia of the Solomons seems to be a case of parallel evolution in a different stock, namely in Cornufer or an allied genus. Its omosternum is forked. It may be described as a Cornufer with extensively webbed fingers and toes.

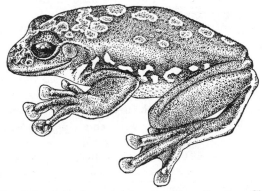

Fig. 171.—*Polypedates dennysi*, a tree frog of southeastern China.

Family 2. Polypedatidae.—The diplasiocoelous frogs with cylindrical sacral diapophyses and intercalary cartilages represent very probably a natural family which has evolved from the Ranidae in much the same way that the Hylidae did from the Bufonidae. They are distinguished from ranids only by the presence of the intercalary cartilage. The 13 genera in the family are not regrouped into subfamilies, for they represent too uniform a stock. The Polypedatidae inhabit southern Asia, Japan, the Philippines, the East Indian Islands, Africa, and Madagascar.

It has been frequently claimed that the Polypedatidae do not represent a natural group but that ranid stocks in different parts of the world have independently developed an intercalary cartilage. This is certainly not true in Africa, where Chiromantis, Leptopelis, Hylambates, Hyperolius, Megalixalus, and Kassina show in their skeletal and external anatomy closer affinity to one another than to any other African ranids. Further, the Madagascan Mantidactylus, Aglyptodactylus, Hemimantis, and Mantella are very closely allied and seem to have arisen from the same polypedatid ancestor as the African genera. Polypedates (Fig. 171) differs anatomically from Staurois (as defined here) only in the presence of the intercalary. But it differs remarkably in life history and it is not improbable that the resemblance may be due to convergent evolution. Whether or not Polypedates arose from Staurois, the anatomical evidence at present available points toward the Polypedatidae as being a natural group.

Most of the Polypedatidae are tree frogs. A few have given up their arboreal habit and have returned to the sod while retaining almost the entire digital adhesive mechanism of their relatives (see page 95).

The most primitive genus in the family is the widespread Polypedates which inhabits the entire range of the family except Africa. It has a horizontal pupil, an entire or slightly notched omosternum, and a long, bony sternum. Its terminal phalange, may be either bluntly or broadly Y-shaped. Philautus has arisen from Polypedates in many parts of its range by that ofts repeated process, a loss of the vomerine teeth. Most species of Philautus are small and have the metatarsals more or less united-while the species of Polypedates are larger and usually have more distinct webs between the metatarsals. Phrynoderma is a Burman Polypedates which has lost its vomerine teeth and reduced its tongue until it lacks any suggestion of a notch behind.

The African Chiromantis is very closely allied to Polypedates, differing only in that the two inner fingers diverge more from the others than do those of Polypedates. Chiromantis is a tree frog and has the same breeding habits as Polypedates. Leptopelis, represented in Africa by many arboreal and some disced terrestrial species, differs from Chiromantis in its vertical pupil, less diverging fingers, and claw-shaped phalanges. Hylambates has developed a broadly Λ-shaped omosternum and its sternum has changed into a broad cartilaginous (or calcified) plate. It retains the vertical pupil and claw-shaped phalanges of Leptopelis. Megalixalus may be described as a Hylambates which has lost its vomerine teeth. The widespread and dominant genus Hyperolius (Rappia of authors) is merely a Megalixalus with horizontal pupil. Lastly, the terrestrial Kassina is merely a Hylambates with very small (apparently absent) digital discs. A close parallel occurs in the terrestrial species of Leptopelis. The widespread *K. senegalensis* has a small tongue and frequently lacks vomerine teeth. This has led to its being described several times as a "new genus and species." It is remarkable that the arboreal and terrestrial species of Leptopelis retain the same skeletal organization and differ only in the extent of the digital dilations. A close parallel, however, occurs in the species of Hyla.

The Madagascan genera exhibit even a closer affinity to one another than do the African genera. Polypedates has reached Madagascar and has apparently given rise to Mantidactylus by a reduction in width of the terminal dilations and by increasing the notch in the omosternum until it formed a λ. Mantidactylus retains the same specialized pads of Polypedates, with ventral and lateral grooves as in the latter. It is sometimes said that Mantidactylus is merely a Rana which has developed an intercalary cartilage. But the discs of Mantidactylus with ventral pads marked off by a groove do not occur in Rana. Further, the skull of Mantidactylus, with its small widely separated nasals and broadly exposed ethmoids, is characteristic of Polypedates.

Aglyptodactylus, including Gephyromantis, is a Mantidactylus with the metatarsals bound together. It retains the same femoral glands (Fig. 42, A), a typical secondary sexual character of Mantidactylus. Hemimantis is a Gephyromantis without vomerine teeth. Mantella, the most disputed genus in the series, is a Hemimantis which has lost the maxillary teeth and reduced the webs between the toes. Mantella has been referred to the Ranidae and to the "Dendrobatidae" by various authors. Its true affinities are, however, disclosed by its skeleton. It possesses an intercalary cartilage, Y-shaped terminal phalanges, λ-shaped omosternum, and narrow bony sternum. The terminal dilations, although small, agree in detailed structure with those of Polypedates. The webs between the toes may be very short or absent. In the Hylidae certain genera such as Acris and Hemiphractus have become secondarily adapted to terrestrial life. Their digital dilations are reduced greatly in size but retain the skeletal and histological detail of the broadest hylid pads. Similarly, the polypedatid Mantella may be considered a terrestrial tree frog, for its pads, although small, agree with those of Polypedates.

Family 3. Brevicipitidae.—The narrow-mouthed toads form a large group of often specialized forms distributed throughout the Americas, Africa and Madagascar, southern and eastern Asia, and the adjacent islands including the whole of the Indo-Australian Archipelago, two genera reaching Queensland. The less specialized genera agree closely with the Ranidae, differing only in the more dilated sacral diapophyses. The Brevicipitidae represent a natural group of genera except for two subfamilies, the Cacosterninae and the Hemisinae, which seem to have arisen independently from African ranids. All other brevicipitids either pass the larval stages within the egg capsule or hatch out to form a very distinctive tadpole with a median spiracle, a toothless and expansible mouth, and no external nares until just before metamorphosis.

The brevicipitid toads exhibit the greatest range of skeletal modification found in any family of Salientia. Different stocks have often undergone a rapid and parallel evolution, making it extremely difficult to recognize natural groups of genera. The more primitive genera might be considered ranids with the sacrum more or less dilated, but they differ from most ranids in their heavy build, large vomers, and ridged palate. The last feature is remarkably constant throughout the family, only a few genera lacking the ridges. These ridges are usually described as a pair of glandular folds, one bounding the entrance to the oesophagus and the other, smaller and anterior to this, on the roof of the palate. Sections reveal that neither is more glandular than the adjacent palate. Both owe their character to a projecting fold of the connective tissue underlying the mucosa. They may serve as pads which strengthen the grip on struggling prey. At least they are not to be confused with the palatine glands which empty near the internal nares. Similar ridges are not found paired in any ranid and, therefore, usually serve as a ready means of identifying the more ranid-like brevicipitids.

The more specialized brevicipitids have lost their teeth and all the ventral elements of the shoulder girdle (Fig. 172) save the coracoids. Their heads and feet may be variously modified for arboreal or fossorial life. Brevicipitids in the Asiatic, East Indian, and Malagasy regions seem to have independently run through a series of structural changes, often parallel in the three regions. In arranging the genera in subfamilies it is very difficult to distinguish between groups showing the same grade of evolution and groups which have descended from a common ancestor. The present arrangement, although not entirely satisfactory, will serve to identify the more conspicuous groups of genera. Three genera have been placed in separate monotypic subfamilies. When the anatomy of other Brevicipitidae becomes better known, they will probably be grouped with other genera, but at the present moment their immediate relationships are unknown.

Subfamily 1. Dyscophinae.—Brevicipitids with large, entire prevomers, surrounding the internal nares except on the outer side; omosternum, clavicles, procoracoids, and sternum present. Dyscophus of Madagascar and Calluella of Sumatra, India, and southern China are the most primitive genera. They agree in having large prevomers with the teeth arranged in a transverse row behind the internal nares. The sacrum in these genera is only slightly dilated, the omosternum is small. They possess maxillary teeth and resemble the semifossorial species of Rana in general appearance. From these two stocks there has arisen in different regions a host of genera. Only three of these derived genera have diverged so slightly from the ancestral stocks that they are grouped in the same subfamily with them.

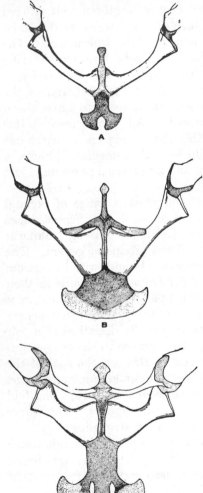

FIG. 172.—Reduction of the pectoral girdle in the breviciptid toads. *A. Microhyla pulchra. B. Kaloula verrucosa. C. Kalophrynus pleurostigma.*

Callulina, known only from *kreffti* of Tanganyika Territory, is a toothless form which retains the large prevomers of Dyscophus. Its omosternum and sternum are cartilaginous but well developed. Its sacrum is much expanded and the terminal phalanges are T-shaped. It represents the primitive brevicipitid stock in Africa.

The two Madagascan genera Pseudohemisus and Scaphiophryne are outwardly very different from Dyscophus but they retain the undivided prevomer of that genus. Maxillary teeth are lacking in both, and the prevomer forms a posteriorly directed process which partially overlies the palatine (see Noble and Parker, 1926). In Pseudohemisus the clavicle is a narrow splint reaching the scapula and midline of the girdle, while in Scaphiophryne it is further reduced and does not reach the midline The former genus lacks, the latter possesses, digital dilations. The former includes four species, the latter, only one.

Dyscophus is one of the most distinctive of all Salientia. It is known from six species, most of which when fully adult are large and tinged with bright purplish red. This color is very unusual among Salientia, and it is perhaps not mere coincidence that Calluella, Calliglutus, and a few other brevicipitids are similarly tinged, though to a lesser degree. It is interesting to note that Calluella and Dyscophus are more closely allied to each other than either is to Callulina. This would seem to afford evidence of a former Indo-Madagascan connection at some earlier time (see page 452), whether or not this connection ran via Africa.

Subfamily 2. Rhombophryninae.—Brevicipitidae with the prevomers of each side divided into two pieces, the posterior overlying the palatines (apparently replacing it in Anodontohyla and Stumpffia). The Rhombophryninae are peculiar to Madagascar. They apparently arose from Dyscophus-like ancestors, although some genera are equipped with very large adhesive finger discs (Fig. 173) and others have simple toes without pads. Within this single subfamily confined to a limited area there has developed arboreal, terrestrial, and fossorial types, none of which shows a close affinity to genera living on the mainland of Africa or Asia. That the Rhombophryninae actually represent a single closely allied group of genera is shown by their palatal bones. In no other Salientia are the prevomers divided into two parts. The only other Amphibia which exhibit a similar splitting of the prevomers are the Plethodontidae, which are obviously a natural group of genera. The posterior part of the prevomer overlies

the palatine, not the parasphenoid as in the plethodontids.   The
teeth on these posterior prevomers have been called "palatine."
As a matter of fact, true teeth are never found on the palatine
bones of any Salientia.

The genera of Rhombophryninae are best distinguished by
comparing their skull and pectoral girdle elements.   Mantipus,
Platyhyla, Platypelis, and Plethodontohyla retain the maxillary
teeth, and their posterior prevomer is a broad transverse plate
overlying the palatines.   In Plethodontohyla the clavicles are

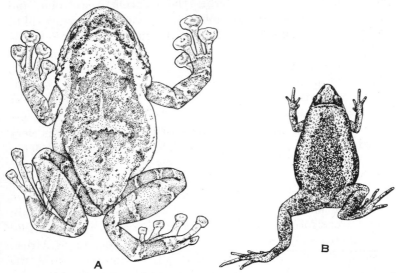

Fig. 173.—Brevicipitid toads.   The Brevicipitidae exhibit a wide range of
adaptive radiation.   Some species, such as *Platyhyla verrucosa* (*A*) of Madagascar are arboreal and have large adhesive discs.   Many, such as the American
Gastrophryne carolinensis (*B*), are fossorial, and have narrow, pointed heads and
rotund bodies.

absent; in the others, present.   Mantipus retains the complete
clavicle of Dyscophus, while in Platyhyla and Platypelis it is
reduced and does not reach the scapula.   Platyhyla retains a
complete row of vomerine teeth, while in Platypelis the vomerine
teeth are restricted to the mesial end of the posterior prevomer.
The most distinctive genus in this series is Platyhyla, with its
enormous discs and hyla-like appearance (Fig. 173, *A*).

The remaining genera of Rhombophryninae are more easily
distinguished than the preceding.   Rhombophryne is a little
toadlike creature with a peculiar warty face (Fig. 34, *B*).   It

lacks maxillary teeth, but the posterior prevomers bear toothlike structures on their whole width. The clavicle is lacking and the procoracoid is reduced to a narrow slip not resting on the coracoid. Cophyla is a very small tree frog with large digital dilations. It retains maxillary teeth, but the posterior prevomers are fused in the midline to form a small dentigerous plate. Anodontohyla and Stumpffia are recognized by their small first (inner) finger. In both these the clavicles and procoracoids are present as in Dyscophus, but in Stumpffia the clavicle extends only two-thirds the length of the procoracoid. Anodontohyla possesses maxillary teeth, and Stumpffia, which is a very small form, lacks them. In both Anodontohyla and Stumpffia the prevomer is small, closely pressed to the mesial side of the internal nares, and without teeth. This suggests that the posterior part has been lost or fused to the palatines. Neither genus is closely related to any other member of the subfamily, and it is perhaps doubtful if they should be included in the same group with the other genera, which apparently represent a natural series.

Subfamily 3. *Sphenophryninae.*—Brevicipitidae with the characters of the Dyscophinae, except that the omosternum is lacking. The Sphenophryninae range from the Philippines, Borneo, and the Celebes through New Guinea to northern Queensland. Two of the four genera are restricted to New Guinea. The Sphenophryninae were obviously derived from Dyscophinae and apparently from Calluella, which they approach closely in structure.

Liophryne of New Guinea seems to be the most primitive. It approaches Calluella closely in body form. The prevomers have the same extent as in Calluella but the vomerine teeth of the latter are replaced by a single row of small odontoids. Maxillary teeth are absent.

The other genera in the subfamily were described as lacking the vomerine teeth. All, however, have a sharp, crenulated ridge across the posterior edge of the prevomers. In some species of Sphenophryne the ridge is lacking, but in others it simulates a row of small teeth. Sphenophryne is identical to Liophryne except that it lacks the·vomerine odontoids and usually has larger digital dilations. The large *L. rhododactyla*, however, has a large calcified omosternum. Oxydactyla, known from a species confined to New Guinea, is a Sphenophryne without digital dilations, the terminal phalanges being simple. Oreophryne is merely a

Sphenophryne with clavicles tilted at a sharp angle to the coracoids and not reaching the scapulae.

It is interesting to note that a modification of the clavicles, identical to that of Oreophryne, has occurred in a very different stock of brevicipitids. The South American Chiasmocleis differs from Hypopachus of the same region by its short procoracoids and clavicles set at an angle to the coracoids as in the case of Oreophryne.

Sphenophryne and Oreophryne represent the dominant brevicipitids of the East Indies. Each is represented by 10 or 12 species. Some species of Oreophryne practice direct development (as in the case of all East Indian brevicipitids, as far as known), but one species of Sphenophryne is said to pass through the tadpole stage.

Subfamily 4. *Cacopinae.*—Brevicipitids with the prevomers surrounding the internal nares as in the Dyscophinae; the omosternum, clavicles, and procoracoids (except in Colpoglossus) absent. The Cacopinae seem to have arisen partly in the East Indies from the Sphenophryninae and partly in southern Asia from Dyscophinae. They have a broad distribution throughout southern Asia and the Indo-Australian Archipelago.

The most primitive genus of Cacopinae seems to be Colpoglossus, of Borneo. It retains true teeth on the maxillaries and in a long row across the prevomers as in Calluella and Dyscophus. The digits are without discs but the terminal phalanges are bluntly T-shaped. The sacrum is only slightly dilated. The body form is depressed as in Calluella. The pectoral girdle is more primitive than in other Cacopinae, for a distinct rudiment of the procoracoid cartilage is retained. Colpoglossus is specialized in that the posterior part of the tongue is tightly bound to the middle of the floor of the mouth. This makes the posterior edges of the tongue curl over to form a shallow pocket. In Glyphoglossus among the Cacopinae and in many other subfamilies of brevicipitids, a parallel modification has occurred, except that in these the whole median portion of the tongue is usually tightly fixed, producing a crease for the greater part of its length (Fig. 174).

Calliglutus of Borneo is apparently identical to Colpoglossus, except that the tongue is not creased and the body is less depressed.

The two burrowing toads of India, Cacopus and Glyphoglossus, are closely related. The maxillaries are toothless and the prevomers are very similar in the two forms.   In Glyphoglossus the prevomers are studded with two or three bony swellings of which the posterior mesial ones form a pair of rounded projections.   In Cacopus these same processes are present but longer and pointed. In life they are covered with pigmented mucosa.   The palates are otherwise identical in the two genera.   The chief difference between Glyphoglossus and Cacopus lies in the tongue, which is modified in the former as in Colpoglossus except that the pocket extends forward as a median groove or fold to the anterior part of the tongue.   As already pointed out, this is a modification which has cropped up many times in the Brevicipitidae.

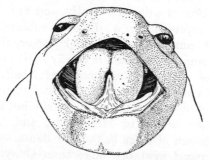

Fig. 174.—Head of *Glyphoglossus molossus*, showing the grooved tongue characteristic of various brevicipitids.

The remaining genera of Cacopinae seem very closely related. The widespread Phrynomantis (Hylophorbus of authors) appears to be the central type.   It ranges from the Philippines to New Guinea and Australia.   It has a crenulated ridge across the posterior margins of the large prevomers.   The usual soft ridges across the back of the roof of the mouth are present.   It has digital dilations, T-shaped terminal phalanges, but no webs.

Copiula of New Guinea differs from Phrynomantis in its slightly more pointed head and in lacking the anterior of the two soft-palatal ridges.   This is hardly a generic difference in view of the extreme variability of the ridge in many other brevicipitids. Cophixalus, of New Guinea, has a palate similar to Copiula but its toes are slightly webbed.   Here, again, the question is raised of whether this can be considered a generic difference.   Both genera are represented by only a single species (possibly two in Copiula).   If these forms were not rare species coming from a little known country, they probably never would be considered types of distinct genera.

Choerophryne, also known from only a single New Guinean species, may be considered a Phrynomantis with a long, pointed snout and with large discs. Its prevomers are, however, firmly fused to the ethmoid and lack transverse ridges. Aphantophryne is another monotypic genus from New Guinea. It has a small, round head and no digital discs. Nevertheless, it retains the T-shaped terminal phalanges and seems to differ from Phrynomantis chiefly in the reduced pectoral girdle. The sternum, according to Fry, is entirely absent.

Genyophryne, the last genus in the subfamily, was at one time considered the type of a distinct family, and Van Kampen (1923) retains it as representing a distinct subfamily. A careful inspection of its anatomy will show, however, that it is closely allied to Phrynomantis. It differs chiefly in its prevomers, which bear a patch of odontoids on their mesial half. The extreme anterior margins of the dentaries are slightly crenulated, suggesting a small series of very small teeth. A similar, but more extensive, modification occurs in Megaelosia, and, as pointed out above, many genera of frogs have their dentaries extended into a more pronounced sawtooth edge than Genyophryne. It is possible that Genyophryne was derived from a more Calluella-like frog than Phrynomantis. Its head and body are much depressed. Its sacral diapophyses are only moderately dilated. The toes are slightly webbed. Genyophryne agrees with a few other brevicipitids in reverting to a procoelous vertebral column. The bones of the skull are partly involved in a secondary ossification, although this does not include the derm. The mandibles, squamosals, and frontoparietals are studded with this bony deposit and extended in width. In other families of frogs a secondary deposition of bone on the skull usually brings with it the formation of odontoids on the prevomers or palatines. The same seems to be the case in Genyophryne, which differs from Phrynomantis chiefly in those parts affected by this secondary deposit.

Subfamily 5. *Symphygnathinae.*—Brevicipitids restricted to New Guinea and differing from all other Salientia in that the maxillaries are extended forward and meet in symphysis anterior to the premaxillaries; in other characters agreeing closely with the Cacopinae. There can be very little hesitation in pronouncing the five genera included in this subfamily as closely related, for no other Amphibia exhibit the same type of skull modification. Further, these genera have the same reduced pectoral girdle, and their prevomers extend posterior to the internal nares as a broad plate on each side.

The most primitive genus in the series appears to be the large Callulops. As this genus has been incorrectly defined in most previous texts, it may be described in full: pupil probably horizontal; tongue large, completely attached behind; prevomers large, extending around the choanae and forming a ridge provided with a row of small odontoids transverse to the body axis; a soft, denticulated ridge between the oesophagus and buccal cavity; a narrow, smooth ridge anterior to this and extending almost across the roof of the mouth as a widely open crescent; tympanum distinct; fingers and toes free, the tips with small discs; outer metatarsals united; no procoracoid or clavicle; terminal phalanges T-shaped.

Mantophryne is identical to Callulops but lacks the odontoids on the prevomer ridges. This is again a character hardly of generic value, especially as the odontoids tend to be lost in dried skeletons of Callulops. Xenobatrachus seems to have arisen directly from Callulops in another direction. Its tongue is more firmly attached and bears a deep median groove, as in Glyphoglossus and Ctenophryne. At least this is the case in *rostratus*, *bidens*, and *giganteus*. In *macrops* it is intermediate between this condition and that in Callulops. In all these species of Xenobatrachus the posterior mesial margin of each prevomer is raised into one or two prominant spikes which may or may not pierce the mucosa. This is apparently a parallel modification to that in Cacopus but does not indicate very close affinity. The name Xenorhina is reserved for a single species of Xenobatrachus which lacks the prevomer spikes. Its tongue is grooved, as in most species of Xenobatrachus. Here, again, it is merely a matter of opinion whether the name should be recognized.

The fifth genus in the subfamily has been placed in at least three different families by different authors, who apparently made little attempt to investigate its anatomy. The only species of Asterophrys is a depressed frog similar to Genyophryne. Its head is not involved in cranial ossification, but a sagittal crest, apparently a secondary sheet of bone, separates the two masses of temporal muscles which completely cover the frontoparietals

It possesses a long, crenulated ridge across the posterior edge of each prevomer. These lack odontoids and therefore resemble those of Mantophryne. Its tongue is firmly attached only toward the rear and thus forms a pocket, as in Colpoglossus and in *Mantophryne macrops*. The terminal phalanges are T-shaped, but the digital dilations are small.

The best evidence of its relationships is to be seen in its rostrum. which exhibits an overlapping of the maxillaries on the premaxillaries as in the other genera in the subfamily.

Subfamily 6. *Kalophryninae.*—Brevicipitidae in which the prevomers are small and restricted to the anterior and mesial margins of the choanae; procoracoids and clavicles present, but the omosternum reduced or absent, the usual pair of ridges on the posterior part of the palate. The Kalophryninae were apparently derived directly from Calluella or at least from the Dyscophinae. Only one genus, Kalophrynus, is found today in Asia, the other five are American. Still this genus has a broad distribution from Sumatra and the Malay Peninsula across Borneo and Southern China to Hainan and the Philippines.

Kalophrynus is the most primitive type. It differs from Calluella in its reduced prevomers and toothless maxillaries. It has also a narrower head and smaller mouth. Although Kalophrynus was derived from a type close to Calluella, it has stronger and straighter procoracoids and clavicles than in that genus.

The American Hypopachus is extremely close to Kalophrynus in structure. Its prevomers are slightly more reduced. The pads just posterior to the internal nares of Kalophrynus, and forming such a characteristic feature of this genus and Kaloula, are lacking. Further, the pupil is erect instead of horizontal. Hypopachus is distributed from Paraguay to the United States.

Otophryne of British Guiana is probably not generically distinct from Hypopachus. It is a large, square-headed frog. It is supposed to be distinguished from Hypopachus by its distinct tympanum and round pupil. Neither of these characters in other groups is always of generic value.

Chiasmocleis and Nectodactylus parallel Oreophryne and Platyhyla in the reduction and tilting of the procoracoid and cle. These genera come from Paraguay and Brazil, respec Except for their short procoracoid and clavicle, which the scapula and are directed partly forward, they to Hypopachus in structure. The genera are each known from only a single species. Nectodactylus differs from Chiasmocleis in its short, webbed fingers. The webs are very fleshy and give the hands the appearance of being thrust into bags.

The last genus, Stereocyclops, is not well known. It is supposed to differ from Hypopachus chiefly in having the sclerotic membrane ossified to form an annulus around the eye. The type in the Museum of Comparative Zoology shows that this annulus is merely a feeble development of dermal ossification both over the eyes and over the snout. The genus should not be separated from Hypopachus.

Subfamily 7. *Microhylinae.*—Brevicipitidae with the reduced prevomers of the Kalophryninae but no clavicle or procoracoid present (except in Gastrophrynoides). The Microhylinae were apparently derived from the Kalophryninae. Three genera are found in southeastern Asia, including the western part of the Malay Archipelago, and three others in the Americas.

Microhyla, which has an extensive range in southeastern Asia and adjoining islands, seems to be the most primitive genus. It differs from Kalophrynus in its reduced pectoral girdle, circular pupil, and smooth anterior palate.

Phrynella, from the Malay region, Sumatra, and Borneo, is apparently closely related to Microhyla. Its toes are cylindrical but its fingers are broadly dilated. Its subarticular tubercles (Fig. 162) are enormous and apparently assist it in its tree-climbing habits. As in Microhyla, there is no procoracoid or clavicle but a rudiment of an omosternum. Phrynella is known from two species.

Gastrophryne is perhaps not generically distinct from Microhyla. Most species of the latter are long-limbed forest frogs, very different from the semifossorial, narrow-mouthed toads of the United States. Some species of Microhyla, such as *rubra* of Ceylon, are practically identical to certain species of Gastrophryne as *elegans* of Mexico. Gastrophryne is supposed to differ in its webless toes, but certain species of Gastrophryne, as *aterrimum*, possess webs. It must be admitted that there is no generic difference between Microhyla and Gastrophryne, and if the former name is retained it can be only on the general appearance of the greater number of species.

Ctenophryne of Colombia is one of the more webbed species of Gastrophryne having an adherent grooved tongue as in Gly-

phoglossus, Xenobatrachus, etc.   It is known only from a single
species.   The sudden appearance of this tongue modification in
the American Brevicipitidae is further evidence of the haphazard
nature of its occurrence.

The recently described Dasypops of Brazil is merely a Gastrophryne with the scapula articulated with the base of the skull.
A parallel modification occurs in the African Hemisus.   Gastrophrynoides of Borneo appears to be a Microhyla with a thin
cartilaginous procoracoid.

Subfamily 8.   *Phrynomerinae.*—Brevicipitidae without procoracoid or clavicle; an intercalary cartilage present between the
last two phalanges of each digit.   The African Phrynomerus is
not closely related to any other brevicipitid.   It has, therefore,
been made the type of a distinct subfamily.   Its most peculiar
features are its intercalary cartilages, which are not found in any
other brevicipitid.   Its sacral diapophyses are greatly dilated,
its prevomers are small.   Phrynomerus is known from five species
which are widely scattered over Africa south of the Sahara.

Subfamily 9.   *Kaloulinae.*—Brevicipitids lacking maxillary
teeth and clavicles but retaining an omosternum and a rudiment
of the procoracoids attached to the coracoids near the midline.
Kaloula is the most primitive genus in this small subfamily.   It
has a wide distribution throughout eastern Asia as far north as
Manchuria and as far west as the western part of the Malay
Archipelago.   It retains large prevomers extending posterior to
the internal nares.   The posterior edge of these prevomers is
raised into a sharp, often crenulated, edge which is covered in
life with mucosa.   Ramanella, of India, is a small form of Kaloula
which has reduced the prevomers to small bones which do not
extend posterior to the internal nares.   The fingers of both
Kaloula and Ramanella are often dilated, the terminal phalanges
T-shaped.

Subfamily 10.   *Melanobatrachinae.*—Brevicipitids with a calcified omosternum, clavicle, and procoracoid present; the prevomers small, reduced to a pair of splints mesial to the internal
nares; palate without ridges.   The little black toad of India,
*Melanobatrachus, is unquestionably a primitive brevicipitid, as
     by its very complete pectoral girdle.   But it shows no
              ty to the primitive Dyscophinae of Asia.   Its squarish
         k color, and rough skin give it the appearance of
          elzneri of Brazil, a representative of a very

different family. It is possible that it is related to the Madagascan Dyscophinae with reduced prevomers (Stumpffia), but our knowledge of these is very fragmentary.

Melanobatrachus is known from only a single species. This species probably lays its eggs in the water. A female 31 mm. long had densely pigmented eggs 2 mm. in diameter. Melanobatrachus feeds on termites, beetles, and worms.

Subfamily 11. *Brevicipitinae.*—Brevicipitidae with the roof of the mouth very glandular, either a broad, porous gland covering nearly the entire roof of the mouth or several pairs of glandular folds between internal nares and oesophagus. The African Breviceps and Spelaeophryne are of uncertain affinities. Breviceps includes six or more short-headed, burrowing toads. They retain clavicle and procoracoid without an omosternum or with a very much reduced cartilaginous one. The sacrum and coccyx are fused as well as the first and second vertebrae.

Spelaeophryne is known only from the type. It differs from Breviceps in its slimmer form, free coccyx, and different palate. A clavicle and procoracoid, although broken in the type specimen, are present and very similar to those of Breviceps.

The little African Didynamipus may be referred provisionally to this subfamily. It retains the pectoral girdle of Breviceps, but its palate is unknown. It parallels Breviceps in the reduction of its lateral digits. Didynamipus is, however, a forest frog, known only from the Cameroons and Fernando Po.

Callulina should probably be referred to this subfamily instead of to the Dyscophinae. It has an additional ridge across the palate which is apparently glandular. The Brevicipitinae although often of grotesque appearance retain many of the primitive skeletal characters of the Dyscophinae.

Subfamily 12. *Hoplophryninae.* Small East African toads differing from all other African brevicipitids in the great reduction of the first (inner) finger.

The two genera in the subfamily are closely related and may have descended from Callulina for Parhoplophryne, the more primitive genus, retains a narrow but complete clavicle. In Hoplophryne the clavicle is reduced to a nodule. The reduced prevomers of both genera do not extend posterior to the choanae, and this represents a further divergence from the primitive condition. The eggs of Hoplophryne are laid between the leaves of banana plants or in old bamboo stems, but the larvae which hatch under these cramped conditions agree essentially with other brevicipitid larvae.

Subfamily 13. `Hemisinae.*—Brevicipitids with a very pointed snout, the procoracoid and clavicle present, and the pectoral girdle articulating with the skull. The African Hemisus is of uncertain affinities and has been isolated provisionally in a separate subfamily. It is possibly related to Breviceps, but its palate lacks the large glands of that genus. Its eggs, although laid on land, develop into tadpoles of a ranid type. This strongly suggests that Hemisus has arisen independently from ranids and has no close affinity to the other Brevicipitidae. Hemisus has a wide distribution throughout the more arid parts of Africa. It is, however, represented by only two species.

Subfamily 14. *Cacosterninae.*—Small African brevicipitids, usually with maxillary teeth, no clavicle, the procoracoid either present or rudimentary, the omosternum bony or cartilaginous; no ridges or glandular swellings on the palate, terminal phalanges either simple or knobbed. The Cacosterninae have probably directly evolved from small African ranids, Arthroleptinae. This is suggested by the life history (see page 64), the tadpole being of the Rana type instead of similar to that of other brevicipitids (Noble, 1926*b*). Cacosternum is known from two or three species, one of which, closely related to the others, lacks maxillary teeth. Anhydrophryne is represented by a single South African species. Both Cacosternum and Anhydrophryne resemble Arthroleptis closely. Cacosternum has a more dilated sacrum and a more reduced pectoral girdle than Anhydrophryne has.

References

LITERATURE CITED

ABEL, OTHENIO, 1919: "Die Stämme der Wirbeltiere," Berlin and Leipzig.

BARBOUR, THOMAS, and G. K. NOBLE, 1920: Some amphibians from north-western Peru, with a revision of the genera Phyllobates and Telmatobius, *Bull. Mus. Comp. Zool. Cambridge, Mass.*, LXIII, No. 8, 395–427, 3 pls.

BOULENGER, G. A., 1899: On the American spade-foot (Scaphiopus solitarius Holbrook), *Proc. Zool. Soc. London*, 1899, 790–793, 1 pl.

———, 1918: Aperçu des principes qui doivent régir la classification naturelles des espèces du genre Rana, *Bull. Soc. Zool. France*, XLIII, 111–121.

———, 1918a: Remarks on the batrachian genera Cornufer, Tschudi, Platymantis, Gthr., Simomantis, g. n., and Staurois, Cope., *Ann. Mag. Nat. Hist.*, (9) I, 372–375.

BULMAN, O. M. B., and W. F. WHITTARD, 1926: On Branchiosaurus and allied genera, *Proc. Zool. Soc. London*, 1926, I, 533–579, 4 pls.

DOUTHITT, H., 1917: The structure and relationships of Diplocaulus, *Contrib. Walker Museum*, II, Nr. 1, 3–41.

DUNN, E. R., 1924: Some Panamanian frogs, *Occ. Papers Mus. Zool. Univ. Mich.* 151, 1–16.

——, 1926: "The Salamanders of the Family Plethodontidae," Northampton, Mass.

GADOW, HANS, 1901: "Amphibia and Reptiles," *Cambridge Nat. Hist.*, VIII, London.

HOFFMANN, C. K., 1873–1878: "Bronn's Klassen und Ordnungen der Amphibien," Leipzig and Heidelberg.

LOVERIDGE, ARTHUR, 1925: Notes on East African batrachians collected 1920–1923, with the description of four new species, *Proc. Zool. Soc. London*, 1925, II, 763–791, 2 pls.

NIEDEN, F., 1913: Gymnophiona (Amphibia Apoda), *Das Tierreich*. Lief. 37, Berlin.

NOBLE, G. K., 1924: A new spadefoot toad from the Oligocene of Mongolia with a summary of the evolution of the Pelobatidae, *Amer. Mus. Novit.* 132, 1–15.

——, 1924a: Contributions to the herpetology of the Belgian Congo based on the collection of the American Museum Congo expedition, 1909–1915; Part III, Amphibia, *Bull. Amer. Mus. Nat. Hist.*, XLIX, 147–347.

——, 1925: The integumentary, pulmonary and cardiac modifications correlated with increased cutaneous respiration in the Amphibia: A solution of the "hairy frog" problem, *Jour. Morph. Physiol.*, XL, 341–416.

——, 1926: An analysis of the remarkable cases of distribution among the Amphibia, with descriptions of new genera, *Amer. Mus. Novit.* 212, 1–24.

——, 1926a: The pectoral girdle of the brachycephalid frogs, *Amer. Mus. Novit.* 230, 1–14.

——, 1926b: The importance of larval characters in the classification of South African Salientia, *Amer. Mus. Novit.* 237, 1–10.

NOBLE, G. K., and H. W. PARKER, 1926: A synopsis of the brevicipitid toads of Madagascar, *Amer. Mus. Novit.* 232, 1–21.

OEDER, R., 1906: Die Zahnleiste der Kröte, *Zool. Anz.*, XXIX, 536–538.

PARKER, H. W., 1927: A revision of the frogs of the genera Pseudopaludicola, Physalaemus, and Pleurodema, *Ann. Mag. Nat. Hist.* (9), XX, 450–478.

ROMER, A. S., 1930: The Pennsylvanian tetrapods of Linton, Ohio, *Bull. Amer. Mus. Nat. Hist.*, LIX, 77–147.

SOLLAS, W. J., 1920: On the structure of Lysorophus as exposed by serial sections, *Phil. Trans. Roy. Soc. London.*, Ser. B, CCIX, 481–527.

VAN KAMPEN, P. N., 1923: "The Amphibia of the Indo-Australian Archipelago," Leiden.

VIDAL, L. M., 1902: Sobre la presencia del tramo Kimeridgense en el Montsech (Lérida) y hallazgo de un batracio en sus hiladas, *Mem. R. Acad. Cienc. Artes Barcelona* (3), IV, No. 18, 263–267.

WATSON, D. M. S., 1919: The structure, evolution and origin of the Amphibia—the "orders" Rachitomi and Stereospondyli, *Phil. Trans. Roy. Soc. London*, Ser. B, CCIX, 1–73.

————, 1926: The evolution and origin of the Amphibia, *Phil. Trans. Roy. Soc. London*, Ser. B, CCXIV, 189–257.

————, 1926a: The Carboniferous Amphibia of Scotland, *Palaeontologica Hungarica*, I, 221–252, 3 pls.

WHITTARD, W. F., 1930: The structure of Branchiosaurus flagrifer, sp.n. and further note on Branchiosaurus amblystomus, Credner, *Ann. Mag. Nat. Hist.* (10) V, 500–513.

Comprehensive Taxonomic Works

General:

BOULENGER, G. A., 1882: "Catalogue of the Batrachia Gradientia S. Caudata and Batrachia Apoda in the Collection of the British Museum," 2d ed., London.

————, 1882: "Catalogue of the Batrachia Salientia S. Ecaudata in the Collection of the British Museum," 2d ed., London.

————, 1910: "Les Batraciens et Principalment Ceux d'Europe," Paris.

NIEDEN, F., 1913: Gymnophiona (Amphibia Apoda), *Das Tierreich*, Lief. 37, Berlin.

————, 1923: Anura I, Subordo Aglossa und Phaneroglossa, Sectio I Arcifera, *Das Tierreich*, Lief. 46, Berlin and Leipzig.

————, 1926: Anura II, Engystomatidae, *Das Tierreich*, Lief. 49, Berlin and Leipzig.

North America:

COPE, E. D., The Batrachia of North America, *Bull. U. S. Nat. Mus.* 34.

DICKERSON, MARY C., 1906: "The Frog Book; North American Frogs and Toads, with a Study of the Habits and Life-Histories of Those of the Northeastern States," New York.

DUNN, E. R., 1926: "The Salamanders of the Family Plethodontidae," Northampton, Mass.

HAY, OLIVER P., 1892: The batrachians and reptiles of the State of Indiana, *Ind. Dept. Geol. and Nat. Resources Ann. Rept.*, 1891, 401–602.

HURTER, JULIUS, SR., 1911: "Herpetology of Missouri," St. Louis, Mo.

JORDAN, DAVID STARR, 1929: "Manual of the Vertebrate Animals of the Northeastern United States," New York.

PRATT, H. S., 1923: "A Manual of Land and Fresh Water Vertebrate Animals of the United States," Philadelphia.

RUTHVEN, A. G., CRYSTAL THOMPSON, and HELEN T. GAIGE, 1928: The herpetology of Michigan, *Mich. Handb.*, Ser. 3.

SLEVIN, J. R., 1928: The amphibians of Western North America, *Occ. Papers Cal. Acad. Sci.*, XVI.

STEJNEGER, L., and T. BARBOUR, 1923: "A Check List of North American Amphibians and Reptiles," 2d ed., Cambridge.

STRECKER, J. K., 1915: Reptiles and amphibians of Texas, *Baylor Bull.* XVIII, No. 4.

South America:

MIRANDA-RIBEIRO, ALIPIO DE, 1926: Notas para servirem ao estudo dos Gymnobatrachios (Anura) Brasileiros, *Arch. Mus. Nacion. Rio de Janeiro,* XXVII.

West Indies:

BARBOUR, T., 1914: A contribution to the herpetology of the West Indies, *Mem. Mus. Comp. Zool.,* Cambridge, Mass., XLIV, No. 2.

BARBOUR, T., and C. T. RAMSDEN, 1919: The herpetology of Cuba, *Mem. Mus. Comp. Zool.,* Cambridge, Mass., XLVII, No. 2.

SCHMIDT, K. P., 1928: Amphibians and land reptiles of Porto Rico, *Scientific Survey of Po:to Rico and the Virgin Islands,* X, Part I, N. Y. Acad. Sci.

STEJNEGER, L., 1904: The herpetology of Porto Rico, *Ann. Rep. U. S. Nat. Mus.,* 1902.

Europe:

BOULENGER, G. A., 1897: "The Tailless Batrachians of Europe," Parts 1–2, London, *Ray Soc.*

NIKOLSKY, A. M., 1918: "Faune de la Russie; Amphibiens," Petrograd.

SCHREIBER, EGID., 1912: "Herpetologia Europaea," Jena.

Africa:

NOBLE, G. K., 1924: Contributions to the herpetology of the Belgian Congo based on the collection of the American Museum Congo expedition 1909–15, *Bull. Amer. Mus. Nat. Hist.,* XLIX, 147–347.

Asia:

BOULENGER, G. A., 1890: "Reptilia and Batrachia; The Fauna of British India including Ceylon and Burma," London.

———, 1912: "Reptilia and Batrachia; A vertebrate fauna of the Malay Peninsula," London.

———, 1920: A monograph of the South Asian, Papuan, Melanesian and Australian frogs of the genus Rana, *Rec. Ind. Mus.,* XX, 1–226.

DUNN, E. R., 1923: The salamanders of the family Hynobiidae, *Proc. Amer. Acad. Arts. Sci.,* LVIII, 445–523.

SMITH, M. A., 1930: The Reptilia and Amphibia of the Malay Peninsula, *Bull. Raffles Mus.,* Singapore, No. 3.

STEJNEGER, L., 1907: The herpetology of Japan and adjacent territory, *Bull. U. S. Nat. Mus.* 58.

East Indies:

VAN KAMPEN, P. N., 1923: "The Amphibia of the Indo-Australian Archipelago," Leiden.

INDEX

Bold face type indicates pages where illustrations, section headings, or more important discussions appear.

ELEMENTS OF MATHEMATICAL BIOLOGY
by Alfred J. Lotka

Formerly published as ELEMENTS OF PHYSICAL BIOLOGY, this classic work is the first major attempt to apply modern mathematics to the problems of phylogeny, ontology, ecology, physiology, endocrinology, psychology, and other branches of biology.

One of the most seminal books ever published in its field it has had enormous influence upon the later work of Norbert Wiener and N. Rashevsky. It is still of great interest to social scientists, biologists, mathematicians and engineers interested in applying mathematical concepts to social studies.

PARTIAL CONTENTS. Evolution, a system in the course of irreversible transformation. Statistical meaning of irreversibility. Evolution as redistribution. KINETICS: Fundamental equations of kinetics of evolving systems. General, special cases. Analysis of the growth function. STATICS. General principles of equilibrium. Chemical equilibrium, interspecies equilibrium, circulation of the elements, the carbon dioxide cycle, the nitrogen cycle, the phosphorus cycle, moving equilibria, displacement of equilibrium, parameters of state. DYNAMICS. Energy transformers of nature, relation of the transformation to available sources, correlating apparatus, adjustors, consciousness, function, origin, energy relations of consciousness.

List of publications by A. J. Lotka. 36 tables. Analytical synopsis of chapters. 72 figures. xxx + 460pp. 5⅜ x 8.

Paperbound $2.95

"The only textbook on linear integral equations in the English language . . . conception and exposition are clear and easily understandable and include all fundamental questions on the subject. . . . One of its merits is that nearly half of the volume is devoted to applications . . . an excellent introduction, can be warmly recommended,"

JOURNAL OF THE ROYAL NAVAL SCIENTIFIC SERVICE.

A WAY OF LIFE
and Other Selected Writings
of SIR WILLIAM OSLER

Doctor, humanist, teacher of medicine at McGill University, The University of Pennsylvania, Johns Hopkins University, and Oxford University, William Osler (1849-1919) was also a curator of the Bodleian Library at Oxford and (after 1911) a baronet of the British Empire.

His work embraced many fields. But it is as a man with the gift of inspiring other men by his example, his speech, and his writings that he is most assured of immortality. A doctor deeply learned in the classics, a humanist with profound religious convictions, a devotedly thoughtful man, he—like Sir Thomas Browne, whose works were his lifelong companions—reconciled the old truths of literature, philosophy, and religion with the new science.

Here, in this selection of essays which reveal his greatness as a writer, are to be found such works as "A Way of Life" in which Osler presents his practical philosophy of everyday living in vivid and memorable language. Here also is included the brilliant address "The Student Life," which details his advice to young men. Such essays as "Creators, Transmuters, and Transmitters" and "The Collecting of a Library" reflect his deepest humanistic convictions. Included also are the incomparable "Letters to my House Physicians" in which Osler minutely describes his visits to continental hospitals and towns. "The Growth of Truth, as Illustrated by the Discovery of the Circulation of the Blood by William Harvey," is a fascinating and thought-provoking account of one of the most dramatic episodes in medicine; while the famous articles on such great physicians as Thomas Browne, Robert Burton, Gui Patin, Michael Servetus, and William Beaumont are masterpieces of medical history.

5 photographs. Introduction by G. L. Keynes, M.D., F.R.C.S. Index. xx + 278pp. 5⅜ x 8.   Paperbound $

SCIENCE AND METHOD

by Henri Poincare

Written by Henri Poincare, who has been termed the last mathematical universalist and the greatest mathematician since Gauss, this volume is concerned with the basic methodology and psychology of scientific discovery, especially in mathematics and mathematical physics. It explains how the scientist analyzes and selects facts with which he must work, and analyzes the nature of experimentation, theory, and the human mind, as they are applied to the acquisition of organized knowledge.

Examples from many fields of science illustrate Poincare's discussion of the germination of ideas. Besides special topics, this volume also contains Poincare's famous discussion of his own idea-creating mental processes, and the use of the unconscious mind. Especially valuable for the modern mathematician or logician is a searching examination of the ideas of Whitehead, Hilbert, and Russell.

"Vivid . . . immense clarity . . . the product of a brilliant and extremely forceful intellect," JOURNAL OF THE ROYAL NAVAL SCIENTIFIC SERVICE. "Still a sheer joy to read," MATHEMATICAL GAZETTE. "Should be read by any student, teacher or researcher in mathematics," MATHEMATICS TEACHER.

Table of contents. THE SCIENTIST AND SCIENCE. Selection of facts. The future of mathematics. Mathematical discovery. Chance. MATHE-MATICAL REASONING. Relativity of space. Mathematical difinitions and education. Mathematicians and logic. The new logics. The last efforts of the logisticians. THE NEW MECHANICS. Mechanics and radium. Mechanics and optics. The new mechanics and astronomy. ASTRONOMICAL SCIENCE. The Milky Way and the theory of gases. French geodesy. Conclusions.

Translated by Francis Maitland. 288pp.

S222 Paperbound **$1.25**

GUIDE TO PHILOSOPHY
by C. E. M. Joad

Joad's GUIDE TO PHILOSOPHY examines systematically the central questions of all philosophical thought since classical times: Is there a plan to the universe? Is mind unique and independent, or a mere secretion of the brain? Is there such a thing as free will?

These and similar questions in theory of knowledge, critical and constructive metaphysics are examined, for the most part, in terms of opposed solutions: subjective idealism vs. realism, teleology vs. chance, causation vs. temporalism, logical positivism vs. vitalism and modern idealism.

Under each problem are considered the solutions and contributions of the great philosophers: Plato, Aristotle, the Scholastics, Kant, Hegel, Leibniz, William James, Whitehead, and many others.

This clear and impartial book by the most gifted expositor in modern philosophy is written for the intelligent reader without specialized training in philosophy. It is not simply a catalogue of varied opinions about varied questions, but a brilliant integration of the greatest problems in human life, done with full awareness of modern needs and special problems.

"The finest introduction to philosophy," BOSTON TRANSCRIPT. "Especially successful in relating classical difficulties to . . . modern physics," JOURNAL OF PHILOSOPHY.

Classified bibliography. Index. 592pp.

T138 Paperbound. $1.95

STUDIES ON THE STRUCTURE AND DEVELOPMENT OF VERTEBRATES

by Edwin S. Goodrich

This monumental work by the greatest comparative anatomist of modern times was recognized as the definitive study of the field immediately upon publication. Its wealth of factual detail plus brilliant exposition and theory have made it an indispensable text and reference work for anatomists, medical students, morphologists, histologists, embryologists, students of evolution, zoologists, and every person interested in biology, no matter what his field of specialization.

The skeleton, fins and limbs, head, vascular, respiratory, excretory, genital and nervous systems, and the subdivision of the body-cavity, are covered from fish to the higher mammals. Among the features of the book is the account of the structure and evolutionary history of the ossicles of the ear, extensive cranial studies, a detailed and complete classification of the vertebrate phylum including the sub-orders, the treatment of the separate divisions of the coelom and the diaphragm, the concise and lucid coverage of embryology, and the illustrations (over 300 of them by the author) which are among the very finest ever presented in a single work. The entire study is characterized by the unity and meticulous attention to detail of one man thoroughly familiar with his subject.

"For many a day this will certainly be the standard text-book," JOURNAL OF ANATOMY. "The reviewer knows of no other book in English which covers so thoroughly the more modern work on many aspects of the subject," SCIENCE PROGRESS.

Enlarged by a 69-page biographical study of his life and work by A. C. Hardy. 754 figures. Bibliography of 1186 references. Index. 2 volumes; total 906pp. 5⅜ x 8. 2 vol. set.

S449, 450 Paperbound **$0.00**

FLATLAND
by Edwin A. Abbott

This is the 7th edition of a perennial science-fiction classic about life in a two-dimensional world. Written by a noted Shakespearean scholar whose hobby was the study of higher mathematics, it is still a first-rate fictional introduction to the concepts of relativity and multiple dimensions of space.

Besides being fascinating reading, FLATLAND will help you understand certain aspects of modern science better than most texts. A very clear description of how three-dimensional objects must be perceptible to two-dimensional beings will offer you a very helpful technique for imagining and visualizing multi-dimensional forms such as tesseracts and hyperspheres.

"Delightful," SCIENCE NEWS LETTER. "One of the best things of its kind that have ever been written," SATURDAY REVIEW OF LITERATURE. "Instructive, entertaining, and stimulating to the imagination," THE MATHEMATICS TEACHER. "Never been equalled for clarity of thought," THE NATION.

New introduction for this edition by Banesh Hoffmann. 16 illustrations. 128pp. 5⅜ x 8.   T1 Paperbound **$1.00**

CONCERNING THE NATURE OF THINGS
by Sir William Bragg

Anyone who wonders about the world around him will enjoy this remarkably clear explanation of certain aspects of modern science by a Nobel Prize-winning physicist. CONCERNING THE NATURE OF THINGS was developed from Sir William Bragg's Royal Institution Christmas lectures dealing with the nature of atoms, gases, liquids, and various types of crystals.

This book requires no scientific background of its readers. In language an intelligent child can understand, it answers such questions as

How birds fly
How uranium is transmuted to lead
How X-rays work
Why a spinning ball travels in a curved track
Why bubbles bounce from each other

plus many other scientific topics that are seldom explained in simple terms.

CONTENTS: The Atoms of Which Things are Made. The Nature of Gases. The Nature of Liquids. The Nature of Crystals: the Diamond. The Nature of Crystals: Ice and Snow. The Nature of Crystals: Metals.

"More interesting than any bestseller among novels which we have ever seen," LONDON MORNING POST. "A detailed, easy-to-follow explanation of gases, liquids, and solids," INDUSTRIAL BULLETIN.

Unabridged reissue of last English printing. 135 illustrations. xi + 232pp. 5⅜ x 8.

T31 Paperbound $1.25

PRIMITVE ART
by Franz Boas

This classic of modern anthropology is now available complete and unabridged for the first time in an inexpensive edition. Penetrating, lucid, exhaustive, it is a major work of Franz Boas, one of the most influential scientists of our century, who has deservedly been called "the father of American anthropology."

PRIMITIVE ART covers all aspects of its field, ranging over the Americas, Africa, Asia, Oceania; pottery, woodwork, bone, stone, metal, weaving, etc. It examines and illustrates specimens from all times—from paleolithic cave paintings to basketry by modern acculturated Indians—and analyzes definitively such fundamental traits as physiological rhythms, symbolism, representation, and styles, all carefully placed in social context. It does not limit itself to the material arts, but also considers primitive literature, music, and the dance. A detailed 115-page study of the art of the North Pacific Coast of North America is included.

"The soundest, most penetrating, and probably most comprehensive work . . . monumental," AMERICAN ANTHROPOLOGIST. "In detail of treatment, in comprehensiveness, in methodological rigor . . . the book stands unique," BOOKMAN.

Unabridged reproduction of original edition, with original introduction, preface, documentation and 950 illustrations. Name index compiled for this edition. 376pp. 5⅜ x 8.

T25 Paperbound $1.95

AN INTRODUCTION TO THE STUDY OF EXPERIMENTAL MEDICINE

by Claude Bernard

Here is the only major work of Claude Bernard now available in English. Ninety years ago, this great French physiologist saw that medicine could be a science rather than an art, and set down his observations in AN INTRODUCTION TO THE STUDY OF EXPERIMENTAL MEDICINE.

This classic of medical science records Bernard's far-reaching efforts to transform physiology into an exact science. Here he explains his principles of scientific research, illustrating them by specific case histories from his own work. He examines frankly the roles of chance and error, and even preliminary false conclusions, in leading eventually to scientific truth; and discusses with equal candor the use of hypothesis. Bernard is considered to be one of the fathers of biochemistry; and much of the modern application of mathematics to biology rests upon a foundation set down by him in this book.

Claude Bernard is remembered today for such major contributions to physiology as the discovery of the vasomotor system; the action of curare, carbon monoxide and other poisons; the functions of the pancreas in digestion; and the glycogenic function of the liver. These considerable achievements give authority to his description of a dedicated scientist attacking his problem some 90 years ago. This account, writes Professor I. Bernard Cohen, in a new Foreword, continues to be "as splendid a statement of the basic features of scientific research as has ever been written."

Translated by Henry C. Greene. Introduction by Lawrence J. Henderson. New Foreword by Professor I. Bernard Cohen of Harvard University. xxv + 266pp. 5⅜ x 8.

T400 Paperbound $1.50

HIGHER MATHEMATICS FOR STUDENTS OF CHEMISTRY AND PHYSICS

by J. W. Mellor

This standard text, which has aided generations of physicists and chemists, has not been superseded as a practical introduction to higher mathematics. Practical in approach rather than abstract. it builds its many examples and exercises out of familiar material from actual laboratory situations, and presupposes only a working knowledge of elementary algebra and the meaning of a few trigonometric formulas.

Beginning with differential calculus, the author proceeds through analytical geometry, infinite series, probability, determinnts and, similar topics. Treatment is full and detailed, and presentation is exceptionally clear.

CONTENTS: Differential calculus. Coordinate or analytical geometry. Functions with singular properties. Integral calculus. Infinite series and their uses. How to solve numerical equations. How to solve differential equations. Fourier's theorem. Probability and the theory of errors. Calculus of variations. Determinants. Appendix I: Collection of formulae and tables of reference. Appendix II: Reference tables.

"An excellent reference work. If the reader is not familiar with this book . . . it will repay him to examine it," CHEMICAL AND EN-GINEERING . NEWS. "Has served generations of physicists, chemists and astronomers . . . a classic," ASTROPHYSICAL JOURNAL. "An eminently readable and thoroughly practical treatise," NATURE (London)

Unabridged republication of 4th edition. Prefatory note by Donald G. Miller. Index. 800 problems. 189 figures. xxi' + 641pp. 5⅜ x 8.

S193 Paperbound **$2.00**

Catalogue of Dover
SCIENCE BOOKS

DIFFERENTIAL EQUATIONS
(ORDINARY AND PARTIAL DIFFERENTIAL)

INTRODUCTION TO THE DIFFERENTIAL EQUATIONS OF PHYSICS, L. Hopf. Especially valuable to engineer with no math beyond elementary calculus. Emphasizes intuitive rather than formal aspects of concepts. Partial contents: Law of causality, energy theorem, damped oscillations, coupling by friction, cylindrical and spherical coordinates, heat source, etc. 48 figures. 160pp. 5⅜ x 8. S120 Paperbound **$1.25**

INTRODUCTION TO BESSEL FUNCTIONS, F. Bowman. Rigorous, provides all necessary material during development, includes practical applications. Bessel functions of zero order, of any real order, definite integrals, asymptotic expansion, circular membranes, Bessel's solution to Kepler's problem, much more. "Clear . . . useful not only to students of physics and engineering, but to mathematical students in general," Nature. 226 problems. Short tables of Bessel functions. 27 figures. x + 135pp. 5⅜ x 8. S462 Paperbound **$1.35**

DIFFERENTIAL EQUATIONS, F. R. Moulton. Detailed, rigorous exposition of all non-elementary processes of solving ordinary differential equations. Chapters on practical problems; more advanced than problems usually given as illustrations. Includes analytic differential equations; variations of a parameter; integrals of differential equations; analytic implicit functions; problems of elliptic motion; sine-amplitude functions; deviation of formal bodies; Cauchy-Lipshitz process; linear differential equations with periodic coefficients; much more. Historical notes. 10 figures. 222 problems. xv + 395pp. 5⅜ x 8. S451 Paperbound **$2.00**

PARTIAL DIFFERENTIAL EQUATIONS OF MATHEMATICAL PHYSICS, A. G. Webster. Valuable sections on elasticity, compression theory, potential theory, theory of sound, heat conduction, wave propagation, vibration theory. Contents include: deduction of differential equations, vibrations, normal functions, Fourier's series. Cauchy's method, boundary problems, method of Riemann-Volterra, spherical, cylindrical, ellipsoidal harmonics, applications, etc. 97 figures. vii + 440pp. 5⅜ x 8. S263 Paperbound **$2.00**

ORDINARY DIFFERENTIAL EQUATIONS, E. L. Ince. A most compendious analysis in real and complex domains. Existence and nature of solutions, continuous transformation groups, solutions in an infinite form, definite integrals, algebraic theory. Sturmian theory, boundary problems, existence theorems, 1st order, higher order, etc. "Deserves highest praise, a notable addition to mathematical literature," Bulletin, Amer. Math. Soc. Historical appendix. 18 figures. viii + 558pp. 5⅜ x 8. S349 Paperbound **$2.55**

ASYMPTOTIC EXPANSIONS, A. Erdélyi. Only modern work available in English; unabridged reproduction of monograph prepared for Office of Naval Research. Discusses various procedures for asymptotic evaluation of integrals containing a large parameter; solutions of ordinary linear differential equations. vi + 108pp. 5⅜ x 8. S318 Paperbound **$1.35**

LECTURES ON CAUCHY'S PROBLEM, J. Hadamard. Based on lectures given at Columbia, Rome, discusses work of Riemann, Kirchhoff, Volterra, and author's own research on hyperbolic case in linear partial differential equations. Extends spherical cylindrical waves to apply to all (normal) hyperbolic equations. Partial contents: Cauchy's problem, fundamental formula, equations with odd number, with even number of independent variables; method of descent. 32 figures. iii + 316pp. 5⅜ x 8. S105 Paperbound **$1.75**

NUMBER THEORY

INTRODUCTION TO THE THEORY OF NUMBERS, L. E. Dickson. Thorough, comprehensive, witn adequate coverage of classical literature. Not beyond beginners. Chapters on divisibility, congruences, quadratic residues and reciprocity, Diophantine equations, etc. Full treatment of binary quadratic forms without usual restriction to integral coefficients. Covers infinitude of primes, Fermat's theorem, Legendre's symbol, automorphs, Recent theorems of Thue, Siegal, much more. Much material not readily available elsewhere. 239 problems. 1 figure. viii + 183pp. 5⅜ x 8.   S342 Paperbound **$1.65**

ELEMENTS OF NUMBER THEORY, I. M. Vinogradov. Detailed 1st course for persons without advanced mathematics; 95% of this book can be understood by readers who have gone no farther than high school algebra. Partial contents: divisibility theory, important number theoretical functions, congruences, primitive roots and indices, etc. Solutions to problems, exercises. Tables of primes, indices, etc. Covers almost every essential formula in elementary number theory! "Welcome addition . . . reads smoothly," Bull. of the Amer. Math. Soc. 233 problems. 104 exercises. viii + 227pp. 5⅜ x 8.   S259 Paperbound **$1.60**

PROBABILITY THEORY AND INFORMATION THEORY

SELECTED PAPERS ON NOISE AND STOCHASTIC PROCESSES, edited by Prof. Nelson Wax, U. of Illinois. 6 basic papers for those whose work involves noise characteristics. Chandrasekhar, Uhlenbeck and Ornstein, Uhlenbeck and Ming, Rice, Doob. Included is Kac's Chauvenet-Prize winning "Random Walk." Extensive bibliography lists 200 articles, through 1953. 21 figures. 337pp. 6⅛ x 9¼.   S262 Paperbound **$2.35**

A PHILOSOPHICAL ESSAY ON PROBABILITIES, Marquis de Laplace. This famous essay explains without recourse to mathematics the principle of probability, and the application of probability to games of chance, natural philosophy, astronomy, many other fields. Translated from 6th French edition by F. W. Truscott, F. L. Emory. Intro. by E. T. Bell. 204pp. 5⅜ x 8. S166 Paperbound **$1.25**

MATHEMATICAL FOUNDATIONS OF INFORMATION THEORY, A. I. Khinchin. For mathematicians, statisticians, physicists, cyberneticists, communications engineers, a complete, exact introduction to relatively new field. Entropy as a measure of a finite scheme, applications to coding theory, study of sources, channels and codes, detailed proofs of both Shannon theorems for any ergodic source and any stationary channel with finite memory, much more. "Presents for the first time rigorous proofs of certain fundamental theorems . . . quite complete . . . amazing expository ability," American Math. Monthly. vii + 120pp. 5⅜ x 8. S434 Paperbound **$1.35**

VECTOR AND TENSOR ANALYSIS AND MATRIX THEORY

VECTOR AND TENSOR ANALYSIS, G. E. Hay. One of clearest introductions to increasingly important subject. Start with simple definitions, finish with sure mastery of oriented Cartesian vectors, Christoffel symbols, solenoidal tensors. Complete breakdown of plane, solid, analytical, differential geometry. Separate chapters on application. All fundamental formulae listed, demonstrated. 195 problems. 66 figures. viii + 193pp. 5⅜ x 8. S109 Paperbound **$1.75**

APPLICATIONS OF TENSOR ANALYSIS, A. J. McConnell. Excellent text for applying tensor methods to such familiar subjects as dynamics, electricity, elasticity, hydrodynamics. Explains fundamental ideas and notation of tensor theory, geometrical treatment of tensor algebra, theory of differentiation of tensors, and a wealth of practical material. "The variety of fields treated and the presence of extremely numerous examples make this volume worth much more than its low price," Alluminio. Formerly titled "Applications of the Absolute Differential Calculus." 43 illustrations. 685 problems. xii + 381pp. S373 Paperbound **$1.85**

VECTOR AND TENSOR ANALYSIS, A. P. Wills. Covers entire field, from dyads to non-Euclidean manifolds (especially detailed), absolute differentiation, the Riemann-Christoffel and Ricci-Einstein tensors, calculation of Gaussian curvature of a surface. Illustrations from electrical engineering, relativity theory, astro-physics, quantum mechanics. Presupposes only working knowledge of calculus. Intended for physicists, engineers, mathematicians. 44 diagrams. 114 problems. xxxii + 285pp. 5⅜ x 8.   S454 Paperbound **$1.75**

MATHEMATICAL ANALYSIS OF ELECTRICAL AND OPTICAL WAVE-MOTION, H. Bateman. By one of century's most distinguished mathematical physicists, a practical introduction to developments of Maxwell's electromagnetic theory which directly concern the solution of partial differential equation of wave motion. Methods of solving wave-equation, polar-cylindrical coordinates, diffraction, transformation of coordinates, homogeneous solutions, electromagnetic fields with moving singularities, etc. 168pp. 5⅜ x 8.   S14 Paperbound **$1.60**

THERMODYNAMICS, Enrico Fermi. Unabridged reproduction of 1937 edition. Remarkable for clarity, organization; requires no knowledge of advanced math beyond calculus, only familiarity with fundamentals of thermometry, calorimetry. Partial Contents: Thermodynamic systems, 1st and 2nd laws, potentials; Entropy, phase rule; Reversible electric cells; Gaseous reactions: Van't Hoff reaction box, principle of LeChatelier; Thermodynamics of dilute solutions: osmotic, vapor pressures; boiling, freezing point; Entropy constant. 25 problems. 24 illustrations. x + 160pp. 5⅜ x 8.   S361 Paperbound **$1.75**

FOUNDATIONS OF POTENTIAL THEORY, O. D. Kellogg. Based on courses given at Harvard, suitable for both advanced and beginning mathematicians, Proofs rigorous, much material here not generally available elsewhere. Partial contents: gravity, fields of force, divergence theorem, properties of Newtonian potentials at points of free space, potentials as solutions of LaPlace's equation, harmonic functions, electrostatics, electric images, logarithmic potential, etc. ix + 384pp. 5⅜ x 8.   S144 Paperbound **$1.98**

DIALOGUES CONCERNING TWO NEW SCIENCES, Galileo Galilei. Classic of experimental science, mechanics, engineering, as enjoyable as it is important. Characterized by author as "superior to everything else of mine." Offers a lively exposition of dynamics, elasticity, sound, ballistics, strength of materials, scientific method. Translated by H. Grew, A. de Salvio. 126 diagrams. xxi + 288pp. 5⅜ x 8.   S99 Paperbound **$1.65**

THEORETICAL MECHANICS; AN INTRODUCTION TO MATHEMATICAL PHYSICS, J. S. Ames, F. D. Murnaghan. A mathematically rigorous development for advanced students, with constant practical applications. Used in hundreds of advanced courses. Unusually thorough coverage of gyroscopic baryscopic material, detailed analyses of Corilis acceleration, applications of Lagrange's equations, motion of double pendulum, Hamilton-Jacobi partial differential equations, group velocity, dispersion, etc. Special relativity included. 159 problems. 44 figures. lx + 462pp. 5⅜ x 8.   S461 Paperbound **$2.00**

STATICS AND THE DYNAMICS OF A PARTICLE, W. D. MacMillan. This is Part One of "Theoretical Mechanics." For over 3 decades a self-contained, extremely comprehensive advanced undergraduate text in mathematical physics, physics, astronomy, deeper foundations of engineering. Early sections require only a knowledge of geometry; later, a working knowledge of calculus. Hundreds of basic problems including projectiles to moon, harmonic motion, ballistics, transmission of power, stress and strain, elasticity, astronomical problems. 340 practice problems, many fully worked out examples. 200 figures. xvii + 430pp. 5⅜ x 8.   S467 Paperbound **$2.00**

THE THEORY OF THE POTENTIAL, W. D. MacMillan. This is Part Two of "Theoretical Mechanics." Comprehensive, well-balanced presentation, serving both as introduction and reference with regard to specific problems, for physicists and mathematicians. Assumes no prior knowledge of integral relations, all math is developed as needed. Includes: Attraction of Finite Bodies; Newtonian Potential Function; Vector Fields, Green and Gauss Theorems; Two-layer Surfaces; Spherical Harmonics; etc. "The great number of particular cases . . . should make the book valuable to geo-physicists and others actively engaged in practical applications of the potential theory," Review of Scientific Instruments. xii + 469pp. 5⅜ x 8.   S486 Paperbound **$2.25**

DYNAMICS OF A SYSTEM OF RIGID BODIES (Advanced Section), E. J. Routh. Revised 6th edition of a classic reference aid. Partial contents: moving axes, relative motion, oscillations about equilibrium, motion. Motion of a body under no forces, any forces. Nature of motion given by linear equations and conditions of stability. Free, forced vibrations, constants of integration, calculus of finite differences, variations, procession and mutation, motion of the moon, motion of string, chain, membranes. 64 figures. 498pp. 5⅜ x 8.   S229 Paperbound **$2.35**

THE DYNAMICS OF PARTICLES AND OF RIGID, ELASTIC, AND FLUID BODIES: BEING LECTURES ON MATHEMATICAL PHYSICS, A. G. Webster. Reissuing of classic fills need for comprehensive work on dynamics. Covers wide range in unusually great depth, applying ordinary, partial differential equations. Partial contents: laws of motion, methods applicable to systems of all sorts; oscillation, resonance, cyclic systems; dynamics of rigid bodies; potential theory; stress and strain; gyrostatics; wave, vortex motion; kinematics of a point; Lagrange's equations; Hamilton's principle; vectors; deformable bodies; much more not easily found together in one volume. Unabridged reprinting of 2nd edition. 20 pages on differential equations, higher analysis. 203 illustrations. xi + 588pp. 5⅜ x 8.   S522 Paperbound **$2.35**

PRINCIPLES OF MECHANICS, Heinrich Hertz. A classic of great interest in logic of science. Last work by great 19th century physicist, created new system of mechanics based upon space, time, mass; returns to axiomatic analysis, understanding of formal, structural aspects of science, taking into account logic, observation, a priori elements. Of great historical importance to Poincaré, Carnap, Einstein, Milne. 20 page introduction by R. S. Cohen, Wesleyan U., analyzes implications of Hertz's thought and logic of science. 13 page introduction by Helmholtz. xlii + 274pp. 5⅜ x 8.　　　　　　　　　S316 Clothbound **$3.50**
　　　　　　　　　　　　　　　　　　　　　　　　　　　　　　　　　S317 Paperbound **$1.75**

MATHEMATICAL FOUNDATIONS OF STATISTICAL MECHANICS, A. I. Khinchin. A thoroughly up-to-date introduction, offering a precise and mathematically rigorous formulation of the problems of statistical mechanics. Provides analytical tools to replace many commonly used cumbersome concepts and devices. Partial contents: Geometry, kinematics of phase space; ergodic problem; theory of probability; central limit theorem; ideal monatomic gas; foundation of thermodynamics; dispersion, distribution of sum functions; etc. "Excellent introduction . . . clear, concise, rigorous," Quarterly of Applied Mathematics. viii + 179pp. 5⅜ x 8.　　　　　　　　　　　　　　　　　　　　　　　　　　　S146 Clothbound **$2.95**
　　　　　　　　　　　　　　　　　　　　　　　　　　　　　　　　　S147 Paperbound **$1.35**

MECHANICS OF THE GYROSCOPE, THE DYNAMICS OF ROTATION, R. F. Deimel, Prof. of Mechanical Engineering, Stevens Inst. of Tech. Elementary, general treatment of dynamics of rotation, with special application of gyroscopic phenomena. No knowledge of vectors needed. Velocity of a moving curve, acceleration to a point, general equations of motion, gyroscopic horizon, free gyro, motion of discs, the damped gyro, 103 similar topics. Exercises. 75 figures. 208pp. 5⅜ x 8.　　　　　　　　　　　　　　S66 Paperbound **$1.65**

MECHANICS VIA THE CALCULUS, P. W. Norris, W. S. Legge. Wide coverage, from linear motion to vector analysis; equations determining motion, linear methods, compounding of simple harmonic motions, Newton's laws of motion, Hooke's law, the simple pendulum, motion of a particle in 1 plane, centers of gravity, virtual work, friction, kinetic energy of rotating bodies, equilibrium of strings, hydrostatics, sheering stresses, elasticity, etc. Many worked-out examples. 550 problems. 3rd revised edition. xii + 367pp.　　S207 Clothbound **$3.95**

A TREATISE ON THE MATHEMATICAL THEORY OF ELASTICITY, A. E. H. Love. An indispensable reference work for engineers, mathematicians, physicists, the most complete, authoritative treatment of classical elasticity in one volume. Proceeds from elementary notions of extension to types of strain, cubical dilatation, general theory of strains. Covers relation between mathematical theory of elasticity and technical mechanics; equilibrium of isotropic elastic solids and aelotropic solid bodies; nature of force transmission, Volterra's theory of dislocations; theory of elastic spheres in relation to tidal, rotational, gravitational effects on earth; general theory of bending; deformation of curved plates; buckling effects; much more. "The standard treatise on elasticity," American Math. Monthly. 4th revised edition. 76 figures. xviii + 643pp. 6⅛ x 9¼.　　　　　　　　　　　S174 Paperbound **$2.95**

NUCLEAR PHYSICS, QUANTUM THEORY, RELATIVITY

MESON PHYSICS, R. E. Marshak. Presents basic theory, and results of experiments with emphasis on theoretical significance. Phenomena involving mesons as virtual transitions avoided, eliminating some of least satisfactory predictions of meson theory. Includes production study of π mesons at nonrelativistic nucleon energies contracts between π and u mesons, phenomena associated with nuclear interaction of π mesons, etc. Presents early evidence for new classes of particles, indicates theoretical difficulties created by discovery of heavy mesons and hyperons. viii + 378pp. 5⅜ x 8.　　　　S500 Paperbound **$1.95**

THE FUNDAMENTAL PRINCIPLES OF QUANTUM MECHANICS, WITH ELEMENTARY APPLICATIONS, E. C. Kemble. Inductive presentation, for graduate student, specialists in other branches of physics. Apparatus necessary beyond differential equations and advanced calculus developed as needed. Though general exposition of principles, hundreds of individual problems fully treated. "Excellent book . . . of great value to every student . . . rigorous and detailed mathematical discussion . . .. has succeeded in keeping his presentation clear and understandable," Dr. Linus Pauling, J. of American Chemical Society. Appendices: calculus of variations, math. notes, etc. 611pp. 5⅝ x 8⅜.　　　　　　　T472 Paperbound **$2.95**

WAVE PROPAGATION IN PERIODIC STRUCTURES, L. Brillouin. General method, application to different problems: pure physics—scattering of X-rays in crystals, thermal vibration in crystal lattices, electronic motion in metals; problems in electrical engineering. Partial contents: elastic waves along 1-dimensional lattices of point masses. Propagation of waves along 1-dimensional lattices. Energy flow. 2, 3 dimensional lattices. Mathieu's equation. Matrices and propagation of waves along an electric line. Continuous electric lines. 131 illustrations. xii + 253pp. 5⅜ x 8.　　　　　　　　　　　S34 Paperbound **$1.85**

THEORY OF ELECTRONS AND ITS APPLICATION TO THE PHENOMENA OF LIGHT AND RADIANT HEAT, H. Lorentz. Lectures delivered at Columbia Univ., by Nobel laureate. Unabridged, form historical coverage of theory of free electrons, motion, absorption of heat, Zeeman effect, optical phenomena in moving bodies, etc. 109 pages notes explain more advanced sections. 9 figures. 352pp. 5⅜ x 8.
S173 Paperbound **$1.85**

SELECTED PAPERS ON QUANTUM ELECTRODYNAMICS, edited by J. Schwinger. Facsimiles of papers which established quantum electrodynamics; beginning to present position as part of larger theory. First book publication in any language of collected papers of Bethe, Bloch, Dirac, Dyson, Fermi, Feynman, Heisenberg, Kusch, Lamb, Oppenheimer, Pauli, Schwinger, Tomonoga, Weisskopf, Wigner, etc. 34 papers: 29 in English, 1 in French, 3 in German, 1 in Italian. Historical commentary by editor. xvii + 423pp. 6⅛ x 9¼.
S444 Paperbound **$2.45**

FOUNDATIONS OF NUCLEAR PHYSICS, edited by R. T. Beyer. 13 of the most important papers on nuclear physics reproduced in facsimile in the original languages; the papers most often cited in footnotes, bibliographies. Anderson, Curie, Joliot, Chadwick, Fermi, Lawrence, Cockroft, Hahn, Yukawa. Unparalleled bibliography: 122 double columned pages, over 4,000 articles, books, classified. 57 figures. 288pp. 6⅛ x 9¼.
S19 Paperbound **$1.75**

THE THEORY OF GROUPS AND QUANTUM MECHANICS, H. Weyl. Schroedinger's wave equation, de Broglie's waves of a particle, Jordon-Hoelder theorem, Lie's continuous groups of transformations, Pauli exclusion principle, quantization of Mawell-Dirac field equations, etc. Unitary geometry, quantum theory, groups, application of groups to quantum mechanics, symmetry permutation group, algebra of symmetric transformations, etc. 2nd revised edition. xxii + 422pp. 5⅜ x 8.
S268 Clothbound **$4.50**
S269 Paperbound **$1.95**

PHYSICAL PRINCIPLES OF THE QUANTUM THEORY, Werner Heisenberg. Nobel laureate discusses quantum theory; his own work, Compton, Schroedinger, Wilson, Einstein, many others. For physicists, chemists, not specialists in quantum theory. Only elementary formulae considered in text; mathematical appendix for specialists. Profound without sacrificing clarity. Translated by C. Eckart, F. Hoyt. 18 figures. 192pp. 5⅜ x 8.
S113 Paperbound **$1.25**

INVESTIGATIONS ON THE THEORY OF THE BROWNIAN MOVEMENT, Albert Einstein. Reprints from rare European journals, translated into English. 5 basic papers, including Elementary Theory of the Brownian Movement, written at request of Lorentz to provide a simple explanation. Translated by A. D. Cowper. Annotated, edited by R. Fürth. 33pp. of notes elucidate, give history of previous investigations. 62 footnotes. 124pp. 5⅜ x 8.
S304 Paperbound **$1.25**

THE PRINCIPLE OF RELATIVITY, E. Einstein, H. Lorentz, M. Minkowski, H. Weyl. The 11 basic papers that founded the general and special theories of relativity, translated into English. 2 papers by Lorentz on the Michelson experiment, electromagnetic phenomena. Minkowski's "Space and Time," and Weyl's "Gravitation and Electricity." 7 epoch-making papers by Einstein: "Electromagnetics of Moving Bodies," "Influence of Gravitation in Propagation of Light," "Cosmological Considerations," "General Theory," 3 others. 7 diagrams. Special notes by A. Sommerfeld. 224pp. 5⅜ x 8.
S93 Paperbound **$1.75**

STATISTICS

ELEMENTARY STATISTICS, WITH APPLICATIONS IN MEDICINE AND THE BIOLOGICAL SCIENCES, F. E. Croxton. Based primarily on biological sciences, but can be used by anyone desiring introduction to statistics. Assumes no prior acquaintance, requires only modest knowledge of math. All basic formulas carefully explained, illustrated; all necessary reference tables included. From basic terms and concepts, proceeds to frequency distribution, linear, non-linear, multiple correlation, etc. Contains concrete examples from medicine, biology. 101 charts. 57 tables. 14 appendices. lv + 376pp. 5⅜ x 8.
S506 Paperbound **$1.95**

ANALYSIS AND DESIGN OF EXPERIMENTS, H. B. Mann. Offers method for grasping analysis of variance, variance design quickly. Partial contents: Chi-square distribution, analysis of variance distribution, matrices, quadratic forms, likelihood ration tests, test of linear hypotheses, power of analysis, Galois fields, non-orthogonal data, interblock estimates, etc. 15pp. of useful tables. x + 195pp. 5 x 7⅜.
S180 Paperbound **$1.45**

FREQUENCY CURVES AND CORRELATION, W. P. Elderton. 4th revised edition of standard work on classical statistics. Practical, one of few books constantly referred to for clear presentation of basic material. Partial contents: Frequency Distributions; Pearsons Frequency Curves; Theoretical Distributions; Standard Errors; Correlation Ratio—Contingency; Corrections for Moments, Beta, Gamma Functions; etc. Key to terms, symbols. 25 examples. 40 tables. 16 figures. xi + 272pp. 5½ x 8½.
Clothbound **$1.49**

HYDRODYNAMICS, ETC.

HYDRODYNAMICS, Horace Lamb. Standard reference work on dynamics of liquids and gases. Fundamental theorems, equations, methods, solutions, background for classical hydrodynamics. Chapters: Equations of Motion, Integration of Equations in Special Gases, Vortex Motion, Tidal Waves, Rotating Masses of Liquids, etc. Excellently planned, arranged, Clear, lucid presentation. 6th enlarged, revised edition. Over 900 footnotes, mostly bibliographical. 119 figures. xv + 738pp. 6⅛ x 9¼. S256 Paperbound **$2.95**

HYDRODYNAMICS, A STUDY OF LOGIC, FACT, AND SIMILITUDE, Garrett Birkhoff. A stimulating application of pure mathematics to an applied problem. Emphasis is on correlation of theory and deduction with experiment. Examines recently discovered paradoxes, theory of modelling and dimensional analysis, paradox and error in flows and free boundary theory. Classical theory of virtual mass derived from homogenous spaces; group theory applied to fluid mechanics. 20 figures, 3 plates. xiii + 186pp. 5⅜ x 8. S22 Paperbound **$1.85**

HYDRODYNAMICS, H. Dryden, F. Murhaghan, H. Bateman. Published by National Research Council, 1932. Complete coverage of classical hydrodynamics, encyclopedic in quality. Partial contents: physics of fluids, motion, turbulent flow, compressible fluids, motion in 1, 2, 3 dimensions; laminar motion, resistance of motion through viscous fluid, eddy viscosity, discharge of gases, flow past obstacles, etc. Over 2900-item bibliography. 23 figures. 634pp. 5⅜ x 8. S303 Paperbound **$2.75**

ACOUSTICS AND OPTICS

PRINCIPLES OF PHYSICAL OPTICS, Ernst Mach. Classical examination of propagation of light, color, polarization, etc. Historical, philosophical treatment unequalled for breadth and readability. Contents: Rectilinear propagation, reflection, refraction, dioptrics, composition of light, periodicity, theory of interference, polarization, mathematical representation of properties, etc. 279 illustrations. 10 portraits. 324pp. 5⅜ x 8. S170 Paperbound **$1.75**

THE THEORY OF SOUND, Lord Rayleigh. Written by Nobel laureate, classical methods here will cover most vibrating systems likely to be encountered in practice. Complete coverage of experimental, mathematical aspects. Partial contents: Harmonic motions, lateral vibrations of bars, curved plates or shells, applications of Laplace's functions to acoustical problems, fluid friction, etc. First low-priced edition of this great reference-study work. Historical introduction by R. B. Lindsay. 1040pp. 97 figures. 5⅜ x 8. S292, S293, Two volume set, paperbound **$4.00**

THEORY OF VIBRATIONS, N. W. McLachlan. Based on exceptionally successful graduate course, Brown University. Discusses linear systems having 1 degree of freedom, forced vibrations of simple linear systems, vibration of flexible strings, transverse vibrations of bars and tubes, of circular plate, sound waves of finite amplitude, etc. 99 diagrams. 160pp. 5⅜ x 8. S190 Paperbound **$1.35**

APPLIED OPTICS AND OPTICAL DESIGN, A. E. Conrady. Thorough systematic presentation of physical and mathematical aspects, limited mostly to "real optics." Stresses practical problem of maximum aberration permissible without affecting performance. Ordinary ray tracing methods; complete theory ray tracing methods, primary aberrations; enough higher aberration to design telescopes, low powered microscopes, photographic equipment. Covers fundamental equations, extra-axial image points, transverse chromatic aberration, angular magnification, similar topics. Tables of functions of N. Over 150 diagrams. x + 518pp. 5⅜ x 8⅝. S366 Paperbound **$2.98**

RAYLEIGH'S PRINCIPLE AND ITS APPLICATIONS TO ENGINEERING, G. Temple, W. Bickley. Rayleigh's principle developed to provide upper, lower estimates of true value of fundamental period of vibrating system, or condition of stability of elastic system. Examples, rigorous proofs. Partial contents: Energy method of discussing vibrations, stability. Perturbation theory, whirling of uniform shafts. Proof, accuracy, successive approximations, applications of Rayleigh's theory. Numerical, graphical methods. Ritz's method. 22 figures. ix + 156pp. 5⅜ x 8. S307 Paperbound **$1.50**

OPTICKS, Sir Isaac Newton. In its discussion of light, reflection, color, refraction, theories of wave and corpuscular theories of light, this work is packed with scores of insights and discoveries. In its precise and practical discussions of construction of optical apparatus, contemporary understanding of phenomena, it is truly fascinating to modern scientists. Foreword by Albert Einstein. Preface by I. B. Cohen, Harvard. 7 pages of portraits, facsimile pages, letters, etc. cxvi + 414pp. 5⅜ x 8. S205 Paperbound **$2.00**

DOVER SCIENCE BOOKS

ON THE SENSATIONS OF TONE, Hermann Helmholtz. Using acoustical physics, physiology, experiment, history of music, covers entire gamut of musical tone: relation of music science to acoustics, physical vs. physiological acoustics, vibration, resonance, tonality, progression of parts, etc. 33 appendixes on various aspects of sound, physics, acoustics, music, etc. Translated by A. J. Ellis. New introduction by H. Margenau, Yale. 68 figures. 43 musical passages analyzed. Over 100 tables. xix + 576pp. 6⅛ x 9¼.

S114 Clothbound **$4.95**

ELECTROMAGNETICS, ENGINEERING, TECHNOLOGY

INTRODUCTION TO RELAXATION METHODS, F. S. Shaw. Describes almost all manipulative resources of value in solution of differential equations. Treatment is mathematical rather than physical. Extends general computational process to include almost all branches of applied math and physics. Approximate numerical methods are demonstrated, although high accuracy is obtainable without undue expenditure of time. 48pp. of tables for computing irregular star first and second derivatives, irregular star coefficients for second order equations, for fourth order equations. "Useful. . . . exposition is clear, simple . . . no previous acquaintance with numerical methods is assumed," Science Progress. 253 diagrams. 72 tables. 400pp. 5⅜ x 8.

S244 Paperbound **$2.45**

THE ELECTROMAGNETIC FIELD, M. Mason, W. Weaver. Used constantly by graduate engineers. Vector methods exclusively; detailed treatment of electrostatics, expansion methods, with tables converting any quantity into absolute electromagnetic, absolute electrostatic, practical units. Discrete charges, ponderable bodies. Maxwell field equations, etc. 416pp. 5⅜ x 8.

S185 Paperbound **$2.00**

ELASTICITY, PLASTICITY AND STRUCTURE OF MATTER, R. Houwink. Standard treatise on rheological aspects of different technically important solids: crystals, resins, textiles, rubber, clay, etc. Investigates general laws for deformations; determines divergences. Covers general physical and mathematical aspects of plasticity, elasticity, viscosity. Detailed examination of deformations, internal structure of matter in relation to elastic, plastic behaviour, formation of solid matter from a fluid, etc. Treats glass, asphalt, balata, proteins, baker's dough, others. 2nd revised, enlarged edition. Extensive revised bibliography in over 500 footnotes. 214 figures. xvii + 368pp. 6 x 9¼.

S385 Paperbound **$2.45**

DESIGN AND USE OF INSTRUMENTS AND ACCURATE MECHANISM, T. N. Whitehead. For the instrument designer, engineer; how to combine necessary mathematical abstractions with independent observations of actual facts. Partial contents: instruments and their parts, theory of errors, systematic errors, probability, short period errors, erratic errors, design precision, kinematic, semikinematic design, stiffness, planning of an instrument, human factor, etc. 85 photos, diagrams. xii + 288pp. 5⅜ x 8.

S270 Paperbound **$1.95**

APPLIED HYDRO- AND AEROMECHANICS, L. Prandtl, O. G. Tietjens. Presents, for most part, methods valuable to engineers. Flow in pipes, boundary layers, airfoil theory, entry conditions, turbulent flow, boundary layer, determining drag from pressure and velocity, etc. "Will be welcomed by all students of aerodynamics," Nature. Unabridged, unaltered. An Engineering Society Monograph, 1934. Index. 226 figures. 28 photographic plates illustrating flow patterns. xvi + 311pp. 5⅜ x 8.

S375 Paperbound **$1.85**

FUNDAMENTALS OF HYDRO- AND AEROMECHANICS, L. Prandtl, O. G. Tietjens. Standard work, based on Prandtl's lectures at Goettingen. Wherever possible hydrodynamics theory is referred to practical considerations in hydraulics, unifying theory and experience. Presentation extremely clear. Though primarily physical, proofs are rigorous and use vector analysis to a great extent. An Engineering Society Monograph, 1934. "Still recommended as an excellent introduction to this area," Physikalische Blätter. 186 figures. xvi + 270pp. 5⅜ x 8.

S374 Paperbound **$1.85**

GASEOUS CONDUCTORS: THEORY AND ENGINEERING APPLICATIONS, J. D. Cobine. Indispensable text, reference, to gaseous conduction phenomena, with engineering viewpoint prevailing throughout. Studies kinetic theory of gases, ionization, emission phenomena; gas breakdown, spark characteristics, glow, discharges; engineering applications in circuit interrupters, rectifiers, etc. Detailed treatment of high pressure arcs (Suits); low pressure arcs (Langmuir, Tonks). Much more. "Well organized, clear, straightforward," Tonks, Review of Scientific Instruments. 83 practice problems. Over 600 figures. 58 tables. xx + 606pp. 5⅜ x 8.

S442 Paperbound **$2.75**

PHOTOELASTICITY: PRINCIPLES AND METHODS, H. T. Jessop, F. C. Harris. For engineer, specific problems of stress analysis. Latest time-saving methods of checking calculations in 2-dimensional design problems, new techniques for stresses in 3 dimensions, lucid description of optical systems used in practical photoelectricity. Useful suggestions, hints based on on-the-job experience included. Partial contents: strain, stress-strain relations, circular disc under thrust along diameter, rectangular block with square hold under vertical thrust, simply supported rectangular beam under central concentrated load, etc. Theory held to minimum, no advanced mathematical training needed. 164 illustrations. viii + 184pp. 6⅛ x 9¼.

S137 Clothbound **$3.75**

7

MICROWAVE TRANSMISSION DESIGN DATA, T. Moreno. Originally classified, now rewritten, enlarged (14 new chapters) under auspices of Sperry Corp. Of immediate value or reference use to radio engineers, systems designers, applied physicists, etc. Ordinary transmission line theory; attenuation; parameters of coaxial lines; flexible cables; tuneable wave guide impedance transformers; effects of temperature, humidity; much more. "Packed with information . . . theoretical discussions are directly related to practical questions," U. of Royal Naval Scientific Service. Tables of dielectrics, flexible cable, etc. ix + 248pp. 5⅜ x 8.
S549 Paperbound **$1.50**

THE THEORY OF THE PROPERTIES OF METALS AND ALLOYS, H. F. Mott, H. Jones. Quantum methods develop mathematical models showing interrelationship of fundamental chemical phenomena wtih crystal structure, electrical, optical properties, etc. Examines electron motion in applied field, cohesion, heat capacity, refraction, noble metals, transition and di-valent metals, etc. "Exposition is as clear . . . mathematical treatment as simple and reliable as we have become used to expect of . . . Prof. Mott," Nature. 138 figures. xiii + 320pp. 5⅜ x 8.
S456 Paperbound **$1.85**

THE MEASUREMENT OF POWER SPECTRA FROM THE POINT OF VIEW OF COMMUNICATIONS ENGINEERING, R. B. Blackman, J. W. Tukey. Pathfinding work reprinted from "Bell System Technical Journal." Various ways of getting practically useful answers in power spectra measurement, using results from both transmission and statistical estimation theory. Treats: Autocovariance, Functions and Power Spectra, Distortion, Heterodyne Filtering, Smoothing, Decimation Procedures, Transversal Filtering, much more. Appendix reviews fundamental Fourier techniques. Index of notation. Glossary of terms. 24 figures. 12 tables. 192pp. 5⅜ x 8⅝.
S507 Paperbound **$1.85**

TREATISE ON ELECTRICITY AND MAGNETISM, James Clerk Maxwell. For more than 80 years a seemingly inexhaustible source of leads for physicists, mathematicians, engineers. Total of 1082pp. on such topics as Measurement of Quantities, Electrostatics, Elementary Mathematical Theory of Electricity, Electrical Work and Energy in a System of Conductors, General Theorems, Theory of Electrical Images, Electrolysis, Conduction, Polarization, Dielectrics, Resistance, much more. "The greatest mathematical physicist since Newton," Sir James Jeans. 3rd edition. 107 figures, 21 plates. 1082pp. 5⅜ x 8.
S186 Clothbound **$4.95**

CHEMISTRY AND PHYSICAL CHEMISTRY

THE PHASE RULE AND ITS APPLICATIONS, Alexander Findlay. Covers chemical phenomena of 1 to 4 multiple component systems, the "standard work on the subject" (Nature). Completely revised, brought up to date by A. N. Campbell, N. O. Smith. New material on binary, tertiary liquid equilibria, solid solutions in ternary systems, quinary systems of salts, water, etc. Completely revised to triangular coordinates in ternary systems, clarified graphic representation, solid models, etc. 9th revised edition. 236 figures. 505 footnotes, mostly bibliographic. xii + 449pp. 5⅜ x 8.
S92 Paperbound **$2.45**

DYNAMICAL THEORY OF GASES, James Jeans. Divided into mathematical, physical chapters for convenience of those not expert in mathematics. Discusses mathematical theory of gas in steady state, thermodynamics, Bolzmann, Maxwell, kinetic theory, quantum theory, exponentials, etc. "One of the classics of scientific writing . . . as lucid and comprehensive an exposition of the kinetic theory as has ever been written," J. of Institute of Engineers. 4th enlarged edition, with new material on quantum theory, quantum dynamics, etc. 28 figures. 444pp. 6⅛ x 9¼.
S136 Paperbound **$2.45**

POLAR MOLECULES, Pieter Debye. Nobel laureate offers complete guide to fundamental electrostatic field relations, polarizability, molecular structure. Partial contents: electric intensity, displacement, force, polarization by orientation, molar polarization, molar refraction, halogen-hydrides, polar liquids, ionic saturation, dielectric constant, etc. Special chapter considers quantum theory. "Clear and concise . . . coordination of experimental results with theory will be readily appreciated," Electronics Industries. 172pp. 5⅜ x 8.
S63 Clothbound **$3.50**
S64 Paperbound **$1.50**

ATOMIC SPECTRA AND ATOMIC STRUCTURE, G. Herzberg. Excellent general survey for chemists, physicists specializing in other fields. Partial contents: simplest line spectra, elements of atomic theory; multiple structure of line spectra, electron spin; building-up principle, periodic system of elements; finer details of atomic spectra; hyperfine structure of spectral lines; some experimental results and applications. 80 figures. 20 tables. xiii + 257pp. 5⅜ x 8.
S115 Paperbound **$1.95**

TREATISE ON THERMODYNAMICS, Max Planck. Classic based on his original papers. Brilliant concepts of Nobel laureate make no assumptions regarding nature of heat, rejects earlier approaches of Helmholtz, Maxwell, to offer uniform point of view for entire field. Seminal work by founder of quantum theory, deducing new physical, chemical laws. A standard text, an excellent introduction to field for students with knowledge of elementary chemistry, physics, calculus. 3rd English edition. xvi + 297pp. 5⅜ x 8.
S219 Paperbound **$1.75**

DOVER SCIENCE BOOKS

KINETIC THEORY OF LIQUIDS, J. Frenkel. Regards kinetic theory of liquids as generalization, extension of theory of solid bodies, covers all types of arrangements of solids; thermal displacements of atoms; interstitial atoms, ions; orientational, rotational motion of molecules; transition between states of matter. Mathematical theory developed close to physical subject matter. "Discussed in a simple yet deeply penetrating fashion . . . will serve as seeds for a great many basic and applied developments in chemistry," J. of the Amer. Chemical Soc. 216 bibliographical footnotes. 55 figures. xi + 485pp. 5⅜ x 8.
S94 Clothbound **$3.95**
S95 Paperbound **$2.45**

ASTRONOMY

OUT OF THE SKY, H. H. Nininger. Non-technical, comprehensive introduction to "meteoritics" —science concerned with arrival of matter from outer space. By one of world's experts on meteorites, this book defines meteors and meteorites; studies fireball clusters and processions, meteorite composition, size, distribution, showers, explosions, origins, much more. viii + 336pp. 5⅜ x 8.
T519 Paperbound **$1.85**

AN INTRODUCTION TO THE STUDY OF STELLAR STRUCTURE, S. Chandrasekhar. Outstanding treatise on stellar dynamics by one of greatest astro-physicists. Examines relationship between loss of energy, mass, and radius of stars in steady state. Discusses thermodynamic laws from Caratheodory's axiomatic standpoint; adiabatic, polytropic laws; work of Ritter, Emden, Kelvin, etc.; Stroemgren envelopes as starter for theory of gaseous stars; Gibbs statistical mechanics (quantum); degenerate stellar configuration, theory of white dwarfs; etc. "Highest level of scientific merit," Bulletin. Amer. Math. Soc. 33 figures. 509pp. 5⅜ x 8.
S413 Paperbound **$2.75**

LES MÉTHODES NOVELLES DE LA MÉCANIQUE CÉLESTE, H. Poincaré. Complete French text of one of Poincaré's most important works. Revolutionized celestial mechanics: first use of integral invariants, first major application of linear differential equations, study of periodic orbits, lunar motion and Jupiter's satellites, three body problem, and many other important topics. "Started a new era . . . so extremely modern that even today few have mastered his weapons," E. T. Bell. 3 volumes. Total 1282pp. 6⅛ x 9¼.
Vol. 1 S401 Paperbound **$2.75**
Vol. 2 S402 Paperbound **$2.75**
Vol. 3 S403 Paperbound **$2.75**
The set **$7.50**

THE REALM OF THE NEBULAE, E. Hubble. One of the great astronomers of our time presents his concept of "island universes," and describes its effect on astronomy. Covers velocity-distance relation; classification, nature, distances, general field of nebulae; cosmological theories; nebulae in the neighborhood of the Milky way; etc. 39 photos, including velocity-distance relations shown by spectrum comparison. "One of the most progressive lines of astronomical research," The Times, London. New Introduction by A. Sandage. 55 illustrations. xxiv + 201pp. 5⅜ x 8.
S455 Paperbound **$1.50**

HOW TO MAKE A TELESCOPE, Jean Texereau. Design, build an f/6 or f/8 Newtonian type reflecting telescope, with altazimuth Couder mounting, suitable for planetary, lunar, and stellar observation. Covers every operation step-by-step, every piece of equipment. Discusses basic principles of geometric and physical optics (unnecessary to construction), comparative merits of reflectors, refractors. A thorough discussion of eyepieces, finders, grinding, installation, testing, etc. 241 figures, 38 photos, show almost every operation and tool. Potential errors are anticipated. Foreword by A. Couder. Sources of supply. xiii + 191pp. 6¼ x 10.
T464 Clothbound **$3.50**

BIOLOGICAL SCIENCES

THE BIOLOGY OF THE AMPHIBIA, G. K. Noble, Late Curator of Herpetology at Am. Mus. of Nat. Hist. Probably most used text on amphibia, most comprehensive, clear, detailed. 19 chapters, 85 page supplement: development; heredity; life history; speciation; adaptation; sex, integument, respiratory, circulatory, digestive, muscular, nervous systems; instinct, intelligence, habits, economic value classification, environment relationships, etc. "Nothing comparable to it," C. H. Pope, curator of Amphibia, Chicago Mus. of Nat. Hist. 1047 item bibliography. 174 illustrations. 600pp. 5⅜ x 8.
S206 Paperbound **$2.98**

THE ORIGIN OF LIFE, A. I. Oparin. A classic of biology. This is the first modern statement of theory of gradual evolution of life from nitrocarbon compounds. A brand-new evaluation of Oparin's theory in light of later research, by Dr. S. Margulis, University of Nebraska. xxv + 270pp. 5⅜ x 8.
S213 Paperbound **$1.75**

9

THE BIOLOGY OF THE LABORATORY MOUSE, edited by G. D. Snell. Prepared in 1941 by staff of Roscoe B. Jackson Memorial Laboratory, still the standard treatise on the mouse, assembling enormous amount of material for which otherwise you spend hours of research. Embryology, reproduction, histology, spontaneous neoplasms, gene and chromosomes mutations, genetics of spontaneous tumor formations, of tumor transplantation, endocrine secretion and tumor formation, milk influence and tumor formation, inbred, hybrid animals, parasites, infectious diseases, care and recording. "A wealth of information of vital concern. . . . recommended to all who could use a book on such a subject," Nature. Classified bibliography of 1122 items. 172 figures, including 128 photos. ix + 497pp. 6⅛ x 9¼.
S248 Clothbound **$6.00**

THE TRAVELS OF WILLIAM BARTRAM, edited by Mark Van Doran. Famous source-book of American anthropology, natural history, geography, is record kept by Bartram in 1770's on travels through wilderness of Florida, Georgia, Carolinas. Containing accurate, beautiful descriptions of Indians, settlers, fauna, flora, it is one of finest pieces of Americana ever written. 13 original illustrations. 448pp. 5⅜ x 8. T13 Paperbound **$2.00**

BEHAVIOUR AND SOCIAL LIFE OF THE HONEYBEE, Ronald Ribbands. Outstanding scientific study; a compendium of practically everything known of social life of honeybee. Stresses behaviour of individual bees in field, hive. Extends von Frisch's experiments on communication among bees. Covers perception of temperature, gravity, distance, vibration; sound production; glands; structural differences; wax production; temperature regulation; recognition, communication; drifting, mating behaviour, other highly interesting topics. "This valuable work is sure of a cordial reception by laymen, beekeepers and scientists," Prof. Karl von Frisch, Brit. J. of Animal Behaviour. Bibliography of 690 references. 127 diagrams, graphs, sections of bee anatomy, fine photographs. 352pp. S410 Clothbound **$4.50**

ELEMENTS OF MATHEMATICAL BIOLOGY, A. J. Lotka. Pioneer classic, 1st major attempt to apply modern mathematical techniques on large scale to phenomena of biology, biochemistry, psychology, ecology, similar life sciences. Partial contents: Statistical meaning of irreversibility; Evolution as redistribution; Equations of kinetics of evolving systems; Chemical, inter-species equilibrium; parameters of state; Energy transformers of nature, etc. Can be read with profit by even those having no advanced math; unsurpassed as study-reference. Formerly titled "Elements of Physical Biology." 72 figures. xxx + 460pp. 5⅜ x 8.
S346 Paperbound **$2.45**

TREES OF THE EASTERN AND CENTRAL UNITED STATES AND CANADA, W. M. Harlow. Serious middle-level text covering more than 140 native trees, important escapes, with information on general appearance, growth habit, leaf forms, flowers, fruit, bark, commercial use, distribution, habitat, woodlore, etc. Keys within text enable you to locate various species easily, to know which have edible fruit, much more useful, interesting information. "Well illustrated to make identification very easy," Standard Cat. for Public Libraries. Over 600 photographs, figures. xiii + 288pp. 5⅝ x 6½. T395 Paperbound **$1.35**

FRUIT KEY AND TWIG KEY TO TREES AND SHRUBS (Fruit key to Northeastern Trees, Twig key to Deciduous Woody Plants of Eastern North America), W. M. Harlow. Only guides with photographs of every twig, fruit described. Especially valuable to novice. Fruit key (both deciduous trees, evergreens) has introduction on seeding, organs involved, types, habits. Twig key introduction treats growth, morphology. In keys proper, identification is almost automatic. Exceptional work, widely used in university courses, especially useful for identification in winter, or from fruit or seed only. Over 350 photos, up to 3 times natural size. Index of common, scientific names, in each key. xvii + 125pp. 5⅝ x 8⅜. T511 Paperbound **$1.25**

INSECT LIFE AND INSECT NATURAL HISTORY, S. W. Frost. Unusual for emphasizing habits, social life, ecological relations of insects rather than more academic aspects of classification, morphology. Prof. Frost's enthusiasm and knowledge are everywhere evident as he discusses insect associations, specialized habits like leaf-rolling, leaf mining, case-making, the gall insects, boring insects, etc. Examines matters not usually covered in general works: insects as human food; insect music, musicians; insect response to radio waves; use of insects in art, literature. "Distinctly different, possesses an individuality all its own," Journal of Forestry. Over 700 illustrations. Extensive bibliography. x + 524pp. 5⅜ x 8.
T519 Paperbound **$2.49**

A WAY OF LIFE, AND OTHER SELECTED WRITINGS, Sir William Osler. Physician, humanist, Osler discusses brilliantly Thomas Browne, Gui Patin, Robert Burton, Michael Servetus, William Beaumont, Laennec. Includes such favorite writing as title essay, "The Old Humanities and the New Science," "Books and Men," "The Student Life," 6 more of his best discussions of philosophy, literature, religion. "The sweep of his mind and interests embraced every phase of human activity," G. L. Keynes. 5 photographs. Introduction by G. L. Keynes, M.D., F.R.C.S. xx + 278pp. 5⅜ x 8. T488 Paperbound **$1.50**

THE GENETICAL THEORY OF NATURAL SELECTION, R. A. Fisher. 2nd revised edition of vital reviewing of Darwin's Selection Theory in terms of particulate inheritance, by one of greatest authorities on experimental, theoretical genetics. Theory stated in mathematical form. Special features of particulate inheritance are examined: evolution of dominance, maintenance of specific variability, mimicry, sexual selection, etc. 5 chapters on man's special circumstances as a social animal. 16 photographs. x + 310pp. 5⅜ x 8.
S466 Paperbound **$1.85**

DOVER SCIENCE BOOKS

THE AUTOBIOGRAPHY OF CHARLES DARWIN, AND SELECTED LETTERS, edited by Francis Darwin. Darwin's own record of early life; historic voyage aboard "Beagle;" furore surrounding evolution, his replies; reminiscences of his son. Letters to Henslow, Lyell, Hooker, Huxley, Wallace, Kingsley, etc., and thoughts on religion, vivisection. We see how he revolutionized geology with concepts of ocean subsidence; how his great books on variation of plants and animals, primitive man, expression of emotion among primates, plant fertilization, carnivorous plants, protective coloration, etc., came into being. 365pp. 5⅜ x 8.
T479 Paperbound **$1.65**

ANIMALS IN MOTION, Eadweard Muybridge. Largest, most comprehensive selection of Muybridge's famous action photos of animals, from his "Animal Locomotion." 3919 high-speed shots of 34 different animals, birds, in 123 types of action; horses, mules, oxen, pigs, goats, camels, elephants, dogs, cats guanacos, sloths, lions, tigers, jaguars, raccoons, baboons, deer, elk, gnus, kangaroos, many others, walking, running, flying, leaping. Horse alone in over 40 ways. Photos taken against ruled backgrounds; most actions taken from 3 angles at once: 90°, 60°, rear. Most plates original size. Of considerable interest to scientists as biology classic, records of actual facts of natural history, physiology. "Really marvelous series of plates," Nature. "Monumental work," Waldemar Kaempffert. Edited by L. S. Brown, 74 page introduction on mechanics of motion. 340pp. of plates. 3919 photographs. 416pp. Deluxe binding, paper. (Weight: 4½ lbs.) 7⅛ x 10⅝.
T203 Clothbound **$10.00**

THE HUMAN FIGURE IN MOTION, Eadweard Muybridge. New edition of great classic in history of science and photography, largest selection ever made from original Muybridge photos of human action: 4789 photographs, illustrating 163 types of motion: walking, running, lifting, etc. in time-exposure sequence photos at speeds up to 1/6000th of a second. Men, women, children, mostly undraped, showing bone, muscle positions against ruled backgrounds, mostly taken at 3 angles at once. Not only was this a great work of photography, acclaimed by contemporary critics as work of genius, but it was also a great 19th century landmark in biological research. Historical introduction by Prof. Robert Taft, U. of Kansas. Plates original size, full of detail. Over 500 action strips. 407pp. 7¾ x 10⅝. Deluxe edition.
7204 Clothbound **$10.00**

AN INTRODUCTION TO THE STUDY OF EXPERIMENTAL MEDICINE, Claude Bernard. 90-year old classic of medical science, only major work of Bernard available in English, records his efforts to transform physiology into exact science. Principles of scientific research illustrated by specified case histories from his work; roles of chance, error, preliminary false conclusion, in leading eventually to scientific truth; use of hypothesis. Much of modern application of mathematics to biology rests on foundation set down here. "The presentation is polished . . . reading is easy," Revue des questions scientifiques. New foreword by Prof. I. B. Cohen, Harvard U. xxv + 266pp. 5⅜ x 8.
T400 Paperbound **$1.50**

STUDIES ON THE STRUCTURE AND DEVELOPMENT OF VERTEBRATES, E. S. Goodrich. Definitive study by greatest modern comparative anatomist. Exhaustive morphological, phylogenetic expositions of skeleton, fins, limbs, skeletal visceral arches, labial cartilages, visceral clefts, gills, vascular, respiratory, excretory, periphal nervous systems, etc., from fish to higher mammals. "For many a day this will certainly be the standard textbook on Vertebrate Morphology in the English language," Journal of Anatomy. 754 illustrations. 69 page biographical study by C. C. Hardy. Bibliography of 1186 references. Two volumes, total 906pp. 5⅜ x 8.
Two vol. set S449, 450 Paperbound **$5.00**

EARTH SCIENCES

THE EVOLUTION OF IGNEOUS BOOKS, N. L. Bowen. Invaluable serious introduction applies techniques of physics, chemistry to explain igneous rock diversity in terms of chemical composition, fractional crystallization. Discusses liquid immiscibility in silicate magmas, crystal sorting, liquid lines of descent, fractional resorption of complex minerals, petrogen, etc. Of prime importance to geologists, mining engineers; physicists, chemists working with high temperature, pressures. "Most important," Times, London. 263 bibliographic notes. 82 figures. xviii + 334pp. 5⅜ x 8.
S311 Paperbound **$1.85**

GEOGRAPHICAL ESSAYS, M. Davis. Modern geography, geomorphology rest on fundamental work of this scientist. 26 famous essays present most important theories, field rescarches. Partial contents: Geographical Cycle; Plains of Marine, Subaerial Denudation; The Peneplain; Rivers, Valleys of Pennsylvania; Outline of Cape Cod; Sculpture of Mountains by Glaciers; etc. "Long the leader and guide," Economic Geography. "Part of the very texture of geography . . . models of clear thought," Geographic Review. 130 figures. vi + 777pp. 5⅜ x 8.
S383 Paperbound **$2.95**

URANIUM PROSPECTING, H. L. Barnes. For immediate practical use, professional geologist considers uranium ores, geological occurrences, field conditions, all aspects of highly profitable occupation. "Helpful information . . . easy-to-use, easy-to-find style," Geotimes. x + 117pp. 5⅜ x 8.
T309 Paperbound **$1.00**

11

DE RE METALLICA, Georgius Agricola. 400 year old classic translated, annotated by former President Herbert Hoover. 1st scientific study of mineralogy, mining, for over 200 years after its appearance in 1556 the standard treatise. 12 books, exhaustively annotated, discuss history of mining, selection of sites, types of deposits, making pits, shafts, ventilating, pumps, crushing machinery; assaying, smelting, refining metals; also salt alum, nitre, glass making. Definitive edition, with all 289 16th century woodcuts of original. Biographical, historical introductions. Bibliography, survey of ancient authors. Indexes. A fascinating book for anyone interested in art, history of science, geology, etc. Deluxe Edition. 289 illustrations. 672pp. 6¾ x 10. Library cloth. S6 Clothbound **$10.00**

INTERNAL CONSTITUTION OF THE EARTH, edited by Beno Gutenberg. Prepared for National Research Council, this is a complete, thorough coverage of earth origins, continent formation, nature and behaviour of earth's core, petrology of crust, cooling forces in core, seismic and earthquake material, gravity, elastic constants, strain characteristics, similar topics. "One is filled with admiration . . . a high standard . . . there is no reader who will not learn something from this book," London, Edinburgh, Dublin, Philosophic Magazine. Largest Bibliography in print: 1127 classified items. Table of constants. 43 diagrams. 439pp. 6⅛ x 9¼. S414 Paperbound **$2.45**

THE BIRTH AND DEVELOPMENT OF THE GEOLOGICAL SCIENCES, F. D. Adams. Most thorough history of earth sciences ever written. Geological thought from earliest times to end of 19th century, covering over 300 early thinkers and systems; fossils and their explanation, vulcanists vs. neptunists, figured stones and paleontology, generation of stones, dozens of similar topics. 91 illustrations, including Medieval, Renaissance woodcuts, etc. 632 footnotes, mostly bibliographical. 511pp. 5⅜ x 8. T5 Paperbound **$2.00**

HYDROLOGY, edited by O. E. Meinzer, prepared for the National Research Council. Detailed, complete reference library on precipitation, evaporation, snow, snow surveying, glaciers, lakes, infiltration, soil moisture, ground water, runoff, drought, physical changes produced by water hydrology of limestone terranes, etc. Practical in application, especially valuable for engineers. 24 experts have created "the most up-to-date, most complete treatment of the subject," Am. Assoc. of Petroleum Geologists. 165 illustrations. xi + 712pp. 6⅛ x 9¼. S191 Paperbound **$2.95**

LANGUAGE AND TRAVEL AIDS FOR SCIENTISTS

SAY IT language phrase books

"SAY IT" in the foreign language of your choice! We have sold over ½ million copies of these popular, useful language books. They will not make you an expert linguist overnight, but they do cover most practical matters of everyday life abroad.

Over 1000 useful phrases, expressions, additional variants, substitutions.

Modern! Useful! Hundreds of phrases not available in other texts: "Nylon," "air-conditioned," etc.

The ONLY inexpensive phrase book **completely indexed.** Everything is available at a flip of your finger, ready to use.

Prepared by native linguists, travel experts.

Based on years of travel experience abroad.

May be used by itself, or to supplement any other text or course. Provides a living element. Used by many colleges, institutions: Hunter College; Barnard College; Army Ordinance School, Aberdeen; etc.

Available, 1 book per language:

Danish (T818) 75¢	**Italian** (T806) 60¢
Dutch (T817) 75¢	**Japanese** (T807) 75¢
English (for German-speaking people) (T801) 60¢	**Norwegian** (T814) 75¢
English (for Italian-speaking people) (T816) 60¢	**Russian** (T810) 75¢
English (for Spanish-speaking people) (T802) 60¢	**Spanish** (T811) 60¢
Esperanto (T820) 75¢	**Turkish** (T821) 75¢
French (T803) 60¢	**Yiddish** (T815) 75¢
German (T804) 60¢	**Swedish** (T812) 75¢
Modern Greek (T813) 75¢	**Polish** (T808) 75¢
Hebrew (T805) 60¢	**Portuguese** (T809) 75¢

MONEY CONVERTER AND TIPPING GUIDE FOR EUROPEAN TRAVEL, C. Vomacka. Purse-size handbook crammed with information on currency regulations, tipping for every European country, including Israel, Turkey, Czechoslovakia, Rumania, Egypt, Russia, Poland. Telephone, postal rates; duty-free imports, passports, visas, health certificates; foreign clothing sizes; weather tables. What, when to tip. 5th year of publication. 128pp. 3½ x 5¼.   **T260 Paperbound 60¢**

NEW RUSSIAN-ENGLISH AND ENGLISH-RUSSIAN DICTIONARY, M. A. O'Brien. Unusually comprehensive guide to reading, speaking, writing Russian, for both advanced, beginning students. Over 70,000 entries in new orthography, full information on accentuation, grammatical classifications. Shades of meaning, idiomatic uses, colloquialisms, tables of irregular verbs for both languages. Individual entries indicate stems, transitiveness, perfective, imperfective aspects, conjugation, sound changes, accent, etc. Includes pronunciation instruction. Used at Harvard, Yale, Cornell, etc. 738pp. 5⅜ x 8.   **T208 Paperbound $ 2.00**

PHRASE AND SENTENCE DICTIONARY OF SPOKEN RUSSIAN, English-Russian, Russian-English. Based on phrases, complete sentences, not isolated words—recognized as one of best methods of learning idiomatic speech. Over 11,500 entries, indexed by single words, over 32,000 English, Russian sentences, phrases, in immediately useable form. Shows accent changes in conjugation, declension; irregular forms listed both alphabetically, under main form of word. 15,000 word introduction covers Russian sounds, writing, grammar, syntax. 15 page appendix of geographical names, money, important signs, given names, foods, special Soviet terms, etc. Originally published as U.S. Gov't Manual TM 30-944. iv + 573pp. 5⅜ x 8.   **T496 Paperbound $2.75**

PHRASE AND SENTENCE DICTIONARY OF SPOKEN SPANISH, Spanish-English, English-Spanish. Compiled from spoken Spanish, based on phrases, complete sentences rather than isolated words—not an ordinary dictionary. Over 16,000 entries indexed under single words, both Castilian, Latin-American. Language in immediately useable form. 25 page introduction provides rapid survey of sounds, grammar, syntax, full consideration of irregular verbs. Especially apt in modern treatment of phrases, structure. 17 page glossary gives translations of geographical names, money values, numbers, national holidays, important street signs, useful expressions of high frequency, plus unique 7 page glossary of Spanish, Spanish-American foods. Originally published as U.S. Gov't Manual TM 30-900. iv + 513pp. 5⅝ x 8⅜.   **T495 Paperbound $1.75**

SAY IT CORRECTLY language record sets

The best inexpensive pronunciation aids on the market. Spoken by native linguists associated with major American universities, each record contains:

> 14 minutes of speech—12 minutes of normal, relatively slow speech, 2 minutes of normal conversational speed.

> 120 basic phrases, sentences, covering nearly every aspect of everyday life, travel—introducing yourself, travel in autos, buses, taxis, etc., walking, sightseeing, hotels, restaurants, money, shopping, etc.

> 32 page booklet containing everything on record plus English translations easy-to-follow phonetic guide.

> Clear, high-fidelity recordings.

> Unique bracketing systems, selection of basic sentences enabling you to expand use of SAY IT CORRECTLY records with a dictionary, to fit thousands of additional situations.

Use this record to supplement any course or text. All sounds in each language illustrated perfectly—imitate speaker in pause which follows each foreign phrase in slow section, and be amazed at increased ease, accuracy of pronunciation. Available, one language per record for

French	Spanish	German
Italian	Dutch	Modern Greek
Japanese	Russian	Portuguese
Polish	Swedish	Hebrew
English (for German-speaking people)		English (for Spanish-speaking people)

7″ (33 1/3 rpm) record, album, booklet. **$1.00 each.**

SPEAK MY LANGUAGE: SPANISH FOR YOUNG BEGINNERS, M. Ahlman, Z. Gilbert. Records provide one of the best, most entertaining methods of introducing a foreign language to children. Within framework of train trip from Portugal to Spain, an English-speaking child is introduced to Spanish by native companion. (Adapted from successful radio program of N.Y. State Educational Department.) A dozen different categories of expressions,. including greeting, numbers, time, weather, food, clothes, family members, etc. Drill is combined with poetry and contextual use. Authentic background music. Accompanying book enables a reader to follow records, includes vocabulary of over 350 recorded expressions. Two 10″ 33 1/3 records, total of 40 minutes. Book. 40 illustrations. 69pp. 5¼ x 10½.   **T890 The set $4.95**

LISTEN & LEARN language record sets

LISTEN & LEARN is the only extensive language record course designed especially to meet your travel and everyday needs. Separate sets for each language, each containing three 33 1/3 rpm long-playing records—1 1/2 hours of recorded speech by eminent native speakers who are professors at Columbia, New York U., Queens College.

Check the following features found only in LISTEN & LEARN:

Dual language recording. 812 selected phrases, sentences, over 3200 words, spoken first in English, then foreign equivalent. Pause after each foreign phrase allows time to repeat expression.

128-page manual (196 page for Russian)—everything on records, plus simple transcription. Indexed for convenience. Only set on the market completely indexed.

Practical. No time wasted on material you can find in any grammar. No dead words. Covers central core material with phrase approach. Ideal for person with limited time. Living, modern expressions, not found in other courses. Hygienic products, modern equipment, shopping, "air-conditioned," etc. Everything is immediately useable.

High-fidelity recording, equal in clarity to any costing up to $6 per record.

"Excellent . . . impress me as being among the very best on the market," Prof. Mario Pei, Dept. of Romance Languages, Columbia U. "Inexpensive and well done . . . ideal present," Chicago Sunday Tribune. "More genuinely helpful than anything of its kind," Sidney Clark, well-known author of "All the Best" travel books."

UNCONDITIONAL GUARANTEE. Try LISTEN & LEARN, then return it within 10 days for full refund, if you are not satisfied. It is guaranteed after you actually use it.

6 modern languages—FRENCH, SPANISH, GERMAN, ITALIAN, RUSSIAN, or JAPANESE *—one language to each set of 3 records (33 1/3 rpm). 128 page manual. Album.

Spanish	the set $4.95	**German**	the set $4.95	**Japanese***	the set $5.95
French	the set $4.95	**Italian**	the set $4.95	**Russian**	the set $5.95

* Available Oct. 1959.

TRÜBNER COLLOQUIAL SERIES

These unusual books are members of the famous Trübner series of colloquial manuals. They have been written to provide adults with a sound colloquial knowledge of a foreign language, and are suited for either class use or self-study. Each book is a complete course in itself, with progressive, easy to follow lessons. Phonetics, grammar, and syntax are covered, while hundreds of phrases and idioms, reading texts, exercises, and vocabulary are included. These books are unusual in being neither skimpy nor overdetailed in grammatical matters, and in presenting up-to-date, colloquial, and practical phrase material. Bilingual presentation is stressed, to make thorough self-study easier for the reader.

COLLOQUIAL HINDUSTANI, A. H. Harley, formerly Nizam's Reader in Urdu, U. of London. 30 pages on phonetics and scripts (devanagari & Arabic-Persian) are followed by 29 lessons, including material on English and Arabic-Persian influences. Key to all exercises. Vocabulary. 5 x 7½. 147pp. Clothbound $1.75

COLLOQUIAL ARABIC, DeLacy O'Leary. Foremost Islamic scholar covers language of Egypt, Syria, Palestine, & Northern Arabia. Extremely clear coverage of complex Arabic verbs & noun plurals; also cultural aspects of language. Vocabulary. xviii + 192pp. 5 x 7½.
  Clothbound $1.75

COLLOQUIAL GERMAN, P. F. Doring. Intensive thorough coverage of grammar in easily-followed form. Excellent for brush-up, with hundreds of colloquial phrases. 34 pages of bilingual texts. 224pp. 5 x 7½. Clothbound $1.75

COLLOQUIAL SPANISH, W. R. Patterson. Castilian grammar and colloquial language, loaded with bilingual phrases and colloquialisms. Excellent for review or self-study. 164pp. 5 x 7½.
  Clothbound $1.75

COLLOQUIAL FRENCH, W. R. Patterson. 16th revised edition of this extremely popular manual. Grammar explained with model clarity, and hundreds of useful expressions and phrases; exercises, reading texts, etc. Appendixes of new and useful words and phrases. 223pp. 5 x 7½. Clothbound $1.75